D1357049

CHEMISTRY AND BIOLOGY OF Proteins

BY FELIX HAUROWITZ

Professor of Chemistry, Indiana University
Bloomington, Indiana

FIRST EDITION
SECOND IMPRESSION

ACADEMIC PRESS INC., PUBLISHERS

NEW YORK · 1950

Second Printing, 1952

PRINTED IN THE UNITED STATES OF AMERICA

FOREWORD

When the author was invited to write a book on Proteins, he was hesitant for a long time to embark upon such a difficult project. What finally induced him to write this book was a request by Indiana University to give a one-semester course on proteins for graduate students in the College of Arts and Sciences. No suitable modern textbook on proteins was available. The few good textbooks on proteins written before 1940 were out of print. It was the author's first task, therefore, to write a textbook which would be understandable to graduate students of chemistry and of the biological sciences.

It has been attempted, moreover, to give a *uniform outline of the present state of the protein problem.* Although the chemistry and the biology of proteins is the subject of many thousands of investigations, the results of experimental work have rarely been correlated systematically with each other. True, each experiment in the protein domain opens new questions and we are still far from a definite solution of the protein problem. Nevertheless, it was considered possible and useful to incorporate the results of both old and recent experiments into a unified concept of the nature of the protein molecule and of its reactions and functions.

Completeness cannot be attained in a book of this kind. In writing the text the needs of those interested in the *fundamental aspects* were kept in mind. Therefore the main topics discussed are (1) protein structure, (2) biological activity of proteins, and (3) biosynthesis of proteins in the living cell. The fundamental importance of the structural problem need not be stressed. Likewise all will agree that protein synthesis is one of the main problems of the biological sciences, inasmuch as growth and reproduction consist essentially of the formation of new protein. Many readers, however, may wonder at the large space devoted in this book to enzymes, hormones and immunologically active proteins. To them it must be recalled, therefore, that the most stable proteins are found among the enzyme proteins, that these enzymes crystallize with particular ease, and that they are more uniform than many of the proteins which lack biological activity. The same is true for many of the hormone proteins. Antigens and antibodies, on the other hand, have been treated in some detail because antibody synthesis is, essentially, a modified protein synthesis; antigens, consequently, are valuable tools which can be used to modify the normal course of protein synthesis. During the last few years a large number of biologically active proteins has been discovered in protein fractions which previously had been regarded as inactive; obviously biological activity cannot be detected unless suitable methods of assay are available. There is no doubt, therefore, that many more biologically active proteins will be discovered in the future.

In a monograph on proteins it is difficult to draw a definite border line between the fundamental and the less important aspects of the problem. It was felt, however, that the technology of proteins could not be treated in this book. Likewise, an account of protein metabolism in different species of the animal and vegetable kingdoms would surpass the limits of this treatise. Readers desirous of orienting themselves in special problems of protein metabolism are referred to numerous review articles in *Advances in Protein Chemistry* and *Annual Reviews of Biochemistry*. Advanced students interested in details of the physical chemistry of proteins will find a wealth of information in the classical book of Edwin J. Cohn and John T. Edsall on "Proteins, Amino Acids and Peptides" (Reinhold Publishing Corporation, New York, 1943).

While the customary textbooks do not endeavor to give an extensive bibliography, it has been attempted to substantiate each statement by quoting the original sources. The numerous references given were not collected *ad hoc*, but were selected from data assembled by the author through many years. By the citation of approximately 1500 original papers the book goes well beyond the usual limits of a textbook. It is hoped that the numerous references will render the book valuable to research workers in biochemistry and in related fields.

When the manuscript of this book was completed, the author felt the necessity of submitting some of the chapters to experts in the topics treated, and to ask them for their criticism. An appeal to several colleagues in protein research resulted in a response which surpassed by far the author's expectations. Dr. Henry B. Bull, Professor of Physiological Chemistry, Northwestern University, Dr. John T. Edsall, Professor of Biochemistry, Harvard Medical School, and Dr. Hans Neurath, Professor of Physical Biochemistry, Duke University, kindly offered to read the whole manuscript, and to send to the author their written comments. Because of this generous help, use could be made of a series of most valuable critical remarks and suggestions, and many pitfalls could be avoided. The author is deeply indebted to Dr. Bull, Dr. Edsall and Dr. Neurath for their invaluable assistance and for the many hours spent on the improvement of his book. The author also wishes to express his best thanks to Dr. Choh H. Li, Professor of Experi-

mental Biology, University of California, for comments on the chapter on hormones.

The author's particular thanks, however, are due to Mr. Charles F. Crampton, Department of Chemistry, Indiana University, who had the difficult task of reading the first draft of the manuscript and of testing it for style and for clarity of presentation. Many sentences and paragraphs were remodelled with Mr. Crampton's help, and several gaps in the deductions were discovered and closed.

In spite of the ample and generous aid of so many colleagues it is unavoidable that the book should contain errors. It is hoped that these are neither too numerous nor too serious, and that the readers will call them to the attention of the author. Obviously none of the abovenamed helpers is to be blamed for these errors. The only person responsible for them and for the mode of presentation is the author.

FELIX HAUROWITZ

Bloomington, Ind.
July, 1950

CONTENTS

Chapter I

Role of Proteins in Biology

Proteins have a unique significance in biology in that they compose the *indispensable substrate of living matter*. To be sure, living organisms also contain carbohydrates and lipids, frequently in even greater abundance than proteins. Thus, green plants are rather poor in proteins, but rich in cellulose, a carbohydrate. There are, however, essential differences between proteins and the other cellular constituents. Wherever the phenomena of *growth* and *reproduction* are seen, proteins are primarily involved. In nucleated cells multiplication is initiated by the nucleus, which contains proteins closely associated with nucleic acids. In bacteria, where there is no visible nucleus, the proteins and nucleoproteins form the bulk of the living substance. Still further down in the order of organisms, we find that viruses consist mainly of proteins and nucleoproteins and that the simplest of them are free of lipids and carbohydrates.

In addition to their role in the functions of growth and multiplication, another important feature of the proteins is their *specificity*, which distinguishes them from other cellular constituents. While we do not know of species-specific lipids, we do know that the proteins of each species of the animal or plant kingdom, and even the proteins of bacteria and of viruses, are typical for the particular species. In some cases we are even able to find variations among the proteins of individuals of the same species. Evidently, proteins must be considered the essential agents in the transmittal of hereditary traits.

A third characteristic property of proteins, in which they differ from other compounds present in the cell, is the phenomenon of *denaturation*. Native proteins are denatured by the same physical or chemical agents which kill or injure living cells. However, denaturation is caused not only by heat, acids or alkalis, and other drastic treatments, but also by the action at room temperature of aqueous solutions of urea and of similar "innocuous" substances. The obvious conclusion to be drawn from such behavior is that the structure of the native protein molecules is so unstable that they are even susceptible to alteration by the impacts of dissolved urea molecules. None of the other cellular constituents exhibits a similar lability.

Proteins have various *functions* in the cell and in organisms. Some of them compose such inert materials as hair, horn, or bones. Also the *contractile substance* of the muscle fiber is a protein. It is somewhat remarkable in that it possesses the capacity to transform chemical energy into mechanical energy. It is thus responsible for the motility of the higher organism. Similarly, in the lower organisms, the movement of flagellae, the coordinated stroking of cilia, and ameboid movement are all ascribed to contractile protein particles. Serving other functions, the *enzymes*, the highly important catalysts of living organisms, are proteins, as are also the respiratory pigments, the *hormones* of the pancreas, the thyroid, and the pituitary gland, the *antibodies*, and the *toxins* of certain bacteria. It is evident that the importance of proteins for the living organism can scarcely be overemphasized.

It is clear, moreover, from the multiple functions of proteins and from their lability that their molecular structure is, in all probability, extremely complicated. We are far from being able to describe the details of this structure. Only in a few instances has it been possible to gain an insight into the arrangement of portions of the protein molecule. The greatest deficiency in our knowledge of proteins lies in our inability to correlate the enzymatic or the hormonal functions of certain of them with a definite chemical arrangement. We do not yet know what molecular groups are responsible for the proteolytic power of crystalline trypsin or for the hormonal activity of crystalline insulin.

These shortcomings in our understanding of proteins are closely connected with the fact that the properties of a protein depend not only on its chemical composition, on the kind and order of the amino acids forming the peptide chains, but also on the *spatial arrangement* of these chains. The properties of a molecule consisting of a closely folded, long peptide chain are quite different from those of the same molecule containing the same peptide chain in an expanded state. In other words, the properties of a protein molecule depend to a large extent on the three-dimensional structure assumed by its peptide chains. In contrast to most other threadlike macromolecules the peptide chains of the proteins are able to maintain their specific constellation over long periods of time.

The specific arrangement of the peptide chains is of the greatest importance for the properties of the protein macromolecule. The solubility of proteins, their serological behavior, their enzymatic and hormonal activities, and many other biological properties depend on the molecular groups present in the surface of the protein molecule, and hence on the spatial arrangement and the mode of folding of the peptide chains. It is, therefore, one of the principal endeavors of protein chemistry to elucidate the *internal structure* of the protein macromolecule and the distribution of functional groups within the large protein molecule. Only in this way will we be able to correlate the biological functions of the proteins with definite molecular structures.

Chapter II

Isolation, Purification, and Determination of Proteins

A. Methods of Isolation. Since most proteins are extremely sensitive to heat, acids, bases, organic solvents, and, in some instances, even to distilled water, the methods generally employed for the isolation of other types of organic compounds can hardly be applied in protein chemistry. The *insoluble cellular proteins* can easily be prepared by extracting the cell with water and with organic solvents to remove fats, carbohydrates, and the soluble proteins. Since some of these soluble proteins are dissolved only in the presence of neutral salts, an extraction by dilute solutions of NaCl or sodium bicarbonate is frequently necessary. If the insoluble protein is resistant to proteolytic enzymes a further purification is achieved by treatment with pepsin at pH 1–2 or with trypsin at pH 8–9. In this way keratin, the insoluble protein of cornified tissues such as horn and hair, can be prepared.

Owing to their insolubility, keratin, collagen, fibroin, and other similar proteins cannot be purified by crystallization. It is impossible to ascertain, therefore, whether the preparations obtained by the usual methods are of a uniform nature or are mixtures of several different proteins.

The isolation and purification of *soluble proteins* involves their extraction from the cells by suitable solvents and their precipitation by altering the concentration of salts and/or of hydrogen ions, or by adding organic solvents. In many instances it has been possible to obtain *crystalline* precipitates by these procedures.

In order *to avoid denaturation* of the protein to be isolated one must work at low temperatures, since solutions of many proteins are subject to denaturation even at room temperature. This is especially true for solutions of proteins in salt-free water. The rate of denaturation is reduced by the addition of neutral salts. For example, crystalline trypsin can be stored in a saturated solution of magnesium sulfate (1). The rate of denaturation is also reduced by storing the protein solution at *low temperatures*. Refrigerators, refrigerated centrifuges, and cold rooms, therefore, form an important part of the equipment required for the preparation of proteins. At low temperatures a second important danger is also reduced, that of bacterial decomposition. Protein solutions form an excellent nutritional medium for bacteria and invariably become infected and are destroyed if kept at room temperature. Owing to the thermolability of protein solutions, they may not be sterilized by heat. Bacterial infection and growth can be inhibited by the addition of disinfectants, but these disinfectants form compounds with the proteins and alter their physicochemical properties. Most of the common disinfectants are denaturing agents and, therefore, cannot be used in preparing native proteins. Bacteria can be removed from protein solutions by centrifugation at high speed or by filtration through Seitz or Berkefeld filters or through filter pads.* The disadvantage of the filtration is that small portions of the protein are adsorbed to the porous filter mass and are lost by denaturation (3). Thus, the adsorption of gliadin to fritted-glass diaphragms was proved by measuring the electrokinetic potential of the glass diaphragms (3).

The best method for storing protein solutions over long periods of time is to keep them in a deep-freeze unit at approximately −10°C. At these temperatures bacteria cannot multiply, making it unnecessary to sterilize the solutions. Antibody solutions and enzyme solutions have been stored in the author's laboratory in the frozen state for many months, some of them for many years without any appreciable loss of their biological activity. One must avoid generalizations, however, since some of the solutions examined lost their antibody activity upon repeated thawing and freezing, although the temperature never was higher than 0°C. (4). Likewise lipoproteins are denatured by freezing and thawing (2). An increase in the activity of zymase is observed when the enzyme solution is frozen and subsequently thawed, the higher activity probably being due to a disaggregation of the enzyme particles in the solution (5). On the other hand it has been found that ovalbumin solutions, on ageing, showed higher turbidity, owing to the aggregation of the ovalbumin molecules, while the crystallizability of the protein was not affected by ageing (6).

The extraction of soluble proteins from tissue cells can only follow the *destruction of the cellular membranes,* since these are impermeable to the massive protein molecules. The destruction of cells can be accomplished mechanically by grinding them with sand or with kieselguhr. In these methods a part of the protein may be adsorbed to the silicate particles, and some denaturation may occur. It is preferable, therefore, to destroy the cells by suitable mills (Latapie mill, Potter-Elvehjem homogenizer). The cellular structure is also destroyed by the action of organic solvents such as alcohol, acetone, or *glycerol.* If the concentration of glycerol does not exceed 85% a large portion of the soluble protein passes into the glycerol extract. In this way hydrolytic enzymes can be

* In the Harvard Department of Physical Chemistry, Hormann or Republic filter pads are used (2).

extracted from the pancreas and other organs. Glycerol extracts are rather stable at room temperature. It would appear that the rate of denaturation is reduced by the loose association of glycerol molecules with the protein, due to the polar hydroxyl groups of glycerol. The same polar groups are responsible for the mutual attraction of glycerol molecules and for the high viscosity of this solvent. The preparation of pure proteins from their solutions in glycerol is very difficult and at present finds infrequent application. The Willstätter school used acetone for the destruction of cells. Use was made of the fact that denaturation of many proteins occurs very slowly in a medium containing more than 80–90% acetone. It is necessary, therefore, to mince the organ to be extracted or to grind it in a meat chopper and then to place the pulp into a large excess of acetone. The advantage of this procedure is that not only the cellular membranes are destroyed, but also that most of the lipids are extracted by the acetone. They can be removed quantitatively by a subsequent treatment with ether. The extracted residue is dried by spreading it over filter paper and is then extracted with water or with dilute solutions of salts or buffers. While many proteins and important enzymes withstand the action of acetone, other less stable proteins are denatured by the action of this solvent.

The simplest and best method for the destruction of the cellular membranes is disintegration by repeated *freezing and thawing*. Since pure ice particles are formed, the concentration of the salts in the cellular liquid increases during freezing, and the cellular membranes burst owing to the heightened osmotic pressure. Mechanical lesions of the cellular membranes by the ice particles may also be involved in the destruction of the cells. Similar osmotic effects are achieved by grinding cells or tissues with dry neutral salts.

The extracts prepared by any of the methods described above are centrifuged to remove insoluble particles. Salts, glycerol, and other substances can be removed by *dialysis* against distilled water. Some proteins are insoluble in salt-free water and are obtained directly as precipitates by dialysis. Thus crystals of horse oxyhemoglobin are formed when oxygen is passed through a solution of reduced horse hemoglobin (7,8). The tendency of rat oxyhemoglobin to crystallize is so great that crystals are formed when rat erythrocytes are mixed with five to ten volumes of water. Many of the vegetable proteins and the euglobulins of blood serum are insoluble in salt-free water and are obtained as precipitates upon prolonged dialysis.

In the past dialysis was performed in *membranes* of animal origin (gut), in parchment paper, or in collodion membranes. The disadvantage of animal membranes is their inhomogeneity, while that of parchment paper and of collodion is their high content of sulfuric and nitric acid ester groups. Many proteins are denatured by adsorption to these groups. The best material at present for dialyzers is cellulose, which is obtainable commercially as *Cellophane*. The only unfortunate feature of Cellophane is the small size of its pores, which renders the rate of diffusion very low, increasing the time required for dialysis and hence the danger of bacterial infection. It is advisable, therefore, to perform the dialysis in the refrigerator. The pore diameter of Cellophane can be increased by treating the membrane with aqueous solutions of zinc chloride. It would considerably facilitate laboratory work involving dialysis if Cellophane membranes of higher permeability were commercially obtainable. The most convenient material for small-scale laboratory experiments is Cellophane tubing; dialyzers of different sizes can easily be prepared by tieing off the tubing at one or at both ends to form sacs of the desired size. Dialysis time can be reduced by a factor of approximately one fourth by stirring the outer liquid. A further increase in the diffusion rate of electrolytes can be achieved by *electrodialysis;* however, one has to avoid acid and alkaline reactions near the surface of the membranes which separate the protein solution from the anodic and the cathodic liquids, respectively. A considerable portion of the protein is denatured when the reaction becomes strongly acid or alkaline.

While some proteins precipitate from their solutions upon dialysis, others are precipitated by the addition of neutral salts to their solutions (*"salting-out" method*). The usual procedure consists first of adjusting the pH of the solution to the isoelectric reaction of the particular protein, for the solubility of proteins has its minimum value here. A saturated solution of the salt or solid salt is next added to the stirred protein solution until a slight opalescence is observed. The solution is then kept at room temperature or in the refrigerator. If the concentration of salts is very high, bacterial multiplication is sharply reduced, so that one can frequently work at room temperature. The salts most frequently used for the precipitation of proteins are sodium sulfate or ammonium sulfate. Thus, if isoelectric solutions of serum albumin or ovalbumin are treated with ammonium sulfate (9) or with sodium sulfate (10) crystals of the albumins are slowly formed and settle at the bottom of the beaker containing the solution. The actual formation of the crystals is due to the slow evaporation of the solution. If an excess of the salt is added amorphous precipitates of the proteins are produced. Crystals can be obtained in such instances by dialysis of the protein solution against a saturated solution of ammonium sulfate.

Crystallization can also be achieved by *increasing the concentration of protein solutions*. While solutions of more stable substances are concentrated by evaporation on the steam bath or under reduced pressure, none of these methods can be applied in dealing with proteins. Heating on the steam bath would obviously denature the protein. It is surprising, however, that some proteins such as trypsin (1) or ribonuclease (11) are resistant to short heating at definite pH and ionic strength. Distillation at reduced pressure cannot be used for concentrating protein solutions, since foaming occurs under these conditions. Small volumes of protein solutions can easily be concentrated in desiccators under slightly reduced pressure over large amounts of water-binding substances. If it is intended to reduce the volume of larger amounts of protein solution, the solution can be placed in a Cellophane bag which is suspended in air in front of an electric fan (pervaporation). As the water evaporates from the surface of the bag, the protein solution becomes more concentrated (12). An increase in protein concentration is also achieved by applying positive or negative pressure during the dialysis (13).

Another method which can be applied to large volumes of protein solutions consists of freezing the solution solid and then thawing it very slowly, without any stirring or shaking. Crystals of ice nearly devoid of protein rise to the surface of the solution, while the bulk of the protein is concentrated in the solution in the lower part of the vessel. The concentrated protein solution is siphoned off and can be submitted repeatedly to the same procedure until high concentrations of protein are obtained. Human hemoglobin was obtained in this way in crystalline form by the author (14). A very efficient method for concentrating proteins is *freeze-drying* (15). A block of the frozen protein solution is exposed to a high vacuum in the presence of a substance which binds water. Sublimation of the ice from the surface of the block takes place. The protein is obtained as an air-dry powder (lyophile method) (16). While most proteins are thus obtained in the native state, some proteins are irreversibly inactivated or denatured by freezing, as was mentioned above.

One of the oldest methods for the preparation of crystalline proteins is the cautious addition of *ethanol* or *acetone* to the cold protein solution. Crystalline oxyhemoglobin was obtained from the blood of many animals in this way by Hoppe-Seyler, and also by Hüfner, toward the end of the last century. While these older methods were purely empirical and their results more or less fortuitous, the systematic purification of proteins by means of organic solvents was recently introduced and successfully elaborated by Cohn, Edsall, Oncley, and co-workers (17). The methodical application of ethanol and other organic solvents is based on the fact that these solvents reduce the dielectric constant of the aqueous protein solutions. The opposite effect, an increase in the dielectric constant, is achieved by the addition of glycine. Since the solubility of proteins depends to a large extent on the dielectric constant of the solvent, these methods can be used for the stepwise reduction of the solubility of proteins and for their separation in crystalline form. Obviously other physicochemical conditions such as temperature, pH, and ionic strength have to be controlled in such a procedure. By varying these conditions the separation of certain protein fractions can be achieved. The results of these methods are described more extensively in Chapter VIII.

Evidently the methods outlined above can be applied repeatedly when it is desired to purify the isolated protein. Soluble proteins can thus be purified by recrystallization. Sometimes it is advantageous to combine different methods of purification in order to remove different sorts of impurities.

B. Fractionation of Protein Mixtures. The extracts of cells or of organs consist of a mixture of various proteins. The same is true for the blood serum and other body fluids. By cautiously increasing or reducing the ionic strength or the dielectric constant of the solution and by adjusting the pH of the solution to the isoelectric point of the different proteins, pure proteins or fractions containing the bulk of one of them can be prepared. The classical method for the preparation of albumins and globulins from the blood serum is based on the fractional addition of ammonium sulfate (see p. 148, Chapter VIII, Sect. B).

In many papers the concentration of the ammonium sulfate used is recorded as the percentage of a saturated solution. Thus a solution containing equal parts of water and of a saturated solution of ammonium sulfate is described as 50% saturated. This mode of designation is rather inaccurate because the saturation depends to a certain degree on the temperature of the solution. It is preferable, therefore, to record the concentration of the ammonium sulfate in the more usual way, *i.e.*, by indication of its molarity. The fractional precipitation with ammonium sulfate or with ethanol has been applied successfully by Cohn and co-workers to the fractionation of serum proteins and a large number of fractions containing biologically active proteins has been prepared in this way (see Chapter VIII). The alcohol method is superior to other methods when proteins are to be prepared on a large scale, since most of the alcohol is easily removed by evaporation, whereas the removal of salts by dialysis is time-consuming and laborious. The essential feature of the new method is, however, the systematic variation of the ionic strength, the hydrogen ion concentration, the temperature, and the dielectric constant of the solution. By varying these factors systematically a large number of new proteins were isolated from the blood serum.

The preparation of a pure protein from its mixtures has in some instances been facilitated by the selective denaturation of the other proteins present. Thus, crude trypsin was purified by heating its solution in 0.5 *N* hydrochloric acid to 90° (18). Inert proteins were removed in this way.

C. Criteria for the Purity of Proteins. In organic chemistry the formation of homogeneous, *uniform crystals* is generally considered conclusive evidence of the uniformity of a compound. If the crystals have a reproducible melting point which remains unchanged after recrystallization, their homogeneity is considered definitely established. This criterion cannot be applied to protein crystals, because proteins decompose when they are heated. Until recently the ability of some proteins to crystallize was considered an indication of their homogeneity. This assumption is, however, invalidated by the electrophoretic behavior of crystalline proteins. Ovalbumin, which can be recrystallized easily, and which had been considered for a long time to be a pure and uniform substance, was found to be a mixture of at least two components which can be separated electrophoretically (19). Similarly crystalline serum albumin (20) and crystalline ricin from castor beans (21) have been shown to be mixtures of two or more compounds. There is no doubt, therefore, that crystallizability alone cannot be taken as a criterion for the purity of a protein.

Solubility has been used as another criterion. It is evident that the solubility of a homogeneous substance is constant and is not altered by an excess of the solid substance. It is hardly possible to apply this method to the solubility of proteins in pure water, because the solubility of proteins is highly dependent on traces of electrolytes and of hydrogen or hydroxyl ions. The influence of these substances can be eliminated if a concentrated salt solution is used as the solvent. When the solubility of crystalline ovalbumin or of carboxyhemoglobin in ammonium sulfate solutions was examined in this way (22), it was found that the solubility was not strictly independent of the amount in the insoluble phase, and it was concluded, therefore, that their molecules must be regarded as systems of reversibly dissociable components. Very careful determinations of the solubility of crystalline chymotrypsinogen (23) and ribonuclease (24) show that these proteins behave as single compounds. It is highly significant that these uniform proteins are enzymes (see Chapter XII).

In recent years *electrophoresis* (see Chapter V, Sect. D) *at different pH values* has been used as a method to test the homogeneity of proteins. It was shown in this way that crystalline ovalbumin, beef serum globulin, β-lactoglobulin, and *all* other proteins examined by this method were mixtures of several proteins (25). It must be considered entirely possible that completely uniform protein molecules do not exist, and that each of the so-called pure proteins is in reality a mixture of very similar protein molecules. Whether the heterogeneity revealed by electrophoresis or by solubility analysis is brought about during the isolation of proteins from their natural medium or whether this heterogeneity exists as such in the cell and in the body fluids remains obscure.

Actually it has been found that the crystalline shape of ovalbumin, its electrophoretic behavior, and its molecular weight are altered by exposure to *Bacillus subtilis* (26). Small amounts of nitrogenous substances are split off and a new similar protein, plakalbumin, is formed. Analogous changes in the properties of ovalbumin were observed on aging of the solutions (27). It is quite possible that similar alterations in the physicochemical behavior of proteins are brought about by the methods of isolation. Obviously, a clear-cut answer to this problem is of the utmost importance. The interpretation of chemical and physicochemical analyses of proteins depends in large measure upon a solution of this problem.

While the formation of crystals and the investigation of the physicochemical properties of protein solutions furnish some criteria of the uniformity or heterogeneity of soluble proteins, no evidence of this sort is available for insoluble proteins such as keratin and collagen. We do not know, therefore, whether these proteins are uniform or whether they are mixtures of different proteins.

D. Color Reactions of Proteins. The textbooks of biochemistry enumerate various color reactions of proteins. Most of these reactions are given by certain amino acids and will be discussed in Chapter III. The phenolic side chain of tyrosine is responsible for the yellow color produced by nitric acid in the xanthoproteic reaction, for the red color given by Millon's reagent, for the diazo test, and for the blue color given in the alkaline solutions of phosphomolybdates. The color reactions brought about by aldehydes such as dimethylaminobenzaldehyde (Ehrlich) or glyoxylic acid (Hopkins-Cole) are due to the presence of tryptophan; the red color reaction with hypochlorite and α-napthol is a reaction of arginine (Sakaguchi), while the dark coloration formed when alkaline solutions of lead acetate are heated with proteins is due to the presence of cystine or cysteine. Occasionally use is made of these reactions for the quantitative colorimetric determination of proteins. It is obvious, however, that the intensity of each of these reactions varies from protein to protein, depending on the percentage of the respective amino acid in the protein molecule.

In this regard the *biuret reaction* differs from all the color reactions mentioned above. The biuret reaction performed by adding a dilute solution of copper sulfate to a strongly alkaline solution of the protein produces a purplish-violet color. Since the same reaction is given by all polypeptides, it is due to the presence of peptide bonds, —CONH—, in the protein molecule. It is assumed that a complex is formed, wherein the copper ion is coordinated with the peptide bond, to form a copper-containing ring of the probable structure:

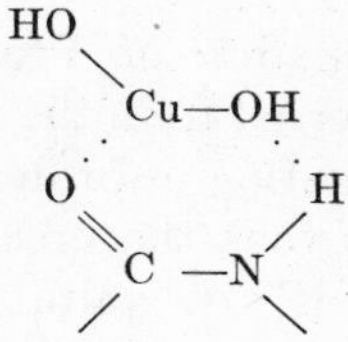

```
HO
  \
   Cu—OH
  .     .
 O       H
  \\    /
   C —N
  /     \
```

or of another similar coordination compound (27*a*). The biuret test is not very sensitive. Its value for scientific purposes is, therefore, restricted. One is not entitled to consider solutions devoid of proteins when the biuret test is negative. On the other hand, a positive biuret test is also given by the amino acid histidine.

In addition to the color reactions of their amino acids and to the biuret test most proteins give a positive Molisch test, *i.e.*, a red color with α-naphthol and sulfuric acid. It is caused by small amounts of carbohydrates present in many proteins.

E. Irreversible Precipitation of Proteins. Proteins are precipitated by the salts of heavy metals (Cu, Pb, Hg, UO_2, Fe), by a series of organic acids including trichloroacetic acid, salicylsulfonic acid, and picric acid, and by colloidal acids (*e.g.*, tungstic acid, tannic acid) and bases (ferric hydroxide). These precipitants, in general, cannot be used for the preparation of pure proteins because many proteins are denatured by their action. Recently it has been found, however, that the heavy-metal salts of some proteins can be obtained in crystalline form if the metal salt is added cautiously and an excess is avoided (28). The proteins are prepared in their native state from their compounds with zinc or other heavy metal salts (28*a*).

If an excess of the precipitating reagents is added to protein solutions, the proteins are denatured and quantitatively precipitated. This method finds extensive use in clinical laboratories in the deproteinization of biological fluids, in the quantitative determination of proteins in the blood serum and similar fluids, and as a qualitative test for the presence of proteins in urine and other biological solutions.

While it is very difficult to separate the precipitated denatured protein from the precipitating agents mentioned above, the protein can be obtained easily in the denatured state by heat coagulation or by Sevag's method (29). In this method the protein is denatured and rendered insoluble by shaking with chloroform. The excess of chloroform is removed by evaporation.

The irreversible precipitation of proteins by phosphotungstic acid has been used as a histochemical test for proteins in tissue sections. The absorption of X rays by the heavy tungsten atom in the dried tissue slices is measured (30).

F. Quantitative Determination of Proteins (31). The precipitate produced by the reagents referred to in the preceding section can be used for the quantitative determination of proteins by Kjeldahl analysis. In this procedure it is assumed that the precipitate contains only protein nitrogen. This assumption is not quite justified because some high-molecular polysaccharidic acids such as chondroitin sulfuric acid and certain nitrogen-containing lipids, such as lecithins or cephalins are precipitated along with the proteins. The Kjeldahl determination consists of converting all the nitrogen into ammonium sulfate by boiling the protein with concentrated sulfuric acid and potassium sulfate in the presence of a catalyst. It is usually assumed that the nitrogen content of all proteins is 16%. Actually this value varies considerably. While ovalbumin contains 15.75% nitrogen, edestin contains 18.7% (32). It is necessary, therefore, to accurately determine the nitrogen content of the protein to be analyzed. Although the Kjeldahl method is one of the standard methods employed in biochemical laboratories, it has been found that the values obtained in the customary procedure are frequently too low. Reliable values have only been obtained with the use of mercury as a catalyst (33,34). The heating of the protein with sulfuric acid, potassium sulfate, and the catalyst should be continued for eight hours (32). When these precautions are observed, precise results are obtained with proteins whose nitrogen-content is known. It is of interest that proteins having an abnormal nitrogen content have been identified in certain pathological body tissues. Thus, proteins containing less nitrogen than the normal serum proteins are found in patients suffering from famine edema (35).

The original Kjeldahl method is rather complicated because it involves distillation or steam distillation of the ammonia formed. Attempts have been made to simplify the method by avoiding the distillation. The ammonium sulfate formed can be oxidized directly by NaOBr and the excess of the hypobromite titrated iodometrically (36). The ammonia content can also be determined colorimetrically by means of Nessler's reagent. Another simplifying modification was introduced by Conway, who devised the distillation of ammonia at room temperature in a closed "unit" (Fig. 1) consisting of two concentric compartments (37,38). In spite of these endeavors toward simplification, the Kjeldahl method remains a tedious procedure. Attempts have been made to replace it by a simpler nephelometric or colorimetric determination of proteins. Nephelometry furnishes only approximate values, the turbidity produced by one of the precipitating agents depending in part upon concentration of salts and other contaminants. Better results have been obtained by the colorimetric evaluation of the biuret reaction (39–41).

Since the specific gravity of the blood serum is largely determined by its protein content, the latter has been evaluated by measuring the specific gravity of the serum in a gradient tube containing a mixture of bromobenzene and kerosene (42). Standardization of the gradient tube is accomplished by using potassium sulfate solutions of differing densities. Copper sulfate solutions have also been used for gradient tubes. Neither of these methods is free from error (43,44), due to the partial dependency

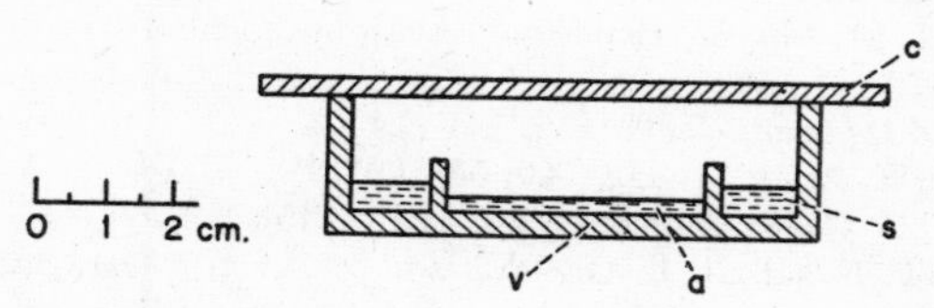

FIG. 1. Cross section through a Conway unit (37). *v*, reaction vessel; *c*, glass cover; *a*, inner compartment containing acid; *s*, solution of ammonium salts made alkaline by potassium carbonate. Diameter of unit, 70 mm.

of the specific gravity of the sera on their content of substances other than proteins.

It is evident from this discussion that the quantitative determination of proteins is no simple procedure. If large amounts of the protein are at hand and if it can be precipitated quantitatively by boiling or by adjusting the isoelectric pH value, the precipitate so formed can be dried and weighed. The main difficulty here consists in removing salts and other soluble compounds, since protein precipitates frequently give rise to colloidal solutions when they are washed with salt-free water. This can often be avoided by washing with dilute acetic acid or by methanol–water (1:1), followed by acetone and ether.

If it is desired to determine very small amounts of protein use can be made of the intensive ultraviolet absorption of tyrosine at 280 mμ (45) or of the blue color caused by the reducing action of proteins on Folin's phenol reagent (*i.e.*, phosphomolybdic acid) (46). Both methods are very simple and rapid. It must not be forgotten, however, that the intensity of the ultraviolet absorption and of the blue color reaction depend on the content of tyrosine and the other aromatic amino acids, and that their percentage varies from protein to protein. It is necessary, therefore, to use a sample of the protein to be determined for standardization.

References

1. J. H. Northrop, M. Kunitz, *J. Gen. Physiol.* **16,** 267 (1932).
2. J. T. Edsall, personal communication.
3. W. M. Martin, *J. Phys. Chem.* **38,** 213 (1934).
4. F. Haurowitz, unpublished experiments.
5. F. F. Nord, *Ber.* **65,** 1148 (1932).
6. M. Bier, F. F. Nord, *Proc. Natl. Acad. Sci. U. S.* **35,** 17 (1949).
7. F. Haurowitz, *Z. physiol. Chem.* **136,** 147 (1924).
8. M. Heidelberger, *J. Biol. Chem.* **53,** 34 (1922).
9. S. Sørensen and M. Høyrup, *Z. physiol. Chem.* **103,** 16 (1918).
10. G. S. Adair, M. Robinson, *Biochem. J.* **24,** 993 (1930).
11. R. J. Dubos, R. H. S. Thompson, *J. Biol. Chem.* **124,** 501 (1938).
12. L. Farber, *Science* **82,** 158 (1935).
13. E. A. Kabat, M. M. Mayer, Experimental Immunochemistry. Thomas, Springfield, 1948, p. 429.
14. F. Haurowitz, *Z. physiol. Chem.* **186,** 141 (1930).
15. G. S. Adair, M. E. Adair, *J. Hyg.* **40,** 548 (1940).
16. E. W. Flosdorf, *J. Chem. Education* **22,** 470 (1945).
17. E. J. Cohn, J. T. Edsall, J. L. Oncley, *et al.*, *J. Am. Chem. Soc.* **68,** 459 (1946); **71,** 541 (1949).
18. J. H. Northrop, Crystalline Enzymes. Columbia Univ. Press, New York, 1948, p. 268.
19. L. G. Longsworth, R. K. Cannan, *J. Am. Chem. Soc.* **62,** 2580 (1940).
20. D. G. Sharp, G. R. Cooper, H. Neurath, *J. Biol. Chem.* **144,** 139 (1942).
21. M. Kunitz , M. McDonald, *J. Gen. Physiol.* **32,** 25 (1948).
22. S. Sørensen, *Compt. rend. trav. lab. Carlsberg. Sèr. chim.* **18,** No. 5 (1930); **19,** No. 11 (1933).
23. M. Kunitz, J. H. Northrop, *Cold Spring Harbor Symposia Quant. Biol.* **6,** 325 (1938).
24. M. Kunitz, *J. Gen. Physiol.* **24,** 15 (1940).
25. E. A. Anderson, R. A. Alberty, *J. Phys. Colloid Chem.* **52,** 345 (1948).
26. K. Linderstrøm-Lang, M. Ottesen, *Nature* **159,** 807 (1947); *Compt. rend. trav. lab. Carlsberg. Sèr chim.* **26,** 404 (1948).
27. G. E. Perlmann, *Nature* **161,** 720 (1948); C. A. Villee *et al.*, *Federation Proc.* **9,** 241 (1950).

27*a*. I. M. Klotz *et al.*, *J. Phys. Colloid Chem.* **54,** 18 (1950).

28. W. L. Hughes, *J. Am. Chem. Soc.* **69,** 1836 (1947).

28*a*. E. J. Cohn *et al.*, *J. Am. Chem. Soc.* **72,** 465 (1950).

29. M. Sevag, D. B. Lackman, J. Smolens, *J. Biol. Chem.* **124,** 425 (1938).
30. A. Engström, M. A. Jakus, *Nature* **161,** 168 (1948).
31. P. L. Kirk, *Advances in Protein Chem.* **3,** 139 (1947).
32. A. C. Chibnall, M. W. Rees, E. F. Williams, *Biochem. J.* **37,** 354 (1943).
33. L. Miller, J. A. Houghton, *J. Biol. Chem.* **159,** 373 (1945).
34. A. Hiller, J. Plazin, D. D. Van Slyke, *J. Biol. Chem.* **176,** 1401 (1948).
35. B. B. Lloyd, H. M. Sinclair, M. C. K. Tweedie, *Biochem. J.* **43,** XVII (1948).
36. F. Rappaport, G. Geiger, *Mikrochemie* **18,** 43 (1935).
37. E. J. Conway, A. Byrne, *Biochem. J.* **27,** 419 (1933). E. J. Conway and E. O'Malley, **36,** 655 (1942).

38. K. Steinitz, *J. Lab. Clin. Med.* **25,** 288 (1939).
39. J. Fine, *Biochem. J.* **29,** 799 (1935).
40. A. Hiller, J. Plazin, D. D. Van Slyke, *J. Biol. Chem.* **176,** 1401 (1948).
41. H. A. Stiff, Jr., *J. Biol. Chem.* **177,** 179 (1949).
42. O. H. Lowry, T. Hunter, *J. Biol. Chem.* **159,** 564 (1945).
43. H. Hoch, J. R. Marrack, *Biochem. J.* **39,** xxxviii (1945).
44. J. Harkness, R. Wittington, *Anal. Chim. Acta* **1,** 249 (1947).
45. H. Eisen, *J. Immunol.* **60,** 77 (1948).
46. M. Heidelberger, C. F. C. McPherson, *Science* **97,** 405 (1943).

Chapter III

Hydrolytic Cleavage of Proteins

A. Methods of Hydrolysis. Acids, bases, and enzymes are the agents used for the hydrolytic cleavage of proteins. In most of the hydrolyses boiling *hydrochloric acid* has been utilized to effect the reaction. Since the constant boiling acid contains only 20.5% HCl, the commercial concentrated acid, which contains 35% HCl is diluted before use. The dry protein is mixed with approximately 10 volumes of the 20.5% acid and kept in a boiling water bath for 30 to 60 minutes. By this procedure the formation of froth during hydrolysis is avoided. Total hydrolysis is achieved by refluxing the protein for 12 to 48 hours with the boiling hydrochloric acid, after which time most of the acid can be removed by distillation or, preferably, by vacuum distillation. The residue contains hydrochlorides of the amino acids which are converted into the amino acids by treatment with moist silver oxide. This procedure is complicated, however, by the formation of complex silver salts by some of the amino acids. It is advantageous to replace the hydrochloric acid by *sulfuric acid* when it is intended to isolate the amino acids. The concentration of the sulfuric acid employed for protein hydrolysis is approximately 8 *N* (20 ml. in 100 ml. solution). The acid is removed from the hydrolyzate by the addition of the equivalent amount of barium hydroxide. The heavy precipitate of barium sulfate must subsequently be extracted several times with boiling water in order to remove the considerable amounts of amino acids which have been adsorbed. The filtrates and washings are evaporated, leaving a mixture of the amino acids.

The advantage of acid hydrolysis is that racemization is avoided, the amino acids being obtained as L-amino acids. Most of the amino acids are resistant to boiling mineral acids. However tryptophan is completely destroyed by the action of boiling acid; moreover, a small portion of the hydroxyamino acids, serine and threonine, undergoes destruction during the acid hydrolysis. The decomposition products of tryptophan are converted into a dark brown substance called humin; it is probably formed by the condensation of the indole nucleus of tryptophan with small amounts of aldehydes which are produced during the hydrolysis (1). The formation of these dark humin substances is prevented by adding tin to the sulfuric acid used for hydrolysis. Although tryptophan is destroyed under these conditions, the oxidation of cysteine to cystine is prevented by the reducing action of tin (2). Another method employed for the same purpose is hydrolysis with an aqueous solution containing 20% HCl and 50% formic acid (3).

The decomposition of tryptophan is avoided when the hydrolysis is conducted with boiling dilute *alkali* or with *baryta*. Since the hydrolyzing action of these bases is very strong, complete hydrolysis is achieved within 10 hours by 4 *N* barium hydroxide (3*a*). The hydrolyzates thus obtained are colorless and free of humin. The disadvantage of the alkaline hydrolysis is that the amino acids undergo racemization, that some of them are deaminated, that arginine is converted into ornithine and urea, and that cystine and cysteine are destroyed by the alkali hydroxides.

Hydrolysis can also be achieved by the action of *proteolytic enzymes*. Although this hydrolysis occurs under very mild conditions, it is rarely utilized for preparative purposes, the reason being that a very long time is necessary for the complete reaction and that the enzymes used as hydrolyzing agents are proteins themselves. The hydrolyzate, therefore, is contaminated with residues from the split enzyme molecules.

If a more complete understanding of the structure of the protein molecules is sought, *partial hydrolysis* may be applied and examination made of the peptide fractions obtained. Partial hydrolysis is achieved by reducing the time of hydrolysis, by decreasing the concentration of the hydrolyzing agent, or by working at lower temperatures (3*b*). Thus a peptide of histidine was obtained from globin using 25 *N* sulfuric acid at 40°C. (4). Similarly dipeptides were isolated from hydrolyzates produced by the action of concentrated hydrochloric acid at 37°C. (5). The formation of peptides indicates that the resistance of various peptide bonds to the hydrolyzing agent is different. Thus only 56 of the peptide bonds of ovalbumin were split rapidly when the protein was exposed to the action of 23% hydrochloric acid at temperatures between 30 and 60°C. (5*a*).

Enzymes can also be used for partial hydrolysis and in this way it has been possible to obtain asparagine (6) and glutamine (7) from edestin and gliadin, respectively. In the usual total hydrolysis, both amides are hydrolyzed to aspartic or glutamic acid and ammonia. Since each of the proteolytic enzymes hydrolyzes only certain types of peptide bonds, leaving the other ones along the chain of the protein molecule uncleaved, different peptide mixtures are obtained by the action of different enzymes. Thus, peptides containing nitrogen-bound proline molecules are attacked by erepsin but not by trypsin (8).

B. Determination of Rate of Hydrolysis. The hydrolysis of proteins consists of the cleavage of peptide bonds according to the following formula:

$$R \cdot CO \cdot NH \cdot R' \xrightarrow{+H_2O} R \cdot COOH + R' \cdot NH_2$$

The extent of hydrolysis can be ascertained at any point by measuring the increase in carboxyl, in amino groups, or in both. All three methods have been applied.

The *increase in carboxyl groups* is followed by titration with alkali in the presence of formaldehyde or ethanol. The *formol titration* was first applied by Sørensen (9) and was originally explained by the formation of *N*-methylene compounds of the formula $R \cdot N{=}CH_2$. Although this interpretation is erroneous (see Chapter VII, Sect. E), it is to be assumed that the formaldehyde does undergo a condensation with the amino groups, so that the basicity of these groups is greatly reduced. Most probably mono- or dimethylol compounds of the formulas $R \cdot NH \cdot CH_2OH$ or $R \cdot N(CH_2OH)_2$, respectively, are formed (9*a*,9*b*). The number of carboxyl groups in amino acids or proteins can also be determined by titration in ethanol (10). The ethanol titration is rendered possible by a shift of the pK value of phenolphthalein used as an indicator; while the color change in aqueous solution occurs near pH 9, it takes place in alcoholic solution near pH 12 (10*a*). At these high pH values the positively charged $\overset{+}{N}H_3$ groups are converted into uncharged NH_2 groups which cannot neutralize the anionic COO^- groups (see Chapter V, Sect. A).

Because amino acids are weaker acids than are peptides (see Chapter V, Sect. A, Table VI) the hydrolysis of peptides is accompanied by a slight decrease in acidity. If carbon dioxide and bicarbonate are present, absorption of carbon dioxide results and the decrease of the carbon dioxide pressure can be measured manometrically in the Warburg apparatus (11).

The classical method for the *determination of free amino groups* liberated during the hydrolysis is the method of Van Slyke (12), which is based upon the reaction of nitrous acid with primary amino groups to form nitrogen gas:

$$R \cdot NH_2 + HONO \rightarrow R \cdot OH + N_2 + H_2O$$

While the α-amino groups of amino acids and the terminal α-amino groups of peptides react very rapidly with nitrous acid, the ϵ-amino groups of lysine react very slowly. A slow formation of nitrogen gas is also caused by ammonia, which is split off by hydrochloric acid from the amide groups of asparagine and glutamine (12). The volume of the nitrogen formed may be measured at atmospheric pressure or manometrically under reduced pressure (13). The Van Slyke method provides excellent results with most of the amino acids and peptides; however, account must be taken of the fact that nitrous acid itself is converted into nitrogen by strongly reducing substances such as cysteine (14). Amounts of nitrogen in excess of the theoretical are also produced by glycine and its peptides (15,16).

The number of amino groups liberated during hydrolysis can also be found by titration with hydrochloric acid in acetone, using naphthyl red as the indicator (17). A similar method is to titrate with perchloric acid, using glacial acetic acid as solvent and brilliant cresyl blue as the indicator (18). In the course of hydrolysis, free water molecules disappear in accordance with the equation:

$$R{\cdot}CO{\cdot}NH{\cdot}R' + H_2O \rightarrow R{\cdot}COOH + R'{\cdot}NH_2$$

The reaction is, therefore, accompanied by a decrease in the total volume which can be measured dilatometrically. This method has been refined to the extent where the rate of enzymatic hydrolysis can be followed in a single drop of the reaction mixture (19).

While the methods outlined above enable us to determine the number of amino and carboxyl groups liberated during the hydrolysis, they do not provide a means of distinguishing between *free amino acids* and peptides. Such a differentiation is accomplished by using reagents which react with the carboxyl and the α-amino group of the same amino acid molecule at the same time. The most important of these reagents is triketohydrindene hydrate, the trade name of which is *ninhydrin*. If ninhydrin is heated with an aqueous solution of an α-amino acid, the amino acid is split oxidatively into the corresponding aldehyde, carbon dioxide, and ammonia:

```
      H       O
      C       C
   //   \   /   \       OH
HC        C       \   /
|         ||        C          + R·CHNH₂·COOH
HC        C       /   \              Amino acid
   \\   /   \   /       OH
      C       C
      H       O
     Ninhydrin

                        H       O
                        C       C
                     //   \   /   \       H
                  HC        C       \   /
          →       |         ||        C          + CO₂ + R·CHO + NH
                  HC        C       /   \
                     \\   /   \   /       OH
                        C       C
                        H       O
```

The aldehyde formed immediately condenses with the reduction product of ninhydrin to give a blue dye, whose concentration is colorimetrically measurable (20). If the heating with ninhydrin is performed at pH 1–5, the carbon dioxide evolved can be measured by gas analysis methods and the amount of free amino acids can be determined. Neither proteins nor peptides give a reaction under these conditions (21).

C. Fractionation and Isolation of Amino Acids and Peptides (22). Methods for the separation and isolation of all amino acids have become available only recently. Previously it was necessary to be content with the separation of certain classes of amino acids. Thus the *basic amino acids* arginine, lysine, and histidine were precipitated by phosphotungstic acid and were separated from each other by precipitation with silver sulfate at different pH values (23).

The principal procedure used for the fractionation of the *monoamino acid* mixtures was the fractional *distillation of their esters* as described in the classical papers of Fischer (24).

According to this method the protein was hydrolyzed with hydrochloric acid, and the insoluble chloride of glutamic acid was first obtained as a crystalline precipitate on cooling the hydrolyzate. After the removal of glutamic acid, the excess of hydrochloric acid was removed by evaporation under reduced pressure and the residue, containing the chlorides of the other amino acids, was esterified by treatment with absolute ethanol and gaseous hydrochloric acid. The insoluble ester of glycine was separated by centrifuging. The chlorides of the other amino acid esters were neutralized by alkali hydroxide, alkali carbonate, alkali ethylate, or by other bases. Distillation *in vacuo* furnished the following fractions:

Fraction I (60°C., 10 mm.) glycine, alanine, leucine, proline
Fraction II (100°C., 10 mm.) valine, leucine, proline
Fraction III (100°C., 0.5 mm.) leucine, proline
Fraction IV (180°C., 0.5 mm.) phenylalanine, glutamic acid, aspartic acid, serine.

The distillation involves great losses, so that the results are far from quantitative. But it was by this method that the peptidelike structure of the proteins and their content of amino acids was conclusively established. The difficulties of the ester distillation led to the search for other, simpler procedures. Important results were obtained by the fractional extraction of amino acids from the hydrolyzate by means of butanol (25).

In the last few years new methods for fractionating protein hydrolyzates have been developed. One of the most efficient of the new procedures is based on the *adsorption of amino acids* by different adsorbents. Thus the aminodicarboxylic acids, aspartic and glutamic acids, are adsorbed by basic adsorbents such as aluminum oxide (26,27) or Amberlite IR-4 (28). While glutamic acid is eluted from the adsorbent by dilute acetic acid, aspartic acid is bound more firmly but can be recovered by the action of 0.5 *N* sodium hydroxide (26). If acid adsorbents such as acid aluminum oxide (27), Amberlite IR 100-H, a phenolic formaldehyde resin (29), or sulfonated phenolic Amberlites (30) are used, the basic diamino acids are adsorbed. When the bases are eluted by treatment with acids, the resin is reactivated in the process and can be used again for other adsorptions (31). From the filtrate containing the monoamino acids, tyrosine and phenylalanine are removed by adsorption to animal charcoal (32). Glycine, serine, threonine, and cysteine are adsorbed by acid alumina following the addition of formaldehyde to the amino acid solution (33).

Synge (34,34*a*) has made use of the *partition* of amino acids between water and butanol, phenol or collidine, *i.e.*, organic solvents which are

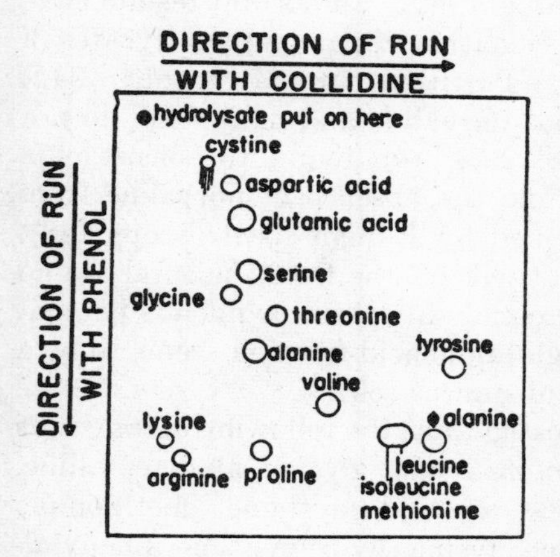

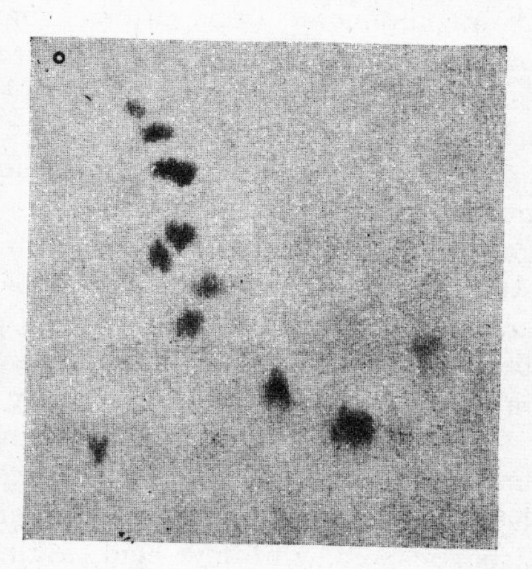

FIG. 2. Two-dimensional chromatogram of a wool hydrolyzate (22). First run with collidine; second run with phenol. 300γ protein used.

immiscible with but partly soluble in water. Mixtures of amino acids are adsorbed on starch (35,36), silica gel (37), or on filter paper strips (38,39), while the organic solvent, saturated with water, flows through the adsorbent. The amino acids are extracted by the solvent at different rates, and are in this way separated from each other. Further fractionation can be achieved by the subsequent application of a second solvent. If filter paper is used as the solid phase and the direction of the flow of the two solvents differs by 90°, the mixtures of amino acids are resolved into "spots" which can be made visible by the ninhydrin test (see Fig. 2). Each of the spots consists of a single amino acid, so that by this method the separation of all amino acids is possible. The ratio "flow rate of amino acid to flow rate of the pure solvent" is a typical constant for each amino acid and has been designated by the symbol R_f. The intensity of the ninhydrin "spots" can be measured spectrophotometrically by the determination of the transmission of the filter paper; in this way a quantitative determination of the various amino acids is possible (12*a*).

While the British authors used extraction by a descending solvent, paper chromatography by capillary ascent has recently been recommended as preferable (40). If radioactive derivatives of amino acids such as *p*-iodophenylsulfonyl derivatives containing I^{131} or S^{35} are used in partition chromatography, the amount of the various amino acids can be determined by measuring the intensity of radiation (41).

In addition to amino acids themselves, mixtures of amino acid derivatives (37,42) and peptide mixtures (43,44) can be resolved into their components by partition chromatography. Important results have been obtained in this way by the fractionation of partial hydrolyzates of insulin (45) and of gramicidin (46). Partition chromatography (34*a*) has provided the important proof that norvaline and norleucine do not exist in proteins (22). "Norleucine" has been found to consist of a mixture of D- and L-leucine (47), while the absence of norvaline from gelatin hydrolyzates has been confirmed by Raman spectroscopy (48). Another amino acid which must be struck off the list of natural amino acids is hydroxyglutamic acid; its presence in casein could not be confirmed (49). The so-called hydroxyglutamic acid fraction seems to be a mixture of aspartic acid with other substances (50).

As a result of these and other investigations the following *amino acids* are to be considered *present in protein molecules:* glycine, alanine, valine, leucine, isoleucine, serine, threonine, cystine, cysteine, methionine, aspartic acid, glutamic acid, arginine, lysine, hydroxylysine, phenylalanine, tyrosine, proline, hydroxyproline, histidine, and tryptophan. Since the amount of these amino acids in some of the proteins which have been analyzed accounts for more than 99% of the total nitrogen content it is apparent that no appreciable amounts of other unknown substances can be present in the molecules of these proteins. That one must, however, beware of generalizations is illustrated by the finding of aminoethanol among the hydrolysis products of gramicidin (see Chapter XV, Sect. B, b) and of diiodo- and dibromotyrosine among those of corals (51) and of spongin (52).

D. Determination of Amino Acids in Proteins and in Protein Hydrolyzates. Since the reactive groups of some amino acids are free even when the amino acids are linked to a peptide chain through their amino and carboxyl groups, attempts have been made to determine these amino acids by measuring the intensity of the color reactions rendered by the protein. It is very doubtful whether such a procedure is justified, for it has been found that the color reaction given by proteins is generally weaker than that given by its hydrolyzate. This is probably due to the fact that some of the reactive groups are hidden inside the globular protein molecules and hence are inaccessible to the color-producing reagents (see Chapter VII, Sect. M).

If it is desired to determine all the amino acids of a protein, it is necessary to hydrolyze the protein completely. Most of the amino acids are determined in the acid hydrolyzate, some of them in another hydrolyzate obtained by barium hydroxide (see Sect. A, above). The separation of the different amino acids from each other is a difficult problem, because all of them are zwitterions, easily soluble in water and insoluble in organic solvents such as ethanol. Only the imino acids proline and hydroxyproline are soluble in ethanol. Owing to their similar physicochemical behavior, the amino acids cannot be separated by fractional addition of alcohol or of neutral salts; however, the solubility of cystine at neutral reaction and that of tyrosine at slightly acid reaction is so low, that the bulk of these two amino acids can be precipitated by adjusting the pH to the proper value. Other amino acids can be precipitated by the addition of suitable precipitating reagents. However, none of these methods is fully satisfactory, because all the precipitates are soluble to a certain extent.

These difficulties of the quantitative precipitation of amino acids have partly been overcome by the "isotope dilution method" (53). To determine a certain amino acid in a hydrolyzate a small amount of the same amino acid containing an isotopic element is added to the hydrolyzate. Precipitation is then brought about by a suitable treatment and the concentration of the isotope in the precipitate and in the supernatant is determined. Since:

$$\frac{\text{isotope in supernatant}}{\text{isotope in precipitate}} = \frac{\text{amino acid in supernatant}}{\text{amino acid in precipitate}}$$

the amount of the respective amino acid in the original hydrolyzate can be calculated. If C_0 is the isotope content of the amino acid added, and C_s, the isotope content of the specimen of amino acid isolated, then B, its amount in the original hydrolyzate, is:

$$B = A(C_0/C_s - 1)$$

where A is the amount of amino acid added. The great advantage of this method is that it can be applied even when the precipitation is incomplete and that no error is introduced by the coprecipitation of other substances which are devoid of the element used as an isotopic label. Glycine, leucine, aspartic and glutamic acids, phenylalanine, tyrosine, arginine, and lysine have been determined in this manner (53). The isotopic elements N^{15}, C^{14}, S^{35}, and deuterium have been used to label the amino acids. In experiments with deuterium it must be borne in mind that α-deuterium atoms are slowly exchanged with hydrogen atoms when the amino acid is boiled with 20% hydrochloric acid (54). Deuterium atoms in β- or γ-position are stable under these conditions (54).

The results of the isotopic dilution method are impaired if the isolated compound is contaminated by compounds containing the element used as an isotopic label. Thus, the ratio C_0/C_s in experiments with N^{15} will, obviously, be altered by the coprecipitation of other amino acids. In order to overcome this difficulty it has been proposed to convert all of the amino acid examined into an isotopically labeled derivative, and to separate it from the isotopic derivatives of the other amino acids by the addition of an overwhelming amount of the nonlabeled derivative (54*a*);

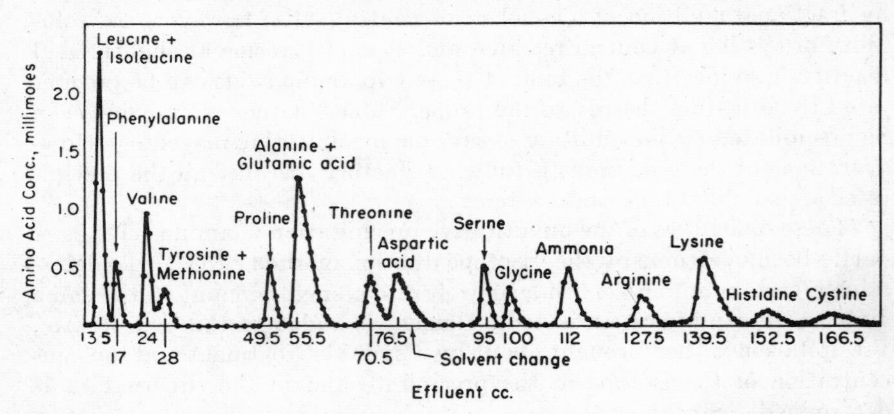

FIG. 3. Chromatographic fractionation of a hydrolyzate of bovine serum albumin according to S. Moore and W. H. Stein (20).

thus the amino acid mixture of a hydrolyzate was treated with *p*-iodophenylsulfonyl chloride to give *p*-iodophenylsulfonamide derivatives of the amino acids, I^{131} being used as radioisotope; large amounts of nonisotopic *p*-iodophenylsulfonylglycine were added as carrier and the isotope content of the isolated *p*-iodophenylsulfonylglycine was measured (54*a*). The method provides a new powerful tool for the determination of amino acids in protein hydrolyzates.

Recently Moore and Stein (20) succeeded in determining more than 99% of the amino acids of bovine serum albumin and of β-lactoglobulin by adsorption of the hydrolyzate to a column of starch and elution of the amino acids with a mixture of *n*-butanol, *n*-propanol, and 0.1 *N* hydrochloric acid (1:2:1), then with propanol and 0.5 *N* hydrochloric acid (2:1). The amino acids pass into the eluate at different rates. Small fractions of the eluate are analyzed for their content of amino acids by means of the ninhydrin test. If the amino acid content of the fractions is plotted against the volume of the eluate a diagram (Fig. 3) is obtained, from which the amount of each of the amino acids can be calculated. Each point of the curve indicates the result of the colorimetric analysis of 0.5 ml. of the effluent; the hydrolyzate was obtained from 2.5 mg. bovine serum albumin.

Another new method for amino acid determination is *microbiological determination,* utilizing *Leuconostoc mesenteroides,* mutant strains of *Neurospora,* or different strains of lactobacilli. The growth of the culture is measured by the turbidity of a suspension of the microbes, by a determination of the lactic acid formed, or by weighing the mycelium of the mold culture (55–57). Another microbiological method is to measure the carbonic acid evolved from an amino acid by the action of decarboxylating microbes. Tyrosine, histidine, lysine, and glutamic acid can be determined in this way (58). For the quantitative determination of an amino acid, the microbes are allowed to grow on a culture medium containing all the necessary amino acids and growth factors, except the amino acid being investigated. The growth response in this medium is compared with the growth response in culture media containing various known amounts of the amino acid to be determined. If the extent of growth is plotted against the amounts of amino acid added, a standard curve is obtained; the amino acid content of the unknown material is then determined by graphic interpolation (55).

The principal advantage of the microbiological methods is their great sensitivity and the fact that the amount of the amino acid required for a determination is less than one milligram, sometimes only several micrograms. On the other hand we are not yet sufficiently informed about the influence of one amino acid on the requirement for another. It is difficult at this point to exclude the possibility of nonspecific inhibition or stimulation produced by traces of amino acids (55) contaminating the amino acid used as standard substance. Therefore the results of microbiological methods must be interpreted with critical caution.

Infrared spectrophotometry has been used as a new method for the identification of amino acids and for their quantitative determination. The infrared absorption is quite typical for each of the amino acids and for α-chloro acids obtained by the action of hydrochloric and nitric acids on the amino acids (59). By means of infrared spectrophotometry it has been proved that the microbiological determination of leucine and isoleucine furnishes values too high for these amino acids (60).

The amino acids obtained by total hydrolysis of the proteins are *optically active,* if racemization is avoided during the hydrolysis. Although some of the amino acids are dextrorotatory and other amino acids levorotatory, all the amino acids isolated from the well known proteins have the same configuration, *i.e.*, the same spatial arrangement of the four substituents of the α-carbon atom. All these natural amino acids are designated L-amino acids. Their mutual relations have been proved by the conversion into identical derivatives (60*a*). In addition to these "natural" amino acids, their optical stereoisomers, the "unnatural" D-amino acids, were found in some ergot alkaloids and bacterial toxins (see Chapter XV) (60*a*). *Glycine* has no asymmetric carbon atom and is, therefore, optically inactive.

There are a number of methods, some of them quite specific, which are commonly used for the determination of the individual amino acids. They are recorded in the following paragraphs.

Glycine $H_2N{\cdot}CH_2{\cdot}COOH$ has been precipitated by trioxalato chromiate (60*b*). It may be determined microbiologically with *Leuconostoc mesenteroides* (61) or by oxidizing it to oxalic acid, COOH·COOH, with permanganate, precipitating the acid as the calcium salt, and titrating to determine the amount of the precipitate (62). Oxalic acid is obtained under the same conditions from serine, so that a separate determination of serine is necessitated.

Alanine is converted by nitrous acid to lactic acid, $CH_3{\cdot}CHOH{\cdot}$-COOH, which is determined in the usual way by converting it to acetal-

$$\begin{array}{c} CH_3 \\ | \\ H_2N\text{—}CH\text{—}COOH \end{array}$$

Alanine

dehyde (63). Alanine can also be precipitated by nitranilic acid (64) or determined by means of *Streptococcus faecalis* (61). On heating with ninhydrin (see Sect. B, above) alanine is converted into acetaldehyde which is distilled off and determined by titration (65).

Valine, leucine, and *isoleucine* also furnish volatile aldehydes under

$$\begin{array}{c} H_3C \quad CH_3 \\ \diagdown \; \diagup \\ CH \\ | \\ H_2N\text{—}CH\text{—}COOH \end{array}$$

Valine

$$\begin{array}{c} H_3C \quad CH_3 \\ \diagdown \; \diagup \\ CH \\ | \\ CH_2 \\ | \\ H_2N\text{—}CH\text{—}COOH \end{array}$$

Leucine

$$\begin{array}{c} \qquad CH_3 \\ \qquad | \\ H_3C \quad CH_2 \\ \diagdown \; \diagup \\ CH \\ | \\ H_2N\text{—}CH\text{—}COOH \end{array}$$

Isoleucine

these conditions and can be determined similarly (65). Each of these three amino acids can be determined microbiologically (55,66). Leucine, owing to its low solubility, can be determined by isotopic dilution (53).

Aspartic acid and *glutamic acid* can be precipitated as calcium or barium salts from alcoholic solution (50,67,68). Both amino acids have

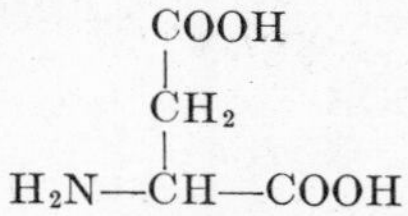

$$H_2N-CH(CH_2-COOH)-COOH$$

Aspartic acid

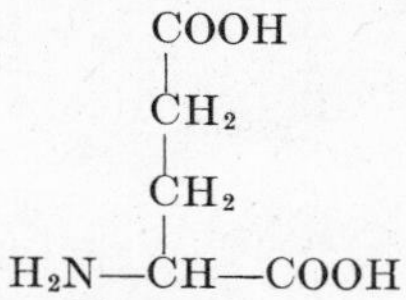

$$H_2N-CH(CH_2-CH_2-COOH)-COOH$$

Glutamic acid

also been determined microbiologically (55,61) and aspartic acid, moreover, by means of isotopic dilution (53). Several new methods have been used for the determination of glutamic acid. Upon oxidation with Chloramine T, $CH_3 \cdot C_6H_4 \cdot SO_2 \cdot NHCl$, glutamic acid is converted into succinic acid, $COOH \cdot CH_2 \cdot CH_2 \cdot COOH$, which is determined manometrically by means of succinoxidase (70). The amount of glutamic acid present in a protein hydrolyzate can also be estimated from the decrease in amino nitrogen on heating of the hydrolyzate under pressure. Under these conditions glutamic acid is converted into pyrrolidonecarboxylic acid (71), which has no free amino group. When heated with ninhydrin, glutamic acid is converted into β-formylpropionic acid, which is determined colorimetrically as its dinitrophenylhydrazone (72). While some of the aspartic and glutamic acid is present in protein molecules as the dicarboxylic acids with free carboxyl groups a portion of these groups is substituted by ammonia and converted into an acid amide group, $-CONH_2$. Although the total amount of the amides is equivalent to the quantity of ammonia liberated upon acid hydrolysis, reliable methods for the separate determination of asparagine and glutamine in proteins are not yet available. In tryptic hydrolyzates of proteins, glutamine can be determined by heating the neutralized hydrolyzate to 100° (73). Asparagine is stable under these conditions but glutamine is rapidly hydrolyzed (74).

Hydroxyamino acids can be determined by means of oxidation with

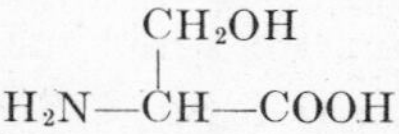

$$H_2N-CH(CH_2OH)-COOH$$

Serine

$$H_2N-CH(CHOH-CH_3)-COOH$$

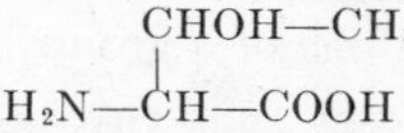

Threonine

periodic acid, HIO_4 (75). By this procedure *serine* is converted to formaldehyde, and threonine to acetaldehyde, one equivalent of ammonia being liberated. Ammonia is also formed from *hydroxylysine*, an amino acid found in noticeable amounts only in gelatin (76). Other proteins contain mere traces of hydroxylysine. For the determination of hydroxylysine, the protein hydrolyzate is precipitated with phosphotungstic acid and the precipitate treated with periodate (76, 76*a*).

Cystine can be determined by precipitation with phosphotungstic acid (77) or by reducing it, and analyzing for cysteine. The reduction

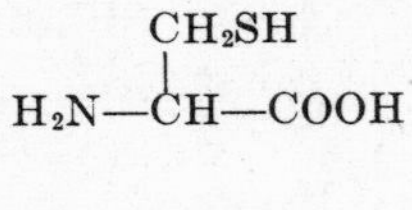

$$\begin{array}{ccc} & CH_2SH & \\ & | & \\ H_2N- & CH & -COOH \end{array} \qquad \begin{array}{ccccc} & CH_2-S-S-CH_2 & & & \\ H_2N-CH & & CH-COOH \\ | & & | \\ COOH & & NH_2 \end{array}$$

Cysteine 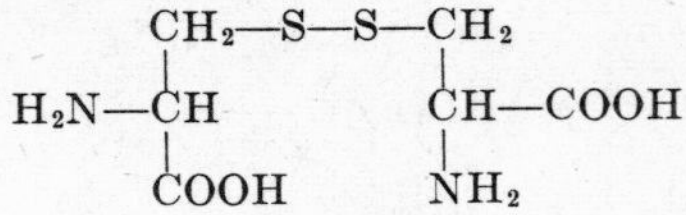　　　　Cystine

can be achieved by thioglycolic acid (78). *Cysteine* is determined colorimetrically with Folin's reagent (79), or by titration of the sulfhydryl group with oxidizing agents such as iodine (80), porphyrindin (81), or ferricyanide (82). The ferrocyanide formed is determined colorimetrically as Prussian blue using ferric chloride to develop the color. Cysteine can also be determined by the electrometric titration of its sulfhydryl groups with silver nitrate (83) or by means of polarography (84). If proteins are treated with alkali cyanides, the dithio bond of cystine is split, yielding first RSH + RSCN, and then the amino acid lanthionine (85,86). The formula of lanthionine obtained in this way or by the action of alkali on cystine or on proteins is:

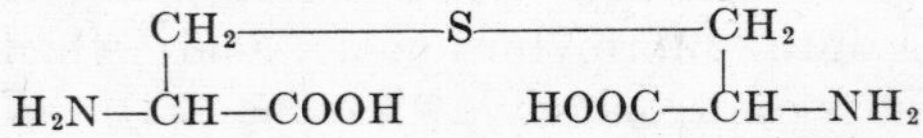

$$\begin{array}{ccc} CH_2 & —S— & CH_2 \\ | & & | \\ H_2N-CH-COOH & & HOOC-CH-NH_2 \end{array}$$

For the quantitative determination of *methionine* advantage is taken

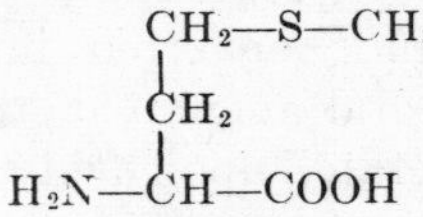

$$\begin{array}{l} CH_2-S-CH_3 \\ | \\ CH_2 \\ | \\ H_2N-CH-COOH \end{array}$$

Methionine

of its property of reacting to form methyl iodide when boiled with hydriodic acid. The methyl iodide evolved is determined in the usual way, titrimetrically (87). Methionine gives a red color with nitroprussides in acid solution (88). A considerable amount of methionine is present in casein.

Arginine is one of a group of basic amino acids which may be isolated

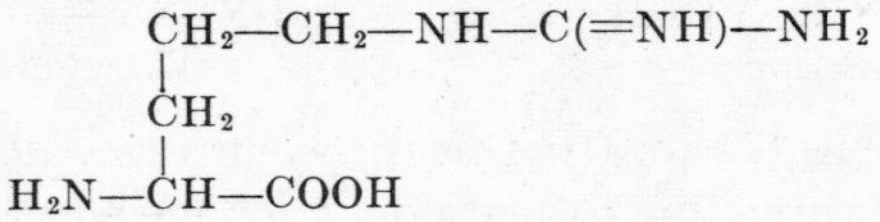

$$\begin{array}{l} CH_2-CH_2-NH-C(=NH)-NH_2 \\ | \\ CH_2 \\ | \\ H_2N-CH-COOH \end{array}$$

Arginine

from the protein hydrolyzate by precipitation with phosphotungstic acid or by electrolysis (89). Boiling with alkali decomposes arginine, forming two molecules of ammonia for each molecule of arginine destroyed. The ammonia liberated may be titrated to find the amount of arginine originally present. The enzyme arginase hydrolyzes arginine, cleaving it to form ornithine and urea. The latter is determined using urease (90).

Arginine is isolated by precipitation with flavianic (1-naphthol-2,4-dinitro-7-sulfonic) acid (91). A very sensitive color reaction given by arginine with α-naphthol and NaOCl was described by Sakaguchi (92). The red color produced is measured colorimetrically for the quantitative determination of arginine (93).

Lysine, another basic amino acid, is separated from the other bases

$$\begin{array}{l} CH_2—CH_2—CH_2—CH_2NH_2 \\ | \\ H_2N—CH—COOH \end{array}$$

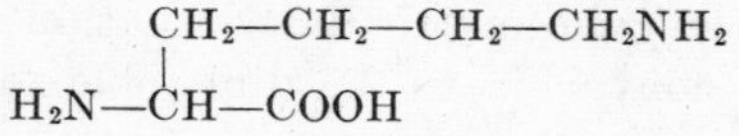

Lysine

by precipitation with picric acid. Lysine has been determined by isotope dilution (53) and can also be determined microbiologically with *Leuconostoc mesenteroides* or by bacterial decarboxylation (94).

Histidine, the third basic amino acid, is separated from the other bases

$$\begin{array}{l} CH—NH \\ \| \qquad \diagdown \\ \| \qquad\quad CH \\ \| \qquad /\!/ \\ C——N \\ | \\ CH_2 \\ | \\ H_2N—CH—COOH \end{array}$$

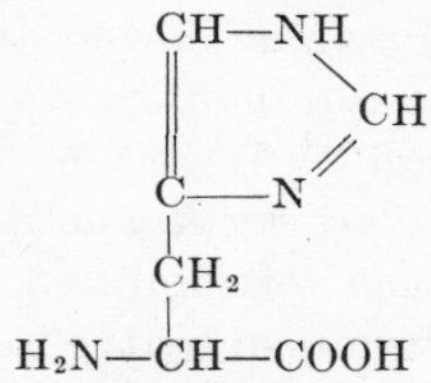

Histidine

as its silver salt. Since histidine gives a red color with diazotized sulfanilic acid, it can be determined colorimetrically (95).

The imino acids *proline* and *hydroxy-proline* differ from the amino

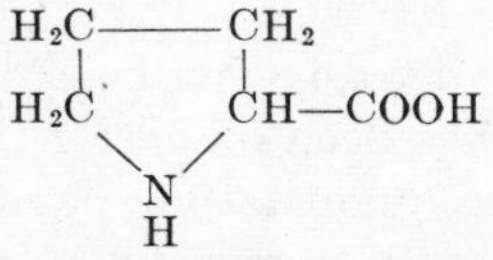

$$\begin{array}{l} H_2C——CH_2 \\ | \qquad\quad | \\ H_2C \qquad CH—COOH \\ \quad \diagdown \;\; \diagup \\ \qquad N \\ \qquad H \end{array} \qquad\qquad \begin{array}{l} HOHC——CH_2 \\ \quad | \qquad\quad | \\ \; H_2C \qquad CH—COOH \\ \qquad \diagdown \;\; \diagup \\ \qquad\quad N \\ \qquad\quad H \end{array}$$

Proline 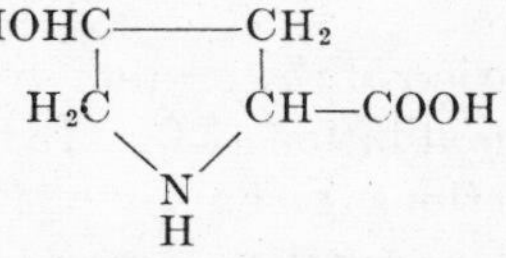 Hydroxyproline

acids by their unusually great solubility in ethanol. Proline is precipitated by the addition of Reineke salt $NH_4Cr(CNS)_4(NH_3)_2$ (96) or by rhodanilic acid, *i.e.*, tetrarhodanatodianilinochromic acid (97). Proline has also been determined microbiologically by means of *Neurospora* (61). For colorimetric analysis, hydroxyproline is oxidized by sodium peroxide to a substance giving a red color with isatin in acid solution (98).

Tryptophan is precipitated from its solution in sulfuric acid by the addition of mercuric sulfate. It can be determined spectrophotometrically by measuring the pronounced absorption in the ultraviolet region (61). Tryptophan gives intense color reactions with aldehydes such as

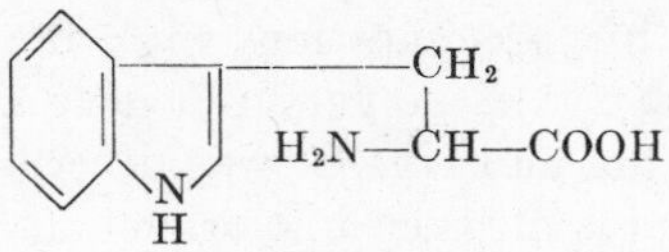

CH_2
$H_2N—CH—COOH$
N
H

Tryptophan

formaldehyde, dimethylaminobenzaldehyde, or glyoxylic acid, which have been used for the colorimetric determination of tryptophan (99).

Phenylalanine is converted to 3,4-dinitrobenzoic acid by treatment

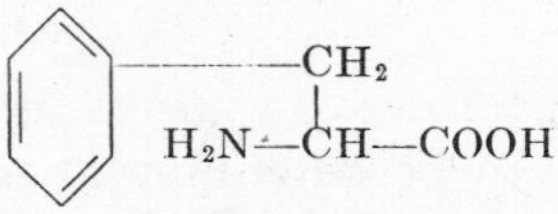

CH_2
$H_2N—CH—COOH$

Phenylalanine

with nitric acid and may then be determined colorimetrically (100). Dinitrophenylalanine is reduced by zinc powder to diaminophenylalanine and coupled with naphthoquinonesulfonic acid to give a dye which is suitable for colorimetric comparison (101). For the microbiological determination of phenylalanine *Lactobacillus arabinosus* has been used (61). Phenylalanine has also been precipitated with 2,5-dibromobenzenesulfonic acid (101*a*) and determined by the isotopic dilution method (53).

The water solubility of *tyrosine* is so low that it precipitates upon

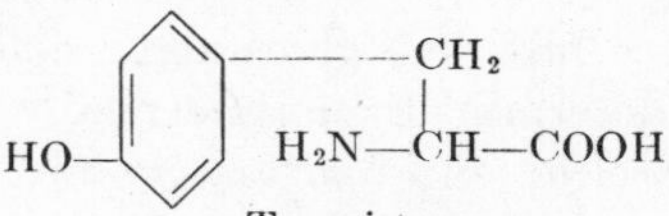

CH_2
HO— $H_2N—CH—COOH$

Tyrosine

neutralization of the protein hydrolyzate. Tyrosine has been determined by isotopic dilution (53). Extensive use has been found for the various color reactions given by tyrosine in its quantitative determination. These color reactions are: (*1*) the diazo test, a red color given after coupling with diazobenzene sulfonic acid (102,103), (*2*) the Millon test, a red color produced by a solution of mercury in nitric acid (104), and (*3*) a blue color resulting from the reducing action of tyrosine on a mixture of phosphotungstic and phosphomolybdic acids (105). Tyrosine, when treated with iodine in slightly alkaline solution, is iodinated and converted to diiodotyrosine and thyroxine (106,107). A similar reaction occurs when proteins are treated with iodine (69).

The last product of protein hydrolysis to be discussed is *ammonia.* It is generally assumed that this ammonia is derived exclusively from asparagine and glutamine. Both amides have been found in enzymatic hydrolyzates of proteins (108). While asparagine is resistant to dilute acids or neutral aqueous solutions, glutamine is converted to ammonia and pyrrolidonecarboxylic acid by heating its solution to 100°C. at pH 2 to 6 (109). Use can be made of this difference for the separate determination of asparagine and glutamine in enzymatic hydrolyzates of proteins (73,110).

```
      H2C—CH2                  H2C———————CH2
        |   |                   |         |
   H2NOC   CH—COOH →           OC        CH—COOH + NH3
           /                     \       /
     H2N                           N
                                   H
       Glutamine              Pyrrolidonecarboxylic acid
```

E. Amino Acid Composition of Proteins (110*a*). By means of the analytical methods indicated above, the amino acid contents of different proteins have been determined. The result of such analyses was customarily expressed in terms of the percentage of the various amino acids. This mode of representation is somewhat erroneous, since the protein molecules do not consist of whole amino acid molecules, $H_2N—R—COOH$, but of their anhydrous residues, —HN—R—CO—. It would certainly be preferable to indicate the number of each of the amino acids per protein molecule. This has been possible in only a few instances, where the molecular weight of the protein has been established definitively. If each of the amino acids is represented by the first three letters of its name, the composition of crystalline β-lactoglobulin is the following: gly$_8$, ala$_{29}$, val$_{21}$, leu$_{50}$, iso$_{27}$, pro$_{15}$, phe$_9$, arg$_7$, his$_4$, lys$_{33}$, asp$_{36}$, glu$_{56}$, ser$_{20}$, thr$_{21}$, cys(SH)$_4$, cys(SS/2)$_8$, met$_9$, tyr$_9$, try$_4$, ammonia$_{32}$ (61). Similarly the formula of pepsin can be represented by the following symbols: gly$_{29}$, ala$_?$, val$_{21}$, leu$_{27}$, iso$_{28}$, pro$_{15}$, phe$_{19}$, arg$_2$, his$_2$, lys$_2$, asp$_{41}$, glu$_{28}$, ser$_{40}$, thr$_{28}$, cys(SH)$_2$, cys(SS/2)$_4$, met$_4$, tyr$_{16}$, try$_4$, ammonia$_{32}$, $(-PO_3H_2)_1$ (111).

Because the molecular weight of proteins varies between wide limits, formulas of this kind are not very suitable for a comparison of the ratio of the different amino acids in the protein molecule. However, it is this ratio which determines the physical and chemical properties of a protein, for these depend mainly on the composition of the side chains R in the peptide formula:

——NH—CHR—CO——NH—CHR—CO——NH—CHR—CO——

According to the composition of these side chains we can classify the amino acids into four groups:

(*a*) Amino acids with *nonpolar* side chains: glycine, alanine, valine, leucine, isoleucine, proline, phenylalanine,

TABLE I

AMINO ACID COMPOSITION OF PROTEINS (MOLES AMINO ACID PER 10^5 GRAM PROTEIN)

	Human serum albumin[a]	Bovine serum albumin[b]	Ovalbumin[a]	β-Lactoglobulin[b]	Human γ-globulin[c]	Fibrin[d,e]	Myosin[d]	Horse myoglobin[f]	Horse hemoglobin[f]	α-Casein[g]	β-Casein[g]	Casein[h]	Insulin[i]	Lactogenic hormone[j]	Growth hormone[k]
Arginine	35	34	33	17	28	44	40	13	21	25	20	23	20	49	52
Histidine	23	26	15	11	16	16	11	55	56	19	20	21	34	29	17
Lysine	84	88	42	86	55	69	70	106	58	61	44	56	18	36	49
Hydroxylysine	0	0	0	—	—	—	—	—	—	—	—	2	—	—	—
Ammonia	63	62	72	77	79	95	85	47	66	—	—	101	126	72	70
Glutamic acid	118	104	109	120	80	101	150	112	56	153	158	150	137	96	88
Aspartic acid	78	82	61	87	66	95	67	62	80	64	37	50	50	101	78
Glycine	21	24	43	19	56	76	25	78	75	38	32	6	61	53	49
Alanine	—	70	75	80		42	73	89	83	42	19	36	33	+	+
Valine	66	50	39	48	83	33	22	35	78	54	87	51	84	50	33
Leucine[1]	91	94	121	118	71	89	119	128	118	60	89	80	125	93	92
Isoleucine[1]	13	20		45	21				0	49	42	40		55	31
Proline	44	41	28	45	70	33	16	29	34	71	139	92	25	54	—
Phenylalanine	47	40	45	23	28	30	26	31	48	28	35	39	48	25	48
Serine	35	40	77	38	109	66	37	33	54	60	65	56	55	63	—
Threonine	42	49	34	41	70	52	41	38	37	41	43	38	27	40	75
Tyrosine	26	28	22	20	37	28	19	13	16	45	18	35	68	26	24
Hydroxyproline	0	0	0	—	—	—	—	—	—	—	—	17	—	—	—
Tryptophan	1	3	13	10	14	16	4	11	8	8	3	13	—	6	4
Cysteine[1]	6	54	13	28	6	13	12	0	4	4	1	3	5	26	19
Cystine (1/2)[1]	46				20			0	5				92		
Methionine	9	5	35	22	7	17	23	11	7	17	23	23	—	29	19
Free basic groups	142	148	90	114	100	129	121	174	135	105	84	102	72	114	118
Free acid groups	133	124	98	130	67	101	132	127	70	116	84	129[2]	61	125	96
Total amino acids found	785	852	805	798	837	820	755	844	834	839	875	831	882	823	678
Nitrogen recovered, %	92.8	99.1	93.4	99.6	96.1	94.1	87.8	96.0	95.3	101.8	103.4	98.4	99	99.9	88.2

	Thyroglobulin[l]	Pepsin[m]	Chymotrypsinogen[m]	Ribonuclease[m]	Aldolase[n]	Glyceraldehyde dehydrogenase[n]	Botulinus toxin[o]	Edestin[h]	Zein[h]	Gliadin[h]	Collagen[p]	Elastin[q]	Keratin, wool[r,s]	Keratin, feather[q]	Fibroin, silk[r,s]
Arginine	47	6	16	30	36	30	27	96	10	16	51	6	59	43	4
Histidine	4	6	8	27	27	32	6	19	8	12	5	0	4	3	0
Lysine	13	6	16	71	58	57	53	16	0	4	31	3	18	9	2
Hydroxylysine	—	—	—	—	—	—	—	—	—	—	8	—	—	—	—
Ammonia	—	93	109	146	65	71	152	126	211	320	47	—	81	—	—
Glutamic acid	45	82	61	88	78	46	106	141	182	310	77	22	96	66	—
Aspartic acid	12	120	85	106	73	93	152	90	35	10	47	4	48	53	—
Glycine	—	84	71	17	75	81	18	51	—	6	350	—	76	—	584
Alanine	—	—	—	—	96	76	44	48	118	24	106	—	46	—	297
Valine	12	61	86	62	63	102	45	41	30	23	29	117	41	71	37
Leucine[1]	87	78	79	24	88	57	79	92	171	90	42	56	86	61	19
Isoleucine[1]	—	82	43		60	70	90					26		46	
Proline	39	44	51	31	50	32	23	31	91	115	132	136	59	76	9
Phenylalanine	—	38	22	22	14	34	7	36	36	39	25	29	23	32	9
Serine	—	126	109	114	63	64	42	60	67	47	33	—	98	—	147
Threonine	—	82	96	75	60	58	71	32	29	18	20	—	54	—	12
Tyrosine	17	47	17	44	29	25	75	24	29	18	8	8	26	12	73
Hydroxyproline	—	—	—	—	—	—	—	—	—	—	107	—	—	—	—
Tryptophan	9	12	27	—	11	10	9	7	1	6	0	9	9	37	—
Cysteine[1]	—	6	11	5	—	—	2	12	7	21	0	5	99	68	0
Cystine (1/2)[1]	13	12	27	13	8	7	4				0				0
Methionine	9	12	8	30	8	18	7	16	16	11	5	0	5	3	17
Free basic groups	—	18	79	128	121	119	86	131	18	28	87	—	81	—	6
Free acid groups	—	109	57	48	86	68	106	105	6	0	77	—	64	—	0
Total amino acids found	—	914	892	—	897	892	861	827	830	770	1076	—	859	—	1210
Nitrogen recovered, %	—	99.2	97.7	98.7	100	100	100	97.8	94.2	92.2	99.8	—	—	—	—

[1] In some of the proteins the sum of leucine and isoleucine and of cysteine and cystine is recorded since analyses of the respective amino acids are not available.
[2] Including phosphoric acid groups.

(*b*) Amino acids with *ionic basic* (cationic) side chains: arginine, histidine, lysine, hydroxylysine,
(*c*) Amino acids with *ionic acid* (anionic) side chains: aspartic and glutamic acids (if their carboxyl groups are free).
(*d*) Amino acids with *polar nonionic* side chains: cysteine, cystine, methionine, serine, threonine, hydroxyproline, tyrosine, tryptophan, asparagine, glutamine.

These four groups of amino acids are shown in Table I. In order to provide grounds for comparison of the composition of different proteins, all figures recorded in Table I refer to protein particles of an equivalent weight of 100,000.

F. Order of Amino Acids in the Peptide Chain. The figures recorded in Table I are indispensable for a complete description of a protein and for the elucidation of its structure. However, these figures do not reveal anything about the order of the amino acids in the long peptide chains and about the distribution of the different amino acids in the globular protein particles. Obviously, the physical and chemical properties of two proteins containing the same amino acids may be very different, if the molecular surface of one of the proteins is formed by ionic amino acids, while that of the second protein is formed by the nonpolar amino acids.

References to Table I

[a] E. Brand *et al.*, *J. Am. Chem. Soc.* **67,** 1524 (1945).
[b] W. Stein, S. Moore, *J. Biol. Chem.* **178,** 79 (1949).
[c] E. Brand, *Ann. N. Y. Acad. Sci.* **47,** 216 (1947).
[d] K. Bailey, *Advances in Protein Chem.* **1,** 311 (1944).
[e] A. A. Albanese, T. M. Barnes, *J. Biol. Chem.* **157,** 613 (1945).
[f] G. R. Tristram, in F. J. W. Roughton, ed., Hemoglobin. Interscience, New York, 1949, p. 109.
[g] W. G. Gordon, W. F. Semmett, M. Morris, *Federation Proc.* **8,** 202 (1949); *J. Am. Chem. Soc.* **71,** 3293 (1949).
[h] A. C. Chibnall, Procter Memorial Lecture, 1946.
[i] E. Brand, *Ann. N. Y. Acad. Sci.* **47,** 487 (1946).
[j] C. H. Li, *J. Biol. Chem.* **178,** 459 (1949).
[k] C. H. Li, *Ann. Rev. Biochem.* **16,** 291 (1947).
[l] E. Brand, B. Kassell, M. Heidelberger, *J. Biol. Chem.* **128,** XI (1939).
[m] E. Brand, cited by J. H. Northrop, *Crystalline Enzymes.* Columbia Univ. Press, New York, 1948, p. 26.
[n] S. F. Velick, E. Ronzoni, *J. Biol. Chem.* **173,** 591, 605, 619, 627 (1948).
[o] J. H. Buehler, E. J. Schantz, C. Lamanna, *J. Biol. Chem.* **169,** 295 (1947).
[p] J. H. Bowes, R. H. Kenten, *Biochem. J.* **43,** 358, 365 (1948).
[q] C. Graham, H. Waitkoff, S. Hier, *J. Biol. Chem.* **177,** 529 (1949).
[r] E. J. Cohn, J. T. Edsall, *Proteins, Amino Acids and Peptides.* Reinhold, New York, 1943, p. 358.
[s] W. T. Astbury, *Advances in Enzymol.* **3,** 78 (1943).

It is impossible, therefore, to predict the physicochemical properties of a protein from the amino acid percentages recorded in Table I.

Until recently nothing was known about the order of the amino acids in the peptide chains of proteins. In the last few years, however, important results have been achieved by the fractionation of partial hydrolyzates. Sanger (45) examined, in this way, the peptides produced by the cleavage of insulin (see Chapter XIII, Sect. C). The terminal amino groups of the peptides were labeled by condensation with dinitrofluorobenzene (see Chapter VII, Sect. C). Since the peptides on further hydrolysis furnished DNP-glycylisoleucine (DNP = dinitrophenyl), DNP-glycylisoleucylvaline and DNP-glycylisoleucylvalylglycine, it is evident that the order of the amino acids in this portion of the insulin molecule was glycine–isoleucine–valine–glycine. Other DNP-peptides were isolated from enzymatic digests of DNP-insulin (112). Similarly, it was found that the partial hydrolysis of the bacterial toxin gramicidin S furnishes the following dipeptides and tripeptides: valylornithine, ornithylleucine, leucylphenylalanine, phenylalanylproline, prolylvalylornithine, valylornithylleucine, and phenylalanylprolylvaline. This led to the conclusion that the amino acids in gramicidin S are arranged in the order L-valine–L-ornithine–L-leucine–D-phenylalanine–L-proline, and that this chain forms a closed cyclopeptide (113) (see Chapter XV, Sect. B). The fractionation of the peptide mixtures in these experiments was accomplished by paper chromatography (22) or by countercurrent distribution between water and butanol or ethyl acetate (112).

Although these analyses reveal only the structure of small parts of the peptide chains, they are extremely important; they represent the first steps in a new phase of protein research, in which the main goal is the reconstruction of the complicated framework of the protein molecule from its hydrolytic cleavage products.

References

1. R. A. Gortner, M. J. Blish, *J. Am. Chem. Soc.* **37,** 1630 (1915).
2. H. B. Vickery, A. White, *J. Biol. Chem.* **99,** 701 (1933).
3. G. L. Miller, V. du Vigneaud, *J. Biol. Chem.* **118,** 101 (1937).
3*a*. A. R. C. Warner, *J. Biol. Chem.* **142,** 741 (1942).
3*b*. H. B. Vickery, *J. Biol. Chem.* **53,** 506 (1922); S. M. Partridge, H. F. Davis, *Nature* **165,** 62 (1950).
4. F. Haurowitz, *Z. physiol. Chem.* **162,** 41 (1926).
5. A. H. Gordon, A. J. P. Martin, R. L. M. Synge, *Biochem. J.* **35,** 1369 (1941); **37,** 79, 87, 92 (1943).
5*a*. H. B. Bull and J. W. Hahn, *J. Am. Chem. Soc.* **70,** 2128, 2132 (1948).
6. M. Damodaran, *Biochem. J.* **26,** 235 (1932).
7. M. Damodaran, G. Jaaback, A. C. Chibnall, *Biochem. J.* **26,** 1704 (1932).

8. M. Bergmann, L. Zervas, H. Schleich, *Ber.* **65,** 1747 (1932).
9. S. Sørensen, *Biochem. Z.* **7,** 45 (1907).
9*a*. M. Levy, D. E. Silverman, *J. Biol. Chem.* **118,** 723 (1937).
9*b*. D. French, J. T. Edsall, *Advances in Protein Chem.* **2,** 278 (1945).
10. R. Willstätter, E. Waldschmidt-Leitz, *Ber.* **54,** 2988 (1921).
10*a*. L. Michaelis, M. Mizutane, *Biochem. Z.* **147,** 7 (1924).
11. H. A. Krebs, *Biochem. Z.* **210,** 7 (1929); **220,** 283 (1930).
12. D. D. Van Slyke, J. *Biol. Chem.* **9,** 185 (1911); **23,** 407 (1915).
12*a*. H. B. Bull, J. W. Hahn, V. R. Baptist, *J. Am. Chem. Soc.* **71,** 550 (1949).
13. D. D. Van Slyke, *J. Biol. Chem.* **83,** 425 (1929).
14. S. A. Lough, H. B. Lewis, *J. Biol. Chem.* **104,** 601 (1934).
15. C. L. A. Schmidt, *J. Biol. Chem.* **82,** 587 (1929).
16. T. L. McMeekin, R. Warner, *Ann. Rev. Biochem.* **15,** 126 (1946).
17. K. Linderstrøm-Lang, H. Holter, *Z. physiol. Chem.* **201,** 9 (1931).
18. L. J. Harris, *Biochem. J.* **29,** 2820 (1936).
19. K. Linderstrøm-Lang, *Nature* **139,** 713; **140,** 108 (1937).
20. S. Moore, W. H. Stein, *J. Biol. Chem.* **178,** 53, 79 (1949).
21. D. D. Van Slyke, R. Dillon, D. McFadyen, P. Hamilton, *J. Biol. Chem.* **141,** 627 (1941).
22. A. J. P. Martin, R. L. M. Synge, *Advances in Protein Chem.* **2,** 1 (1945); A. J. P. Martin, *Ann. N. Y. Acad. Sci.* **49,** 249 (1949).
23. A. Kossel, F. Kutscher, *Z. physiol. Chem.* **31,** 165 (1901). A. Kossel, S. Edlbacher, *ibid.* **110,** 241 (1920).
24. E. Fischer, *Z. physiol. Chem.* **33,** 151 (1901).
25. H. D. Dakin, *J. Biol. Chem.* **44,** 499 (1920).
26. T. Wieland, L. Wirth, *Ber.* **76,** 823 (1943).
27. F. Turba, M. Richter, F. Kuchar, *Naturwissenschaften* **31,** 508 (1943).
28. R. Cannan, *J. Biol. Chem.* **152,** 401 (1944).
29. E. A. H. Sims, *J. Biol. Chem.* **158,** 239 (1945).
30. R. J. Block, *Arch. Biochem.* **11,** 235 (1946).
31. R. A. Baxter, F. S. Spring, *Ann. Repts. on Progress Chem. Soc. London* **42,** 96 (1946).
32. J. L. Wachtel, H. G. Cassidy, *Science* **95,** 233 (1942).
33. E. Lederer, *Un symposium sur les proteines,* Desoer, Liège 1946, p. 227.
34. R. L. M. Synge, *Biochem. J.* **33,** 1913, 1918 (1939).
34*a*. R. L. M. Synge, *Symposia Biochem. Soc.,* No. 3, p. 90 (1949).
35. R. L. M. Synge, *Biochem. J.* **35,** 285 (1944).
36. W. H. Stein, S. Moore, *J. Biol. Chem.* **176,** 337 (1948).
37. A. H. Gordon, A. J. P. Martin, R. L. M. Synge, *Biochem. J.* **37,** 79 (1943).
38. R. Consden, A. J. P. Martin, A. H. Gordon, *Biochem. J.* **41,** 590 (1946).
39. C. E. Dent, *Biochem. J.* **41,** 240 (1946).
40. R. S. Williams, H. Kirby, *Science* **107,** 481 (1948).
41. A. S. Keston, S. Udenfriend, M. Levy, *J. Am. Chem. Soc.* **69,** 3151 (1947).
42. A. J. P. Martin, R. L. M. Synge, *Biochem. J.* **35,** 91 (1941); K. Zeile *et al., Z. physiol. Chem.* **284,** 1, 19, 40 (1949).
43. G. R. Tristram, *Biochem. J.* **40,** 721 (1946).
44. A. J. P. Martin, *Nature* **158,** 474 (1946); J. I. M. Jones, S. E. Michael, *Nature* **165,** 685 (1950).
45. F. Sanger, *Nature* **162,** 491 (1948).
46. F. Sanger, *Biochem. J.* **40,** 261 (1946).

47. R. Consden, A. H. Gordon, A. J. P. Martin, O. Rosenheim, R. L. M. Synge, *Biochem. J.* **39**, 351 (1945).
48. M. Renard, *Mem. Soc. Roy. Sci. Liège*, **1**, No. 1 (1945).
49. B. H. Nicolet, L. A. Shinn, *J. Biol. Chem.* **142**, 139 (1942).
50. K. Bailey, A. C. Chibnall, M. W. Rees, E. F. Williams, *Biochem. J.* **37**, 360 (1943).
51. K. Mörner, *Z. physiol. Chem.* **88**, 138 (1913).
52. D. Ackermann, E. Müller, *Z. physiol. Chem.* **269**, 146 (1941).
53. D. Rittenberg, G. L. Foster, *J. Biol. Chem.* **133**, 737 (1940). G. L. Foster, *ibid.* **159**, 431 (1945). D. Rittenberg, D. Shemin, *Ann. N. Y. Acad. Sci.* **47**, 119 (1946).
54. D. Rittenberg, A. S. Keston, R. Schoenheimer, G. L. Foster, *J. Biol. Chem.* **125**, 1 (1938).
54*a*. A. S. Keston, S. Udenfriend, R. K. Cannan, *J. Am. Chem. Soc.* **71**, 249 (1949). A. S. Keston, S. Udenfriend, M. Levy, *J. Am. Chem. Soc.* **72**, 748 (1950).
55. E. E. Snell, *Advances in Protein Chem.* **2**, 85 (1945).
56. E. G. Kellett, *Ann. Repts. on Progress Chem. Soc. London* **42**, 253 (1946).
57. J. L. Slokes, M. Gunness, I. M. Dwyer, M. C. Caswell, *J. Biol. Chem.* **160**, 35 (1945).
58. E. F. Gale, *Biochem. J.* **39**, 46 (1945).
59. M. Renard, Recherches des acides monoaminés, M. Hayez, Brussels, 1946.
60. S. E. Darmon, G. B. B. M. Sutherland, G. R. Tristram, *Biochem. J.* **42**, 508 (1948).
60*a*. A. Neuberger, *Advances in Protein Chem.* **4**, 298 (1948).
60*b*. M. Bergmann, S. W. Fox, *J. Biol. Chem.* **109**, 317 (1935).
61. E. Brand, L. Seidel, W. H. Goldwater, B. Kassell, F. J. Ryan, *J. Am. Chem. Soc.* **67**, 1524 (1945).
62. S. Rapoport, *Biochem. Z.* **281**, 30 (1935).
63. A. I. Kendall, T. E. Friedemann, *J. Infectious Diseases* **47**, 171 (1930).
64. B. W. Town, *Biochem. J.* **30**, 1833 (1936).
65. A. Virtanen, N. Rautanen, *Biochem. J.* **41**, 101 (1947).
66. F. Ryan, E. Brand, *J. Biol. Chem.* **154**, 161 (1944).
67. F. W. Foreman, *Biochem. J.* **8**, 463 (1914).
68. D. B. Jones, O. Moeller, *J. Biol. Chem.* **79**, 429 (1928).
69. E. Bauer, E. Strauss, *Ber.* **68**, 1108 (1935).
70. P. P. Cohen, *Biochem. J.* **33**, 551 (1939).
71. H. S. Olcott, *J. Biol. Chem.* **153**, 71 (1945).
72. B. A. Prescott, H. Waelsch, *J. Biol. Chem.* **164**, 331 (1946).
73. F. Haurowitz, R. Cindi, unpublished experiments.
74. H. B. Vickery, G. W. Pucher, H. T. Clarke, A. C. Chibnall, R. G. Westall, *Biochem. J.* **29**, 2710 (1935).
75. L. A. Shinn, B. H. Nicolet, *J. Biol. Chem.* **138**, 91 (1941).
76. D. D. Van Slyke, A. Hiller, D. MacFadyen, *J. Biol. Chem.* **141**, 681 (1941).
76*a*. S. Bergström, S. Lindstedt, *Arch. Biochem.* **26**, 323 (1950).
77. K. Kassell, E. Brand, *J. Biol. Chem.* **125**, 131 (1938).
78. A. E. Mirsky, M. L. Anson, *J. Gen. Physiol.* **18**, 307 (1935).
79. O. Folin, J. M. Looney, *J. Biol. Chem.* **51**, 421 (1922).
80. Y. Okuda, *J. Biochem.* (Japan) **5**, 217 (1925).
81. R. Kuhn, P. Desnuelle, *Z. physiol. Chem.* **251**, 14 (1938).
82. H. L. Mason, *J. Biol. Chem.* **86**, 623 (1930).

83. J. Leonis, *Compt. rend. trav. lab. Carlsberg. Sér. chim.* **26,** 315 (1948).
84. R. Brdicka, *Mikrochemie* **15,** 167 (1934).
85. A. Schöberl, E. Ludwig, *Ber.* **70,** 1422 (1937).
86. W. R. Cuthbertson, H. Philipps, *Biochem. J.* **39,** 7 (1945).
87. H. D. Baernstein, *J. Biol. Chem.* **115,** 25, 33 (1936).
88. T. E. McCarthy, M. X. Sullivan, *J. Biol. Chem.* **141,** 871 (1941).
89. G. L. Foster, C. L. A. Schmidt, *J. Am. Chem. Soc.* **48,** 1709 (1926).
90. A. Hunter, J. A. Dauphinee, *J. Biol. Chem.* **85,** 627 (1930).
91. A. Kossel, E. Gross, *Z. physiol. Chem.* **135,** 167 (1924).
92. S. Sakaguchi, *J. Biochem. (Japan)* **5,** 25, 133 (1925).
93. C. J. Weber, *J. Biol. Chem.* **86,** 217 (1930).
94. E. F. Gale, *Biochem. J.* **38,** 232 (1944).
95. M. Hanke, *J. Biol. Chem.* **66,** 475 (1926).
96. J. Kapfhammer, R. Eck, *Z. physiol. Chem.* **170,** 294 (1927).
97. M. Bergmann, *J. Biol. Chem.* **110,** 471 (1935).
98. W. D. McFarlane, G. H. Guest, *Can. J. Research* **17,** 139 (1939).
99. O. von Fuerth, H. Lieben, *Biochem. Z.* **109,** 124 (1920).
100. R. Kapeller-Adler, *Biochem. Z.* **252,** 185 (1932).
101. W. C. Hess, M. X. Sullivan, *Arch. Biochem.* **5,** 165 (1944).
101*a*. D. G. Doherty, W. H. Stein, M. Bergmann, *J. Biol. Chem.* **135,** 487 (1940).
102. H. Pauly, *Z. physiol. Chem.* **94,** 284, 426 (1915).
103. M. Hanke, *J. Biol. Chem.* **79,** 587 (1928).
104. O. Folin, V. Ciocalteu, *J. Biol. Chem.* **73,** 627 (1927).
105. O. Folin, J. M. Looney, *J. Biol. Chem.* **51,** 421 (1922); **69,** 519 (1926).
106. P. von Mutzenbecher, *Z. physiol. Chem.* **261,** 253 (1939).
107. E. P. Reineke, C. W. Turner, *J. Biol. Chem.* **149,** 555 (1943).
108. M. Damodaran, *Biochem. J.* **26,** 135 (1932).
109. J. Melville, *Biochem. J.* **29,** 179 (1935).
110. H. Waelsch, personal communication.
110*a*. G. R. Tristram, *Advances in Protein Chem.* **5,** 84 (1949).
111. E. Brand, *Ann. Rev. Biochem.* **16,** 224 (1947).
112. D. W. Woolley, *J. Biol. Chem.* **179,** 593 (1949).
113. R. Consden, A. H. Gordon, A. J. P. Martin, *Biochem. J.* **41,** 596 (1947).

Chapter IV

Size and Shape of Protein Molecules

A. General Remarks. The molecular weight of small molecules may be determined by dissolving them in suitable solvents and measuring the lowering of the freezing point, the elevation of the boiling point, or the decrease in the vapor pressure of the solvent. Satisfactory values are obtained by these methods if the concentration of the solute is at least 0.01 to 0.1 M. It would be physically impossible, however, to prepare a 0.01 M solution of a protein of molecular weight 100,000, since such a solution would have to contain 1000 g. protein per liter.

Some proteins, such as certain albumins, are highly soluble and with these it is possible to prepare solutions containing 300 g. or more of the protein per liter of water. It is hardly feasible, however, to determine molecular weights using such solutions, because traces of contaminating low-molecular substances would have an enormous influence on the result. Thus, a millimole of carbon dioxide and a millimole of serum albumin will each depress the freezing point of water to the same extent; but whereas a millimole of carbon dioxide is only 0.044 g., a millimole of serum albumin is 68 g. Similar exaggerated errors due to traces of impurities are to be expected in experiments designed to measure the elevation of the boiling point or the lowering of the vapor pressure of the solvent. It is clear that other methods must be employed to determine the molecular weights of macromolecules such as proteins.

The first estimations of the molecular weight of proteins were based on the *chemical determination of elements or of amino acids* occurring in the protein in only *small* amounts. The classical example of this procedure is the estimation of the molecular weight of hemoglobin from its iron content. The hemoglobin of mammals contains 0.34 g. iron in 100 g. hemoglobin. Since the atomic weight of iron is 56, 0.34 g. is equal to $0.34/56 = 1/165$ of an equivalent, and the amount of hemoglobin bound to 1 gram equivalent of iron is $165 \times 100 = 16{,}500$. This value is the minimum molecular weight of hemoglobin and was long considered to be the actual molecular weight. The true molecular weight of hemoglobin in solution has been found to be 68,000, so that each molecule evidently consists of four of the subunits found by iron analysis.

Similarly minimum molecular weights of β-lactoglobulin, serum albumin (1), edestin (1*a*), and other proteins were calculated from their content of certain amino acids. Although such a chemical analysis does not furnish true molecular weights, only minimum values thereof, it is very useful in those cases in which the determination of different constituents indicates the same minimum value.

The *physicochemical methods* used for determining the molecular weights of proteins are founded on various principles and furnish varying results, the interpretation of which is frequently difficult, and many times impossible. This is because the measurements made depend not only on the size and the mass of the protein molecule, but also on its electrical charge and on its shape. The latter factor is particularly important when measuring the rate of molecular movements such as the diffusion rate or the rate of sedimentation in a gravitational field. While sphere-like molecules behave normally in such experiments, the threadlike, elongated molecules of fibrous proteins behave abnormally, because the diffusion rate of the molecules depends on their shape; deviations from the spherical shape give rise to an increase in the frictional coefficient and, consequently, tend to reduce the diffusion rate. In concentrated solutions of threadlike molecules further complications arise by the mutual collisions and by temporary adhesion of the molecules. The results of these dynamic methods are also affected by the hydration of particles, since the motion of a protein through its solvent will be retarded if its cross-sectional area is increased by hydration.

Interference by these factors need not be feared, however, when we examine protein solutions which are in a state of equilibrium, *e.g.*, by measuring their osmotic pressure or by measuring their concentration gradient in the gravitational field of an ultracentrifuge. In the following sections we will first discuss these equilibrium methods, next the dynamic methods, and finally various other procedures for obtaining the molecular weights of proteins.

B. Osmotic Pressure of Proteins. The osmotic pressure is measured with an osmometer, which consists essentially of a semipermeable membrane containing the protein solution and a capillary serving as manometer (Fig. 4). If the semipermeable membrane containing the protein solution is placed in water, water will flow into the protein solution and the level in the capillary will rise until the hydrostatic pressure, p, is equal to the osmotic pressure of the protein solution. The osmotic pressure is approximately proportional to the molar concentration, C, of the protein and to the absolute temperature, T, or, mathematically expressed, $p = KCT$, where K is a constant. Van't Hoff found that K is identical with the gas constant, R, the value of which is 0.08207 liter-atmospheres per degree; the molar concentration, C, is equal to c/M, where c is the concentration in grams per liter and M the molecular weight of the protein. By substituting these values in the above equation we obtain, $p = RTc/M$ and $M = RTc/p$, which is van't Hoff's equation for the osmotic pressure. It is identical with the Gay-Lussac law for gases; the osmotic pressure is evidently the pressure which the same substance would exert if it were present in the form of a gas of the same molecular concentration. The osmotic pressure was actually regarded as due to the impact of the solute particles on the wall of the membrane.

Accurate measurements of the osmotic pressure of proteins showed, however, that proportionality between pressure and concentration is

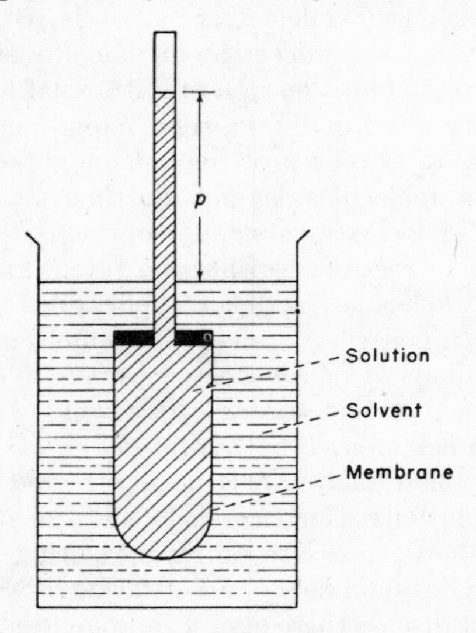

FIG. 4. Osmometer.

found only in very dilute solutions over a limited range of concentration (2,3). The deviation from ideal behavior is accounted for by the equation:

$$M = RTc/(p - Kc^2)$$

where K is a constant of the system examined (4). If K in the above equation is substituted by $B \times R \times T$, and p/c is plotted against c, the slope gives the factor B, while the intercept is proportional to $1/M$ (4*a*,4*b*). At very low concentrations of the solute, c^2 becomes so small that the term Kc^2 can be neglected. The molecular weight can, therefore, be determined by plotting the osmotic pressure, p, against the concentration, c, and extrapolating the curve to $c = 0$. The intercept on the p-axis is considered as the osmotic pressure of an ideal solution and is used to compute M according to van't Hoff's law.

The constant K in the above equation corrects for the volume occupied by the protein molecules themselves. Deviation from ideal behavior is particularly large in solutions containing threadlike molecules, because these immobilize molecules of the solvent (5). Evidently the osmotic pressure cannot arise directly from impacts of the protein molecules on the membrane.

A more adequate concept (6) describes the osmotic pressure as determined by the difference in the activities of the water molecules on both sides of the membrane. While the water in which the osmometer is immersed has the full activity of free water, the activity of the water inside the membrane is reduced by hydration of the proteins and also by the immobilizing action of threadlike protein molecules. From the thermodynamic standpoint the flow of water into the protein solution can also be viewed as due to the tendency for an increase in entropy; by applying a high hydrostatic pressure the intermolecular distances and the entropy are reduced (4).

The osmotic pressure of protein solutions is affected by the pH of the solution because the number of anionic and cationic groups in the protein molecule depends on pH. In acid solutions the proteins are present as cations, in alkaline solutions as anions, so that dialyzable anions and cations, respectively, are required to balance the charge of the proteins, and an unequal distribution of these dialyzable ions inside and outside the membrane results (Donnan effect). Owing to this phenomenon the osmotic pressure of acid or alkaline protein solutions is higher than that of isoelectric solutions. Thus the osmotic pressure of a 1.2% solution of hemoglobin at pH 5.4, 6.5, 7.2, and 10.2 was found to be 13.4, 3.2, 5.0, and 21.4 mm. Hg, respectively (2*a*). It is evident from these figures that the osmotic pressure has its minimum value near the isoelectric point of hemoglobin (pH 6.9).

Although the equipment required for osmometry is simple (Fig. 4), accurate determinations are very difficult. In order to avoid bacterial decomposition of the protein, the determinations must be made at low temperatures and over short periods of time. Capillary glass tubing is frequently used to hasten the attainment of equilibrium. Complications by capillary phenomena (6*a*) are avoided by replacing the water in the capillary by toluene. In order to reduce Donnan effects and to eliminate errors arising from traces of salts present in the protein solution, a concentrated salt solution is employed as solvent and the osmometer membrane is immersed in a salt solution of equal concentration. The measurement of membrane potentials permits the calculation of that part of the pressure, p, which is due to differences in the ion activities.

In this manner the molecular weight of ovalbumin was found to be

45,000 (7–9), that of serum albumin 69,000 (11), and that of hemoglobin 72,000 (11). While these values agree closely with those obtained by other methods, lower values of the osmotic pressure, *p*, are obtained in measurements made on protein mixtures (12), indicating that protein complexes are probably formed in such mixtures.

Since proteins dissolve more readily in concentrated solutions of urea than in water, 6.66 *M* urea solutions have been used as a solvent in osmotic measurements (3).

The molecular weights of amandin and excelsin were 30,300 and 35,700 in urea solution, but 206,000 and 214,000 in the native aqueous solutions, respectively (13). Ovalbumin, serum albumin, gliadin, and other proteins, however, have the same molecular weights in water and in urea solution (13*a*), while many proteins undergo aggregation after denaturation by urea and other similar agents (13*a*).

Osmometric determinations of molecular weights below about 150,000 are more accurate than other methods and are less dependent upon the shape and the hydration of the protein molecules; however, they do not provide us with any basis for deciding whether the protein in the solution examined is homogeneous, or whether it is a mixture of proteins of different molecular weights. If the solution contains more than one kind of protein, the molecular weight computed from the osmotic pressure is a mean value, equal to the sum of the molecular weights of all protein molecules divided by the total number of protein molecules.

C. Sedimentation Equilibrium. If a protein solution is centrifuged at high speed, the protein molecules, owing to their high specific gravity, will tend to sediment, with the result that their concentration increases from the center of the centrifuge to the periphery. The centrifugal force exerted upon the protein molecules is, however, counteracted by the more highly concentrated protein in the periphery, which causes the protein molecules to diffuse back toward the more dilute, central part of the system. At equilibrium the molecular weight, M, is equal to:

$$M = \frac{2RT \ln (c_2/c_1)}{\left(1 - \frac{\rho}{\sigma}\right) \omega^2 (x_2^2 - x_1^2)}$$

where R is the gas constant, T the absolute temperature, c_2 and c_1 the concentrations of the protein at the distances x_2 and x_1 from the center of rotation, ω the angular velocity, and ρ and σ the densities of the solvent and of the sedimenting particles, respectively.

The attainment of the high speeds necessary for experiments of this kind was accomplished by Svedberg, who constructed an oil turbine "ultracentrifuge" with a stainless-steel rotor. Since the sedimentation equilibrium would be disturbed by stopping the centrifuge, the observation had to be made during the centrifugation. For this purpose the protein solutions were placed in transparent chambers and the gradient of the protein concentration was measured by a refractive-index method, similar to that used in electrophoresis (Chapter V, Sect. D), or by other optical devices (14). The very expensive oil-driven steel centrifuge has been replaced by the cheaper air-driven Duraluminum rotor suspended electromagnetically in a vacuum (15), or by electrically driven ultracentrifuges.

The principal disadvantage of the equilibrium method is that a very long time, amounting to as much as several days, may be necessary for equilibrium to be attained. In contrast with the osmometric method, the sedimentation method does permit a decision to be made with regard to whether or not the protein under investigation is homogeneous, since protein mixtures form more than one boundary in the centrifuged solution. A large number of proteins has been examined by Svedberg and coworkers by means of the ultracentrifugal equilibrium method. The results of these investigations will be discussed when we consider a second ultracentrifugal method, in which the rate of sedimentation is measured (Sect. E, p. 45).

D. Diffusion Rate of Proteins (16). When a protein solution is placed in contact with the protein-free solvent, diffusion of protein molecules into the solvent will occur. The quantity, dS, of protein diffusing through an area Q in time dt is, according to Fick's law:

$$dS = -DQ(dc/dx)dt$$

where dc is the difference in protein concentration over the distance dx, and dc/dx is the concentration gradient. D is called the diffusion coefficient. Its order of magnitude is 10^{-5} cm.^{2} sec.$^{-1}$ for amino acids, and 10^{-6} to 10^{-7} cm.^{2} sec.$^{-1}$ for proteins. The diffusion rate is proportional to the absolute temperature and inversely proportional to a quantity called the frictional constant, f. Stated more concisely:

$$D = RT/Nf$$

where R and T are the gas constant and the absolute temperature, respectively, and N the Avogadro number (6.02×10^{23}). For spherical molecules of radius r the frictional constant is proportional to the radius and to η, the viscosity of the solvent:

$$f = 6\pi\eta r \quad (1)$$

$$D = RT/Nf = RT/6\pi\eta rN \quad (2)$$

Since the volume of a sphere of radius r is $4r^3\pi/3$, the molecular weight of a spherelike protein molecule can be calculated by means of the equation $M = 4r^3\pi N\sigma/3$, where σ is the density of the dissolved protein particle. Substituting r from equation (2) we obtain:

$$M = (4\pi N\sigma/3)(RT/6D\pi\eta N)^3 \tag{3}$$

Since most of the protein molecules are nonspherical, their frictional constant, f, is larger than f_0, the frictional constant of a spherical molecule of an equal molecular weight. The frictional ratio, f/f_0, is therefore greater than one. The magnitude of the frictional ratio can be calculated for regularly shaped particles such as cylinders, rods, and ellipsoids. If, however, the shape of the molecule is not known, one is unable to calculate the molecular weight from the diffusion rate.

It is usually assumed that the protein molecule is an ellipsoid of revolution with a long axis, a, and two short axes, b, or with a smaller than b; the axial ratio a/b is greater than one for a prolate ellipsoid and less than one for an oblate ellipsoid. a/b can be calculated if M and f/f_0 are known. The frictional constant of a protein depends, however, not only on its molecular weight and its shape but also on its hydration, because swelling of the dissolved particle through binding water of hydration clearly results in an increase of the friction (17). If the protein has a spherelike shape the frictional ratio depends solely on the degree of hydration; this can be calculated from the relationship:

$$w = (f/f_0 - 1)\rho/\sigma$$

where w is the weight of water bound by one gram of protein and ρ and σ are the densities of the solution and of the dissolved protein, respectively. In computing the molecular weight of nonspherical molecules a value of 0.3 to 0.5 is usually assumed for w.

The diffusion constant is determined experimentally by forming a sharp horizontal boundary between protein solution and solvent in a vertical tube and by measuring the rate at which the boundary spreads by means of one of the optical methods used in sedimentation and electrophoresis (see Chapter V, Sect. D) (16,17). If the protein investigated is homogeneous, the concentration gradient dc/dx will decrease according to a Gaussian distribution curve, while the curve of the gradients in protein mixtures will not fit the Gaussian curve.

Since the formation of a sharp boundary between protein solution and solvent is difficult to accomplish experimentally, the two solutions have been studied when separated by a porous disc of sintered glass (18). The rate of diffusion is measured by determining the amount of protein diffusing through the disc into the water (Fig. 5). By placing the heavier protein solutions above the solvent, S, the diffusion is accelerated by gravity. The diffusion tube is calibrated with solutions of known diffusion coefficient. If the substance used for standardization is a protein of known molecular weight M_1, with diffusion coefficient D_1, according to equation (3) the molecular weight, M_2, of the unknown protein is:

$$M_2 = M_1 \frac{\sigma_2}{\sigma_1} \left(\frac{D_1 f_1}{D_2 f_2} \right)^3$$

If the frictional ratios and the densities of both proteins are the same the molecular weight is:

$$M_2 = M_1 (D_1/D_2)^3$$

The results obtained by this method are somewhat less reliable than those obtained by means of the free-boundary method.

Molecular weights calculated from diffusion rates are of the same order of magnitude as values obtained by other methods. Owing to the variable factors introduced by hydration and by deviations of the molecules from the spherical shape, determinations of the diffusion rate are rarely used for the direct calculation of molecular weights. Frequently they are combined with the sedimentation velocity method.

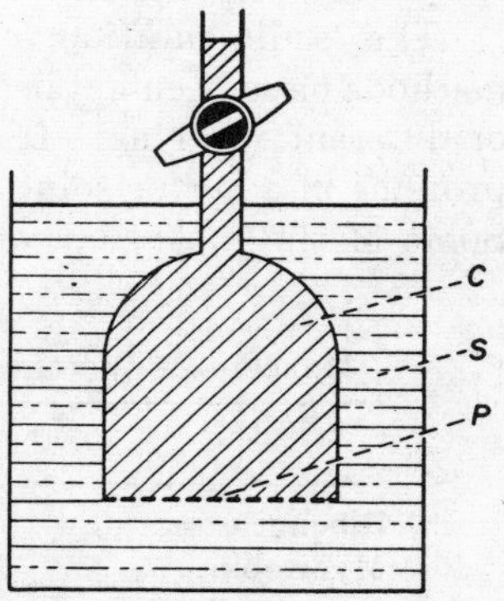

FIG. 5. Diffusion apparatus. C, colloid solution; S, solvent; P, porous disc.

E. Sedimentation Velocity of Proteins. If protein solutions are spun in an ultracentrifuge at very high speeds, so that the centrifugal field developed becomes equivalent to approximately 500,000g (g = earth's gravitational field), the protein particles sediment at a much higher rate than in the equilibrium method. If the molecular weight of the protein molecules is high, the rate of diffusion can be neglected, since the rate of sedimentation increases and the diffusion rate decreases considerably the greater the molecular weight of the solute studied in such experiments. The molecular weight is computed according to the equation:

$$M = \frac{RTs}{D(1 - \rho/\sigma)}$$

where R, T, ρ, and σ have the same significance as noted above; D is the diffusion coefficient, and s the sedimentation constant. The sedimentation constant is defined as the rate of sedimentation in a centrifugal field of unity. It is equal to:

$$s = (dx/dt)(1/\omega^2 x)$$

where x is the distance of the moving boundary from the center of the rotor at time t and ω the angular velocity of the rotor. The sedimentation constant of proteins is of the order of 10^{-12} to 10^{-13} sec. It is evident that the diffusion coefficient, D, must be known if M is to be calculated from this equation. It is usually determined by the diffusion method described in the preceding section. Although the sedimentation rate depends on the electrical charge of the protein molecules this factor can be eliminated to a certain extent by addition of salts (19).

The sedimentation equilibrium and the sedimentation velocity methods have been applied by Svedberg and coworkers to a large number of different proteins. It was found that the molecular weights of the proteins in aqueous solutions vary from about 12,000 to several million. Some of the molecular weights found are shown in Table II. Edestin

TABLE II

Molecular Weights Determined by Sedimentation Velocity

Protein	Mol. wt.	Ref.
Ribonuclease	12,700	19*a*
Myoglobin	17,000	14
Cytochrome c	17,000	14
Bence-Jones protein	35,000	14
β-Lactoglobulin	35,400	19*b*
Ovalbumin	45,000	9
Serum albumin	68,000	14
Human hemoglobin	63,000	14
Thyroglobulin (pig)	630,000	14
Apoferritin	465,000	19*c*
Jack bean urease	473,000	19*d*
Hemocyanin (*Helix pomatia*)	6,700,000	14
Tobacco mosaic virus	~40,000,000	27

from hemp seed, excelsin from brazil nuts, and phycocyan and phycoerythrin from algae had molecular weights of 280,000–310,000 (14).

A solution containing a mixture of several proteins produces more than one boundary so that the method reveals whether or not a particular protein is uniform. Thus, gelatin was found to be heterogeneous and to consist of particles of molecular weight 10,000–70,000 (20). Casein, zein, and serum globulin were also found to be mixtures.

While no difficulties are encountered in the interpretations of results obtained with homogeneous protein solutions, complications arise in mixtures due to the formation of mixed protein-protein compounds (21).

Svedberg had originally assumed that all molecular weights of proteins are multiples of 17,000. Later, however, it was found that some of the values required correction (see Table II) so that it is not clear at present whether the figures of 68.000, 35,000 and 17,000 recorded in the table are significant in this respect. Higher molecular weights, above 200,000, cannot shed light on this important problem, because the experimental error increases with the molecular weight, approaching 17,000 when the value of M exceeds 200,000 (22).

F. Flow Birefringence (23). If a solution of a macromolecular substance such as a protein is placed between two crossed Nicol prisms, the field will remain dark. If, however, the solution is made to flow, a light

FIG. 6. Flow birefringence. *a*, particles at rest; *b*, particles oriented owing to flow.

field is observed in solutions of rodlike or threadlike proteins, while solutions of spherelike proteins remain dark. The appearance of light in the dark field of the crossed Nicol prisms is due to the same phenomenon as the birefringence of crystals and other anisotropic structures. It is believed that rodlike protein molecules undergo a uniform orientation in the streaming solution (Fig. 6). Quantitative measurements of flow birefringence are carried out by means of a device in which the protein solution is placed between two concentric cylinders. While one of the cylinders is fixed, the other one rotates, so that the rodlike protein molecules tend to assume a position tangential to the direction of flow. The angle between the long axis of the rods and the direction of flow decreases as the speed of the moving cylinder increases and as the axial ratio of the rods increases; this ratio can, then, be calculated from the angle of orientation (24,25). In the rotating system a dark cross, the cross of isocline, is visible; it is similar to the cross observed in starch grains under a polarizing microscope. The average angle of orientation of the rods is equal to 90° minus the angle of isocline. By means of this device it has been found that the molecules of myosin from muscle (25), fibrinogen from blood plasma (26), and tobacco mosaic virus (27) are elongated threadlike molecules with high axial ratios, while those of γ-globulin are less asymmetric (26); β_1-globulin was found to be highly symmetric (see Table XI, p. 152).

G. Viscosity of Protein Solutions (23). It is a familiar observation that solutions of some proteins such as gelatin are extremely viscous,

TABLE III

RELATIVE VISCOSITIES OF AQUEOUS SOLUTIONS OF OVALBUMIN AND GELATIN (29)

Ovalbumin								
Concentration, %	3.02	8.88	14.53	20.12	28.15			
Relative viscosity	1.22	1.57	2.21	3.60	9.99			
Gelatin								
Concentration, %	1	2	3	4	5	6	8	10
Relative viscosity	2.39	3.44	4.54	5.78	7.12	9.06	14.2	22.0

while solutions of others such as ovalbumin or the serum proteins flow much more easily, even if their concentration is much higher than that of gelatin. This is evident from Table III, which shows the viscosity of ovalbumin (28) solutions at 25.2°C. and that of gelatin solutions at 37°. At the lower temperature the viscosity of gelatin cannot be measured because its solutions form a gel (29). The high viscosity of gelatin solutions is due to the threadlike shape of the gelatin molecules which, owing to Brownian motion, occupy a larger volume of the solvent than spherical molecules of the same molecular weight would occupy. Additional work is therefore required to maintain a given velocity of flow in such a solution of asymmetric molecules.

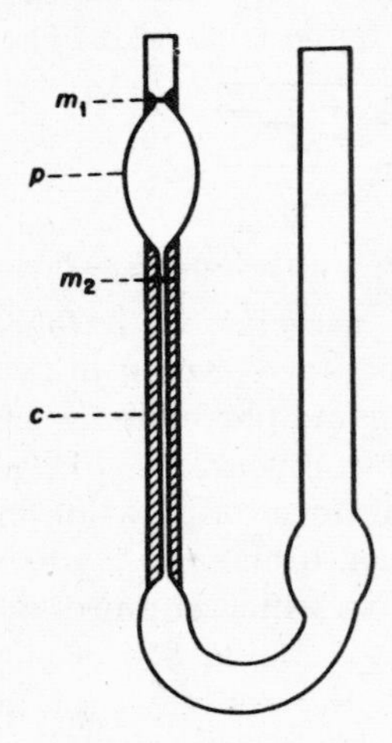

FIG. 7. Ostwald viscometer.

Measurements of viscosity are frequently made because there are no experimental difficulties encountered. The type of viscometer most commonly used is the Ostwald viscometer (Fig. 7). The aqueous solution of the protein is allowed to flow from the pipet, p, through the capillary, c, and the time, t, required for the level to drop from m_1 to m_2 is noted. If the viscosity of the protein solution does not differ too greatly from that of water and if the dimensions of the capillary are appropriate, the viscosity, η, is directly proportional to t, the time of outflow, and to d, the density of the solution:

$$\eta = Cdt$$

If η_0 is the viscosity of water and η that of the protein solution, the relative viscosity:

$$\eta_r = \eta/\eta_0 = Cd_pt_p/Ct_w = d_pt_p/t_w$$

where d_p is the density of the protein solution, and t_p and t_w the time of flow of the protein solution and of water, respectively. The relative viscosity, η_r, is evidently independent of the constant C, which is a function of the dimensions of the capillary.

For very dilute suspensions of spherelike particles Einstein formulated the equation:

$$\eta = \eta_0(1 + 2.5Nv/V) \tag{4}$$

where N is the number of suspended particles, v the volume of each particle, and V the total volume of the solution. If we know N, the number of protein molecules dissolved, we can calculate the volume occupied by each particle and can thus determine the extent to which it is hydrated. On the other hand, if the hydration is known we can calculate from equation (4) the number of molecules, N, and the particle weight, which is equal to the total weight of the protein divided by N. Reasonable values for the hydration are obtained in this way for ovalbumin, hemoglobin, and other proteins with spherelike molecules (30). Most of the proteins have a nonspherical shape, so that this method is of very limited applicability.

Since the viscosity, η, of a protein solution is always higher than η_0, the viscosity of water, the relative viscosity $\eta_r = \eta/\eta_0$ is always greater than one. The increase in relative viscosity, which is equal to $\eta_r - 1$, has been called the specific viscosity, η_{sp}. According to Staudinger (31) the specific viscosity of solutions of threadlike macromolecules is directly proportional to the concentration and to the molecular weight of the dissolved macromolecule. In the equation:

$$\eta_{sp} = KcM$$

K is a constant for a given series of homologous chain molecules of the same structural pattern but of different lengths; c is the concentration, and M the molecular weight.

If chain molecules are dissolved, their molecules will only rarely be present in the fully extended shape. They will fold and unfold continually, owing to free rotation around the valence bonds, and will assume different constellations at different times (Fig. 8).

According to statistical considerations (32) the average chain length of the molecule, *i.e.*, the distance between the two ends of the chain, is proportional to $\sqrt{L}$, where L is the chain length of the fully extended molecule. Since M is proportional to L, the average chain length is also proportional to $\sqrt{M}$.

The viscosity of the solution depends not only on this average chain length, but also on the shape resistance of the molecule, *i.e.*, on the resistance of the chain molecule to rearrangement of the constellation. In order to account for these factors the value M of Staudinger's equation has been replaced by its power-function M^{α}, where α assumes values between 0.5 and 1.5 (33,34).

If viscosity measurements are performed at different concentrations of the macromolecular solution, different values of η_r or of η_{sp} are obtained. By plotting the specific viscosity against the concentration of the solution and by extrapolation to the concentration $c = 0$, the *intrinsic viscosity*, $[\eta]$, of a molecule can be determined. It is (35–37):

$$[\eta] = (\eta_{sp}/c)_{c\rightarrow 0} = (\ln \eta_r/c)_{c\rightarrow 0}$$

While viscosity measurements allow the determination of the molecular weight of chain molecules such as those of rubber and of cellulose esters, the situation in solutions of proteins is complicated by the electrostatically interacting anionic and cationic protein side chains and by

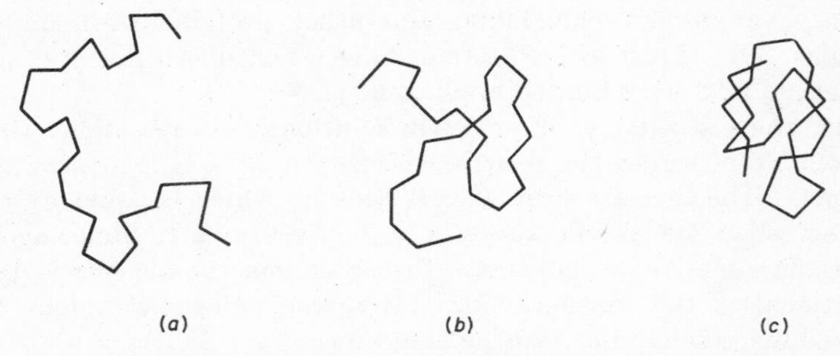

FIG. 8. Different constellations of a threadlike macromolecule.

their action on water molecules. The viscosity of a protein solution will depend, therefore, on the pH of the solution. The electrostatic action of the ionic groups can be minimized by the addition of salts; the viscosity of polyelectrolytes is reduced by the addition of sodium chloride (38,39). While it is hardly possible to calculate the weight and shape of protein molecules from viscosity measurements alone, the results of viscometric investigations in combination with other methods give valuable information concerning these properties of proteins. Thus, by combining the results of viscometry and of diffusion measurements, the following values were obtained for the molecular weights: ovalbumin 40,500, lactoglobulin 41,500, serum albumin 67,100, serum globulin 150,000–200,000, amandin (from almonds) 330,000 thyroglobulin 676,000, hemocyanin from octopus 2.78 millions (40,41). The molecular weight of tobacco mosaic virus was found to be 63.2 and 42.6 million; the dimensions of the virus particles were 11.5 × 725 mμ and 12.3 × 430 mμ (42) in excellent agreement with the results of diffusion measurements (43).

If the rodlike particles of a solution are very long and if they possess sufficient rigidity, the phenomenon of *thixotropy* is observed (44). This consists of the formation of a gel during prolonged standing of the solution, and of the liquefaction of the gel upon agitation. Thixotropy has been observed in gels of myosin, the contractile muscular protein.

H. Light Scattering by Proteins. The fact that colloidal solutions such as those of proteins are turbid and that they scatter part of the incident light, an effect called the *Tyndall phenomenon,* has long been known. The intensity of the scattered light increases with the number and size of the colloidal particles. This is evident from the formula:

$$\tau = MHc \tag{5}$$

where τ is the excess turbidity, M the molecular weight, c the concentration in grams per cm.^{3}, and H a proportionality constant. If μ is the refractive index of the solution, μ_0, that of the solvent, and λ, the wave length of the light used, H can be determined according to the following equation:

$$H = \frac{32\pi^3}{3}\frac{\mu_0{}^2}{N\lambda^4}\left(\frac{\mu - \mu_0}{c}\right)^2 \tag{6}$$

where N is the Avogadro number (44*a*). The equation shows that the intensity of the turbidity, τ, depends on the magnitude of the refractive index and on the difference between the two refractive indices μ and μ_0, moreover, that it is inversely proportional to the fourth power of the wave length, λ. If solvent and solution have the same refractive index, the last term becomes zero and no scattering will occur. Since all the values of equation (6) can be determined experimentally, the molecular weight, M, can be calculated according to equation (5).

Molecular weights obtained in this manner are: ovalbumin 38,000, serum albumin 74,000, hemocyanin from *Helix* 6,340,000 (45), tobacco mosaic virus 40,000,000 (46). The light scattering method is of a particular value for protein chemistry because it permits a rapid determination of the molecular weight, so that one has not to fear changes caused by contamination with bacteria or by traces of proteolytic enzymes.

If the size of the protein molecule is so great as to be comparable with the wave length of the incident light, interference occurs and the intensity of the scattered light is no longer symmetrically distributed about the right-angle position. The intensities $\dot{I}_1$ and $\dot{I}_2$ of light scattered at 45° and 135°, *i.e.*, forward and backward from 90° direction, are found to be different. The value $q = (\dot{I}_1/\dot{I}_2) - 1$ has been called the dissymmetry coefficient. With increasing dilution of the solution, q approaches a limiting value called the "intrinsic dissymmetry coefficient"; this value is a measure of the spatial extension of the colloidal molecule and can be used to determine directly the size of the molecule in solution. In this way the length of the tobacco mosaic virus was found to be 2750 Å, in agreement with electron microscope measurement which furnished the value 2800 Å (47).

I. X-Ray Analysis of Soluble Proteins (48). While the fibrous structural proteins show regular periodicities in one or two dimensions (see Chapter IX, Sect. B) many of the soluble proteins can be obtained in the form of true, three-dimensional crystals. Analysis of such crystals with the older X-ray equipment furnished less typical interferences, than analysis of fibers or of denatured proteins in powder form. The reason for this unexpected result was that the older X-ray analysis showed only short-range periodicities, not those to be expected in large molecules.

TABLE IV

Protein	Dimensions of unit cell, Å (1 Å = 10^{-8} cm.) *a*	*b*	*c*	Mol. wt. of unit cell	Ref.
Insulin					
Wet	144	83	34	52,400	(54)
Dry	130	74.8	30.9	39,500	
Lactoglobulin					
Wet	67.5	67.5	154	67,000	(55,56)
Dry	60	63	110	40,000	
Ribonuclease					
Wet	30.8	38.5	53.5	~23,000	(57)
Dry	28.7	29.3	45.2	~14,500	

The interferences obtained in these first analyses were due to periodicities of the amino acids along the peptide chain (49) or to periodicities in the distances between parallel peptide chains within the protein molecule. Thus, all denatured proteins furnish interferences corresponding to periodicities of 4.6 and 10 Å (50,51). Obviously this method could not furnish any information about the true dimensions of the unit cells in protein crystals.

New X-ray equipment, however, permits measurement of periodicities of a higher order by means of small-angle scattering (52). With this method the dimensions of the unit cells of several crystalline proteins have been measured. The main difficulty lies in the preparation of large single crystals of proteins since only X-ray diagrams given by single crystals can be interpreted unequivocally. Powder diagrams are virtually worthless (53).

While the methods discussed in the preceding sections provide information concerning only two of the three axes of the molecule, X-ray analysis enables us to determine the extension of the unit cell in all three dimensions. Some of these values are shown in Table IV, where *a*, *b*, and *c* are the dimensions of the unit cells and *M* the molecular weight corresponding to this unit cell.

Hemoglobin crystals were found to consist of cylindrical units with a height of 33.5 (dry) or 40.1 (wet) Å, and a diameter of 57 Å (58). In lactoglobulin, ribonuclease, and hemoglobin the unit cell seems to be identical with the protein molecule. In other proteins, however, the unit cell is formed by two or more protein molecules.

J. Electron Micrography of Proteins (59). This method furnishes direct information concerning the dimensions of the molecules. In its present state electron micrography is limited to the determination of the dimensions of only the largest protein molecules, chiefly those of the viruses. Particularly beautiful pictures are obtained by first shadowing the particles, *i.e.*, by exposing them to the oblique evaporation of chromium or of gold. The metal is deposited on one side of the particle, giving the suggestion of a shadow and imparting depth to the picture obtained (60). The first electron micrographs of proteins were produced by von Ardenne (61), who found a molecular diameter for hemocyanin of 220 Å. Each of the hemocyanin particles is apparently a bundle of four subunits (62). Edestin forms approximately spherical particles; their diameter is about 70 Å (62*a*). Myosin, the muscular protein, consists of threads 50–100 Å broad and several thousand Å in length (63). The transverse diameter of tobacco mosaic virus particles was found to be 150 Å, and their length 2800 Å (64).

K. Comparison of Molecular Weights Found by Different Methods. In the preceding sections the difficulties encountered in determining the molecular weights of dissolved proteins were emphasized. These were seen to be partly due to the fact that diffusion, sedimentation, and other similar phenomena depend not only on the molecular weight of the protein, but also on the shape and the hydration of the molecule.

In a number of the formulas quoted above there appears the term σ, the density of the protein particles in solution. This value cannot be determined experimentally, nor can an adequate interpretation be assigned it. It is sometimes replaced by $1/V$, where the partial specific volume, V, is the increase in volume of a large volume of solvent brought about by the addition of 1 g. of the solute (see Chapter VI, Sect. A). In view of these complicating factors one would expect that the molecular weights found by different methods differ widely. This is, however, not the case. Table V shows a surprisingly fair agreement between most of the values obtained by different methods. This correspondence is most probably due to the fact that all proteins contain approximately the same amount of water of hydration (see Chapter VI) and that the error made in determining σ is the same in most of the methods. In this way two of the factors which cause deviations are abolished.

Nevertheless it is somewhat astonishing that agreement is also found in the case of serum albumin, lactoglobulin, and certain other proteins, which as revealed by electrophoresis are mixtures of several compounds. While the molecular weights determined by X-ray analysis (Table V) agree fairly well with molecular weights found by the other methods, great differences exist between the axial ratios calculated from viscosity or diffusion on the one hand, and from X-ray analysis on the other (66). Thus axial ratios, a/b, of 3–4 were calculated for serum albumin, hemoglobin, and for lactoglobulin in solution, while X-ray analysis showed that the axial ratio in the wet crystals is less than 3 for lactoglobulin and less than 2 for hemoglobin and serum albumin.

TABLE V
MOLECULAR WEIGHTS OF PROTEINS (65)

Protein	Method employed				
	Osmometry	Sedimentation equilibrium	Sedimentation velocity	X-ray analysis	Light scattering
Pepsin	36,000	39,000	35,500	~39,300	—
Lactoglobulin	—	38,500	41,500	40,000	—
Ovalbumin	44,000	40,500	44,000	—	38,000
Hemoglobin	67,000	68,000	68,000	66,700	—
Serum albumin	73,000	68,000	70,000	<82,800	74,000
Excelsin	214,000	—	295,000	305,800	280,000
Insulin	48,000	41,000	35,000	36,000	—

A thorough examination of insulin demonstrated that the difference between the value 48,000 found osmometrically and the value 36,000 found by X-ray analysis is a true difference in molecular weights and not due to analytical error. A simultaneous chemical analysis of insulin led to the conclusion that the molecule is formed from subunits of equivalent weight 12,000 (see Chapter XIII, Sect. C); it is assumed, therefore, that the particles of insulin in solution consist of four subunits, while the insulin crystal is formed from three subunits of the equivalent weight 12,000 (67).

The question arises as to whether the structural units of the crystals, or the particles which are present in aqueous solutions, or, finally, the so-called subunits are true "molecules." We must remember that such *subunits* are also found osmometrically and by sedimentation methods when proteins are dissolved in concentrated urea solutions (see Sect. B, above). Disaggregation of protein particles is also accomplished by other mild procedures, for instance by lowering the temperature (68), or by small pH changes (69–71). The cleaved molecules combine again on readjustment to the original pH value. The ease of the fragmentation of protein molecules into subunits shows that these subunits are linked together by very weak bonds, possibly by hydrogen bonds or by electrostatic forces between anionic and cationic groups. This being the case, and if the notion "molecule" is used for particles held together by strong covalent bonds, the subunits are the true protein molecules and the particles present in the aqueous solution are micelles, *i.e.*, aggregates of subunits (71,72).

The phenomenon of *reversible dissociation* of protein particles into smaller particles is not only interesting from the theoretical point of view, but also is of great biological importance. If such a disaggregation occurred within the living cell, it would precipitate an increase in the osmotic pressure, a swelling of the cell, and a sudden drop in the viscosity of the cellular fluid, the reverse of those changes occurring upon reaggregation. Similar changes might well be involved in the alterations of the cellular shape which characterize ameboid movement and muscular contraction. Myosin, the contractile protein of muscle, seems to be a polymer of tropomyosin, another muscular protein, and a mutual conversion *in vivo* is to be considered entirely possible.

References

1. E. Brand, L. J. Seidel, W. H. Goldwater, B. Kassell, F. J. Ryan, *J. Am. Chem. Soc.* **67,** 1524 (1945).

1*a*. A. C. Chibnall, *Proc. Roy. Soc. London* **B131,** 136 (1942).

2. S. Sørensen, *Proteins.* The Fleischmann Company, New York, 1925.

2*a*. G. S. Adair, *Proc. Roy. Soc. London* **A108,** 627 (1925); **109,** 292 (1925).

3. N. F. Burk, D. M. Greenberg, *J. Biol. Chem.* **87,** 197 (1930).

4. G. Gee, *Ann. Repts. on Progress Chem., Chem. Soc. London* **39, 7** (1942).

4*a*. G. Scatchard, A. C. Batchelder, A. Brown, *J. Am. Chem. Soc.* **68,** 2320 (1946).

4*b*. J. T. Edsall, personal communication.

5. H. Staudinger, G. Schulz, *Ber.* **68,** 2320, 2336 (1935).

6. E. J. Cohn, J. T. Edsall, *Proteins, Amino Acids, and Peptides.* Reinhold, New York, 1943, p. 382.

6*a*. G. Jones, H. F. Fornwaldt, *J. Am. Chem. Soc.* **60,** 1683 (1938).

7. J. R. Marrack, L. F. Hewitt, *Biochem. J.* **23,** 1079 (1929).

8. H. B. Bull, *J. Biol. Chem.* **137,** 143 (1941).

9. H. Gutfreund, *Nature* **153,** 406 (1944).

10. A. Roche, M. Dorier, F. Marquet, *Compt. rend. soc. biol.* **119,** 50 (1935).

11. G. S. Adair, M. Robinson, *Biochem. J.* **24,** 1864 (1930).

12. A. G. Ogston, *Biochem. J.* **31,** 1952 (1937).

13. N. F. Burk, *J. Biol. Chem.* **120**, 63 (1937).
13*a*. H. Neurath, J. P. Greenstein, F. W. Putnam, J. O. Erickson, *Chem. Revs.* **34**, 158 (1944).
14. T. Svedberg, K. O. Pedersen, *The Ultracentrifuge.* Oxford Univ. Press, London, 1940.
15. R. G. W. Wyckoff, *Science* **85**, 390 (1937).
16. H. Neurath, *Chem. Revs.* **30**, 357 (1942).
17. J. L. Oncley, *Ann. N. Y. Acad. Sci.* **41**, 121 (1941).
17*a*. E. G. Pickels, *Chem. Revs.* **30**, 341 (1942).
18. J. H. Northrop, M. L. Anson, *J. Gen. Physiol.* **12**, 543 (1929).
19. A. Tiselius, *Kolloid-Z.* **59**, 306 (1938).
19*a*. A. Rothen, *J. Gen. Physiol.* **24**, 203 (1940).
19*b*. R. Cecil, A. G. Ogston, *Biochem. J.* **44**, 33 (1949).
19*c*. A. Rothen, *J. Biol. Chem.* **152**, 679 (1944).
19*d*. J. B. Sumner, N. Gralèn, B. Erickson-Quensel, *Science* **87**, 395 (1938).
20. K. Krishnamurti, T. Svedberg, *J. Am. Chem. Soc.* **52**, 2897 (1930).
21. K. O. Pedersen, *Compt. rend. trav. lab. Carlsberg. Sèr. chim.* **22**, 427 (1938).
22. A. Norris, *Nature* **157**, 408 (1946).
23. J. T. Edsall, *Advances in Colloid Sci.* **1**, 269 (1942).
24. A. von Muralt, J. T. Edsall, *J. Biol. Chem.* **89**, 315, 351 (1930).
25. G. Boehm, R. Signer, *Helv. Chim. Acta* **14**, 1370 (1931).
26. J. T. Edsall, J. F. Foster, H. Scheinberg, *J. Am. Chem. Soc.* **69**, 2731 (1947); J. F. Foster, J. T. Edsall, *ibid.* **70**, 1860 (1948).
27. M. A. Lauffer, *J. Biol. Chem.* **126**, 443 (1938).
28. H. Chick and E. Lubrzynska, *Biochem. J.* **8**, 59 (1914).
29. M. Kunitz, *J. Gen. Physiol.* **10**, 811 (1926–1927).
30. W. Pauli, E. Valko, *Kolloidchemie der Eiweisskörper*, T. Steinkopff, Dresden, 1933, p. 241.
31. H. Staudinger, *Ber.* **65**, 267 (1932).
32. W. Kuhn, *J. Colloid Sci.* **3**, 11 (1948).
33. T. Alfrey, A. Bartovics, H. Mark, *J. Am. Chem. Soc.* **61**, 2319 (1939).
34. P. Debye, A. Bueche, *J. Chem. Phys.* **16**, 573 (1948).
35. H. B. Bull, *Physical Biochemistry.* Wiley, New York, 1943, p. 258.
36. J. G. Kirkwood, J. Riseman, *J. Phys. Chem.* **16**, 565 (1948).
37. L. H. Cragg, *J. Colloid Sci.* **1**, 261 (1946).
38. H. Staudinger, H. Becker, *Ber.* **70**, 879 (1937).
39. R. Fuoss, *Science* **108**, 545 (1948).
40. A. Polson, *Nature* **137**, 740 (1936).
41. H. Neurath, G. R. Cooper, *J. Am. Chem. Soc.* **62**, 2248 (1940).
42. M. A. Lauffer, *J. Biol. Chem.* **126**, 443 (1938).
43. H. Neurath, A. M. Saum, *J. Biol. Chem.* **126**, 435 (1938).
44. A. S. C. Lawrence, *Ann. Repts. on Progress Chem., Chem. Soc. London* **37**, 101 (1941).
44*a*. P. Debye, *Ann. N. Y. Acad. Sci.* **51**, 575 (1949); *J. Phys. Colloid Chem.* **53**, 1 (1949).
45. P. Putzeys, T. Brosteaux, *Trans. Faraday Soc.* **31**, 1314 (1934).
46. G. Oster, P. M. Doty, B. H. Zimm, *J. Am. Chem. Soc.* **69**, 1193 (1947).
47. P. M. Doty, W. Affens, B. H. Zimm, *Trans. Faraday Soc.* **42**, B66 (1946).
48. I. Fankuchen, *Advances in Protein Chem.* **2**, 387 (1945).
49. E. W. Hughes, W. J. Moore, Jr., *J. Am. Chem. Soc.* **64**, 2236 (1942).
50. J. D. Bernal, I. Fankuchen, and M. Perutz, *Nature* **141**, 523 (1938).

51. G. Clark, J. Shenk, *Radiology* **28,** 58 (1937).
52. R. G. W. Wyckoff, R. B. Corey, *J. Biol. Chem.* **114,** 407 (1936).
53. I. Fankuchen, *Ann. Rev. Biochem.* **14,** 207 (1945).
54. D. Crowfoot, D. Riley, *Nature* **144,** 1011 (1939).
55. D. Crowfoot, D. Riley, *Nature* **141,** 521 (1938).
56. F. Senti, R. Warner, *J. Am. Chem. Soc.* **70,** 3318 (1948).
57. I. Fankuchen, cited by E. J. Cohn, J. T. Edsall, *Proteins, Amino Acids and Peptides.* Reinhold, New York, 1943, p. 382.
58. J. Boyes-Watson, O. Davidson, M. F. Perutz, *Proc. Roy. Soc. London* **A191,** 83 (1947).
59. L. Marton, *Ann. Rev. Biochem.* **12,** 587 (1943).
60. R. C. Williams, R. G. W. Wyckoff, *Proc. Soc. Exptl. Biol. Med.* **58,** 265 (1945).
61. M. von Ardenne, *Z. physik. Chem.* **187,** 1 (1940).
62. A. Polson, R. G. W. Wyckoff, *Nature,* **160,** 153 (1947).
62*a*. C. E. Hall, *J. Am. Chem. Soc.* **71,** 2951 (1949).
63. M. von Ardenne, H. H. Weber, *Kolloid-Z.* **97,** 322 (1941).
64. W. M. Stanley, T. F. Anderson, *J. Biol. Chem.* **139,** 325 (1941).
65. P. Johnson, *Ann. Repts. on Progress Chem., Chem. Soc. London* **43,** 53 (1948).
66. D. Crowfoot, *Chem. Revs.* **28,** 215 (1941).
67. D. Riley, in *Symposium sur les Proteines.* Desoer, Liège, 1946, p. 35.
68. F. F. Nord, *Naturwissenschaften* **24,** 481 (1936); **23,** 722 (1935).
69. B. Erickson-Quensel, T. Svedberg, *Biol. Bull.* **71,** 498 (1936).
70. S. Brohult, *J. Phys. Colloid Chem.* **51,** 206 (1947).
71. K. O. Pedersen, *Ann. Rev. Biochem.* **17,** 185 (1947).
72. H. Staudinger, *Ber.* **68,** 2313 (1935).

Chapter V

Electrochemistry of Proteins

A. Amino Acids as Dipolar Ions. It was long believed that amino acids go into water solution in the form of neutral molecules having the general formula $H_2N \cdot R \cdot COOH$. That amino acids in acidic or alkaline solution migrate to the cathode or to the anode, respectively, was ascribed to the following set of reactions:

$$H_2N \cdot R \cdot COOH + H^+ \rightleftharpoons H_3\overset{+}{N} \cdot R \cdot COOH \tag{1a}$$
$$H_2N \cdot R \cdot COOH + \overset{-}{O}H \rightleftharpoons H_2N \cdot R \cdot CO\overset{-}{O} + H_2O \tag{2a}$$

It was first proposed by Adams (1) and by Bjerrum (1*a*) that the neutral formula of amino acids, $H_2N \cdot R \cdot COOH$, has to be replaced by the dipolar formula, $H_3\overset{+}{N} \cdot R \cdot CO\overset{-}{O}$, and that only negligibly small amounts of the amino acids can be present as uncharged, neutral molecules. If we accept this view equations (1*a*) and (2*a*) have to be replaced by the equations (1b) and (2b):

$$H_3\overset{+}{N} \cdot R \cdot CO\overset{-}{O} + H^+ \rightleftharpoons H_3\overset{+}{N} \cdot R \cdot COOH \tag{1b}$$
$$H_3\overset{+}{N} \cdot R \cdot CO\overset{-}{O} + \overset{-}{O}H \rightleftharpoons H_2N \cdot R \cdot CO\overset{-}{O} + H_2O \tag{2b}$$

Hydrogen ions, according to the older concept, are bound to uncharged amino groups, NH_2, converting them into positively charged ammonium groups $\overset{+}{N}H_3$ (equation 1a); according to the new concept, hydrogen ions combine with the negatively charged $CO\overset{-}{O}$ groups to form COOH. In an analogous manner hydroxyl ions, $\overset{-}{O}H$, react with COOH or with $\overset{+}{N}H_3$ according to equations (2a) and (2b), respectively.

Comparing equation (1a) with (1b), and (2a) with (2b), we find that the right sides are identical. Actually amino acids are present in acid solutions as cations of the formula $H_3\overset{+}{N} \cdot R \cdot COOH$, and in alkaline solutions as anions of the formula $H_2N \cdot R \cdot COO^-$. While this can be proved by the migration of the amino acid ions in an electric field, no decision between the neutral formula $H_2N \cdot R \cdot COOH$ and the dipolar formula $H_3\overset{+}{N} \cdot R \cdot CO\overset{-}{O}$ is possible in this way; for dipolar ions, owing to their positive and negative groups, are attracted with the same force by both the anode and the cathode, and therefore do not migrate as do true anions or cations. As a result dipolar ions (zwitterions, hybrid ions) fail to contribute to the conductance of the solution, behaving, in other words, as though they were neutral, uncharged molecules. Thus the question of whether a solution contains neutral molecules of the formula $H_2N \cdot R \cdot COOH$ or dipolar ions of the formula $H_3\overset{+}{N} \cdot R \cdot COO^-$ cannot be decided by conductivity measurements.

The dipolar formula of the amino acids was, however, fully confirmed by other physicochemical methods. One of the first methods applied was the calorimetric determination of the *heat of ionization* of amino acids in acid and in alkaline solutions (2). It is well known that the heat of the reaction:

$$R \cdot COOH \rightleftharpoons R \cdot CO\bar{O} + H^+$$

in aliphatic carboxylic acids, approximately +1000 cal. per mole, is quite different from the heat of ionization of aliphatic amines:

$$R \cdot \overset{+}{N}H_3 \rightleftharpoons R \cdot NH_2 + H^+$$

which is close to +12000 cal. per mole. Actually it was found that the heat of ionization of amino acids in acid solution varies from −1300 to +2100 cal. and the heat of ionization in alkaline solution from +10,000 to +13,300 cal. per mole. Evidently hydrochloric acid reacts with the carboxyl groups of the amino acids, sodium hydroxide with their ammonium groups.

The dipolar formula of amino acids is also strongly supported by the fact that amino acids raise the *dielectric constant* of water in which they are dissolved (see Chapter VII, Sect. K). The older representation of amino acids as neutral molecules would be quite inadequate in this respect. The existence of COO^- groups rather than COOH groups in neutral solutions of amino acids is also indicated by their Raman spectra (3), which depend on the vibrations and hence on the structure of the molecular groups involved.

The dipolar structure of amino acids in their aqueous solutions is, finally, confirmed by the phenomenon of *electrostriction*, *i.e.*, by an excessive contraction when the solid amino acid is dissolved in water. Slight contractions are also observed in other substances. Thus a large volume of water increases by 56.2 ml. when one mole (75 g.) of glycolamide, $CH_2OH \cdot CONH_2$, is dissolved, whereas if one mole (75 g.) of the isomeric glycine, $H_3\overset{+}{N} \cdot CH_2 \cdot CO\bar{O}$, is dissolved, the volume increase amounts only to 43.5 ml. The pronounced electrostriction indicated is due to the strong attraction and resultant compression of water molecules by the electrostatic forces of the ionized groups of the amino acid (4).

That the *solid amino acids* also exist as dipolar ions rather than as neutral molecules is shown by their high densities and their high melting points. Both properties indicate strong electrostatic attraction between the oppositely charged ionic groups of adjacent molecules, making it more difficult for them to separate than would be the case with adjacent, neutral molecules. While the density and the melting points of glycolamide are 1.390 and 117°, respectively, the isomeric glycine has a density of 1.607 and a melting point of 232°C. (4).

The main advantage of the new concept of a dipolar structure of amino acids is the agreement of the dissociation constants of their acid and basic groups with the dissociation constants of aliphatic acids and aliphatic amines. If the older equations (1a) and (1b) are used as a basis for the calculation of dissociation constants, values are obtained which differ widely from the typical dissociation constants of the aliphatic acids and amines; thus, constants of the order of 10^{-9} were found for the acid groups of amino acids, and 10^{-11} for their basic groups, while the dissociation constant of acetic acid is 1.8×10^{-5}, and that of ethylamine 1.2×10^{-3}. The dissociation of the carboxyl groups of amino acids, according to this old concept, would be lower than that of carbonic acid ($k_a = 4.5 \times 10^{-7}$). Actually, these contradictory results gave rise to the proposition of a dipolar formula for amino acids.

Before discussing the dissociation of the acid and the basic groups of amino acids, we have, however, to modify equation (2b) in order to make it consistent with Brönsted's theory of acids and bases. Brönsted has defined acids as substances which are capable of giving up protons, and bases as substances which are capable of taking up protons. If we accept this definition, the groups $CO\bar{O}$ and NH_2 are to be regarded as basic groups because they combine with protons, H^+; likewise the groups COOH and $\overset{+}{N}H_3$ are to be regarded as acid groups because they are proton donors. Accordingly equation (2b) (p. 58) has to be replaced by equation (2c):

$$H_3\overset{+}{N}{\cdot}R{\cdot}CO\bar{O} \rightleftharpoons H_2N{\cdot}R{\cdot}CO\bar{O} + H^+ \qquad (2c)$$

While the designation of $R{\cdot}COO^-$ as basic and of $R{\cdot}\overset{+}{N}H_3$ as acid is free from objection, the older designation of the carboxyl group as acid and of the amino group as basic is frequently used. Care must be taken to avoid confusion in terminology.

Brönsted's theory on the nature of acids and bases was advanced in order to explain the reaction between acids and bases in nonaqueous solvents, where hydroxyl ions, $\bar{O}H$, do not occur. In aqueous solutions one has to take account of the fact that water can act both as an acid, *i.e.*, as proton donor ($H_2O \rightarrow H^+ + \bar{O}H$), and as a base, *i.e.*, as proton acceptor ($H_2O + H^+ \rightarrow H_3O^+$); in the latter case hydronium ions, H_3O^+, are formed. It is possible, therefore, to formulate the reaction of amino acids with bases in aqueous solution according to equation (2b). In the absence of water, only equation (2c) is adequate. One must not forget, however, that the proton shown on the right side of the equation is not free, but is bound by the base added, so that the equation (2c) can also be written in the following manner:

$$H_3\overset{+}{N}\cdot R\cdot COO^- - H^+ \rightleftharpoons H_2N\cdot R\cdot COO^-$$

Since hydroxyl ions are not essential for bases, according to Brönsted's theory, and since acids and bases are defined as proton donors and proton acceptors, respectively, we can represent the dissociation of acid and of basic groups by the general formula:

$$A \rightleftharpoons B + H^+ \tag{3}$$

where A is an acid (proton donor) and B a base (proton acceptor). The dissociation constant of the acid, A, is, from equation (3):

$$K_A = \frac{a_B a_{H^+}}{a_A}$$

where a_A, a_B, and a_{H^+} are, respectively, the activities of the acid, the base, and the hydrogen ions. According to equation (1b), the dissociation constants of the carboxyl groups of amino acids are represented by:

$$K_a = \frac{a_{H_3\overset{+}{N}\cdot R\cdot CO\bar{O}} \times a_{H^+}}{a_{H_3\overset{+}{N}\cdot R\cdot COOH}}$$

and the dissociation constants of the amino groups, according to (2c) by:

$$K_b = \frac{a_{H_2N\cdot R\cdot CO\bar{O}} \times a_{H^+}}{a_{H_3\overset{+}{N}\cdot R\cdot CO\bar{O}}} \tag{2d}$$

If equation (2b) instead of (2c) is used for the calculation of the dissociation of amino groups, we obtain:

$$K_{b'} = \frac{a_{H_3\overset{+}{N}\cdot R\cdot CO\bar{O}} \times a_{\bar{O}H}}{a_{H_2N\cdot R\cdot CO\bar{O}}}$$

In dilute solutions, where they are not very different from unity the activity coefficients can be neglected and the activity terms of the above equations replaced by the molar concentrations. The last equation can then, from equation (2b), be written as:

$$K_{b'} = \frac{[H_3\overset{+}{N}\cdot R\cdot CO\bar{O}][\bar{O}H]}{[H_2N\cdot R\cdot CO\bar{O}]} \tag{3a}$$

Since the concentration of hydrogen ions and that of hydroxyl ions are determined by the equation:

$$K_W = [H^+][\bar{O}H] \tag{4}$$

the term $[\bar{O}H]$ in the above equation can be replaced by $K_W/[H^+]$, and the equation, from equations (3a) and (4), may be rewritten as:

$$K_{b'} = \frac{[H_3\overset{+}{N}\cdot R\cdot CO\bar{O}]\, K_W}{[H_2N\cdot R\cdot CO\bar{O}][H^+]}$$

Since K_b in dilute solutions, according to equations (2c) and (2d), is:

$$K_b = \frac{[H_2N\cdot R\cdot CO\bar{O}][H^+]}{[H_3\overset{+}{N}\cdot R\cdot CO\bar{O}]}$$

the relation of $K_{b'}$ to K_b is represented (see equations 2b, 3, and 4) by the equation:

$$K_{b'} = K_W/K_b$$

where K_W, the dissociation constant of water, is approximately 10^{-14}. When the dissociation constants of carboxyl groups, K_a, or of amino groups, K_b or $K_{b'}$, are determined employing these equations, values between 10^{-2} and 10^{-3} are obtained for K_a, the dissociation constants of carboxyl groups. The $K_{b'}$ values found for the amino groups vary from 10^{-4} to 10^{-5}, the K_b values from 10^{-9} to 10^{-10}. The meaning of these dissociation constants becomes clearer when we consider those cases in which the concentration of the proton donor, A, is equal to that of the proton acceptor, B. When [A] = [B], the dissociation constant, K, is equal to the hydrogen ion concentration:

$$K = \frac{[B][H^+]}{[A]} = [H^+]$$

The hydrogen ion concentration is, under these conditions, a measure of the dissociation of the acid or base. It indicates the region where the ratio $[H_3\overset{+}{N}\cdot R\cdot COO^-]/[H_3\overset{+}{N}\cdot R\cdot COOH]$ or $[H_2N\cdot R\cdot COO^-]/[H_3\overset{+}{N}\cdot R\cdot COO^-]$ is unity. Since it is usual to indicate the hydrogen ion concentration by the negative logarithm, pH = $-\log[H^+]$, we can apply the same method to the dissociation constants and write $pK_a = -\log K_a$, and $pK_b = -\log K_b$. Evidently pK_a and pK_b are equal to those pH values at which 50% of the amino acid is present as dipolar ion and 50% as cation or anion, respectively. They are determined by electrometric titration of the amino acids with hydrochloric acid or with sodium hydroxide (5). If pH is plotted against the amount of acid or base added to the amino acid, the pK_a and pK_b values are equal to those pH values of the titration curve which correspond to the addition of 0.5 equivalent of acid, or of base, per mole amino acid.

While the dissociation of amino groups was previously represented by their $K_{b'}$ values, at present K_b values are preferred, because these show directly the pH value of 50% dissociation; the $K_{b'}$ values are related to the concentration of hydroxyl ions, which generally is not noted and is easily obtained by subtracting pH from 14. The main advantage of the new manner of representing dissociation constants is, however, that we are able to determine and to indicate such constants also in those cases in which the nature of the reacting group is not known. Thus, it was not clear, for some time, whether the pK value 9.1 found in the electrometric titration of tyrosine corresponds to the dissociation of its phenolic hydroxyl group into hydrogen ion and an anion, or to the dissociation of the ammonium group $\overset{+}{N}H_3$ into an amino group, NH_2, and a hydrogen ion. Obviously, the electrometric titration does not furnish any information on the mode of the reaction taking place; it indicates only the number of protons bound at different pH values. It is not necessary, therefore, to use the different symbols K_a and K_b for carboxyl and amino groups; it is preferable to number the dissociation constants in sequence of increasing pK values as pK_1, pK_2, pK_3, etc. This mode of indication of dissociation constants has been used in the Table VI. Table VI shows

TABLE VI
IONIZATION CONSTANTS OF MONOAMINO ACIDS AND PEPTIDES (6)

Substance	pK_1	pK_2	Isoelectric point
Glycine	2.35	9.78	6.1
Glycylglycine	3.12	8.07	5.6
Alanine	2.34	9.87	6.1
Alanylalanine	3.17	8.42	5.8
Valine	2.32	9.62	6.0
Leucine	2.36	9.60	6.0
Hexaglycine	3.05	7.60	5.32
Serine	2.21	9.15	5.68
Proline	1.99	10.60	6.30
Tryptophan	2.38	9.39	5.89

that the acid and the basic ionization constants of the *aliphatic monoamino acids* vary only slightly. The aliphatic side chain of the amino acids recorded in the table has, apparently, no great influence on the dissociation of the amino and the carboxyl groups. The table shows, moreover, that the pK_1 values of peptides are higher by 0.8 pH unit, but the pK_2 values lower by 1.4 to 1.7 pH units than those of the corresponding amino acids. This means that the acidity of peptides is slightly lower, but their basicity much lower, than that of the corresponding amino acids. It is understandable, therefore, that peptides are more strongly acidic than amino acids and that the hydrolysis of peptides is accompanied by decrease in the acidity of the solution which is sufficiently marked to be manometrically measurable in an atmosphere of carbon dioxide (see Chapter III, Sect. B).

Since amino acids migrate in alkaline solutions to the anode and in acid solutions to the cathode there is a pH value at which no migration occurs. This pH value has been called the *isoelectric point.* It can easily be calculated from the ionization constants according to the equation:

$$pH_I = \frac{pK_1 + pK_2}{2}$$

and is recorded in the last column of Table VI.

If the acid and the basic groups of an amino acid were ionized to the same extent, its salt-free water solution would have the same pH value as pure water. Since the ionization of the carboxyl groups is higher than that of the amino groups, monoamino acids are slightly acid substances, whose isoelectric points are in the neighborhood of pH 6. An aqueous solution of a monoamino acid contains, therefore, small amounts of hydrogen ions and of the anions $H_2N{\cdot}R{\cdot}CO\bar{O}$ in addition to large amounts of the dipolar ion $H_3\overset{+}{N}{\cdot}R{\cdot}CO\bar{O}$.

Since the amino acids are weak acids and weak bases at the same time, their mixtures with strong acids and bases are used as buffer solutions. Figure 9 (p. 65) shows pH values of mixtures of glycine with hydrochloric acid or sodium hydroxide. If the volume of hydrochloric acid or of sodium hydroxide indicated in the diagram is v, the volume of 0.1 N glycine solution used is $10-v$ ml.

If the amino acids contain ionized groups other than the α-amino and the α-carboxyl groups, the titration curve will be complicated by new inflection points. The ionization constants of some amino acids containing functional groups in their side chains are recorded in Table VII. This table shows that the aminodicarboxylic acids possess a stronger acid group than do the monoamino acids. This is in agreement with the well known strength of the organic dicarboxylic acids. The table shows, moreover, that the pK value for the phenolic hydroxyl group of tyrosine is approximately 10.1; it is evidently a very weak acid, being

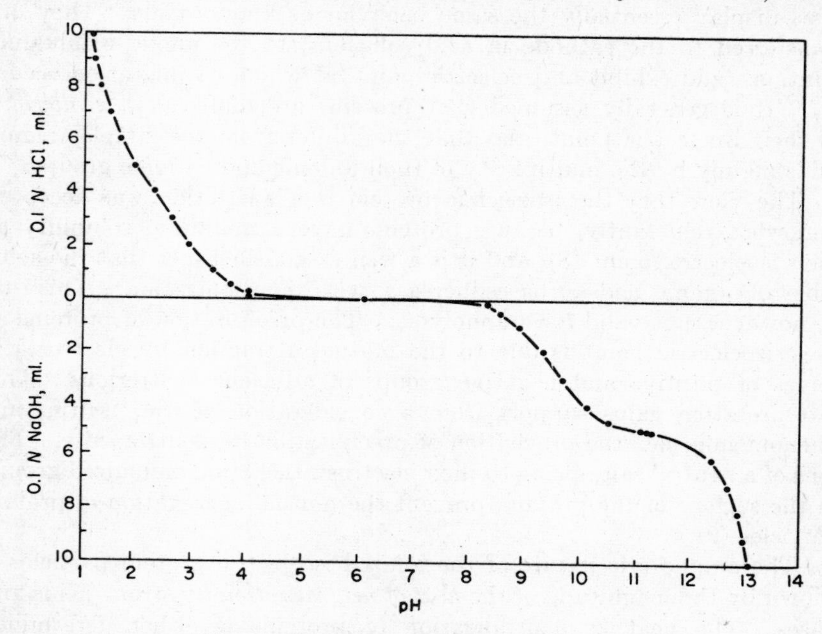

FIG. 9. Buffering action of glycine (6a).

practically uncharged in neutral solutions and ionized only in alkaline solutions.

The basic groups of arginine and of lysine (pK 12.48 and 10.53) are strongly basic, their ionization being more pronounced than that of the amino groups of monoamino acids; the imidazole group of histidine is but

TABLE VII

Amino acid	pK_1	pK_2	pK_3	Isoelectric point
Aspartic acid	2.09 (COOH)	3.87 (COOH)	9.82 (NH_3^+)	3.0
Glutamic acid.......	2.19 (COOH)	4.28 (COOH)	9.66 (NH_3^+)	3.2
Tyrosine............	2.20 (COOH)	9.11 (NH_3^+)	10.1 (OH)	5.7
Cysteine............	1.96 (COOH)	8.18 (NH_3^+)	10.28 (SH)	5.07
Arginine............	2.02 (COOH)	9.04 (NH_3^+)	12.48 (guanido)	10.8
Lysine..............	2.18 (COOH)	8.95 (α-NH_3^+)	10.53 (ϵ-NH_3^+)	9.7
Histidine...........	1.77 (COOH)	6.10 (imidazole)	9.18 (NH_3^+)	7.6

weakly basic. The ionization constants of amino acids are only slightly affected by remote molecular groups. One can expect, therefore, that ionization constants similar to amino acids will be found for proteins.

B. Ionization of Proteins. Combination with Hydrogen Ions. Proteins display essentially the same behavior as amino acids. They are transferred to the cathode in acid solutions, to the anode in alkaline solutions, and exhibit an isoelectric point, at which no migration occurs (7). It is generally assumed that proteins are multivalent *zwitterions* at their isoelectric point, and that they differ from the simpler amino acids mainly by the multiplicity of their anionic and cationic groups.

The view that the isoelectric protein is a zwitterion was accepted somewhat reluctantly, because proteins have a minimum solubility at their isoelectric point (8), and it is a well established fact that the solubility of organic acids or bases increases with their ionization. This rule is, however, not valid for ampholytes. The precipitation of proteins at their isoelectric point is due to the mutual attraction by electrostatic forces of positive and negative groups of adjacent zwitterions. This interpretation gains support from a consideration of the "salting-in" phenomenon, *i.e.*, the prevention of precipitation by neutral salts. The ions of a neutral salt, owing to their electrostatic action on ionized groups in the surface of the protein, prevent the mutual aggregation of protein particles (9).

The amphoteric nature of the ionized isoelectric protein particles is shown by the magnitude of the *heat of neutralization* by strong acids and bases. The heat of neutralization of proteins is either determined calorimetrically (10) or calculated from the temperature coefficient of the ionization constant (11). Both methods furnish values of approximately +10,000 cal. per equivalent of hydrogen ion when acids are added to the slightly alkaline solution of the protein (pH about 8–9). This value is of the same order of magnitude as values obtained on the addition of strong acids (hydrogen ions) to organic bases, but is much higher than the heat of ionization (12) (see above Sect. A) of the reaction:

$$R \cdot COO^- + H^+ \rightleftharpoons R \cdot COOH$$

It is therefore evident that the reaction taking place at pH 8–9 corresponds not to this reaction but to the equilibrium:

$$R \cdot NH_2 + H^+ \rightleftharpoons R \cdot \overset{+}{N}H_3$$

The most convincing proof for the *zwitterion structure of the isoelectric protein* is furnished by a comparison of the electrometric titration in the presence and absence of formaldehyde. Formaldehyde, as we know (see Chapter VII, Sect. E), combines with the amino groups of proteins so as to eliminate their basicity. If amino acids or proteins are titrated with sodium hydroxide in the presence of formaldehyde, the typical inflection of the titration curve at pH 9 which corresponds to the conversion of $\overset{+}{N}H_3$ into NH_2, disappears (see Figs. 10 and 11), thereby showing conclusively that the buffering action of proteins in this pH region is due to their amino groups and not to the ionization of carboxyl groups (13). The same result is obtained when the amino groups are converted into hydroxyl groups by the action of nitrous acid (14). The course of the electrometric titration curve is also changed by the addition of

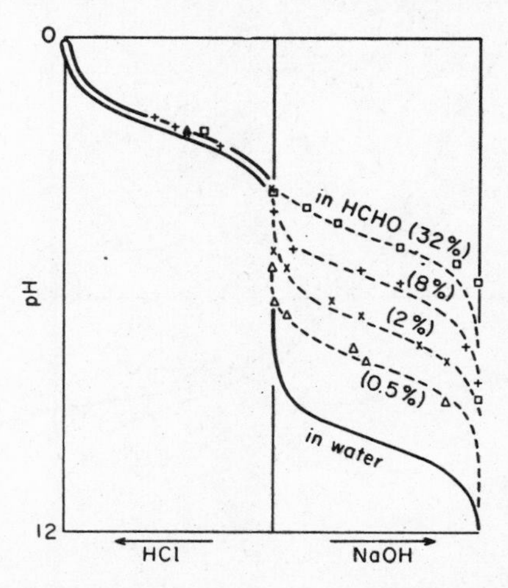

FIG. 10. Titration curve of glycine in the presence of increasing concentrations of formaldehyde (15*a*).

ethanol, which reduces considerably the dissociation constant of the carboxyl group, while the dissociation constant of the ammonium groups is only slightly reduced (15).

Although the curves obtained by the *electrometric titration of proteins* are similar to those of amino acids, several important differences are to be noted. The ionization of monoamino acids is due to the electrolytic dissociation of the grouping:

$$\begin{array}{ccc} R & & CO\bar{O} \\ & \diagdown \; \diagup & \\ & C & \\ & \diagup \; \diagdown & \\ H & & \overset{+}{N}H_3 \end{array}$$

i.e., to the ionization of an α-amino group and of the adjacent carboxyl group. Owing to the proximity of these two groups there will be electrostatic interaction between them and also between nearby hydrogen and hydroxyl ions. The positive hydrogen ion, which is attracted by the negative carboxyl group, will be repelled from the neighborhood of this group by the positively charged ammonium group. The negative charge of the carboxyl group will be weakened by the closely adjacent positive ammonium group. Evidently a very complicated interaction of electrostatic forces will take place, the result of which cannot be predicted. From Table VI, however, it is apparent that the α-carboxyl groups of

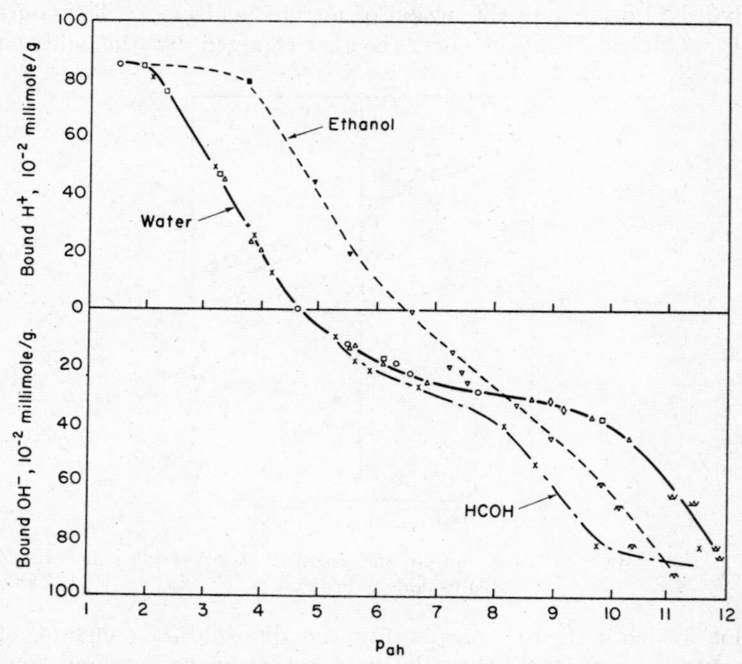

FIG. 11. Electrometric titration of ovalbumin in water, 80% ethanol, and 1% formaldehyde (13).

monoamino acids (pK about 2.2) are more strongly acidic than those of the corresponding fatty acids (pK about 4.8) and that the amino groups (pK about 9.8) are less basic than those of organic amines (pK about 10.6).

The *ionic groups of proteins* are essentially the same as those of the amino acids. However, most of the α-amino groups and α-carboxyl groups are bound to one another by peptide bonds. The acid groups of proteins are mainly the free carboxyl groups of aspartic and glutamic acids, whose ionization, according to Table VII corresponds to pK 3.87 and 4.28. The basic groups of proteins are the guanido groups of arginine (pK 12.48) and the ϵ-amino groups of lysine (pK 10.53). The hydroxyl groups of tyrosine and the sulfhydryl groups of cysteine lose their protons in the same pH range (pK about 10), whereas the imidazole groups of histidine are titrated close to pH 6 (Table VII).

The electrometric titration curve of proteins distinctly shows the inflections due to the buffering action of the carboxyl and amino groups at pH 3–4 and 10–12, respectively. It is not possible, however, to differentiate electrometrically the few terminal α-carboxyl groups of proteins from the β- and γ-carboxyl groups of aspartic and glutamic acid, and the terminal α-amino groups from the ϵ-amino groups of lysine; the only conclusion to be drawn from the titration curves is that the number of terminal α-carboxyl groups cannot be very large (see Chapter VII, Sect. D); otherwise the inflection of the curve would be shifted from pH 3–4 toward pH 2. The inflection near pH 6–7 which is visible in many titration curves corresponds to the buffering action of the imidazole groups of histidine (see Fig. 11).

The electrometric titration of proteins is carried out by adding strong acids such as hydrochloric acid or strong bases such as sodium hydroxide to the isoelectric solution of the protein. If we add hydrochloric acid to an isoelectric protein solution, one portion of the hydrogen ions (protons) will be bound by the COO^- groups of the proteins and these will be converted into carboxyl groups (see equation 1b, page 58). Moreover some of the few NH_2 groups present in the isoelectric protein will be converted into positively charged ammonium groups, $\overset{+}{N}H_3$. The maximum acid binding is represented in the titration curve by the distance between the horizontal line which corresponds to the isoelectric point and the horizontal part of the titration curve at pH 1–2. Similarly the maximum base bound is determined by electrometric titration of the isoelectric protein with sodium hydroxide. It is difficult, however, to determine precisely the amount of base bound, because the end point is less sharp here than in the titration of acid-binding groups (16,17). It must be borne in mind, moreover, that the hydroxyl ions used as a base in the electrometric titration actually are not bound to the protein, but that they combine with protons furnished by the positively charged guanidonium groups of arginine or by ammonium groups ($R{\cdot}\overset{+}{N}H_3 + {}^-OH \rightarrow R{\cdot}NH_2 + H_2O$) or by the uncharged hydroxyl or sulfhydryl groups of tyrosine (17*a*) and cysteine, respectively ($R{\cdot}OH + {}^-OH \rightarrow R{\cdot}O^- + H_2O$). Obviously, we are not dealing here with true base binding, but with the transfer of protons from acid groups of the protein to hydroxyl ions.

In many proteins the results of the electrometric titration agree satisfactorily with the results of amino acid analyses. Thus the total number of anionic and cationic groups found electrometrically in ovalbumin, lactalbumin (16), or serum albumin (18) is almost identical with the number of acidic and basic amino acids found by analysis. In other proteins such as insulin, however, a considerable excess of groups titrated in the alkaline pH range has been found (18) and is attributed to the presence of numerous terminal α-amino groups.

The *isoelectric protein* contains positively and negatively charged groups in equal amounts, its resulting *free charge* being zero, so that no unilateral migration occurs if an electrical field is applied. However, the isoelectric protein is not a truly homogeneous substance, but a mixture of particles containing a slight excess of positive and negative charges. Thus, in a solution of isoelectric hemoglobin at pH 6.9 only 22.4% of the hemoglobin molecules are strictly isoelectric (free charge 0), while the percentage of molecules carrying 1, 2, 3, or more positive charges is 17, 9.4, 3.9, and 1.5%, that of groups carrying 1, 2, 3, or more negative charges 21.2, 14.2, 3.0, and 2.5% respectively (18*a*).

The isoelectric point of a protein depends on the number of the ionized groups and on their ionization constants. Since the dissociation of each of the ionic groups is affected by the electrostatic action of neighboring ionic groups, no fixed relationship exists between the ratio:

$$\frac{\text{maximum number of protons taken up}}{\text{maximum number of protons given off}}$$

on the one hand, and the isoelectric point of the protein on the other hand; this is evident from Table VIII, where $\dot{I}$ is the isoionic point (pH of electrodialyzed protein solution), a the maximum amount of protons in g. equivalent taken up per 10^5 g. protein, and b the maximum amount of protons given off per 10^5 g. protein.

TABLE VIII

Protein	$\dot{I}$	a	b	a/b
Ovalbumin	4.74	110	134	0.82
Serum albumin	5.34	148	159	0.92
Hemoglobin	6.97	156	127	1.23

The dependence of the isoelectric point on the ionization constants of the ionic groups is evident from determinations of the isoelectric point in the presence of various concentrations of ethanol. Since ethanol reduces mainly the dissociation constants of the carboxyl groups (see Sect. A), it shifts the isoelectric point to higher pH values. In gelatin solutions containing 80% ethanol the isoelectric pH value is 6.0, while the isoelectric point in aqueous solutions is 4.9 (13).

While the interpretation of the electrometric titration of amino acids and simple peptides is relatively easy, difficulties in the interpretation of the titration curves of proteins arise due to the following facts:

(*1*) Proteins are *multivalent* zwitterions containing a large number of positively and negatively charged groups. The titration curves show that approximately one millimole of acid or of base is required for the neutralization of one gram of protein. Since the molecular weight of proteins is of the order of 100,000, there are approximately 100 negative and 100 positive groups per protein molecule. These figures agree fairly well with the number of aminodicarboxylic acids, of ammonia, and of basic amino acids found by analysis. However, a precise statement concerning the number of ionized groups is hardly possible because some overlapping occurs, chiefly in the alkaline region between pH 8 and 12. The assumption of pH 8.5 as the end point for the neutralization of the basic groups is somewhat arbitrary (19).

(*2*) A second difficulty lies in the *lability of proteins* in the presence of acids and bases. Some of them are denatured at pH values of less than 2, or more than 11, so that accurate determinations of the ionization of the native protein in these pH regions are impossible. By working at low temperatures the rate of denaturation can be minimized. If denaturation is unavoidable, its influence can be eliminated to a certain extent by measuring pH immediately after mixing the protein with acid or base and subsequently at regular intervals. The neutralization of the ionized groups occurs immediately, while denaturation, in general, takes place slowly. Both reactions can, therefore, be differentiated from each other (20).

(*3*) Considerable difficulties are met with in the ready *combination of proteins with ions other than hydrogen ions.* Proteins combine particularly with calcium, magnesium, phosphate, and bicarbonate ions. The linkages which they form are so stable that the ions are removed neither by dialysis nor by electrophoresis, although it may be possible to remove them by electrodialysis (21). The stability of the bond formed between protein molecules and calcium or phosphate ions is due to the high electrostatic action of the bivalent inorganic ions. Univalent ions such as those of sodium, potassium, or chlorine are less firmly bound; therefore sodium and potassium hydroxide, and hydrochloric acid are used for electrometric titrations. Recently, it was found, however, that proteins also combine with chloride ions (22). They are bound, most probably, to positively charged groups of the protein molecules.

In the process of adsorbing counterions the ionized groups of the protein become neutralized; the over-all effect is a modification of the electrochemical properties of the protein (23). Actually it has been found that the isoelectric point of a protein depends on the kind and on the concentration of the various ions present (24,25).

The shift of the isoelectric point is particularly large when multivalent ions such as phosphate are present. Unfortunately, most of the salts commonly employed as buffers between pH 6 and 7 possess multivalent ions. To obviate such complications as might arise, the use of barbiturate as a buffer for this pH region has been recommended by Michaelis (26). Since the isoelectric point of a protein depends on the presence of extraneous ions, it is not constant; the term *isoionic point* is used to designate the pH of the pure protein dissolved in salt-free water (27). The determination of the isoionic point is difficult and frequently impossible because many proteins are insoluble in the absence of salts and because the conductance of salt-free solutions is very low. The isoionic point of carbon monoxide hemoglobin from sheep blood is pH 7.6 while the isoelectric point in ammonium phosphate buffer varies between 6.70 and 7.16 (28).

(*4*) One must consider, finally, *interactions between the protein zwitterions.* Two or more protein molecules can form an aggregate (micelle) by means of saltlike bonds between positively and negatively charged groups of adjacent molecules. It has been mentioned above that the formation of insoluble protein precipitates is inhibited by neutral salts. The same is true for the formation of soluble aggregates; thus, aggregation occurs during electrodialysis of serum globulin (30) when most of the salts are removed. Besides the proteins, the simple amino acids also display a tendency to combine with each other and form such saltlike compounds (30).

While the difficulties mentioned in the preceding paragraphs (*1–4*) are inherent in the complicated structure of the proteins, another difficulty of a general character must be considered when it is attempted to interpret the results of electrometric titrations and of electrophoresis. In most of these experiments the *hydrogen ion concentration* is determined by means of the usual electrodes. These measure not the actual concentration of hydrogen ions $[H^+]$, but their electromotive activity, a_{H^+}, which is equal to $[H^+]\gamma$, where γ is the activity coefficient. The results of electrometric titrations and of electrometric measurements are customarily referred to hydrogen ion activities and the term pH is frequently replaced by pa_{H^+}. But this also is an oversimplification since the activity of the hydrogen ions depends on the nature and the concentration of other ions present. The true concentration and activity of the hydrogen ions are not determinable (31). One can, nevertheless, use the values measured for purposes of comparison and can consider them close to the true hydrogen ion activities, but not identical with them (32,33).

C. Combination of Proteins with Other Ions (see also pages 72 and 188). It was mentioned in the preceding section that proteins combine not only with hydrogen ions, but also with other ions present in the solution and that this phenomenon affects electrometric titrations and determinations of the isoelectric point. The combination of proteins with other ions is attributable to the electrostatic forces of the ionic groups. Anions are bound to positively charged groups of the protein, while cations are attracted by the negatively charged COO^- groups. The linkage of foreign ions to protein molecules is of the greatest biological importance, because a portion of the inorganic ions present in the body fluids is bound in this manner.

The existence of *ion–protein complexes* can be demonstrated by dialyzing the body fluid containing the respective ion against a protein-free solution containing the same ion in the same concentration (34). If all the ion in the body fluid is unbound, no change in its concentration will be observed. In the event that some of the ion is bound to protein, ions will migrate from the dialyzate into the body fluid until an equilibrium is attained between the free ions on both sides of the membrane.

The linkage of inorganic ions to protein molecules is also demonstrated by electrophoresis experiments; when a transfer of cations, such as Ca^{++}, to the anode, or anions to the cathode occurs, as is frequently the case, one must conclude that the ion is linked to a protein molecule and that the resultant complex migrates as a whole.

A comparison of different ions shows that their fixation to proteins depends chiefly on their valence. While the univalent ions of the alkali metals and the chlorine ion are either free or bound only to a minor extent (22), a considerable part of the calcium, magnesium, and phosphate ions present in body fluids is bound to proteins. The fact that proteins are precipitated by salts of heavy metals indicates that the ions of these metals combine firmly and extensively with proteins. The combination of proteins with inorganic and organic ions occurs not only in body fluids but also *in vitro* where buffer solutions are used. If we are to avoid the combination of ions with proteins it is necessary to employ buffer solutions of univalent ions such as the alkali salts of acetate, diethyl barbiturate, or monohydrogen phthalate.

Among the ions which combine with proteins, *calcium* has been investigated with the most thoroughness. About 40% of the calcium of muscle juice (35) and about one third of the calcium of the blood serum is bound to protein molecules (36). One gram of the serum proteins is capable of binding 0.062 millimole of calcium (37). The combination of proteins with Ca^{++} takes place in accordance with the law of mass action (38). In milk a considerable part of the calcium is bound to the phosphoric acid groups of casein (39). The physicochemical behavior of magnesium is similar to that of calcium, the magnesium ions in the muscle juice and in the serum being attached in considerable amounts to protein molecules (35,36).

The combination of *phosphate* with protein molecules is of negligible importance in the physicochemical equilibrium of the blood serum, because the phosphate content of the serum is very low. Great importance is attributed, however, to the combination of *carbonic acid* with proteins. It had been shown by Siegfried (41) that amino acids combine with carbonates to form *carbamino acids:*

$$NH_2{\cdot}R{\cdot}COO^- + CO_2 \rightarrow \begin{matrix} HO \diagdown \\ C{\cdot}NH{\cdot}R{\cdot}COO^- \\ O \diagup\!\!\diagup \end{matrix}$$

The reaction occurs only in alkaline solutions. In an analogous manner one part of the carbonic acid present in the blood is assumed to combine with the protein component of hemoglobin to form carbhemoglobin (42–46*a*). This assumption is based on the fact that blood combines with carbon dioxide in two phases; the second, slow phase corresponds to the well known slow conversion of carbon dioxide to bicarbonate; this phase is preceded by a rapid uptake of carbon dioxide ascribed to the formation of a carbamino compound. Actually it has been shown that one portion of the carbonic acid cannot be precipitated by barium hydroxide.

On the other hand, the formation of typical carbamates takes place only in strongly alkaline solutions, when the ammonium groups, NH_3^+ are converted into amino groups, NH_2; it is not quite clear, therefore, whether carbamino compounds are formed under physiological conditions to a noticeable extent. One has also to consider the possibility that bicarbonate ions combine with positively charged groups of the protein to form bicarbonates (47):

$$RNH_3^+ + HCO_3^- \rightarrow RNH_3^+ \cdots HCO_3^-$$

This has been observed in electrodialyzed salt-free protein solutions (17,47). The combination of carbon dioxide with hemoglobin is of great importance in the physicochemical equilibrium of blood, because the affinity of hemoglobin for oxygen is lowered by carbonic acid, a phenomenon well known in physiology as the Bohr effect. The influence of carbonic acid on the oxygen affinity of hemoglobin is attributed to the fact that carbon dioxide combines with a basic amino group or imidazole group in the neighborhood of the iron atom to which oxygen is bound (46*a*,48).

Electrometric titrations and determinations of the conductance of protein solutions in the presence of *alkali chlorides* show that small amounts of these univalent ions are bound to the protein (22,49,50). The amount of alkali chloride bound to the proteins of the blood serum is, however, so small that it cannot be determined by compensation dialysis (34) or by electrophoretic measurement of the transport number (51). By an evaluation of electrometric titrations and of measurements of conductance it was found that about ten groups per molecule of serum albumin combine rather tightly with chloride or thiocyanate ions, and that a further considerable number of these anions is bound by weaker bonds (22). The maximum number of ions bound to a protein corresponds satisfactorily with the number of groups of the opposite sign present in the protein. For instance, it has been found that ovalbumin combines with metaphosphoric acid to give a crystalline metaphosphate containing approximately one molecule of metaphosphoric acid per positively charged group of the protein (52).

Among the heavy-metal compounds of proteins deserving mention are the natural *protein–copper* compounds which include hemocuprein from the red cells of ox blood (53), hepatocuprein from the liver (53), the hemocyanins from the blood of certain invertebrates (see Chapter XI, Sect. D), and copper-containing oxidases (54). Copper is present not only in the soluble proteins of the liver, but also in the insoluble residue obtained after extraction with dilute ammonia (55). It seems that in all these compounds cupric ions are bound to negatively charged protein groups. *In vitro* proteins combine with copper in a similar way. The binding of copper to serum albumin is accompanied by a release of free energy, the ΔF decreasing from -5179 cal. per equivalent for the first copper ion bound to -1271 cal. for the sixteenth copper ion bound; the simultaneous increase in entropy indicates that molecules of water of hydration are displaced by the copper ions and are released from their linkage with the protein (56).

D. Electrophoresis of Proteins (57–60). Electrophoresis was originally used for determining the isoelectric point of proteins and their mobility at different pH values. The apparatus consisted of a simple U-tube, in which was placed a solution of the protein to be examined, buffered at a definite pH. A protein-free solution of the same buffer was cautiously placed over the protein solution. The two arms of the U-tube were connected to nonpolarizable electrodes and the motion of the protein–buffer boundary under the influence of a direct current of a potential of about 100 volts was observed (Fig. 12) (61,62).

In order to ensure equal concentrations of buffer in both solutions, the protein–buffer mixture may be dialyzed against the buffer solution. The difficulties of obtaining sharp boundaries are overcome by a U-tube (Fig. 13) consisting of three cells which can be slid over one another along

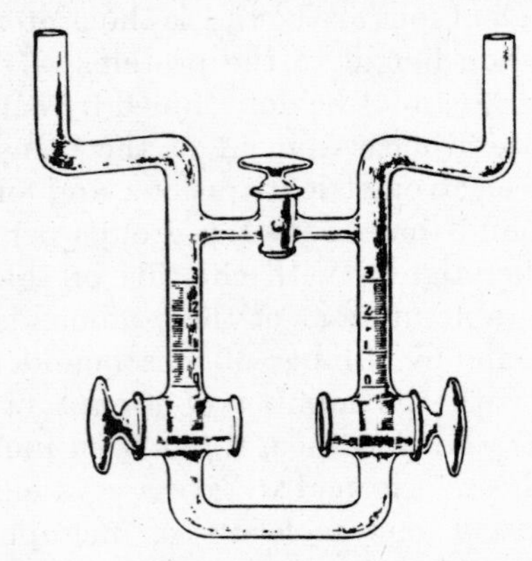

Fig. 12. U-tube for electrophoresis (62*a*).

two horizontal planes. The protein–buffer mixture is placed in the bottom compartment and the cathodic middle compartment, while the anodic middle compartment and the top cells are occupied by the buffer solution (63).

The motion of the protein–buffer boundaries in the middle cell can be followed visually when colored proteins such as hemoglobin or hemo-

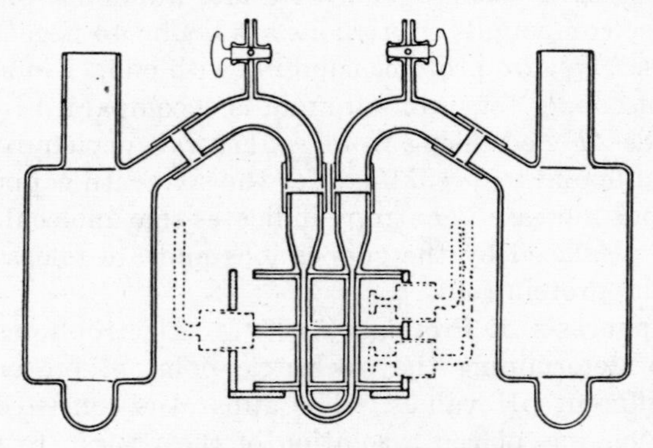

Fig. 13. Electrophoretic cell (63).

cyanin are being examined. Since all proteins absorb ultraviolet light, ultraviolet photography was used to record the movement of colorless proteins. This required that the glass vessels be replaced by quartz vessels.

The difficulties presented by the invisibility of the boundary were finally overcome by an ingenious method introduced by Tiselius (63). In this procedure use is made of the difference in *refraction* between the protein–buffer mixture and the protein-free buffer solution. The refractive index of a solution is considerably increased by the addition of protein, the increment amounting to approximately 0.0018 to 0.0019 per gram protein in 100 ml. solution (64). Since refractive indices can be measured with great precision, small changes in the concentration of the protein cause the observable refractive increment to be large. The refractive increment varies slightly from protein to protein; its magnitude is 0.001876 for 1 g. ovalbumin in 100 ml. solution, 0.001901 for beef serum albumin, and 0.001887 for human serum albumin (65).

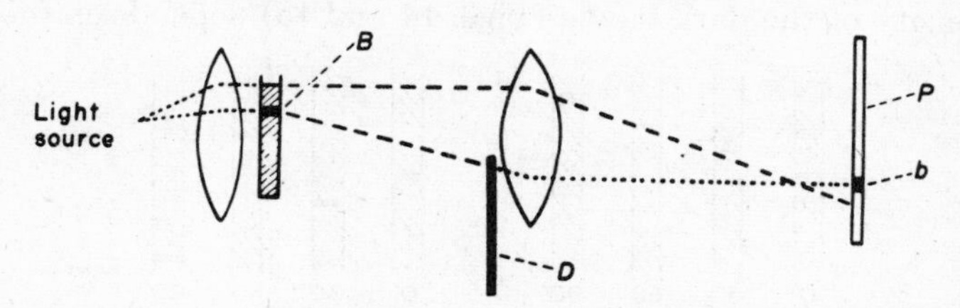

FIG. 14. Schlieren-scanning system of electrophoresis according to Longsworth (58).

Owing to the higher refractive index of the protein layer, light passing through the boundary is bent in the direction of the protein solution, *i.e.*, downward. By a suitable optical system the difference in refraction is made visible as a shadow on a ground-glass screen or on a photographic plate; the appearance of differences in light intensity caused by differences in refraction is called the "Toepler schlieren" phenomenon. Since the refractive increment is proportional to the concentration of the protein, the angle of deflection will increase with increasing protein concentrations.

Two different principles are used at present for automatically recording movements of the protein boundary. In the equipment designed by Longsworth and McInnes (66) the maximally deflected light is intercepted by a *diaphragm*, *D* (knife edge), raised against the beam of light (Fig. 14). This causes the appearance of a dark band, *b*, which indicates the position of the protein boundary on the photographic plate, *P*. If pictures are taken at regular time intervals the displacement of the boundary is recorded and the mobility of the protein can be calculated. Each of the arms of the U-tube can be used for this purpose; since both the boundaries will be displaced toward the same electrode, one of them will descend, while the other ascends. The movement of both boundaries is measured, with the result that an ascending and a descending diagram are obtained. If a dark screen with a narrow vertical slit is placed before the plate, pictures such as are reproduced in Figure 15 are obtained.

The boundary between the protein–buffer mixture and the buffer solution is not strictly a single geometrical plane but rather a narrow region of refractive index, varying between that of the homogeneous protein mixture and that of the homogeneous buffer solution. If we designate the height of the arm of the U-tube by h (in millimeters) and the refractive index of the solution by n, the gradient of refraction, *i.e.*, the increase or decrease in refraction per unit height is represented by the differential quotient dn/dh. The gradient is obviously zero in the two homogeneous solutions and has its maximum value in the boundary. It increases when the concentration of protein in the solution increases. The intensity of the dark bands (Figs. 14 and 15) depends on the magni-

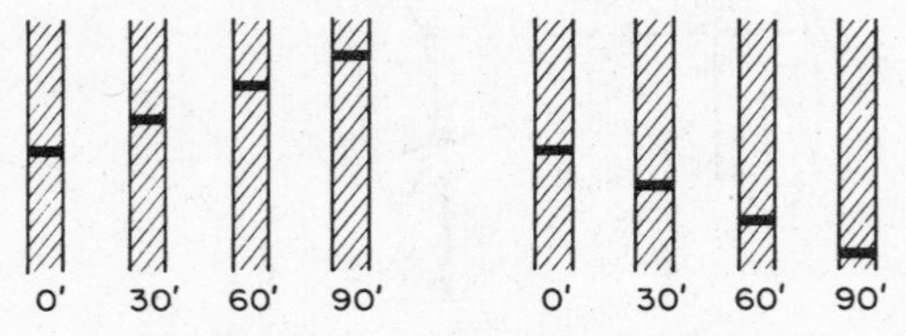

FIG. 15 Diagram of ascending (left) and descending (right) boundaries of a homogeneous protein solution observed at 30-minute intervals.

tude of the gradient of refraction, so that the maximum of the shadow will correspond to the maximum of the gradient of refraction and of concentration.

It is evident that the shapes of the dark bands (Figs. 14 and 15) also depend on the position of the diaphragm which intercepts the deflected light (Fig. 14). The higher the diaphragm is raised, the broader the dark band will be. An accurate position of the boundary (B) cannot be determined from such wide bands. On the other hand, boundaries with a lower angle of deflection, *i.e.*, with a lower gradient of refraction, can be detected only at higher positions of the diaphragm D; to detect them it is necessary, therefore, to raise D (Fig. 14). In the Longsworth electrophoresis apparatus the upward movement of the diaphragm is coupled with a lateral movement of the photographic plate (P), so that a continuous electrophoretic diagram (Fig. 16) is produced instead of a series of individual pictures.

While a single dark band is produced by solutions containing only one protein, two or more bands are obtained when the solution contains two or more proteins of different mobility. In such a case only at the time $t = 0$ is a single boundary present. Under the influence of the direct current the different proteins will migrate at different rates so that a multiplicity of regions of varying refraction is produced. The single dark band in Figure 16 will be replaced by a number of horizontal dark bands.

The protein mixture which has been most frequently examined is that of normal and pathological blood sera. The diagrams of its ascending and descending boundaries are commonly presented horizontally, *i.e.*,

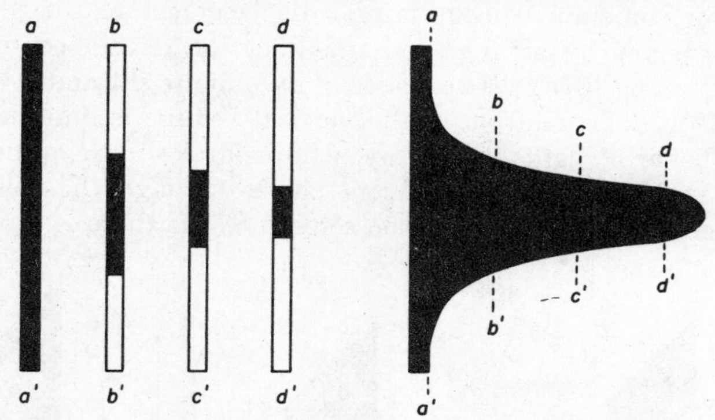

FIG. 16. Schlieren phenomenon. *aa'*, *bb'*, *cc'*, and *dd'* are Schlieren bands at different diaphragm settings.

turning them through 90°. The ascending and the descending diagrams are mirror images of each other. However, small differences are always observed. Usually only the descending boundary is shown (Fig. 17).

At pH 7.35, which is the value of normal blood serum, and at higher pH values, the serum proteins are present as anions. Hence, all of them

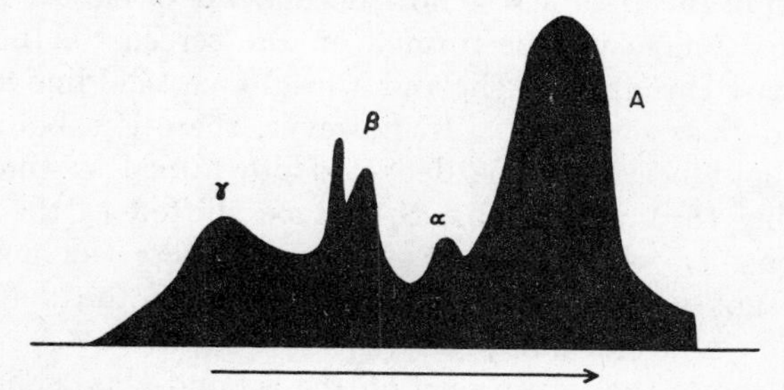

FIG. 17. Electrophoretic pattern of normal human serum (descending boundary).

migrate in the same direction, indicated in Figure 17 by an arrow. Serum albumin, whose isoelectric point is near pH 4.6, moves anodically with the greatest velocity, while the globulins, whose isoelectric points are between pH 5 and 6, are transferred at a lower rate. The maxima of the curves shown in Figure 17 indicate the position of the respective boundaries at the time at which the picture was taken. The height of the curves indicates the magnitude of dn/dh, the gradient of refraction, while the concentration of the protein is indicated by the area included under each of the curves.

While such diagrams were originally obtained by the successive exposure of the photographic slide at different positions of the diaphragm, *D*, the complicated mechanism required for the vertical displacement of *D* and for the simultaneous lateral displacement of the plate, *P*, is made unnecessary by an ingenious modification developed by Philpot (67) and Svensson (67*a*). It consists of an oblique slit and a cylindrical lens (Fig. 18). The solution in the vertical U-tube is illuminated by a horizontal beam of light defined by a horizontal slit, *H*, which can be considered self-luminous. The beam passes through the solution and then through the oblique slit in the screen, *S*. If there is no boundary

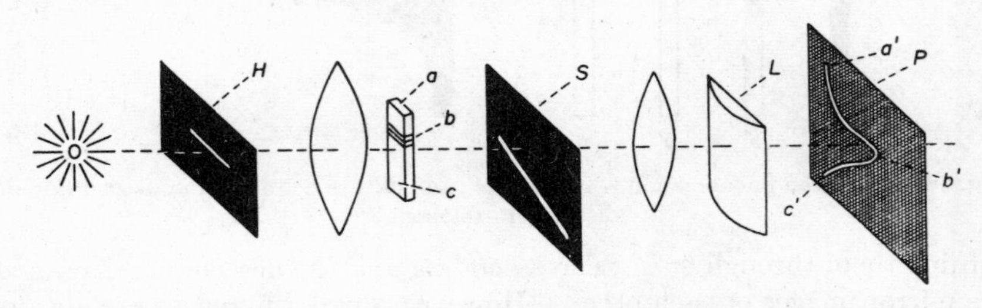

FIG. 18. Cylindrical lens system of electrophoresis. *a* and *c* are projections of the homogeneous solution in *a* and *c*; *b* is the projection of the boundary *b*.

in the solution in the U-tube, the horizontal beam of light is not deflected and its vertical image will be formed on the screen. A narrow pencil of light will pass through the slit and a bright vertical line a′–c′ appears on the ground-glass screen, *P*. If, however, there is a boundary in the U-tube, the light beam will be deflected downward so that the pencil of light passing through the slit, *S*, will be shifted to the right. The cylindrical lens, *L*, whose axis is vertical, deflects the pencil of light laterally but not vertically, so that the image of the deflected pencil appears on *P* as a lateral hump, *b*′.

Figure 19 shows the image seen on the ground-glass slide, *P*, or on a photographic plate which may be mounted in its place; it is a bright line on a dark background. If the narrow slit is replaced by a metal wire, black curves on a white background are obtained. In the original method of Philpot where two edges were used instead of the slit, a picture similar to that of Figure 19 was obtained. The great advantage of these two methods is that the course of the electrophoresis can be controlled visually by observing the diagram projected onto the ground-glass screen, P, and that photographic pictures can then be taken at suitable intervals of time.

By means of electrophoresis the *isoelectric points* of proteins can readily be determined. From the mobility at different pH values the *valence* of the protein ions can be calculated. The valence is obviously zero at the isoelectric point; the approximate valence of ovalbumin in its neutral solutions was found to be 10–12, and that of serum albumin 16–17 (57).

By means of electrophoresis studies it was found that serum globulin, which had been considered a uniform protein, is a *mixture* of at least three types of globulins called α-, β- and γ-globulin (68). Likewise crystalline β-lactoglobulin (69,70), crystalline serum albumin (71), and crystalline ovalbumin (72,73) have been found to be mixtures of more

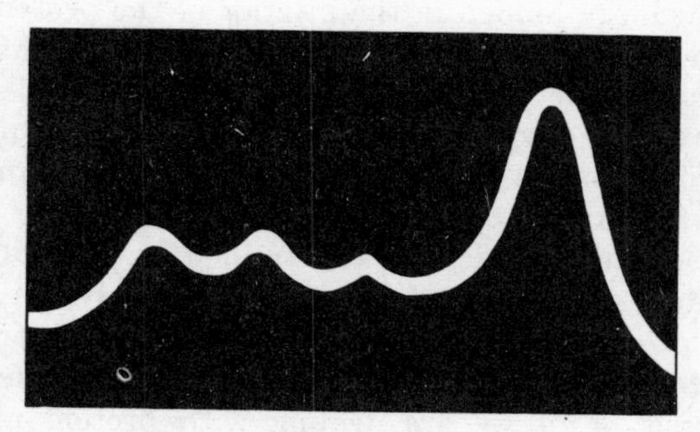

FIG. 19. Electrophoresis diagram of blood serum obtained by Svensson's method.

than two components which can be separated by electrophoresis at their isoelectric point or at other pH values (74).

Electrophoresis has been used both for the *separation* of proteins and for the *preparation* of pure protein fractions; since the U-tube used for electrophoretic analysis is too small for this purpose, it was modified for preparative purposes (75,76).

While electrophoresis is an excellent tool for determining isoelectric points, mobilities, and the uniformity of proteins, difficulties arise when an attempt is made to interpret the results quantitatively. These difficulties are partly due to the fact that the protein boundary is subject to *diffusion*, even when no current passes through the solution. Owing to diffusion and to *thermal convection* the boundary widens with time (77). This can be reduced by working at low temperatures; actually, electrophoresis is carried out at 4°C., where water has its maximum density. Another more serious difficulty is that migration of the protein molecules might lead to *chemical reactions in the boundary*, for instance to the formation of saltlike compounds between more and less acid proteins or between proteins and the buffer ions (77). If such reactions take place, the observed electrophoretic behavior will not be that of the protein, to which we ascribe it, but that of a protein complex (78).

Since all electrophoresis diagrams are based on the refractive indices of the solutions, the results will be highly dependent on all *factors which might influence the refraction.* Although the refractive index of the protein solution depends chiefly on the protein concentration, it is also dependent on the buffer ions.

The electrophoretic motion of protein particles is certainly due to their electrical charges, *i.e.*, to the ionized groups of the protein molecule. The question arises as to whether only *ionic groups on the surface* of globular protein particles are responsible for the migration or whether ionic groups which are hidden in the interior of the protein particle also contribute. In experiments on cells and on bacteria it has been shown that the electrophoretic behavior is determined by the surface layers. Moreover it has been demonstrated in some cases that quartz particles coated with protein behave electrophoretically in the same way as the protein from which the coating layer was formed (79). Evidently the mobility of the protein particles is determined by the potential of their surfaces. Because this potential manifests itself only during the motion of the particle or of the surrounding solution in an electrical field, it is called *electrokinetic potential* or ζ-potential. Its magnitude is determined by electrophoresis or, if we are dealing with protein membranes, by electroosmosis or by measuring streaming potentials; the latter are produced by forcing solutions through the pores of the protein membrane. All three methods furnish the same ζ-potential when applied to protein-covered surfaces, such as glass capillaries coated with protein (80). This supports the assumption that the electrophoretic behavior of proteins is determined by their electrokinetic potential.

The ζ-potential, according to Gouy's theory, is attributable to a diffuse ionic atmosphere surrounding the protein molecule, each ionic group of the protein attracting one or more ions of the opposite sign. The thickness of the double layer depends on the ionic strength of the solution according to the equation (81):

$$d = 3.05 \times 10^{-8} \times \frac{1}{\sqrt{\mu}} \text{ cm.}$$

where d is the thickness of the double layer and μ the ionic strength of the solution. If A and C are the molar concentrations and a and c the valences of the anion and the cation, respectively, the ionic strength of the solution is:

$$\mu = (Aa^2 + Cc^2)/2$$

Hence, the ionic strength of 0.01 M sodium chloride is $(0.01 + 0.01)/2 = 0.01$ and that of 0.01 M calcium chloride is $(0.02 + 0.04)/2 = 0.03$. The thicknesses of the double layers in these solutions, according to the above equation, are 30 and 18 Å, respectively.

Attempts have been made to calculate the actual charge of the protein molecule from its electrophoretic behavior. In view of the unknown size and shape of the protein molecule, only approximate results could be expected; they agree remarkably well with the number of charges calculated from electrometric titration curves (40,82) (see Sect. B, Table VIII).

REFERENCES

1. E. Q. Adams, *J. Am. Chem. Soc.* **38,** 1503 (1916).
1*a*. N. Bjerrum, *Z. physik. Chem.* **104,** 147 (1923).
2. L. Ebert, *Z. physik. Chem.* **121,** 385 (1926).
3. J. T. Edsall, *J. Chem. Phys.* **4,** 1 (1936).
4. F. T. Gucker, Jr., W. L. Ford, C. E. Moser, *J. Phys. Chem.* **43,** 153 (1939); **45,** 309 (1941).
5. S. Miyamoto, C. L. A. Schmidt, *J. Biol. Chem.* **90,** 165 (1931).
6. D. I. Hitchcock, in C. L. A. Schmidt, Chemistry of the Amino Acids and Proteins. Thomas, Springfield, Ill., 1944, p. 613.
6*a*. S. Sørensen, *Biochem. Z.* **71,** 174 (1909).
7. W. Hardy, *J. Physiol.* **24,** 288 (1899).
8. L. Michaelis, P. Rona, *Biochem. Z.* **28,** 193 (1910).
9. H. G. B. de Jong *et al. Rec. trav. chim.* **53,** 607 (1934).
10. O. Meyerhof, *Arch. ges. Physiol. (Pflügers)* **195,** 53 (1922).
11. W. C. Stadie, K. Martin, *J. Biol. Chem.* **60,** 191 (1924).
12. H. H. Weber, *Biochem. Z.* **218,** 1 (1930).
13. I. Lichtenstein, *Biochem. Z.* **303,** 26 (1939).
14. Z. Loebel, *J. Phys. Chem.* **32,** 763 (1928).
15. H. A. Abramson, Electrokinetic Phenomena, Chemical Catalog Co., New York, 1939.
15*a*. L. J. Harris, *Biochem. J.* **24,** 1080 (1930).
16. R. K. Cannan, *Chem. Revs.* **30,** 395 (1942).
17. W. Pauli, *Helv. Chim. Acta* **30,** 79 (1947).
17*a*. A. Neuberger, *Biochem. J.* **28,** 1982 (1934).
18. J. T. Edsall, *Ann. N. Y. Acad. Sci.* **47,** 229 (1946).
18*a*. E. J. Cohn, J. T. Edsall, Proteins, Amino Acids and Peptides, Reinhold, New York, 1943, p. 467.
19. H. Neurath, J. P. Greenstein, *Ann. Rev. Biochem.* **13,** 117 (1944).
20. G. Ettisch, G. V. Schulz, *Biochem. Z.* **265,** 338 (1933).
21. J. T. Edsall, private communication.
22. G. Scatchard, *Ann. N. Y. Acad. Sci.* **51,** 661 (1949); *J. Am. Chem. Soc.* **72,** 535, 540 (1950).
23. H. G. B. de Jong, *Kolloid-Beihefte* **48,** 33 (1938).
24. E. L. Smith, *J. Biol. Chem.* **108,** 187 (1935).
25. B. D. Davis, E. J. Cohn, *J. Am. Chem. Soc.* **61,** 470 (1941).
26. L. Michaelis, *J. Biol. Chem.* **87,** 33 (1930).
27. S. Sørensen, K. Linderstrøm-Lang, E. Lund, *J. Gen. Physiol.* **8,** 543 (1927).

28. S. G. Adair, M. E. Adair, *Biochem. J.* **28,** 1230 (1934).
29. P. von Mutzenbecher, *Biochem. Z.* **235,** 425 (1931).
30. C. L. A. Schmidt, *Ann. Rev. Biochem.* **1,** 159 (1932).
31. R. Bates, *Chem. Revs.* **42,** 1 (1948).
32. J. Sendroy, Jr., *Ann. Rev. Biochem.* **7,** 231 (1939).
33. D. A. McInnes, *Science* **108,** 693 (1948).
34. P. Rona, F. Haurowitz, H. Petow, *Biochem. Z.* **149,** 393 (1924).
35. G. Quagliarello, *Atti reale acad. naz. Lincei* **9,** 1029 (1929).
36. H. Benjamin, A. F. Hess, J. Gross, *J. Biol. Chem.* **103,** 629, 383 (1933).
37. D. M. Greenberg, *Ann. Rev. Biochem.* **8,** 278 (1939).
38. I. M. Klotz, *Arch. Biochem.* **9,** 109 (1946).
39. D. M. Greenberg, C. L. A. Schmidt, *J. Gen. Physiol.* **8,** 271 (1926).
40. R. K. Cannan, A. H. Palmer, A. C. Kibrick, *J. Biol. Chem.* **142,** 803 (1942)
41. M. Siegfried, *Ber.* **39,** 397 (1906).
42. O. Henriques, *Biochem. Z.* **260,** 58 (1933).
43. A. Ferguson, F. J. W. Roughton, *J. Physiol.* **81,** 2 (1934); **88,** 40 (1936).
44. D. D. Van Slyke, *Proc. Natl. Acad. Sci. U. S.* **132,** 242 (1934).
45. W. C. Stadie, H. O'Brien, *J. Biol. Chem.* **117,** 439 (1937).
46. C. L. Evans, Recent Advances in Physiology. Blakiston, Philadelphia, 1936, p. 125.
46*a*. J. Wyman, Jr., *Advances in Protein Chem.* **4,** 410 (1948).
47. W. Pauli, *Biochem. Z.* **205,** 71 (1929); *Helv. Chim. Acta* **30,** 77 (1946).
48. F. J. W. Roughton, *Physiol. Revs.* **15,** 241 (1936).
49. J. H. Northrop, M. Kunitz, *J. Gen. Physiol.* **11,** 481 (1927–1928).
50. W. C. Stadie, F. Sundermann, *J. Biol. Chem.* **91,** 227 (1931).
51. S. Miyamoto, C. L. A. Schmidt, *J. Biol. Chem.* **99,** 335 (1933).
52. G. E. Perlman, H. Hermann, *Biochem. J.* **32,** 926, 932 (1938).
53. T. Mann, D. Keilin, *Nature* **142,** 148 (1938); *Proc. Roy. Soc. London* **B126,** 303 (1938).
54. C. R. Dawson, M. Valette, *Advances in Protein Chem.* **2,** 179 (1945).
55. H. Turnwald, F. Haurowitz, *Z. physiol. Chem.* **181,** 176 (1929).
56. I. M. Klotz, H. Curme, *J. Am. Chem. Soc.* **70,** 939 (1948).
57. H. A. Abramson, L. S. Moyer, M. H. Gorin, Electrophoresis of Proteins, Reinhold, New York, 1942, p. 159.
58. L. G. Longsworth, *Chem. Revs.* **24,** 271 (1939); **30,** 323 (1942).
59. J. A. Luetscher, Jr., *Physiol. Revs.* **27,** 621 (1947).
60. C. Stern, *Ann. N. Y. Acad. Sci.* **39,** 147 (1939).
61. K. Landsteiner, W. Pauli, cited by Pauli and Valko, Kolloid Chemie der Eiweisskörper. T. Steinkopff, Dresden, 1933, p. 17.
62. L. Michaelis, H. Davidsohn, *Biochem. Z.* **41,** 102 (1912).
62*a*. L. Michaelis, P. Rona, Praktikum der Physikalische Chemie. J. Springer, Berlin, 1930, p. 126.
63. A. Tiselius, *Kolloid-Z.* **85,** 129 (1938).
64. G. S. Adair, M. Robinson, *Biochem. J.* **24,** 993 (1930).
65. G. E. Perlman, L. G. Longsworth, *J. Am. Chem. Soc.* **70,** 2719 (1948).
66. L. G. Longsworth, D. A. McInnes, *J. Am. Chem. Soc.* **62,** 705 (1940).
67. J. E. L. Philpot, *Nature* **141,** 283 (1938).
67*a*. H. Svensson, *Kolloid-Z.* **87,** 181 (1939).
68. A. Tiselius, *Biochem. J.* **31,** 1464 (1937).
69. T. L. McMeekin, B. D. Polis, E. della Monica, J. Custer, *J. Am. Chem. Soc.* **70,** 881 (1948).

70. J. A. Bain, H. F. Deutsch, *Arch. Biochem.* **16,** 223 (1948).
71. D. G. Sharp, G. R. Cooper, J. O. Erickson, H. Neurath, *J. Biol. Chem.* **144,** 139 (1942).
72. A. Tiselius, B. Erickson-Quensel, *Biochem. J.* **33,** 1752 (1939).
73. L. G. Longsworth, R. K. Cannan, D. A. McInnes, *J. Am. Chem. Soc.* **62,** 2580 (1940).
74. R. Alberty, E. Anderson, J. Williams, *J. Phys. Chem.* **52,** 217 (1948).
75. L. Hahn, A. Tiselius, *Biochem. Z.* **314,** 389 (1943).
76. H. Svensson, *Advances in Protein Chem.* **4,** 251 (1948).
77. R. Alberty, J. Nichols, *J. Am. Chem. Soc.* **70,** 1675, 2297 (1948).
78. H. Svensson, *Arkiv. Kemi Mineral. Geol.*, **22,** 156 (1946).
79. L. S. Moyer, H. A. Abramson, *J. Gen. Physiol.* **19,** 727 (1936).
80. H. B. Bull, *J. Phys. Chem.* **39,** 577 (1935).
81. H. B. Bull, Physical Biochemistry. Wiley, New York, 1947, p. 181.
82. L. G. Longsworth, *Ann. N. Y. Acad. Sci.* **41,** 267 (1941).

Chapter VI

Interaction of Proteins with Water

A. Hydration. Hydration is said to occur when water molecules are bound to the molecules of a dry or dissolved substance. Proteins are the principal water-binding substances which occur in living organisms and, since water is the universal medium of biological reactions, the great importance of the phenomenon of protein hydration is obvious. The literature dealing with protein hydration is very confusing, because the hydration of dry proteins and hydration of proteins in solution have been investigated by different authors who used varying methods. Moreover, the expression "dry protein" is used by some authors to describe air-dried materials, while others use it to designate what are really water-free proteins. Since an essential hydration takes place even on exposure of dry proteins to air of normal humidity, a serious error is introduced when this hydration is neglected.

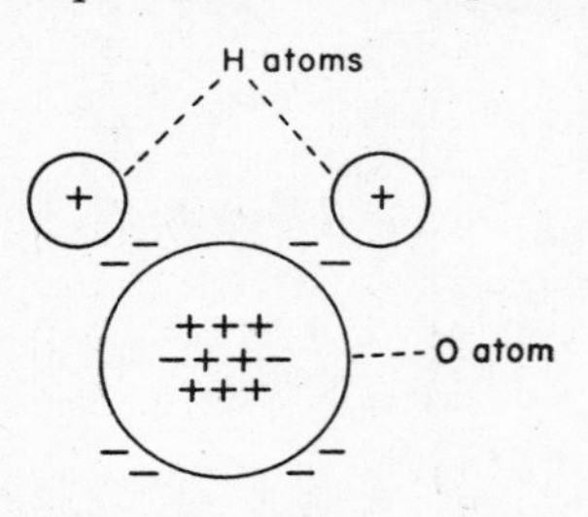

FIG. 20. Electron formula of water.

Let us first consider the mechanism of hydration. The phenomenon of hydration is due to the polar properties of water molecules. The electronic formula of water shows that the center of charge of the negatively charged electrons is nearer to the oxygen atom than to the positively charged hydrogen nuclei (Fig. 20). On the other hand the center of the positive charges is nearer the two hydrogen atoms. We call such a molecule, in which the centers of the positive and the negative charges do not coincide, a polar molecule or a *dipole*. The diagram (Fig. 21)

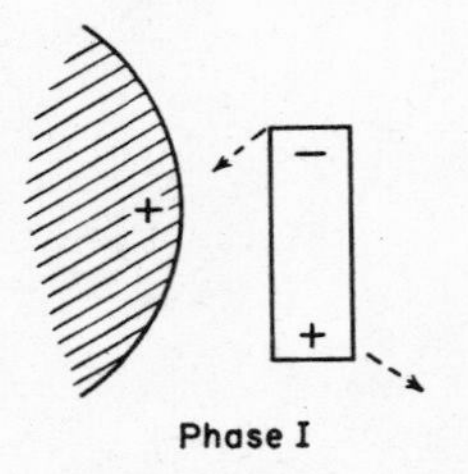

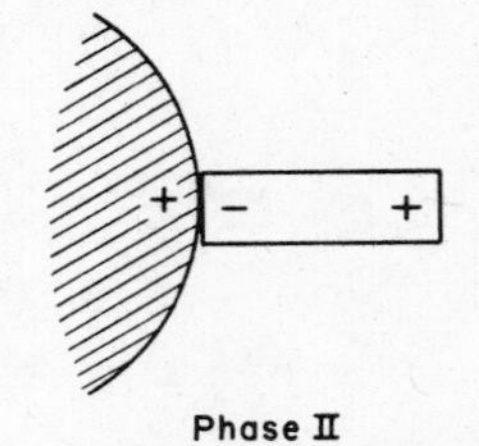

FIG. 21. Mutual attraction of a dipole and a positively charged ionic group.

shows that dipoles are *always* attracted by ions; the ion, in a first phase, attracts the opposite pole and repels the pole of the same sign with the same force; in a second phase attraction is stronger than repulsion, because the attracted pole is nearer the ion than is the repelled pole. For similar reasons attraction takes place between two dipoles, as shown by the following diagram (Fig. 22).

The forces operating between dipoles are less effective over large distances than those operating between ion and dipole. They are however responsible for the mutual association of water molecules and for the high boiling temperature of water as compared with that of analogous molecules such as H_2S or H_2Se.

Hydration consists of the binding of water dipoles to ions or ionic groups, to dipoles or to polar groups. Hydration takes place in solid substances as well as in solution. In some cases hydrates of a definite

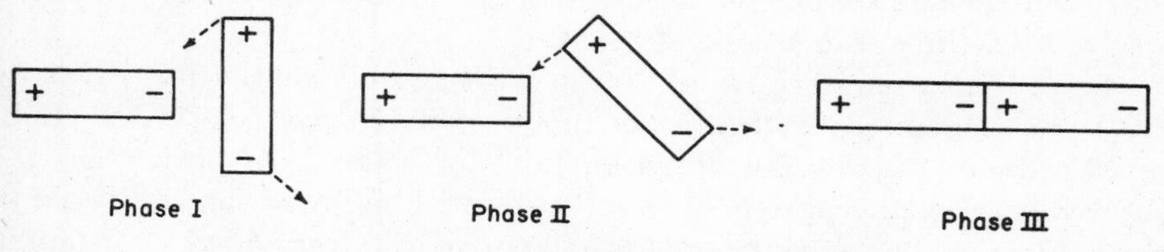

FIG. 22. Dipole association.

stoichiometric composition are formed. A well known example is the hydration of copper sulfate. The dry substance, $CuSO_4$, attracts water from the air to form the hydrate, $CuSO_4 \cdot 5H_2O$.

Since the components of a compound are linked to each other in such a way that they have lost some of their free translational mobility, the volume of a hydrated molecule is always smaller than the sum of the volumes of its components. In other words, *hydration is accompanied by a decrease of the total volume.* This decrease can be determined by measuring directly the volume before and after the reaction, or, more precisely by measuring the density, D, *i.e.*, the weight in grams per milliliter. The reciprocal value of the density, which is the volume occupied by one gram of the substance, is called the specific volume, $V_{sp} = 1/D$.

In order to better understand the relationships existing between the factors involved, we will discuss the volume changes occurring on hydration of copper sulfate. The density of anhydrous $CuSO_4$ is 3.58, that of $CuSO_4 \cdot 5H_2O$ is 2.29. The respective specific volumes are $1/3.58 = 0.28$ and $1/2.29 = 0.436$. Hence the volume of one mole of dry copper sulfate (mol. wt. 159.6) is $159.6 \times 0.28 = 44.5$ ml.; the volume of five moles of water (5×18 ml.) is 90 ml. The total volume of one mole of dry copper sulfate plus five moles of water is $44.5 + 90 = 134.5$ ml. The volume occupied by one mole of $CuSO_4 \cdot 5H_2O$ is, however, $249.7 \times 0.436 = 109$ ml. (where 249.7 is the molecular weight of the pentahydrate). Evidently the volume contraction in mixing one mole of copper sulfate with five moles of water is $134.5 - 109 = 25.5$ ml.

While all this is clear, difficulties arise when we attempt to determine the actual volumes occupied by copper sulfate and by water molecules. For purposes of calculation we can subtract all the volume decrease from the volume of the dry copper sulfate and say that copper sulfate in its pentahydrate has shrunk from an original volume of 44.5 ml. per mole to an "apparent" volume of $44.5 - 25.5 = 19$ ml. per mole $CuSO_4$. Or we can deduct all the volume decrease from the volume of the five water molecules and say that their volume has shrunk by 25.5 ml. from 90 to 64.5 ml., so that the apparent molar volume of water would be $64.5/5 = 12.9$ instead of 18 ml. per mole, and its apparent density $18/12.9 = 1.4$ g. per ml. Obviously, none of these assumptions is correct. The volume decrease is actually due to the fact that the water molecules, the copper ions, and the sulfate ions of the hydrate have lost their ability to move freely in all three dimensions of space.

In protein chemistry we are faced with a similar situation when we try to determine the hydration of dry proteins exposed to water vapor or of proteins dissolved in large amounts of water. In both cases the total volume of the protein–water system will be lower than the sum of the volume of the dry protein and the volume of water added. Although small changes in the volume of a system cannot be measured easily, changes in the density may be determined very precisely by means of pycnometers, a procedure which is frequently used. If the density of the protein–water mixture is D, the specific volume, V_{sp}, *i.e.*, the volume occupied by one gram of the system, is $V_{sp} = 1/D$. The density of protein solutions is determined by weighing the protein solution in a pycnometer of an accurately known volume, V. If the weight of the solution is P and the volume of the pycnometer is V, the density is $D = P/V$.

While it is easy to measure the density of protein solutions, great difficulties arise in the determination of the density of dry proteins or of wet protein preparations. Many proteins are denatured by drying, so that we are not able to use the dry preparations for experiments investigating hydration. This complication can be overcome by first determining the density of the wet protein crystal or the protein solution and subsequently drying the protein. The principal problem remains, however, that of determining the density of dry or wet protein preparations. One of the methods used consists of placing the protein in a pycnometer, weighing it, and then filling the pycnometer with a liquid of known density. Obviously water cannot be used because it would increase the extent of hydration. Ethanol, acetone or diethyl ether, on the other hand, would attract water and, consequently, reduce the extent of hydration of the protein. Benzene, bromobenzene, and other hydrophobic liquids are used for these purposes. Even so, the results obtained are not very satisfactory, since proteins are denatured at the water–solvent interface and because small amounts of water are dissolved by these solvents. Difficulties arise also due to the formation of small air bubbles in the protein powder when it is suspended in the organic liquid.

Another method applied for the determination of density consists of measuring the rate of sedimentation of the protein particles in aqueous salt solutions of different densities (1). The interpretation of results obtained in this way is complicated by the fact that the protein combines not only with water but also with salts (see Chapter V, Sect. C). The densities found are, therefore, the densities of the hydrated protein-salt compound and not those of the hydrated protein.

It is evident from these few remarks that we are confronted with great experimental obstacles when we attempt to determine the density of dry or hydrated proteins. Moreover, the interpretation of the results which are obtained is very uncertain. Since we are not able to indicate the amount of hydrated protein and of free water in the protein-water system, the thermodynamic notion of *partial specific volume* has been introduced and is frequently determined.

Let us consider a system consisting of n_P moles of protein and n_W moles of water. If the total volume of the system is V, we can consider this volume as the sum of the volumes of the two components forming the system. Let us further assume that the volume contribution per mole of protein is $\bar{v}_P$ and that per mole of water $\bar{v}_W$; then the total volume will be $V = n_P\bar{v}_P + n_W\bar{v}_W$. The value $\bar{v}_P$ and $\bar{v}_W$ are called the *partial molar volumes*. Since the molecular weight of proteins is not always known, the partial molar volumes $\bar{v}_P$ and $\bar{v}_W$ are frequently replaced by the *partial specific volumes*, $\bar{v}_p$ and $\bar{v}_w$. Their relation to V_{sp} is shown by the equation:

$$V_{sp} = g_p\bar{v}_p + g_w\bar{v}_w \tag{1}$$

where g_p and g_w are the amounts of protein and water, respectively, in one gram of the mixture. Obviously, $g_p + g_w = 1$ gram. Since V_{sp}, g_p, and g_w can be determined, equation (1) contains only two unknowns, $\bar{v}_p$ and $\bar{v}_w$. Their magnitude can be determined by varying the protein: water ratio ($= g_p/g_w$) and plotting V_{sp} against g_p. This furnishes a curve instead of a straight line, indicating that the partial specific volume of the protein depends on its concentration. An approximate value for $\bar{v}_p$ is obtained by drawing the best smooth curve through the points of the plot and determining the slope of the line (2).

Another less rigorous procedure is based on the arbitrary assumption that the partial specific volume of water remains unchanged and is always $v_w = 1.0$. Then equation (1) is reduced to the simpler form:

$$V_{sp} = g_p(v_p)_{app} + g_w$$

The term $(v_p)_{app}$ is called the *apparent specific volume* of the protein.

It must be emphasized again that neither the partial specific volume, $\bar{v}_p$, nor the apparent specific volume, $(v_p)_{app}$ indicates the true volume occupied by the protein in the protein–water mixture. We have obtained

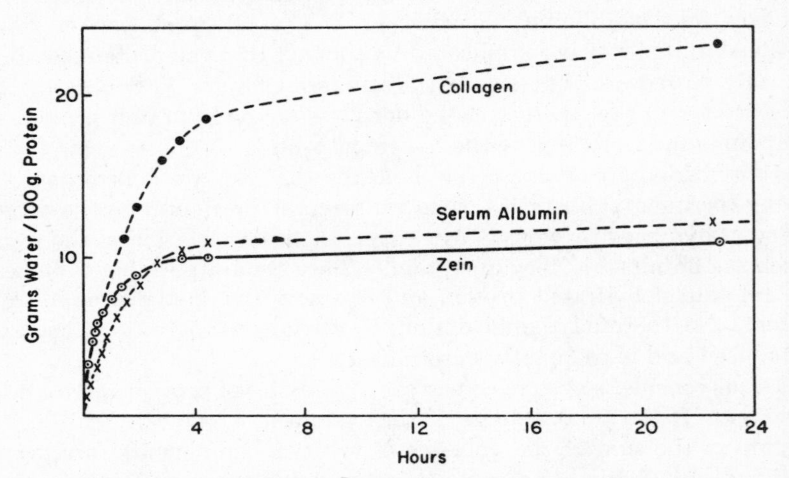

FIG. 23. Adsorption of water vapor by dry proteins (15). 20°C.; relative humidity 50%.

these values by assuming that the volume of the protein–water mixture is the sum of the volume of a water phase and a protein phase. In this assumption the presence of hydrated protein molecules was not taken into account. Therefore, we are not able to calculate the extent of hydration from $\bar{v}_p$ or $(v_p)_{app}$. Nevertheless these values are important for the evaluation of results obtained by other methods. Their determination is also necessary for the calculation of molecular weights from the sedimentation velocity in the ultracentrifuge (see Chapter IV, Sect. C and E).

B. Hydration of Dry Protein. It is a well known fact that the length of keratin fibers depends on their water content and, because of this, hair is used in hygrometers. Keratin, however, is not unique since all proteins bind water when exposed to an atmosphere containing water vapor. Figure 23 shows the adsorption of water by powdered proteins which had been dried at room temperature in a vacuum over phosphorus pentoxide. It is evident from the figure that the adsorption of water takes place at a rather rapid rate until a certain saturation is reached.

The amount of water bound depends on the temperature and the water vapor pressure (see Fig. 24) (2*a*,2*b*). The figure shows a sigmoid curve. Similar curves have been obtained for all proteins hitherto investigated (2*a*). The curves reveal that a certain amount of water, *a*, is bound very firmly and is given off only at extremely low pressures; a second amount, *b*, approximately equal to *a* is bound if the water vapor

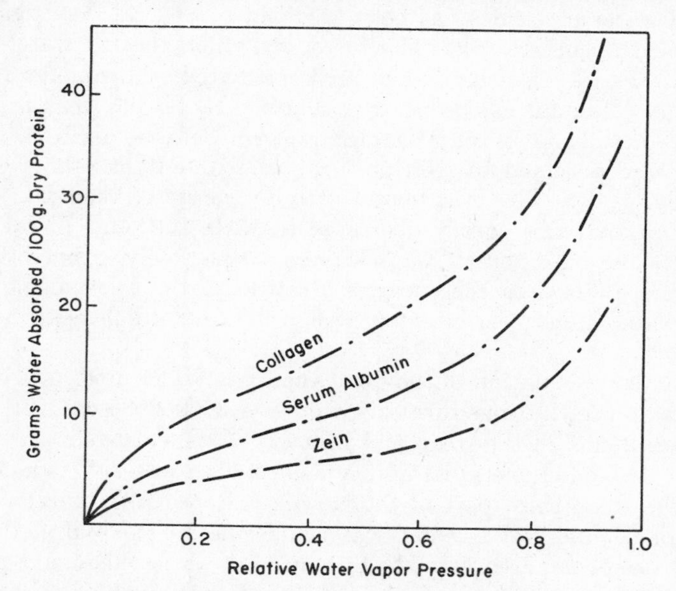

FIG. 24. Adsorption of water vapor by dry proteins (2*a*). 25°C.

pressure is increased further. At high water vapor pressures a sharp rise in the amount of water bound to the protein is observed, until about 40 g. of water are bound to 100 g. serum albumin. The amount *a* varies from 4 to 10 g., and the maximum amount of water bound from 20 to 60 g. per 100 g. protein (2*a*,3,4).

The particular shape of the curve of hydration cannot be accounted for by a simple adsorption of water or by the formation of stoichiometric hydrates. The amount, *a*, corresponding to the first steep part of the curve, is about one fifth of the amount of water required to cover the whole protein molecule with a monomolecular layer. It is assumed, therefore, that this water is bound to certain hydrophilic groups forming, between the peptide chains, a layer of water one molecule in thickness

(2,2*a*). The amount *b*, which is of the same order of magnitude as *a*, probably represents a second layer formed over the same hydrophilic groups, so that in these areas each of the adjacent peptide chains has its own water layer.

The question arises as to whether or not the second water layer, and also additional layers of water molecules, could possibly be bound by dipole induction to the primarily oriented layer of water molecules. This matter is of significance in our understanding of the forces operating in biological systems. Actually the occurrence of multiple layers of oriented water molecules has been assumed by several investigators (5) and denied by others (6). The force, by which the mth water layer is bound to the $(m-1)$st layer, has been calculated by Brunauer, Emmett, and Teller (7) and it has been found that it is by far too weak to fix more than the first layer of water molecules in a definite position. Similar results were obtained by Harkins (8), who found that the first water layer adsorbed to TiO_2 was bound with an energy of 6550 cal. per mole water, but that this energy decreased to 1380, 220, and 70 cal. for the second, third, and fourth water layers, respectively. Since the latter values are lower than the energies involved in the thermal movements of the water molecules, oriented layers of water dipoles can hardly be formed.

A similar calculation of the bond energy of water molecules bound to dry protein preparations furnishes values of 3000–6000 cal. per mole for the water bound in the steep first part (*a*) of the curve shown in Figure 24 (9). The bond energy of additionally bound water, *b*, is much lower (9). The steep third part of the curve (*c*) is probably due to the condensation of randomly oriented water molecules on the hydrated surfaces and has been compared with the formation of water clusters in gases (7). While the first process (*a*) consists of the adsorption of an oriented layer of polar water molecules and results in a higher degree of order in the system, *i.e.*, in a decrease of entropy, the last part of the curve is due to the tendency of the peptide chains to dissolve in water as a solvent; it results in a less ordered system, *i.e.*, in an increase in entropy (10).

The great strength by which the first portions of water are bound to a protein is evident from the appreciable contraction of the volume attending this process. The density of dry ovalbumin, $D = 1.2655$, increases to 1.2855 when 6.15% of water is bound. The specific volume of the protein decreases accordingly from $1/1.2655 = 0.792$ ml. per g. to $1/1.2855 = 0.777$ ml. per g. On further binding of water the density decreases; ovalbumin containing 56.26 g. water per 100 g. has a density of 1.1280 ($V_{sp} = 0.887$) (11). Important information on the hydration of protein crystals has been obtained by X-ray analysis of the crystals.

It has been found that the crystals maintain their shape when they are exposed to water vapor of different pressures or to aqueous salt solutions of a different salt content, but that stepwise swelling or shrinking of the unit cells occurs. The conclusion has been drawn that the water bound to the crystals is mainly bound at the surface of the protein molecules and that it does not penetrate their interior (12). The water content found in the crystals of proteins varied within wide limits; thus 32% water was found in insulin crystals, but more than 90% in crystals of tropomyosin (12*a*).

There is no general agreement at present concerning the chemical grouping in proteins to which water is bound. While X-ray analyses, as mentioned above, suggest that this water covers the surface of the molecule, some authors attribute the water of hydration to the ionic groups of the protein or to other polar groups such as the peptide bonds. The total number of water molecules bound corresponds approximately to the number of positively and negatively charged ionic groups (13). The extent of hydration decreases on benzoylation of the protein (14), but is hardly affected by the reduction of dithio bonds (14) or by methylation; methylated zein, fibroin, and hemoglobin bind approximately the same amount of water as the untreated proteins (15).

Not only the ionic groups, but also the peptide bonds, —CO·NH—, are to be considered points of attachment for water molecules, since it has been shown that peptides synthesized from nonhygroscopic amino acids are hygroscopic, *i.e.*, able to bind water molecules (16). Moreover, Nylon, which can be considered an artificial polypeptide of the formula . . . NH·R·NH—CO·R·CO—NH·R·NH—CO·R·CO— . . . also binds water in accordance with the typical sigmoid curve (Fig. 24) (2*a*). Since Nylon has no ionic side chains, there is no doubt but that most of the water is bound to the peptide bonds; possibly the water molecules are interlinked between two peptide bonds of adjacent peptide chains. The amount of water bound by different proteins is, however, not proportional to the number of peptide bonds. Fibroin from silk, which is particularly rich in peptide bonds (see Table I, Chapter III, Sect. E) binds less water than keratin, which has considerably fewer peptide bonds (2*a*).

C. Hydration of Proteins in Solution (16*a*). Attempts to determine the hydration of proteins in solution were made before the behavior of dry proteins, described in the preceding section, was known. It was assumed at that time that a definite part of the water in protein solutions is free and another definite part bound to the protein. One of the methods applied to determine these two portions of water consisted of measuring the expansion which occurred when the solution was frozen.

Since the density of ice is considerably lower than that of water, freezing of "free" water is accompanied by a distinct increase in volume, which can be measured dilatometrically. In this way it was found that a certain part of the water of protein solutions did not freeze (17). This was thought to be the water of hydration. The objection raised against experiments of this kind is that water can easily be cooled below its freezing point without solidifying. It is not clear, therefore, whether the unfrozen water is really water of hydration or undercooled water.

The possibility has also to be considered that one portion of the water of hydration of proteins consists of "ice" molecules, which, as is well known, occupy a larger space than molecules of liquid water. The initial excessive volume contraction during the enzymatic hydrolysis of proteins (see Chapter XVI, Sect. A) is possibly due to the conversion of "ice" molecules into water molecules (17*a*).

In a second method used the solubility of urea, glucose, or other nonelectrolytes in a protein solution was determined. It was assumed that the water of hydration, being bound to the proteins, would not be available to function as a solvent for other substances. The solubility of the nonelectrolytes added was determined either chemically or by measuring the lowering of the freezing point or of the vapor pressure. The obvious criticism of this method is that the substance added might compete with the protein for the water molecules and might, therefore, reduce the original degree of hydration of the protein. Another ambiguity is due to our inability to differentiate between adsorption of hydrogen and hydroxyl ions and true hydration, *i.e.*, binding of water molecules to the protein (18). The most serious objection to this method is, however, that the substances added to the protein solution are themselves sometimes bound to the protein, so that an increase in solubility results instead of the expected decrease (19). Nevertheless, important results were obtained by comparative experiments at different pH values and temperatures, in which it was found that the "nonsolvent volume" is almost independent of the pH (20). Accordingly the high viscosity of alkaline protein solutions could not be ascribed to the increase in hydration, to which it had previously been ascribed. Another important finding was that the "nonsolvent volume" decreased only slightly on denaturation and heat coagulation of the protein (21). The water-binding capacity of the protein coagulate was not much lower than that of the native protein in solution.

Since the phenomenon of hydration is accompanied by a decrease in volume, information concerning the extent of hydration can be obtained by determining the density of dry proteins and of protein solutions using one of the methods discussed in Section A, above. The decrease in volume is very considerable, amounting to 5–8 ml. per 100 g. dry protein (22).

Such an experiment showed that the density of dry ovalbumin suspended in benzene was 1.2715, but the "apparent density" of ovalbumin dissolved in water was 1.377. The increase in density corresponds to a decrease in the specific volume from 0.786 ml. per g. dry protein to an "apparent specific volume" of 0.726 ml. per g. dry protein (23).

The densities of most dry proteins are close to 1.27, the "apparent densities" of proteins in solution close to 1.34. A straight line is obtained if the density of the solution is plotted against the concentration of the protein dissolved; the value $\dot{I} = (d_s - d_w)/c_p$ has been called density increment; d_s and d_w are the densities of the protein solution and of its dialyzate, respectively, and c_p is the protein concentration in grams per milliliter. The density increment is almost independent of the concentration of the protein and of pH, but depends on the concentration of the salts present in the solution (1). For carboxyhemoglobin $\dot{I}$ is 0.251 in water and 0.21 in 1% sodium chloride solution.

The amount of water bound to the protein in solution has been determined by Adair and Adair (1,24) who measured the density of protein solutions in equilibrium with their dialyzates. If the density increments of a protein in solutions containing different amounts of a buffer are $\dot{I}_1$ and $\dot{I}_2$ and the densities of the dialyzates are d_1 and d_2, the nonsolvent volume $V_{ns} = (\dot{I}_1 - \dot{I}_2)/(d_2 - d_1)$. The nonsolvent volume is the sum of the "*bound water*" and of the "apparent specific volume" of the protein, that is, the volume occupied by the dissolved hydrated protein in 1 ml. of the solution. The bound water is obtained by subtracting the apparent specific volume from the nonsolvent volume.

The "bound water" of serum albumin in solution is approximately 40 g. per 100 g. dry protein (1). This is close to the maximum amount of water bound by 1 g. of the dry protein (see Fig. 24). Similar results have been obtained with other proteins (24*a*). The values of bound water vary between 20 and 50 g. water per 100 g. protein. An astonishingly low percentage of water (15%) was found in the tobacco mosaic virus (24*b*).

From the foregoing discussion on the hydration of protein crystals and protein solutions it is evident that the main volume contraction occurs in the region of low water pressure (Fig. 24). The apparent specific volume of proteins in their crystals is hardly different from the apparent specific volume found in protein solutions. Both are, however, much lower than the specific volume of dry proteins.

D. Immobilized Water. Although the amount of water bound by hydration amounts to only 20–50 g. per 100 g. protein, much higher amounts of water are bound by living matter. The average water content of muscle and of parenchymatous organs is approximately 70–80%, their protein content 20–30%, so that 200–300 g. water are found in a tissue containing 100 g. protein. In gelatin gels and in the tissues of jellyfish the water: protein ratio is still higher. It was believed for a time that these large amounts of water are bound by proteins; no other explanation was found for the fact that the water of normal muscles and other tissues could not be drained off by introducing a tube into the organ. Examination of organs and of gelatin gels by means of the methods described in the preceding sections proved, however, that most of this water was "free." It freezes at the same temperatures as normal water, has the same solvent power and there is no indication that it is bound to the protein molecules. We must regard it as free water, mechanically immobilized by the network of the cellular protein membranes and protein filaments (25,26).

The existence of solid gelatin gels containing only 2–3% of protein demonstrates that 1 g. gelatin is able to immobilize more than 30 g. water. Most of the water present in living matter must be considered to be immobilized water.

E. Solubility of Proteins in Water. The solubility of proteins in water varies within wide limits. While some proteins dissolve easily in salt-free water, others dissolve only in the presence of certain concentrations of salts; a third group is insoluble in water, but dissolves in mixtures of water and ethanol, while a fourth group, the scleroproteins, do not dissolve in any solvent. This differing behavior of proteins has been chosen as a basis for a classification of proteins into albumins, globulinlike proteins, prolamins, and scleroproteins. Classifications of this kind are more or less artificial and are of restricted value. Thus, some hemoglobins are readily soluble in salt-free water, while other hemoglobins are almost insoluble in the absence of salts, but promptly dissolve upon the addition of salts.

One would expect that those proteins which have a high affinity for water and are strongly hydrated would be the most readily soluble in water. Solubility and hydration, however, do not run parallel. Thus, collagen has a much higher affinity for water than serum albumin and binds more water when its dry powder is exposed to water vapor (see Fig. 23). Nevertheless, it is insoluble in water, while serum albumin dissolves easily.

There is no doubt but that the solubility of a protein in water is determined by its chemical formula, *i.e.*, by the kind and number of the amino acids forming the molecule, and by their arrangement in the molecule. One would expect that a high content of the positively or negatively charged ionic groups would increase both the affinity of the protein for water and its solubility. While this is certainly true, ionic groups at the same time exert the opposite effect by combining readily with ionic groups of the opposite sign, thus forming saltlike bonds within a protein molecule (27) as well as between adjacent protein molecules. While all salt-like bonds result in dehydration (27), the intermolecular bonds give rise to the formation of large insoluble protein aggregates. This explains the insolubility of many proteins in spite of the high content of anionic and cationic groups.

We are not yet able to predict the solubility of a protein in water from its amino acid composition, nor can we explain the solubility of the vegetable prolamins in ethanol. It has frequently been attributed to their high content of proline, which is soluble in alcohol. Collagen, however, in spite of its much higher content of proline is insoluble in alcohol.

If the solubility of synthetic polypeptides is examined it is found that polypeptides containing only one type of amino acid tend to form colloidal solutions; thus alanine hexapeptide, containing six molecules of alanine, is a proteinlike colloidal substance, which is hygroscopic and swells when it binds water (28).

It is well known that the solubility of proteins depends to a great extent on pH and on the concentration of salts present in the solution. The minimum solubility is found at the isoelectric point. The solubility is increased by the addition of acids or bases to the isoelectric protein. Use is made of the low solubility of isoelectric proteins when it is desired to isolate them from mixtures with other proteins. The precipitation of the isoelectric protein is probably due to the mutual formation of saltlike links between anionic and cationic groups of adjacent protein molecules (see Chapter VII, Sect. L).

Neutral salts have a twofold effect on protein solutions. Low concentrations of the salts increase the solubility of proteins, while high concentrations of neutral salts reduce the solubility and give rise to the formation of precipitates. The first of these two effects is known as the *salting-in* effect while the precipitation caused by high concentrations of the salts has been designated as *salting-out.*

The salting-in effect is particularly striking in those cases in which the protein is insoluble in salt-free water. Thus the euglobulins of the blood serum or the vegetable globulins are insoluble in water, but are readily dissolved on the addition of sodium chloride to their suspension in water. The solubility-promoting action of the neutral salts is due to the electrostatic interaction between their ions and the charged groups of the protein (28*b*). It has been mentioned in the preceding chapter (p. 70) that isoelectric solutions of a protein contain not only isoelectric molecules, P, with zero free charge, but also protein anions and cations of the formulas P^{-}, P^{2-}, P^{3-} . . . and P^{+}, P^{2+}, P^{3+} . . . The solubilities of these ions are higher than the solubility of the isoelectric protein (28*a*). Thus the solubility of uncharged molecules of horse carboxyhemoglobin was estimated to be 11 g. per liter of water at zero ionic strength, while the true solubility of the uncharged and charged molecules was 17 g. per liter (28*a*). The content of the solution in protein ions increases not only upon the addition of acids or bases, but also on the addition of neutral salts (28*a*). This may be responsible for the increase in solubility, *i.e.*, for the salting-in effect. It is not necessary to assume the formation of permanent strong bonds between the protein ions and ions of the salt added (28*b*). It is probable, however, that each of the ionic groups of the protein, owing to its electrostatic action, is surrounded by an atmosphere of salt ions of the opposite charge. It is hardly possible to decide whether or not this in some cases leads to the formation of permanent bonds between protein and inorganic ions (see Chapter V, Sect. C).

The solubility of proteins is also increased by glycine and other dipolar molecules which raise the dielectric constant of water (28*c*); on the other hand, the solubility of proteins in water is reduced by organic solvents such as ethanol which lower the dielectric constant of water (28*c*). Use has been made of these actions of glycine and of organic solvents in the fractionation of plasma proteins (see Chapter VIII, p. 150). The influence of the dielectric constant on the solubility of proteins is due to the fact that ionization is enhanced by a higher dielectric constant of the medium.

While the solubility of proteins is increased by the addition of small amounts of salts, it is well known that soluble proteins are precipitated by high concentrations of neutral salts. Use is made of this phenomenon in the preparation of protein crystals (see Chapter II, Sect. A). The *salting-out effect* of high concentrations of salts is evidently due to a competition between the salt and protein for molecules of the solvent. So much water is bound by the salt ions that not enough water is available for the dissolution of the proteins.

The salting-in effect of low salt concentrations and the salting-out effect of higher concentrations of salts is shown by the following table, where μ is the ionic strength of the potassium phosphate buffer solution at pH 7.4 and 0°, and G the amount of muscle globulin dissolved, measured in milligrams nitrogen per liter salt solution (29):

μ	0.1	0.20	0.30	0.50	3.0	3.3	3.4	3.5
G	1.8	3.2	149.0	1275	822	204	41	26

The solubility of proteins is, in general, decreased when the temperature is lowered. If, however, sodium sulfate is used for salting-out, lowered temperature results in heightened solubility, because solid sodium sulfate crystallizes and the sodium sulfate concentration of the solvent decreases. For this reason salting-out by sodium sulfate is carried out at 20°C. or higher.

From the observations noted in this section it is clear that we are not yet able to correlate solubility with the occurrence and content of certain amino acids in the protein molecule. The solubility of a solute in a solvent depends quite generally on the intensity of the mutual interaction between solvent and solute molecules and for similar reasons on the lattice energy of the solid phase, *i.e.*, on the forces effective between molecules of the solute. If the intensity of the attraction between molecules of the solute and the solvent exceeds the mutual attraction of solute molecules, dissolution will result. Since the diameter of globular protein molecules is very large, only the superficial molecular groups will be available for solute–solute interaction. We have to conclude, therefore, that the solubility of proteins will depend mainly on the nature of those groups which form the *surface* of the large particles, and particularly on the distribution of ionic and nonpolar groups between the surface and the interior of the protein molecule (6,21,28*c*,30). Unfortunately our knowledge about this arrangement of polar and nonpolar groups is very limited. Some indications concerning the distribution of polar groups have been obtained by measuring the dielectric increment of protein solutions (see Chapter VII, Sect. K).

G. Proteins in Surfaces and Interfaces (31–34). Proteins are capillary-active substances. Their concentration at the surface of their aqueous solution is higher than in the bulk of the solution. The migration of the protein molecules into the surface requires, however, a certain time (35), which sometimes amounts to several hours.

The most stable films are obtained by spreading proteins on solutions of the pH of the isoelectric point (36,37). The protein is spread from small drops delivered by a capillary pipet. Another method consists in placing a small amount of the dry protein on the water surface from which it slowly dissolves, to furnish a protein film (38).

Soluble proteins such as ovalbumin or hemoglobin readily form surface films on water or on dilute salt solutions. Less soluble proteins such as myosin form films only after a short treatment with trypsin (36). Gelatin does not form films on salt-free water, but can be spread on ammonium sulfate solutions.

The most important result obtained by the investigation of protein films is the fact that all proteins form films of the same type. The area covered by 1 mg. of the protein is about 0.7 to 0.85 m.^{2}; since the specific volume of proteins is approximately 0.75, the volume of 1 mg. protein is 0.75 mm.^{3} and the height of the protein film is equal to its volume divided by its area, *i.e.*, approximately 9–10 Å (35). This is much less than the diameter of most protein molecules and even less than the height of fatty acid films. It must be concluded that the peptide chains of

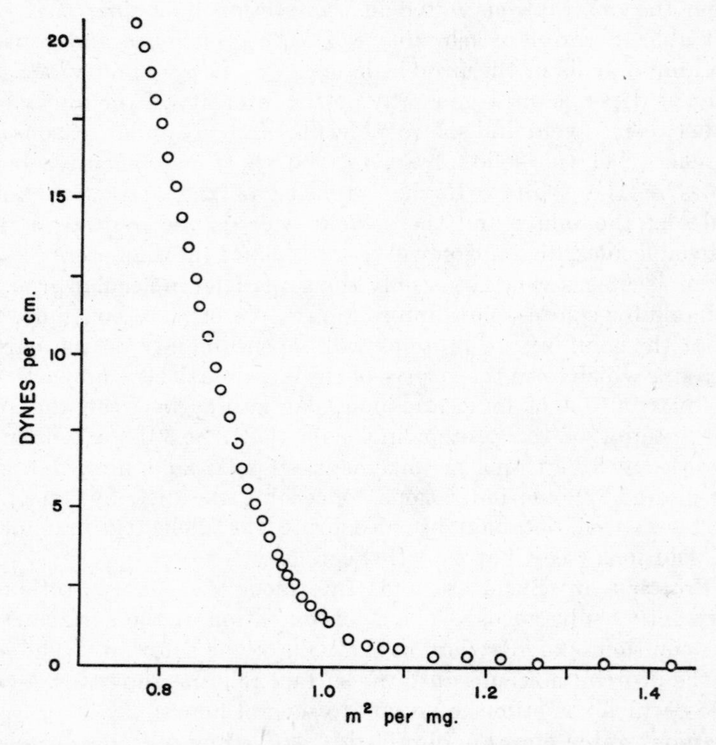

FIG. 25. Force-area curve of egg albumin spread on 35% ammonium sulfate (32).

globular protein molecules unfold and that the film consists of a monomolecular layer of peptide chains, their long axes parallel to the surface of the solution.

The lateral pressure exerted by protein films can be measured by means of a "film balance." When the area of the expanded film is plotted against the film pressure, curves as that shown in Figure 25 are obtained (32). The lower part of the curve shows the behavior of the film in the region of low pressure. In this region the protein molecules behave like a two-dimensional gas. Although they can move freely in two dimensions, parallel to the surface, movement in the third dimension, upward and downward, is not possible. The horizontal pressure exerted by the film is related to the osmotic pressure and depends on the number of protein molecules. If the number of the molecules present in the film is n, the following equation holds:

$$FA = nRT$$

where F is the force (in dynes), A the area (in cm.^{2}), R the gas constant (8.31×10^7 erg per degree per mole), and T the absolute temperature. If W is the weight of the total protein spread, its molecular weight, M, is $M = W/n$ (32). This method furnishes values of 17,100 and 20,100 for the molecular weights of β-lactoglobulin and zein, respectively (32) and 34,400 for pepsin (39). The method has also been used to determine the molecular weight of peptides formed from ovalbumin during the hydrolysis by pepsin (40).

The area occupied by a protein film under low pressure is much larger than the area occupied by the same amount of protein at high pressure, as shown in Table IX (41).

TABLE IX
AREA (IN M.^{2}) OF PROTEIN FILMS FORMED BY 1 MG. PROTEIN (41)

Protein	Low-pressure region extrapolated to zero pressure	High-pressure region at collapsing pressure
Ovalbumin	1.3	0.77
Insulin	1.65	0.77
Serum albumin	1.45	0.79
Gliadin	1.65	0.50
Cytochrome c	1.55	0.70

Our knowledge about the factors causing film formation of proteins is still very limited. It seems that the hydrophilic ionic groups of the proteins are directed toward the aqueous solution, while the nonpolar groups cover the layer of peptide chains and are directed toward the air (31,42). That protein films have a certain structure has been demonstrated by spreading "indicator oils" over the film. Starlike figures or other geometric patterns are made visible in this way by the refraction colors of the indicator oils (43).

Calculations of the film area are based on the assumption that the film is homogeneous and that there are no holes in the film. Such gaps as well as the formation of multimolecular layers can be discovered by darkfield ultramicroscopy of the film surface (44). Multimolecular films of ovalbumin were obtained when the concentration of the protein

solution was higher than 0.1% (45). Nonhomogeneous films were obtained by spreading proteins over stearate layers (31).

If proteins are mixed with lipids, mixed protein–lipid films are formed. Since similar films might be present in organisms, the properties of such mixed films are particularly interesting from the biological point of view. It has been found that protein-lipid films are permeable for water-soluble and also for fat-soluble substances; the permeation of the water-soluble molecules occurs, apparently, through the protein patches of the film, the permeation of fat-soluble substances through the lipid phases. Mixed molecules diffuse, in all probability, along the water–oil interface, the polar head in the protein phase, the nonpolar paraffin group in the lipid phase (46,47).

Proteins spread not only on the surface of aqueous solutions, but also at the interface between water and organic solvents. Thus it was found that gliadin and serum albumin form films at the interface between water and benzene (48). Films of ovalbumin occupy a larger area on the interface between water and bromobenzene than in the water–air surface (49).

The interface tension at the water/*p*-xylene interface is lowered considerably by serum albumin, ovalbumin or pepsin. This effect is particularly strong in the case of solutions of globin (50).

The spreading of proteins in surfaces and interfaces is frequently an irreversible process and involves, therefore, partial or total denaturation. This problem will be discussed in Chapter VII, p. 129.

References

1. G. S. Adair, M. E. Adair, *Proc. Roy. Soc. London* **A190,** 341 (1947).
2. H. B. Bull, Physical Biochemistry. Wiley, New York, 1947, p. 290.
2*a*. H. B. Bull, *J. Am. Chem. Soc.* **66,** 1499 (1944).
2*b*. J. Katz, *Kolloid Beihefte* **9,** 1 (1917).
3. R. Robinson, *J. Chem. Soc.* **1948,** 1083.
4. S. Gregg, T. Jacobs, *Trans. Faraday Soc.* **44,** 524 (1948).
5. H. R. Kruyt, Natuurw. *Tijdschr.* **18,** 38 (1936).
6. F. Haurowitz, *Kolloid-Z.* **74,** 208 (1936).
7. S. Brunauer, P. H. Emmett, E. Teller, *J. Am. Chem. Soc.* **60,** 309 (1938).
8. W. Harkins, *Science* **102,** 294 (1945).
9. M. Dole, A. D. McLaren, *J. Am. Chem. Soc.* **69,** 651 (1947).
10. S. Davis, A. D. McLaren, *Polymer Sci.* **3,** 16 (1948).
11. H. Neurath, H. B. Bull, *J. Biol. Chem.* **115,** 519 (1936).
12. M. F. Perutz, *Trans. Faraday Soc.* **42,** B, 187 (1946). T. Boyes-Watson, O. Davidson, M. F. Perutz, *Proc. Roy. Soc.* **A191,** 83 (1947).
12*a*. M. F. Perutz, *Research* **2,** 52 (1949).
13. L. Pauling, *J. Am. Chem. Soc.* **67,** 555 (1945).
14. E. F. Mellon, A. H. Korn, S. R. Hoover, *J. Am. Chem. Soc.* **69,** 827 (1947); **71,** 2761 (1949).

15. F. Haurowitz, F. Bursa, unpublished experiments; see also S. W. Benson *et al.*, *J. Am. Chem. Soc.* **72,** 2102 (1950).
16. M. Dole, A. D. McLaren, *J. Am. Chem. Soc.* **70,** 3040 (1948).
16*a*. T. L. McMeekin, R. C. Warner, Ann. Rev. Biochem. **15,** 119 (1946).
17. G. Jones, R. A. Gortner, *Colloid Symposium Monograph* **9,** 410 (1931).
17*a*. K. Linderstrøm-Lang, *Cold Spring Harbor Symposia Quant. Biol.* **14,** 117 (1950).
18. R. A. Gortner, *Trans. Faraday Soc.* **26,** 678 (1930).
19. H. B. Bull, *J. Gen. Physiol.* **17,** 83 (1933).
20. H. H. Weber, D. Nachmannsohn, *Biochem. Z.* **204,** 215 (1929); **234,** 62 (1931).
21. F. Haurowitz, *Kolloid-Z.* **71,** 198 (1935).
22. H. Chick, J. Martin, *Biochem. J.* **7,** 92 (1913).
23. F. Haurowitz, unpublished experiments.
24. G. S. Adair, M. E. Adair, *Proc. Roy. Soc. London* **B120,** 422 (1936).
24*a*. T. L. McMeekin and R. C. Warner, *J. Am. Chem. Soc.* **64,** 2393 (1942).
24*b*. H. K. Schachman, M. A. Lauffer, *J. Am. Chem. Soc.* **71,** 536 (1949).
25. W. Pauli, P. Fent, *Kolloid-Z.* **67,** 288 (1934).
26. F. Eirich, H. Mark, *Ergeb. exakt. Naturwiss.* **15,** 1 (1936).
27. W. Pauli, *Helv. Chim. Acta* **30,** 79 (1946).
28. E. Abderhalden, W. Gohdes, *Ber. D. Chem. Ges.* **64,** 2070 (1931).
28*a*. A. A. Green, *J. Biol. Chem.* **93,** 517 (1931). A. A. Green, E. J. Cohn, M. H. Blanchard, *ibid.* **109,** 631 (1935).
28*b*. E. J. Cohn, in Cohn and J. T. Edsall, Proteins, Amino Acids and Peptides. Reinhold, New York, 1943, pp. 569 and 586.
28*c*. E. J. Cohn, J. D. Ferry, cited by Cohn and J. T. Edsall, Proteins, Amino Acids and Peptides. Reinhold, New York, 1943, p. 615.
29. J. T. Edsall, *J. Biol. Chem.* **89,** 289 (1930).
30. F. Haurowitz, F. Marx, *Kolloid-Z.* **77,** 65 (1936).
31. H. Neurath, H. B. Bull, *Chem. Revs.* **23,** 391 (1938).
32. H. B. Bull, *Advances in Protein Chem.* **3,** 95 (1947).
33. A. Rothen, *Advances in Protein Chem.* **3,** 123 (1947).
34. N. Adam, Physics and Chemistry of Surfaces. Oxford Univ. Press, London, 1941.
35. E. Gorter, F. Grendel, *Proc. Konink. Nederland. Akad. Wetenschap.* **29,** 1262 (1926); **32,** 770 (1929).
36. E. Gorter, T. van Ormondt, *Biochem. J.* **29,** 38 (1935).
37. H. Neurath, *Science* **85,** 298 (1937).
38. A. H. Hughes, E. K. Rideal, *Proc. Roy. Soc. London* **A137,** 621 (1932).
39. H. A. Dieu, H. B. Bull, *J. Am. Chem. Soc.* **71,** 450 (1949).
40. H. B. Bull, J. Hahn, *J. Am. Chem. Soc.* **70,** 2128, 2132 (1948).
41. H. Neurath, H. B. Bull, *Chem. Revs.* **23,** 391 (1938).
42. D. G. Dervichian, *J. Chem. Phys.* **11,** 236 (1943).
43. V. J. Schaefer, *J. Phys. Chem.* **42,** 1098 (1938).
44. H. Zocher, F. Stiebel, *Z. physik. Chem.* **147,** 401 (1930).
45. H. B. Bull, *J. Biol. Chem.* **123,** 17 (1938).
46. T. H. Schulman, *Proc. Roy. Soc. London* **A155,** 701 (1936).
47. F. Sebba, E. K. Rideal, *Trans. Faraday Soc.* **37,** 273 (1941).
48. A. E. Alexander, H. Teorell, C. G. Åborg, *Trans. Faraday Soc.* **35,** 1200 (1939).
49. F. A. Askew, J. F. Danielli, *Trans. Faraday Soc.* **36,** 785 (1940).
50. F. Haurowitz, P. Boucher, unpublished experiments.

CHAPTER VII

Internal Structure of Globular Proteins (1*a*)

A. General Considerations. Although a very large number of amino acids make up a globular protein, the dimensions of the molecules indicate a chain length of only 10–20 amino acid units. For example, hemoglobin, whose molecular weight is 68,000, consists of molecules the shape of which approximates cylinders 33.5 Å high and 57 Å wide (1*b*). Since the length of an amino acid in the expanded peptide chain is approximately 3.4 Å, the dimensions of each hemoglobin molecule correspond to 10–17 amino acids. The average equivalent weight of the amino acids which form hemoglobin is approximately 130, so that each hemoglobin molecule contains 520–530 amino acids. If these formed a single straight peptide chain, the length of it would be 1780 Å. It is to be concluded from these considerations that the peptide chains forming the globular protein molecule in order to conform with the known dimensions are somehow folded or coiled. The marked species specificity of proteins characteristic further suggests that this folding or coiling must occur in a definite manner. A highly specific *internal structure* exists in the protein molecules; this structure is maintained even when the protein is dissolved in water or salted out by the addition of salts, the specificity of proteins apparently being unaffected by such treatment.

While monoaminomonocarboxylic acids can form only straight peptide chains, cystine with its two amino and two carboxyl groups is capable of linking parallel peptide chains to each other and can, in this way, give rise to branchings of the peptide chain. Branched peptide chains could also conceivably be formed by those amino acids which possess a functional side chain, in particular the aminodicarboxylic acids, the diamino acids, and the hydroxyamino acids. A repetition of such ramifications could lead to the formation of closed rings in the large protein molecule (see Fig. 26). The question of branched peptide chains and of closed peptide rings will be discussed in the following sections of this chapter. Our knowledge in this field is very limited because protein molecules are not only very large and structurally complicated but also very unstable, so that there are but few methods of chemical analysis which can be applied to shed light on this matter.

The lability of proteins is due to the weak forces which operate between adjacent peptide chains to maintain their internal structure.

There is no doubt that chain branching and formation of rings, if they occur at all, occur at only a few points in the macromolecule. This is indicated by the tendency of globular proteins to form monomolecular films at interfaces. The formation of such expanded films would be impossible if the protein molecules were three-dimensional lattices such as those which compose the synthetic resins. The ease with which proteins become spread on the water surface is convincing proof that the molecule consists either of one-dimensional, long peptide chains or of a two-dimensional network of peptide chains. Since films evidently can only be formed from a rather regular pattern of folded peptide chains, and not from a mass of irregularly linked and mutually entangled peptide chains, any complicated coiling of the peptide chains is ruled out by the ease with which they spread (2).

Branching, rings, and bonds other than peptide linkages can be only exceptional structures in the protein molecule; *its bulk*, without any

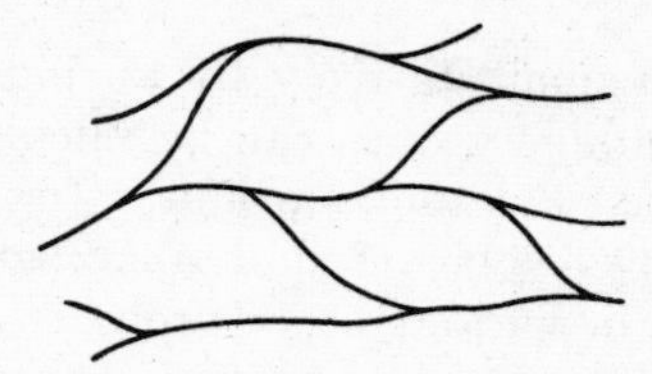

FIG. 26. Branching of peptide chains and formation of rings.

doubt, *consists of long peptide chains*, in accordance with the classical views advanced by E. Fischer and F. Hofmeister, the pioneers of protein chemistry. On the other hand, however, it is a well known fact in the chemistry of macromolecules that the properties of long chain molecules are radically altered by the formation of a few bridges between parallel chains. Thus vulcanized rubber, owing to the formation of a few sulfur bridges between the hydrocarbon chains, is insoluble in benzene, while the native rubber dissolves readily. It is clear, therefore, that ramifications or rings, even if their number in the macromolecule is very small, will produce a pronounced influence on the properties of proteins.

B. End Groups of Peptide Chains (3). The question of whether or not a peptide chain is straight or branched can be decided by determining the number of the terminal α-amino and α-carboxyl groups (groups *a* and *e* p. 106). An unbranched peptide chain will possess only a single α-amino and a single α-carboxyl group, while branched chains, unless the chains form rings, will have a number of these groups. In determining terminal α-amino groups it must be borne in mind that free ϵ-amino groups will occur in the side chains of lysine (group *c* in formula p. 106). Hence the determination of the total free amino groups according to the method of Van Slyke (see Chapter III, Sect. B) gives the sum of α-amino and ϵ-amino groups.

```
                                                                     OH
                                                                     |
                                                                 (C6H4 ring)
                                  NH2                                |
                                  |                                  |
     CH3                         (CH2)4                              CH2
     |                            |                                  |
H2N·CH·CO—NH·CH·CO—NH·CH·CO—NH·CH·CO—NH·CH·COOH
             |                        |
             CH2                      CH2
             |                        |
             COOH                     CH2
                                      |
                                      COOH
    (a)          (b)          (c)          (d)          (e)
```

Peptide chain

If lysine is determined quantitatively by an independent method, the number of terminal α-amino groups can be calculated by deducting the ϵ-amino groups from the total amino groups. In this way a considerable excess of α-amino groups has been found in lactoglobulin (4), insulin (4), cytochrome c (5), and in various other proteins. The values obtained by this indirect method are not, however, entirely reliable, because some amino acids such as glycine or cysteine give more than the theoretical amount of N_2 when treated with nitrous acid in the Van Slyke determination.

The electrometric titration of the proteins cannot be used to establish the number of terminal amino groups because there is no sharp break in the curve between the end point of the titration of the amino groups and the beginning of the neutralization of imidazole groups of histidine (6). Cautious electrometric titrations of ovalbumin and lactoglobulin gave only one to two free amino groups in excess of the ϵ-amino groups of lysine (7).

Similar difficulties arise when it is intended to determine quantitatively the terminal carboxyl groups of the peptide chains. Here we must also differentiate between the terminal α-carboxyl groups of the peptide chains, the β-carboxyl groups of aspartic, and the γ-carboxyl groups of glutamic acid (see above formula, groups *b* and *d*). A considerable part of these two types of carboxyl groups exists as the amide $—CONH_2$ (see Table I, p. 32). Another part of these groups is, however, present as free carboxyl groups and is titrated electrometrically together with the terminal α-carboxyl groups.

Difficulties are encountered when an attempt is made to calculate the number of free α-carboxyl groups by deducting the number of β- and γ-carboxyl groups from the total number of carboxyl groups determined electrometrically. Since the number of terminal α-carboxyl groups is much lower than the number of total carboxyl groups, small analytical errors in the determination of the dicarboxylic acids lead to exaggerated errors in the number of α-carboxyl groups.

It is evident from the foregoing discussion that the important question of whether or not peptide chains are branched cannot be decided by the direct determination of end groups, since there are no truly adequate methods to accomplish such determinations. A different approach has been to label these end groups by chemical substituents and to investigate the protein hydrolyzate for the presence of substituted amino acids. The main difficulty here consists in finding a substituent which will not be split off during the hydrolysis of the protein.

C. Substitution of Terminal Amino Groups. The free amino groups of proteins are easily acylated or alkylated. Treatment with dimethyl sulfate, $(CH_3)_2SO_4$ (8), or with diazomethane, CH_2N_2 (9), furnishes

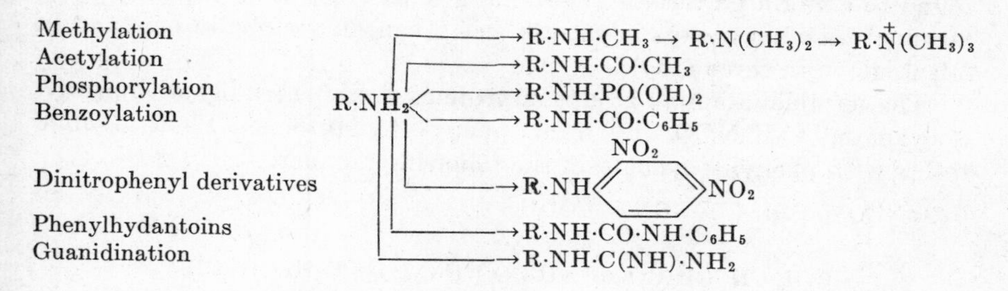

O- and *N*-methyl derivatives. Acetyl proteins are prepared by heating proteins with acetic anhydride, $(CH_3CO)_2O$ (9), or, preferably, by passing gaseous ketene, $CH_2{=}CO$, through the protein solution (10). Phosphoproteins are obtained (11,12,12*a*) through reaction with phosphorus oxychloride, $POCl_3$. Benzoyl proteins are prepared by treating proteins dissolved in dilute sodium carbonate with benzoyl chloride, C_6H_5COCl (13). The acyl groups are split off when the protein is hydrolyzed with acids or alkalis, so that substitution with acyl residues does not provide any information concerning the terminal amino groups. By the action of *O*-methylisourea the amino groups of lysine are converted into guanido groups (13*a*), thus providing guanidinated proteins.

$$\underset{\text{Lysine}}{HOOC{\cdot}CH(NH_2){\cdot}CH_2{\cdot}CH_2{\cdot}CH_2{\cdot}CH_2NH_2} \rightarrow \underset{\text{Homoarginine}}{HOOC{\cdot}CH(NH_2){\cdot}CH_2{\cdot}CH_2{\cdot}CH_2{\cdot}CH_2{\cdot}NH{\cdot}C(NH){\cdot}NH_2}$$

Important results were obtained by Sanger and Porter (14), who alkylated proteins in bicarbonate solution with 1-fluoro-2,4-dinitrobenzene. The *N*-dinitrophenyl proteins were hydrolyzed and the yellow dinitrophenylamino acids separated by chromatographic technique. It was found in this way that the terminal α-amino groups of horse hemoglobin are provided by six valine molecules. Myoglobin has only one terminal amino group, that of glycine. Insulin furnished two molecules of dinitrophenylglycine and two of dinitrophenylphenylalanine per unit of equivalent weight 12000 (15). Similar results were obtained by countercurrent distribution of the dinitrophenyl peptides (15*a*). All the hydrolyzates also contain the dinitrophenyl derivatives of lysine. The great importance of these experiments is that they prove the presence of more than one terminal α-amino group per protein molecule. Accordingly the molecules of hemoglobin and of insulin cannot consist of a straight unbranched peptide chain; they contain either branched peptide chains or multiple peptide chains held together by cystine molecules or by other bonds. Ovalbumin in contrast to hemoglobin and insulin was found to contain no terminal α-amino groups (16), while the number of terminal α-amino groups in edestin was seven, in γ-globulin one, and in β-lactoglobulin three (16*a*).

The terminal α-amino groups of proteins combine readily with phenyl isocyanate, C_6H_5NCO, to form phenyl hydantoins. Phenylalanine reacts with phenylisocyanate in the following manner:

$$C_6H_5{\cdot}NCO + C_6H_5{\cdot}CH_2{\cdot}CHNH_2{\cdot}COOH$$

$$\rightarrow C_6H_5{\cdot}CH_2{\cdot}CH(COOH)NH{\cdot}CO{\cdot}NH{\cdot}C_6H_5 \rightarrow C_6H_5{\cdot}CH_2{\cdot}CH\begin{matrix} \diagup NH-CO \\ \\ \diagdown CO-N{\cdot}C_6H_5 \end{matrix}$$

The phenylhydantoin derivatives of phenylalanine have been obtained from insulin (17), and, in small amounts also from casein, globin, and ovalbumin (18). With carbon suboxide, C_3O_2, the free amino groups of proteins combine to form malonyl proteins (19):

$$R{\cdot}NH_2 + C_3O_2 \rightarrow R{\cdot}NH{\cdot}CO{\cdot}CH_2{\cdot}COOH$$

An interesting substitution reaction of amino groups is that with mustard gas, which leads to the formation of thiazan rings (20–22):

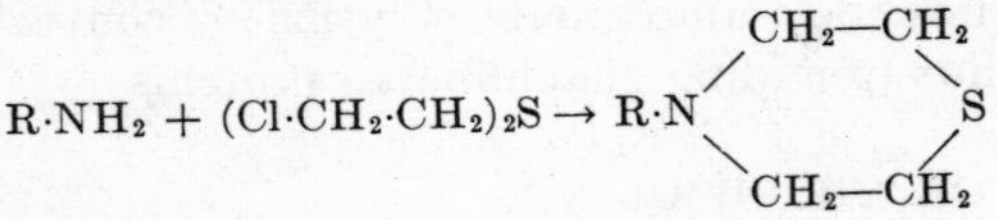

$$R{\cdot}NH_2 + (Cl{\cdot}CH_2{\cdot}CH_2)_2S \rightarrow R{\cdot}N\begin{matrix} \diagup CH_2-CH_2 \diagdown \\ \\ \diagdown CH_2-CH_2 \diagup \end{matrix}S$$

Although most of these substituents are also bound to the OH of hydroxyl or of carboxyl groups, the *O*-derivatives are more easily split by hydrolysis than the *N*-derivatives, so that a differentiation is still possible. Complications arise by the alkylation or acylation of the NH groups of the peptide bonds; methylation with dimethyl sulfate as well as acetylation with acetic anhydride lead to substitution at the peptide nitrogen (23,24).

Attempts have also been made to determine which amino acids provide the terminal amino group by isolating the product of oxidative destruction. This method is based on the fact that an amino acid is easily oxidized if its α-amino group is free but that it is stable if the amino group composes a peptide bond. Treatment of peptides with NaOBr results in oxidation of the terminal amino acid to carbon dioxide and a nitrile (25):

$$R^1NH{\cdot}CO{\cdot}CHR^2{\cdot}NH{\cdot}CO{\cdot}CHR^3{\cdot}NH_2 \rightarrow R^1NH_2 + R^2{\cdot}CO{\cdot}COOH + NH_3 + CO_2 + R^3C{\equiv}N$$

Similarly chromic acid oxidizes only those valine and leucine molecules of casein possessing a free α-amino group (26).

Since free amino groups are converted to hydroxyl groups by nitrous acid, this method has also been applied to proteins, and the protein hydrolyzates have been examined to find which amino acids carried the terminal amino groups (27). It has been found in this way that neither the glutamic acid nor the glutamine molecules of proteins possess free amino groups (28).

D. Terminal α-Carboxyl Groups. The free carboxyl groups of proteins are readily esterified by treating the protein with ethanol in the presence of small amounts of mineral acids (29) or treating them with other alkylating reagents:

$$R{\cdot}COOH \rightarrow R{\cdot}COOCH_3$$

Since the ester bond formed is easily hydrolyzed and since the free carboxyl groups of aspartic and glutamic acids are alkylated at the same time this method is not suitable for the determination of terminal α-carboxyl groups. The terminal α-carboxyl groups can be differentiated from the carboxyl groups of aspartic and glutamic acids by virtue of the fact that they will condense with thiocyanate to form thiohydantoins (30,31):

```
R·CO·NH·CHR'·COOH + NH4CNS → R·CO·N———CHR'
                                  |      |
                                  SC     CO
                                   \    /
                                     N
                                     H
```

It is evident from the formulas that an α-amino group, either free or linked by a peptide bond, is required for the formation of the thiohydantoin ring. Consequently, the free carboxyl groups of aspartic and glutamic acid cannot react to form thiohydantoin rings. In the author's laboratory it has been found that not only amino acids and peptides, but also proteins combine with thiocyanates; however, it has not yet been possible to isolate thiohydantoin derivatives (32,33).

E. Substitution of Other Groups (34,35). One of the reagents frequently used in protein chemistry is *formaldehyde* (36). It has been noted (Chapter III, Sect. B) that formaldehyde reacts with amino groups in such a way that in its presence amino acids can be titrated with sodium hydroxide. It was generally believed that formaldehyde condensed with free amino groups to form methylene imine groups (Schiff bases) according to the equation:

$$R{\cdot}NH_2 + HCOH \rightarrow R{\cdot}N{=}CH_2 + H_2O$$

In the last few years it was shown, however, that the reaction between formaldehyde and amino acids or proteins is much more complicated. Formaldehyde combines with *two* free amino groups of adjacent peptide chains forming methylene bridges of the type $N{-}CH_2{-}N$ (37,38). One of these amino groups can also be replaced by the acid amide group, $-CONH_2$, by the indole ring of tryptophan, by the benzene ring of tyrosine, by the imidazole ring of histidine (39), or by the NH group of a peptide bond (40). The various bonds which may so be formed act as cross links between the peptide chains of the protein with the result that soluble proteins are converted into substances which are insoluble, but which swell to a limited extent by taking up water (41).

The hydroxyl groups of the *hydroxyamino acids* are esterified by the action of concentrated sulfuric acid, chlorosulfonic acid, or phosphorus pentoxide (29,42). The oxygen atom of the hydroxyl group, in contrast to that of the carboxyl group, does not exchange with O^{18} when the proteins are treated with H_2O^{18} (43).

Substitution of the aromatic ring of *tyrosine* is easily accomplished by treating proteins with halogens, nitric acid, or diazo compounds. *Iodoproteins* are prepared by the addition of iodine dissolved in potassium iodide solutions, to proteins at slightly alkaline reaction (44). Iodine substitutes the 3- and 5- position of the phenol ring (45). Prolonged action of iodine results in the production of thyroxine:

$$HO{-}C_6H_4{-}CH_2{\cdot}CHNH_2{\cdot}COOH \rightarrow HO{-}C_6H_2I_2{-}CH_2{\cdot}CHNH_2{\cdot}COOH$$

$$\rightarrow HO{-}C_6H_2I_2{-}O{-}C_6H_2I_2{-}CH_2{\cdot}CHNH_2{\cdot}COOH$$

Nitric acid reacts not only with the aromatic rings but also with the guanido groups of arginine (46):

$$R{\cdot}NH{\cdot}C(NH)NH_2 + HNO_3 \rightarrow R{\cdot}NH{\cdot}C(NH)NH{\cdot}NO_2$$

In order to prevent deamination, the nitrous acid produced from nitric acid is destroyed by adding urea. The reaction is complicated by the hydrolyzing and oxidizing actions of nitric acid.

The coupling of proteins with *diazo compounds* has found extensive use because this reaction takes place at low temperatures and at slightly alkaline reactions so that there is little danger of denaturing the protein. Landsteiner (47) in this way prepared a great number of *azo proteins* which were used as specific antigens. By varying the amount of the diazo compound, azo proteins containing different amounts of the azo group can be prepared (48,49). The diazo compounds combine mainly with the aromatic ring of tyrosine and the imidazole ring of histidine (50):

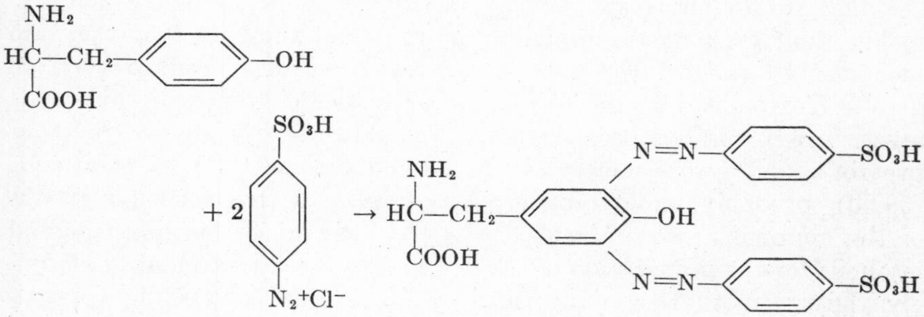

NH_2 | HC—CH_2—C_6H_4—OH | COOH

+ 2 SO_3H—C_6H_4—$N_2^+Cl^-$ → NH_2 | HC—CH_2—C_6H_2(—OH)(—N=N—C_6H_4—SO_3H)$_2$ | COOH

If an excess of the diazo compound is used, it also combines with amino acids other than tyrosine and histidine (51–53). Under such conditions the diazo compounds couple with amino groups and other functional groups of the proteins.

An evaluation of the results obtained by applying these many substitution reactions leads to the conclusion that at least a portion of the hydroxyl groups of hydroxyamino acids, of the imidazole rings of histidine, and of the guanido groups of arginine in the proteins exist in the form of "free" reactive groups. Quantitative determinations show, however, that not all these free groups in the native protein are reactive. A considerable number of them are concealed among the closely folded peptide chains and are therefore inaccessible to the substituting agents. By denaturing the protein and unfolding the peptide chains, the previously hidden functional groups become available for substitution reactions (see page 127).

F. Ring Structures in Proteins. By heating the methyl or ethyl esters of amino acids cyclic peptides are obtained. The simplest ring obtained in this way is the diketopiperazine ring:

```
        CHR—COOR'                CHR—CO
       /                        /      \
   H2N      +        NH2  →  HN          NH
                    /           \       /
        R'OOC—CHR                CO——CHR
```

Diketopiperazines have also been obtained by the partial hydrolysis of proteins; thus fibroin treated with 70% sulfuric acid at room temperature gave glycylalanyl-anhydride and glycyltyrosyl-anhydride (54). Although no anhydrides were formed from amino acids under the same conditions the secondary formation of these cyclic anhydrides in a medium containing little water can hardly be excluded (55). If the proteins originally contained diketopiperazines, the question of the manner of their linkage within the macromolecule would arise. No attempt has been made hitherto to answer this question satisfactorily. Proteolytic enzymes are unable to split diketopiperazines (56,57), a fact which also makes their existence in proteins doubtful and suggests that they are secondarily formed. The same is true for anhydrides obtained by more drastic treatment, *e.g.*, by heating proteins to 130–150°C. in anhydrous glycerol (58). It has been demonstrated that the free amino groups of protein-bound lysine molecules are altered by such a heat treatment (59,60), probably undergoing condensation with free carboxyl groups of the aminodicarboxylic acids. Use has been made of these thermal methods for the preparation of cyclic peptides; heat treatment of alanylglycylglycyl methyl ester furnished cyclic peptides containing approximately 20 amino acid residues in their cyclopeptide ring (61). Since these cyclic peptides have no terminal free amino or carboxyl groups, some of them are cleaved by "endopeptidases," *i.e.*, by proteolytic enzymes attacking endopeptide groups (62). Natural cyclopeptides of this type have been found among the bacterial toxins (see Chapter XV).

Cyclic anhydrides are provided not only by the condensation of amino with carboxyl groups, but both amino and carboxyl groups may presumably combine with hydroxyl or thio groups to form oxazoles, azlactones, or thiazolines:

```
  CH2OH  O             CH2SH  O             NHCOCH3
  |      ||            |      ||            |
 —CH-NH-C—            —CH-NH-C—            —CH-COOH
      ↓                    ↓                    ↓
  H2C————O             H2C————S             N====CCH3
  |      |             |      |             |     |
 —HC     C—           —HC     C—           —HC    O
    \   //               \   //               \  /
      N                    N                   CO
 Oxazole ring         Thiazole ring        Azlactone ring
```

The possibility of the presence of these ring systems in proteins has been discussed from time to time (63,64). But no experimental evidence for these assumptions has been furnished to date. The existence of —S·CO— bonds has in fact been disproved by the finding that there is no increase in acid groups when the sulfhydryl groups of native proteins react with iodine (65).

When proteins are subjected to the action of sodium in amyl alcohol, pyrrole bases and other heterocyclic compounds are obtained. The opinion has been expressed that these cyclic compounds are present in the original protein (66). Similar compounds are, however, formed from amino acids by heat treatment, as when glutamine or glutamic acid on heating are readily and almost quantitatively converted into pyrrole derivatives:

```
CH2—CONH2              CH2—CO
|                      |     \
|        NH2    →      |      NH     + NH3
|       /              |     /
CH2—CH                 CH2—CH
       \                     \
        COOH                  COOH
   Glutamine           Pyrrolidonecarboxylic
                               acid
```

The existence of heterocyclic rings in proteins, moreover, would be incompatible with the optical properties of the proteins (see Chapter VII, Sect. J).

The X-ray diagrams of protein crystals have been interpreted to indicate the presence of trihydroxytriazine rings formed by the condensation of three enolized peptide linkages (67):

```
       R    R                         R    R
       |    |                         |    |
       N    COH                       N—C—OH
      //       \\                    /      \
R—COH            N—R    →    R——C            N—R
                                /   \        /
   R—N=C—R                   HO      N—C—OH
       |                             |   |
       OH                            R   R
  Enolized peptides            Trihydroxytriazine
                                    (cyclol)
```

This interpretation has been criticized by the X-ray analyst (68) as well as by the chemist and physical chemist. The assumption of trihydroxytriazine rings is invalidated by the fact that proteins do not possess the large number of hydroxyl groups required for the postulated structure (69). It has been demonstrated moreover that the lattice of polymeric trihydroxytriazine rings is so restricted in size that it could not contain amino acids other than glycine and alanine; there would be no space for the side chains of the other amino acids (70). Finally, it has been shown that the existence of trihydroxytriazine rings is energetically impossible (71). By the examination of a large number of compounds containing the —CO·NH— group it was revealed (71*a*) that the rearrangement into —C(OH)=N— depends on the formation of an aromatic ring system. The energy released on aromatization is required for the formation of the enolized lactim bond (71*a*).

The existence of other ring systems is just as unlikely as that of trihydroxytriazine rings. If proteins contained heterocyclic rings which are split by hydrolyzing agents, hydrolysis with deuterium oxide should furnish compounds containing firmly bound deuterium. This was not observed when casein was hydrolyzed by trypsin in heavy water (72). It is very improbable, therefore, that proteins contain rings other than those of the aromatic and heterocyclic amino acids.

G. Branching (Ramification) in Peptide Chains. Among the amino acids, *cystine* is unique in that it is a diaminodicarboxylic acid, possessing two α-amino and two α-carboxyl groups. As a result it is able to form bridges between parallel peptide chains (formula *a*) and, in this way, to link together parallel chains (*b*) or to form loops as shown in formula (*c*). The dissolution of keratin in reducing agents such as sulfides has been ascribed to the rupture of the dithio bridges of existing cystine molecules as represented in formula (*b*) (see Chapter IX, Sect. B).

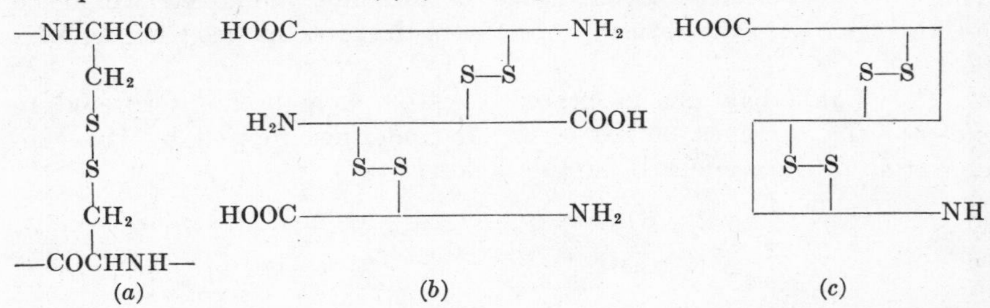

On the other hand the molecular weight of ovalbumin is not altered when the sulfhydryl groups of its cysteine molecules are oxidized to dithio groups (73). Oxidation of the dithio bridges of cystine is accomplished by the action of periodate (74); such a treatment of ovalbumin or of serum albumin does not noticeably alter the viscosity of the protein solution (75). The behavior of ovalbumin and serum albumin would therefore seem to indicate a structure such as that represented by formula (*c*) rather than by (*b*), since there is no indication of the disaggregation of these molecules upon oxidation of their dithio bonds.

It was assumed until recently that *glutamic acid*, a dicarboxylic acid, forms peptide bonds only by means of its α-carboxyl group. Glutathione, however, a tripeptide, is γ-glutamylcysteylglycine, in which glutamic acid is bound to the cysteine molecule by the γ-carboxyl group. γ-Glutamyl bonds have also been found in a polymeric glutamic acid (76), which constitutes the capsular substance of *Bacillus anthracis*. The hypothesis has been advanced, therefore, that the carboxyl or amide groups in the side chains of the glutamyl or glutaminyl radicals combine with functional groups of other amino acids, thus forming points of ramification of the main peptide chain (4,32).

Branching of the peptide chains by means of aminodicarboxylic and diamino acids has been considered to be responsible for the characteristic properties of collagen and gelatin (77). The tryptic digestion of casein and of other proteins produces small amounts of γ-glutamyl peptides, the presence of which is proved by the formation of succinyl peptides on oxidation with NaOBr or with Chloramine T (32,78). It remains to be discovered, however, whether or not the γ-glutamyl residues actually do form points of ramification in the peptide chains of the protein molecules (formula *d*) or whether some of the glutamic acid molecules are linked according to formula (*e*).

```
    CO—NH·CHR·COOH
    |
    CH2
    |
    CH2                          COOH
    |                            |
—HN·CH·CO—                   —HN·CH·CH2·CH2·CO—
      (d)                             (e)
```

It should be mentioned, finally, that branching of the peptide chains by means of *ureido residues* has been considered possible (64,79). Ureido bridges would be formed by the condensation of carbonic acid with two adjacent amino groups: R·NH·CO·NH·R′. The existence of ureido compounds is suggested by the ease with which carbamino acids are formed from amino acids and carbonates, and by the formation of small amounts of carbon dioxide during the hydrolysis of proteins. Peptides of carbamic acid furnish carbon dioxide and ammonia on hydrolysis (80):

$$R{\cdot}CO{\cdot}NH{\cdot}CO{\cdot}NH{\cdot}R' \rightarrow RCOOH + NH_3 + CO_2 + H_2NR'$$

It seems, however, that most if not all the carbon dioxide liberated from protein hydrolyzates originates from HCO_3^- ions adsorbed by positively charged groups of the protein (81).

H. Order of Amino Acids in Peptide Chains. The order of occurrence of amino acids in short peptide chains containing five to ten amino acids can be determined in a very difficult and laborious way by a combination of various analytical methods. In this manner the structure of the cyclopeptide gramicidin S has been elucidated (82) (see Chapter

XV). Similarly the structure of different peptides obtained by the partial hydrolysis of insulin and of hemoglobin has been established, mainly by labeling the terminal amino groups with dinitrofluorobenzene (14,83). The results of these analyses reveal that insulin and hemoglobin are built up from quite heterogeneous fragments. Thus a peptide A isolated from insulin contains glycine, isoleucine, valine, and tyrosine, but is free of arginine, histidine, lysine, phenylalanine, and threonine; peptide B from insulin contains phenylalanine, valine, aspartic acid, glutamic acid, lysine, threonine, and alanine (83) (see also Chapter III, Sect. F and Chapter XIII, Sect. C). There is evidently no indication of a periodic arrangement of the amino acids such as had been proposed by Bergmann (84).

While the sequence of amino acids in the shorter peptide chains can be determined, it would be hopeless to endeavor to fully characterize peptide chains containing 100 or more amino acids. However, attempts have been made to gain insight into the distribution of the amino acids in proteins by partially hydrolyzing them. Hydrolysis of proteins by concentrated hydrochloric acid at 30, 45, and 60°C. demonstrates that some of the peptide bonds are more resistant than others; splitting by the acid does not occur at random, but at certain linkages of the peptide chain (85). Peptide bonds formed by the amino groups of hydroxyamino acids are split more easily than other peptide bonds, because the hydroxyamino acids tend to form oxazoline rings (16), so that they are stabilized and cannot recombine with adjacent amino acids to form the original peptide bond.

It has long been known that certain amino acids appear in the hydrolyzate earlier than other amino acids; this is in agreement with recent quantitative investigations. Thus it was found that leucine is split off rapidly when casein is hydrolyzed, while valine is liberated at a much lower rate; the early liberation of leucine has been attributed to the terminal position of leucine molecules (86). It may be mentioned, finally, that the partial hydrolysis of certain proteins by hydrochloric acid at 37° furnishes peptides formed mainly from basic amino acids (87). On the other hand, glutamylglutamic acid was isolated from partially hydrolyzed wool (87*a*). Such findings make it evident that the distribution of amino acids in the globular protein molecule is far from homogeneous.

I. Salt Linkages and Hydrogen Bonds in Proteins. From the preceding sections it is clear that branching and cyclization play a secondary role in the formation of the globular protein molecules. The tight folding of the long peptide chains is apparently not due to strong chemical bonds, but to weaker forces, mainly to the mutual attraction of ionic and polar groups. It has been emphasized that proteins contain positively and negatively charged ionic groups. Groups of the opposite charge will attract each other by electrostatic forces. Similarly dipoles will attract each other by dipole association (see Fig. 22, p. 87). While the mutual attraction of ionic groups decreases with r^{-2}, *i.e.*, is proportional to the reciprocal of the square of their distance apart, dipole association decreases approximately with r^{-6} or r^{-7}; this means that the forces operating between dipoles are effective only over very short distances and can therefore link together only those dipoles which are closely adjacent (87*b*).

The electrostatic forces which give rise to the mutual attraction of ions and dipoles are also responsible for the so-called hydrogen bond (88,88*a*). In proteins most of the hydrogen bonds are formed between the imino groups of peptide linkages on the one hand and carbonyl groups of adjacent peptide linkages on the other:

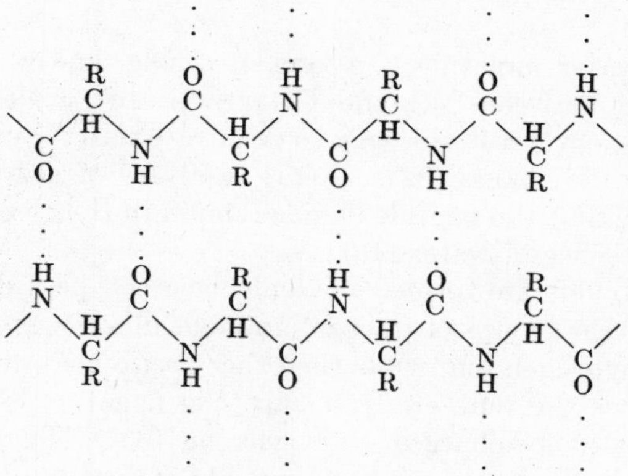

Hydrogen bonds
(dotted lines)

The structure of the hydrogen bonds is shown by the electronic formula:

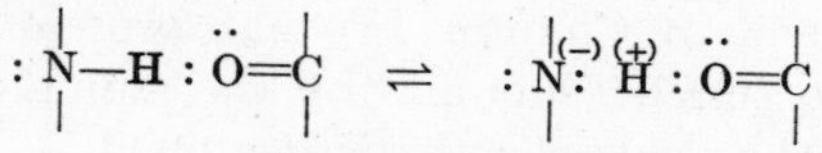

$$:\overset{|}{\underset{|}{N}}-H:\ddot{O}=\overset{|}{\underset{|}{C}} \quad \rightleftharpoons \quad :\overset{|}{\underset{|}{N}}\!\!:^{(-)}\ \overset{(+)}{H}:\ddot{O}=\overset{|}{\underset{|}{C}}$$

Hydrogen bond

in which the unshared electron pairs of the electron octets are represented by double dots, while each of the shared electron pairs is represented by the usual dash. It is evident from the formula that attraction must result between the positively charged proton (H^{+}) and the unshared electron pair of the oxygen atom. Owing to this force of attraction a hydrogen bond will be formed, as shown by the formula on the right. It was assumed originally that hydrogen bonds are symmetrical and that the proton is pulled by equal forces to the nitrogen and to the oxygen atom. This is, however, not the case; symmetrical hydrogen bonds are energetically improbable (89). One must assume that the hydrogen nucleus forming the hydrogen bond is nearer the nitrogen than the oxygen atom. In addition to the hydrogen bonds between nitrogen and oxygen atoms, proteins also contain hydrogen bonds between two oxygen or two nitrogen atoms. The presence of hydrogen bonds between the phenolic hydroxyl groups of tyrosine and free carboxyl groups has been proved by a shift of the typical absorption maximum of tyrosine in the ultraviolet region of the spectrum (90).

```
                    HO
                      \
 ===>—O—H . . . O=C—
```

The bond energy of the different types of hydrogen bonds varies from 2 to 9 kcal. (91).

Since the water molecule is a typical dipole, one would expect the hydrogen bond between NH and CO groups to be cleaved by water molecules and the water in this way to penetrate into the crevices between the folded peptide chains (92). X-ray analyses of crystalline proteins show, however, that the peptide chains remain in the closely folded state even in the presence of water (1*b*).

Hydrogen bonds are formed not only between peptide linkages, but also between other groups of the protein molecules. One of these groups furnishes the hydrogen ion, while the other group containing nitrogen or oxygen furnishes the lone electron pair, the negative charges of which attract the positively charged hydrogen ion (93). There are far more peptide linkages than other groups capable of forming hydrogen bonds and as a result most of the hydrogen bonds form cross links between parallel peptide chains (94,95). In this way, the specific internal structure of the globular protein molecules is maintained (96).

It was mentioned in Chapter IV that protein molecules undergo disaggregation into smaller subunits by the action of urea. This also seems to be due to the cleavage of hydrogen bonds. It is not yet known, however, what type of group holds together the subunits in the macromolecule. Possibly we are confronted here with the phenomenon of complementarily shaped surfaces; these can approach one another so closely that the short-range forces between polar groups become effective and may result in a very strong mutual attraction (see Chapter XIV Sect. C).

J. Optical Properties of Proteins. Optical methods are valuable tools in the elucidation of the structure of organic compounds. It has been attempted to gain an understanding of the internal structure of proteins by measuring the refraction, rotation, and absorption of light by proteins.

In discussing electrophoresis it was mentioned that aqueous solutions of proteins have a higher *refractive index* than pure water and that use is made of this fact to determine the position of the moving boundary. The refractive index of protein solutions increases linearly with the concentration of the protein. The difference between the refractive indices of an 1% protein solution and water is called the *specific refractive increment.* It varies slightly from protein to protein; the following typical values have been found: bovine serum albumin 0.001901, human serum albumin 0.001887, ovalbumin 0.001876, and human γ-globulin 0.001875 (97). Since the temperature and the presence of salts do not greatly alter the refractive increment, the concentration of proteins can be determined very rapidly by measuring the refractive index of their solution and subtracting the refractive index of their dialyzate. It must be borne in mind, however, that the refractive increment of lipoproteins, 0.00171, is much lower than that of fat-free proteins (97*a*).

The molecular refraction of organic substances is an additive property, and is equal to the sum of the atomic refractions. The same is true for proteins. However, no use can be made of the refractive indices for the elucidation of the protein structure because the carbon, hydrogen, oxygen, and nitrogen contents of the various proteins are very similar and because the number of atoms in the molecule is so large that the contribution of single atoms or of atomic groups to the molecular refraction is negligibly small.

The same is true for determinations of the *optical rotation* of polarized light (98,99). Since amino acids, with the exception of glycine, are optically active, and since the asymmetric carbon atoms remain asymmetric in the peptide chains, peptides and proteins are optically active. The sign and the magnitude of the specific rotation depend on the number and the type of the amino acids forming the protein molecule; the net value resulting from the contribution of hundreds of amino acids does not permit any conclusions to be drawn concerning the arrangement of the amino acids or other details of the internal structure of the protein molecules. The specific rotation observed has its minimum at the isoelectric point; it varies from -30 to $-70°$ (99). Very high values up to $-313°$ were observed in gelatin gels (100).

Some information on the structure of proteins is obtained, however, by measuring the *absorption of light* of different wave lengths. Visible light is absorbed only by colored proteins such as hemoglobin, the yellow enzyme, visual purple, and other chromoproteins. While very important information concerning the colored prosthetic group is obtained by measuring the visible absorption spectrum between 450–650 mμ, the absorption curves of visible light do not permit conclusions concerning the structure of the colorless protein carrier.

All proteins strongly absorb ultraviolet light; the maximum of the absorption is near 270 mμ (101,102), and it corresponds to the absorption maximum of the amino acids tryptophan, tyrosine, and phenylalanine. Conclusions concerning the amounts of these amino acids in the protein molecule can, therefore, be drawn by a consideration of the intensity of the absorption maximum. If the protein is hydrolyzed by

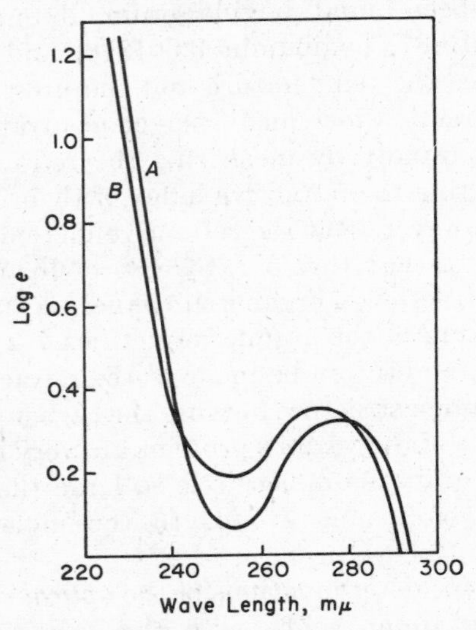

FIG. 27. Spectral absorption of serum globulin (*A*) and its tryptic hydrolyzate (*B*) (103).

proteolytic enzymes the absorption curve is not altered essentially (Fig. 27) (103). One can conclude, therefore, that there are no absorbing structures present in the native protein that are not present also in the hydrolyzate. The occurrence of large amounts of heterocyclic rings, as postulated by some authors, is disproved by this finding.

The *infrared absorption* of organic molecules is due to the absorption at characteristic frequencies of certain atomic groups. The main difficulty here consists in the fact that water also absorbs infrared light. It is necessary, therefore, to examine dry protein layers, which are never quite homogeneous, which vary more or less in thickness, and which contain cracks. Because of these factors, it is hardly possible to determine very precisely the intensity of the absorption. It is evident, however, from the examination of proteins in the infrared region that there are typical absorption maxima. The maxima at 3.0 and 3.22 μ have been attributed to the NH groups of the peptide bonds, while maxima near 6 μ are due to the CO groups; there are no indications for absorption caused by enolized peptide bonds —C(OH)=N— (103*a*). Since the absorption band at the wave length 1.90 μ in silk was found to be more intense in the direction perpendicular to the long axis of the fiber, it was suggested that the CO groups lie in a plane perpendicular to the long axis (104,105). On the other hand it was concluded from an analysis of protein in polarized infrared light that the NH groups are oriented in a plane parallel to the long axis of the peptide chains (103*b*).

K. Dielectric Constant of Protein Solutions (106–109). Measurements of the dielectric constant give information concerning the polar properties of the substance examined. The dielectric constant is determined by measuring the electrostatic force between two charged plates of a condenser first *in vacuo* and next in the substance to be tested. If the electrostatic force in a vacuum is v_0 and that in the substance v_s, v_s is always smaller than v_0. The ratio v_0/v_s is called the dielectric constant.

Evidently the dielectric constant is to be correlated with the polar structure of molecules, since high dielectric constants are found in polar molecules, low dielectric constants in nonpolar molecules. Because they are highly polar substances, one would expect that zwitterions should have high dielectric constants. Unfortunately it is not possible to determine the dielectric constants of amino acids or of proteins directly, because they cannot be liquefied; their melting points are so high that decomposition occurs at the temperatures required to melt them.

While it is not possible to measure directly the dielectric constant of proteins and amino acids, significant results have been obtained by measuring the dielectric constant of their aqueous solutions. Water itself has a very high dielectric constant, amounting to 80 at 20°C., while that of ethanol is 24, that of diethyl ether 4.3, and that of the paraffins less than 2. The high dielectric constant of water is due to its polarity, discussed in Chapter VI. If organic molecules are dissolved in water, its dielectric constant is lowered in general. However, if amino acids or proteins are dissolved in water, the dielectric constant increases. This, which is somewhat atypical behavior, is a consequence of the highly polar character of amino acids and proteins. The increase in the dielectric constant, while different for different amino acids, peptides, and proteins, is proportional to the concentration of the dissolved substance. If D_w and D_s are the dielectric constants of water and of the solution, respectively, and C the molar concentration of the dissolved substance, the molar *dielectric increment* is $i_M = (D_s - D_w)/C$. The dielectric increments of α-amino acids vary from 22 to 28, while those of the peptides are much higher; for peptides containing 2, 3, 4, 5, and 6 glycine molecules the following values were found: 70, 113, 159, 215, and 239 (110). One has to bear in mind, however, that molar solutions of the higher peptides contain larger amounts of substance per unit volume. If we divide the values reported by the number of glycyl residues per molecule we obtain the following values for the dielectric increment per equivalent of glycyl residue: 35, 38, 40, 43, and 39. Evidently the increase in the dielectric constant of water is the same, whether we add a certain amount of triglycine or the same weight of hexaglycine.

The dielectric increments in protein solutions vary widely. Since the concentration of proteins is not usually expressed in moles, the molar dielectric increment, i_M, is replaced by dielectric increment per gram, $i_G = (D_s - D_w)/c$, where c is the concentration in grams per liter. The i_M and i_G values found are shown in Table X (111).

TABLE X

Substance	Dielectric increments per mole, i_M	Dielectric increments per gram, i_G	Substance	Dielectric increments per gram, i_G
Glycine	22.6	0.30	Ovalbumin	0.1
Alanine	23.2	0.26	Gliadin	0.1
Valine	25	0.21	Serum albumin	0.17
Leucine	25	0.19	Insulin	0.3
Diglycine	70.6	0.54	Carboxyhemoglobin	0.33
Triglycine	113	0.60	Zein	0.4
Tetraglycine	159	0.65	Edestin	0.7
Pentaglycine	215	0.71	Serum pseudoglobulin	1.1
Hexaglycine	239	0.65	Lactoglobulin	1.5

Calculating the dielectric increments of amino acids per gram of amino acid, we find values between 0.18 and 0.36, *i.e.*, values of the same order of magnitude as those of some of the proteins. It is difficult to interpret the fact that the dielectric constant of water is increased to approximately the same extent by 1 g. of protein as by 1 g. of an amino acid. It seems to be due to two compensating effects. In one case we have in a given unit weight a large number of small dipoles (amino acids), and in the other a small number of large dipoles (proteins). The larger the dipole moment, the larger the dielectric constants to be expected.

The magnitude of the *dipole moment* of α-amino acids can be estimated from the distance between the positively and the negatively charged groups. This distance is approximately 3 Å (3×10^{-8} cm.). The charge of an electron is 4.8×10^{-10} electrostatic unit. Hence, the dipole moment will be roughly 15×10^{-18} electrostatic unit, *i.e.* 15 Debye. Since the distance between positive and negative charge is the same in all α-amino acids, it is not surprising that dielectric increments of the same order of magnitude have been found in most of the amino acids.

As they occur in protein molecules, only a few of the amino acids contain free positive or negative groups. To a first approximation it can be assumed that, of ten amino acids, one has a positively charged group and one a negatively charged group. Hence, the number of charges in 1 g. protein is approximately one tenth of those present in 1 g. of an amino acid mixture. Since the dielectric increment per gram of proteins is not very different from that of amino acids, it is necessary to assume that the distances between the charges are larger. In this case high dipole moments will again result. One must not assume, however, that all the positive charges are located at one side of the protein molecule and all negative charges at the opposite side. If this were so, dielectric increments much higher than these observed would result; the values which are observed indicate a fairly high degree of electrical symmetry in the protein molecules (112).

The dielectric constant of protein solutions, which obviously varies with the pH, will be greatest in the isoelectric range of the protein, because here the electrical charge of the protein is at a maximum (see Chapter V, Sect. B). The dielectric constant will also be affected by the frequency of the applied electrical field. Since it is possible to get information about the axial ratio of protein molecules by examining them at different frequencies, the principle underlying this method will be briefly discussed.

If a polar molecule is placed in an electrical field, the molecule will become oriented, its positive pole shifting in the direction of the externa negative pole, and the negative pole of the molecule shifting toward the external positive pole (Fig. 28). If the polar molecule is spherical and if the distance of the poles from the center is equal, a revolution of the molecule around its center will result, as shown in Fig. 28 by I*a* and I*b*. If, however, the shape of the polar molecule is nonspherical, the molecule as a whole will yield to the electrostatic forces exerted on its two poles and it will be oriented as shown in Fig. 28 by II*a* and II*b*.

The relaxation time, *i.e.*, the time that will be necessary for the completion of such movements can be determined by increasing the frequency of the external alternating electrical field (107). When the frequency exceeds a certain limiting value, the molecule can no longer alter its position rapidly enough. Above this frequency the molecule does not contribute to the dielectric increment of the solution. The "*relaxation time*" is short for small molecules and long for large molecules. For the small water dipoles the relaxation time is approximately 10^{-11} sec.; for amino acids it is 10^{-10} sec., and for proteins 10^{-6} to 10^{-8} sec. If the frequency of the external alternating field is 10^3 cycles per sec. (wave length 3×10^7 cm.) amino acids and proteins give the dielectric increments reported above. At frequencies of 10^7 cycles per second (wave length 3×10^3 cm.) and above, however, proteins do not increase the dielectric constant of water. In fact, a slight decrease is observed because that portion of the water bound by the protein is unable to follow the oscillations of the alternating field (107).

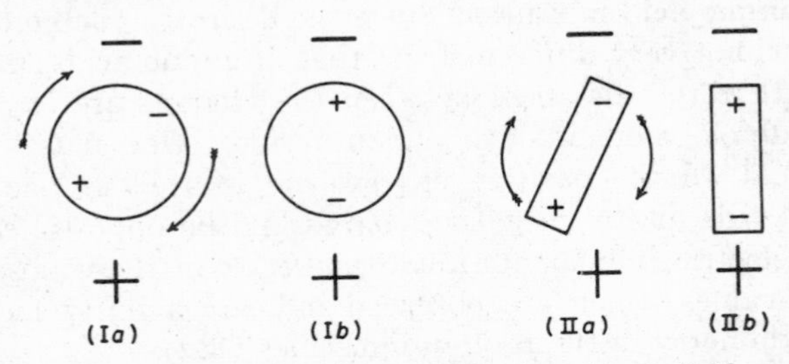

FIG. 28. Orientation of dipoles in an electric field.

By varying the frequencies from high to low the critical frequency corresponding to the relaxation time of the molecule can be determined. If the critical frequency is n, the relaxation time $t = 1/2\pi n$, and the molecular volume $V_M = RTt/3\eta$, where η is the viscosity of the solution. If the particles are not spherical but ellipsoidal two different relaxation times will be found, one of them corresponding to rotation around the short axis, the other corresponding to rotation around the long axis. By determining these two values the axial ratio, a/b, of proteins in their aqueous solutions has been estimated. The values obtained for a/b, neglecting hydration, are (109,111,113,113*a*):

Serum albumin	6	Ovalbumin	5
Horse serum pseudoglobulin	9	Edestin	9
Carboxyhemoglobin	1.6	Zein	7
Lactoglobulin	4		

The axial ratios calculated in this way are approximate values based on the simplifying assumption that the protein molecules are ellipsoids of revolution. The molecules are probably not strictly ellipsoidal in shape; those of hemoglobin have been shown to be cylinders with slightly convex bases (1*b*).

The dipoles represented by I*a* and I*b*, and II*a* and II*b* in Figure 28 are permanent dipoles. Actually, however, all molecules, including even typical nonpolar ones, become dipoles when placed in an external electrical field. This is due to the shift of their electrons toward the external positive pole and the analogous shift of their positive nuclei toward the negative pole. We call the dipoles which arise in an external electrical field "*induced dipoles.*" The total dipole moment of proteins, as well as that of other molecules, is due in part to dipole induction.

In the foregoing discussion the protein molecules have been dealt with as though they were rigid bodies with fixed dipole moments. One has to consider, however, the possibility that some of the peptide chains inside the globular molecule possess a certain freedom of vibration or of rotation and that the relaxation time of these polar elements is lower than that of the macromolecule as a whole (114). These groups might possibly contribute to the dielectric increments observed in the range of intermediate frequencies. It is evident from this discussion that we are as yet unable to make any positive statements concerning the distribution of the electrical charges within globular protein molecules. Although the low values of dielectric increments indicate that this distribution is fairly uniform, differences exist between the electrical charge of the molecular surface and that of the interior of the globular protein particle. Differences up to 0.78 pH units have been observed between pH_s, the pH of the molecular surface, and pH_b, the pH value of the bulk of the protein molecule (115).

By examining the reactions taking place between proteins and macromolecular counterions, it is possible to get information concerning the distribution of ionic groups between the surface and interior of the protein particle. Thus, it has been found that globulins give precipitates with the strongly basic protamines in neutral solutions, while albumins are not precipitated under the same conditions (116). It has been concluded that globulins contain negatively charged groups (exo-groups) in their surface, while the negative charges of albumins are located in the interior of the corpuscular molecules (endo-groups). While both the ionic endo-groups and exo-groups react with counterions of small dimensions such as the hydrogen ion, only the exo-groups are accessible to large counterions. This provides a means of differentiating between endo-groups and exo-groups.

L. Denaturation of Proteins (117). The irreversible coagulation of egg white on heating is a phenomenon familiar to all. Similar changes can be brought about not only by other physical means, such as vigorous shaking or stirring, and irradiation with ultraviolet light or ultrasonic waves, but also by the action of acids, bases, organic solvents, salts of heavy metals, by urea, guanidine, salicylates, detergents, and other compounds. In all these reactions the proteins lose their original solubility; in most instances they become insoluble at their isoelectric range. Collagen, however, becomes soluble if heated with water. We call the changed protein "*denatured*" in contrast to the original "native" protein. Denaturation is frequently accompanied by a loss of the biological activity of the protein; enzymes lose their catalytic activity, hormones their physiological action, and antibodies their ability to combine with antigens. These changes do not always run parallel to the physicochemical changes. Evidently, denaturation is a complex phenomenon. One would hardly expect that the same kind of alteration is brought about by the action of agents so different as urea, sulfuric acid, and heat. Consequently, to speak merely of "denatured ovalbumin" is inadequate; the method of denaturation should be designated.

The phenomenon of denaturation has been explained in a variety of ways. Denaturation by heat was regarded as typical of denaturation in general and this commanded the earliest attention. It was first proposed that heat causes a dehydration of the protein molecule or an establishment of peptide linkages between some of the free amino and carboxyl groups. In addition, the possibility of the reverse reaction, the cleavage of peptide bonds by heat, was also considered possible. Each of these assumptions can be tested by *dilatometry;* since hydration is accompanied by a volume decrease (see Chapter III, Sect. B), dehydration would be revealed by an increase of the total volume. An increase is also to be expected when peptide bonds are formed, because in the reaction:

$$R \cdot NH_2 + HOOC \cdot R' \rightarrow R \cdot NH \cdot CO \cdot R' + H_2O$$

water is liberated. Dilatometric measurements show, however, that denaturation by heat is not accompanied by any noticeable change in volume (118,119). The hydration of denatured proteins in humid air is only slightly lower than that of native proteins; their water-binding power is of the same order of magnitude (23,120).

The first reasonable *theory of denaturation* was advanced by Wu (121). In this theory it was proposed that denaturation consists of a rearrangement of the peptide chains in the protein molecule due to rupture by the denaturing agent of the weak bonds which hold these chains together. Applying these concepts of Wu to the picture outlined in the preceding sections we may safely say that denaturation consists of an alteration of the specific internal structure of the protein, wherein the closely folded peptide chains unfold. The particular mode of denaturation will determine whether the disrupted peptide chains remain in the unfolded state (II), whether they are refolded to give the original specific pattern (I), or whether there will result some other pattern (III) different from the original internal structure (see Fig. 29).

If we consider the phenomenon of denaturation from the standpoint of energetics it is apparent that an energy barrier protects the native protein from denaturation by the thermal agitation of the peptide chains. When this barrier is overcome by the denaturing agent, the peptide chains will be released and will then assume shapes consistent with their bulk and electrical charge, as well as consistent with the mechanical stress which is dependent, in turn, upon adjacent parts of the protein molecule and on the impact of molecules of the solvent (121*a*). Obviously the extent of denaturation can vary from slight structural changes to complete rearrangement of the peptide chains.

That denaturation is accompanied by unfolding of the peptide chains is indicated by the more intensive *color reactions* given by denatured

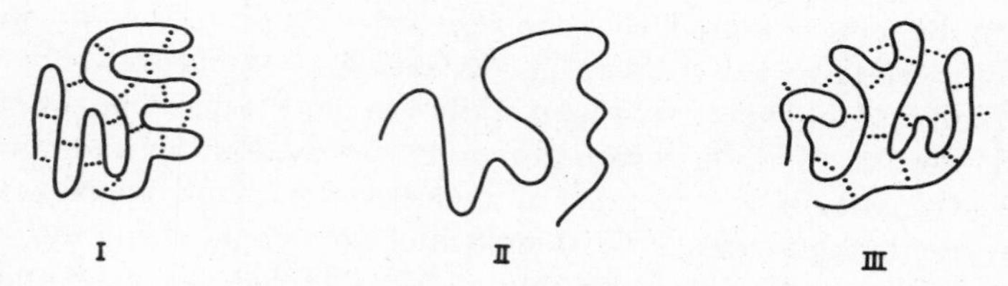

FIG. 29. Diagram of denaturation.

protein than by the same protein in the native state. This was first shown for the sulfhydryl groups of cysteine and the dithio groups of cystine (122). By the nitroprusside test, by titration with ferricyanide (34), by acetylation (123), and by polarography (124) more sulfhydryl and disulfide groups are found in the denatured than in the native protein. Similarly the denatured protein gives more intensive color reactions for tyrosine with phosphomolybdic acid (125,126) and with the diazo reagent (127), for arginine with Sakaguchi's reagent (128), and combines with larger amounts of iodine (129). While only 12 ε-amino groups of lysine combine with dinitrofluorobenzene in native lactoglobulin, all 31 groups combine after denaturation of the protein (130). All these observations support the view that some of the reactive groups of the native protein molecule are inaccessible to the different reagents, but become accessible through the unfolding of the peptide chains.

The *resistance of some native proteins to trypsin,* as compared with the ready tryptic hydrolysis of the same proteins in the denatured state (131) is to be explained on a similar basis. The points of attack for the enzyme become accessible by the loosening of the tight peptide structure of the native protein (132,132*a*). The slow hydrolysis of native proteins by trypsin is probably due to the cleavage of traces of denatured protein, so that the equilibrium "native protein $\rightleftharpoons$ denatured protein" is continually disturbed and shifted to the right (133).

A rearrangement of the peptide chains on denaturation is also indicated by an increase in flow birefringence (133*a*), by a shift of the isoelectric point toward higher pH values (134), and by a loss of the property to combine with acidic dyes (135). The conversion of Congo red to Congo blue at pH 1–2 is inhibited by denatured, but not by native, albumins (135*a*).

Denaturation is in some instances accompanied by the formation of a large protein aggregate, while in other cases the molecule is split into subunits. Osmometric measurements by Burk (135*b*) have shown that hemoglobin, casein, and edestin undergo disaggregation when they are denatured by concentrated solutions of urea. The molecular weights of the split products are 34,300, 33,600, and 49,500, respectively, while the molecular weight of native hemoglobin is 68,000 and that of edestin 212,000. Serum albumin, serum globulin, and ovalbumin had the same molecular weight in water and in concentrated urea solutions. On the other hand, aggregates of 5–20 molecules are formed when ovalbumin is denatured by acids, alkali, or heat (136). Molecules of hemocyanin are cleaved into halves or eighths when they are exposed to slight changes of pH or of salt concentration (136*a*), or to ultrasonic waves (137). Likewise, lactoglobulin molecules of molecular weight 35,000, or insulin molecules dissociate into halves when the protein is spread as a monomolecular film on aqueous salt solutions (138). The dissociation of insulin molecules can be prevented by cupric salts (138*a*).

That the specific structure of native proteins is altered on denaturation is evident from the change in serological specificity. Denatured ovalbumin combines only with 1–2% of the amount of antibodies bound by native ovalbumin (136,139).

It is not surprising that the complicated specific arrangement of the peptide chains in the native protein molecule can be disturbed by agents of different types. Almost any physical or chemical agent will be able to alter the labile structure of the native protein. The denaturing action of mineral acids and of alkali hydroxides is explained by their action on the ionic groups of the proteins. Mineral acids convert the negative $—COO^-$ groups into —COOH groups, so that the salt bridges, $—COO^- \ldots H_3N^+—$, are cleaved and the peptide chains unfold; the positive charges are similarly abolished by added alkali. The unfolding of the protein in acid and in alkaline solutions is indicated by a considerable increase in the viscosity of the solution (118). If the added acid or alkali is neutralized the protein is reconverted to its amphoteric state, whereupon some of the original salt bridges will be re-established. However, some of the positive groups will combine with negative groups other than those to which they were bound originally. Moreover, some of the positive and negative groups at the surface of the rearranged particles may combine with oppositely charged groups belonging to other protein molecules, so that *intermolecular salt bridges* will be formed, thus accounting for the formation of large insoluble aggregates of protein molecules, *i.e.*, for the coagulation of the denatured protein (119).

If denaturation is brought about by *heat*, the protein remains in the zwitterionic state and the original salt bridges are split by the thermal movement of the peptide chains. New intramolecular and intermolecular salt bridges are formed and as a result the protein coagulates (see p. 132). The peptide chains cannot unfold unless water flows into the space between the chains. Therefore, dry proteins are more resistant to heat than proteins in solution. For the same reasons concentrated protein solutions are more stable than dilute solutions. Crystals of serum albumin maintain their crystalline shape when they are heated (140).

Denaturation by vigorous *shaking* or *stirring* is due to the formation of a foam and consists essentially of *surface* denaturation in the protein films extending over the air bubbles constituting the foam. In discussing the spreading of proteins in surface films it was shown that this spreading is accompanied by a total unfolding of the peptide chains and the formation of a thin layer, whose height corresponds to the transverse diameter of one peptide chain (see Chapter VI, p. 100). It is understandable, therefore, that all the sulfhydryl groups will become accessible on spreading and that all can be titrated with ferricyanide (141). On the other hand, denatured proteins cannot be spread as readily as native proteins in monomolecular films since the intramolecular and intermolecular cohesion of their groups is so strong that it is not overcome by the forces which cause spreading of the film (142). If the denatured protein is dissolved, however, it frequently forms monomolecular films. The ability of denatured proteins to form films is also increased by their brief exposure to the action of trypsin (143).

Dry native proteins are denatured when their powder is vigorously ground (144). Denaturation is here, probably, due to the mechanical deformation or disruption of the peptide chains. While many proteins remain in the native state when their solutions are frozen and thawed repeatedly, the solubility of lipoproteins (113*a*) and the biological properties of some antibody proteins are affected by such a treatment (23). The problem of a denaturation by freezing is very important for the technology of frozen food (145).

Denaturation by ultraviolet *radiation* is a complicated reaction. It is clear that only that radiation which is absorbed can have an effect on proteins. As mentioned above (Sect. J) ultraviolet radiation is absorbed mainly by the aromatic rings of tyrosine, phenylalanine, and tryptophan and the absorption curve of proteins is not very different from that of the hydrolyzate (Fig. 27, p. 120). Actually it has been found that peptide bonds adjacent to the aromatic rings are the ones split by photolysis (146). The effective wave lengths are those absorbed by the aromatic amino acids, *i.e.*, approximately 2700 Å. The quantum yield found in such experiments is very low; it was only 0.0025 when pepsin was inactivated by light of the wave length 2537 Å (146*a*). In other words, only one out of 400 absorbed quanta was effective. While light of wave length 2700–2800 Å acts in the same way in aerobic and anaerobic experiments, radiation of wave lengths between 3000 and 4000 Å causes photoxidation of proteins (147).

Similar complications due to oxidation present themselves when proteins are exposed to ultrasonic treatment. The ultrasonic waves act in three different ways: (*1*) by mechanical agitation, (*2*) by thermal effects, and (*3*) by production of oxygen from water (148). The rings of the aromatic amino acids are destroyed by ultrasonic waves (148). While ultrasonic waves of low frequencies cause disaggregation, waves of high frequencies lead to the formation of insoluble aggregates (148*a*).

The most interesting denaturing agents are those substances which are neutral and apparently indifferent such as *urea,* some acid amides, and certain guanidine derivatives. Urea is neither acidic nor basic; it is not toxic or surface active. It is, however, one of the few substances which increase the dielectric constant of water. One has to conclude, therefore, that urea is a dipole and that in aqueous solutions the nonpolar normal structure, $NH_2{\cdot}CO{\cdot}NH_2$ is converted into the polar form (149), $NH_2{-}\overset{-}{C}\overset{-}{O}{=}\overset{+}{N}H_2$. The denaturing action of concentrated solutions of urea is probably due to the formation of hydrogen bonds with the peptide linkages of the peptide chains. Apparently the small polar urea molecules are driven by their thermal movements as wedges between the peptide chains, cleaving the hydrogen bonds and being bound to the liberated peptide linkages by the formation of new hydrogen bonds; this is shown by the following formulas where the long horizontal lines represent two parallel peptide chains.

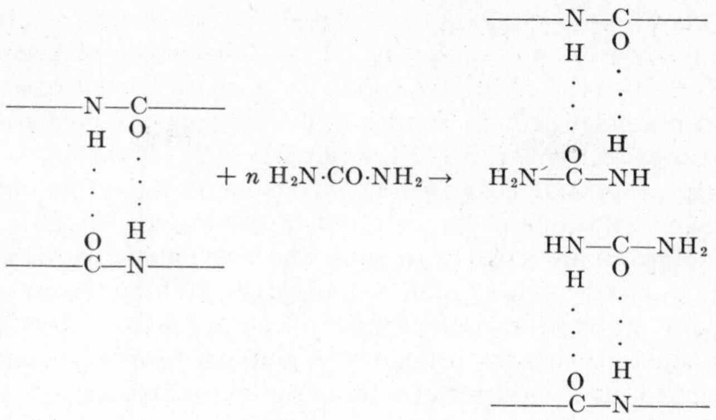

```
                                                ———N—C———
                                                   H  O
                                                   .  .
  ———N—C———                                        .  .
     H  O                                          .  .
     .  .                                          O  H
     .  .    + n H2N·CO·NH2 →                 H2N—C—NH
     .  .
     O  H                                     HN—C—NH2
  ———C—N———                                     H  O
                                                   .  .
                                                   .  .
                                                   .  .
                                                   O  H
                                                ———C—N———
```

In this way the peptide chains are unfolded and the protein denatured. The concentration of the urea solutions used is 40–60%. Similar effects are produced by acid amides (150), whose formula, $R{\cdot}CO{\cdot}NH_2$, is analogous to that of urea which in turn can be considered the diamide of carbonic acid. Denaturation of lactoglobulin by urea takes place very rapidly at 6°C., but more slowly at higher temperatures up to 37°C. (151). The reasons for this peculiar behavior remain obscure.

It has been noted above that several proteins are split by urea into smaller subunits, indicating that the subunits of the macromolecule are held together by hydrogen bonds; according to the classical concepts of chemistry we have to designate these subunits as the true molecules, while the larger units, which are at present called molecules, should be called micelles or multimolecular complexes (152). This view is certainly justified when the "subunits" have the same biological properties as the total complex. Frequently, however, the cleavage of the large complexes into subunits is accompanied by a loss of certain biological activities.

Denaturation frequently goes hand in hand with a drastic alteration in the solubility of the protein. If the denaturing agent is removed and the pH of the solution is near the isoelectric point of the denatured protein, the protein will generally coagulate. It was previously mentioned that *coagulation* is due to the formation of intermolecular salt bridges between ionic groups which are displaced to the surface of the particle through the unfolding of the peptide chains. This supposition is supported by the finding that the basic protamines combine with denatured albumins but not with native albumins (116). In Figure 30, state I shows the native protein molecule containing only *intra*molecular salt bridges. II shows three denatured protein molecules linked to each other by *inter*molecular salt bridges. The figure shows the three-dimensional reaction actually taking place, in a two-dimensional diagram.

The view that coagulation is caused by salt bridges between ionic groups is, however, not shared by all authors; some of them attribute the insolubility of denatured protein to a spatial redistribution of the polar and nonpolar groups, resulting in the transfer of nonpolar, hydrophobic groups to the surface of the particle (121,153,154).

Denaturation and coagulation of certain proteins are inhibited by concentrated solutions of glucose and of other sugars (155). Coagulation of serum albumin by heating is also prevented by the addition of alkali salts of fatty acids (156), anionic dyes such as Congo red (135*a*), urea, and certain other substances. The action of these substances might be due to their adsorption on the globular protein particles, so that the protein forms the center of a large soluble complex.

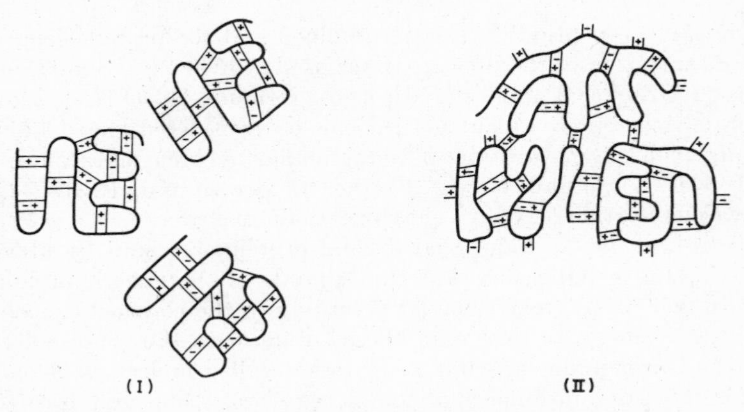

FIG. 30. Intramolecular and intermolecular salt bridges (119).

It seems that denaturation is inhibited to a certain extent by a high viscosity of the solvent, because this retards the movements of the peptide chains and their unfolding. Denaturation is also suppressed by high pressures (157).

The denaturation by sodium hydroxide of the hemoglobins of different species takes place at very different rates. While human hemoglobin is denatured to 50% by 0.05 N sodium hydroxide in 20–30 sec., 50% denaturation of beef hemoglobin requires many hours (158). Denaturation of these two hemoglobins by heat or by hydrochloric acid occurs, however, at the same rate (159). These observations are explained on the basis that the different denaturing agents attack different groups of the protein molecule and produce different end products (160).

Sometimes a reversal of denaturation is observed when the denaturing agent is removed or when the denaturing reaction is otherwise brought to a halt. Thus some enzyme proteins display no loss of activity if their heat-treated solutions are cooled again (see Chapter XII, Sect. H) (161). *Renaturation* has also been observed in hemoglobin (162). Although the behavior of the renatured proteins is very similar to that of the original native proteins, slight differences are revealed by sensitive methods (163). Thus renatured proteins are split by enzymes in the same way that denatured enzymes are split (132*a*). Their solubility, crystalline shape, and electrophoretic mobility are slightly different from those of native proteins (164). Renatured hemoglobin is cleaved by sodium hydroxide at a much higher rate than native hemoglobin (165). All this shows that renaturation is not complete. From the statistical point of view a complete renaturation, *i.e.*, a complete restoration of every minute detail of the original structure, is highly improbable. In a macromolecule of the size of the protein molecule an endless number of energetically equivalent constellations is possible. If the constellation of the peptide chains in the native protein molecule is very stable and if it imposes less strain and distortion upon the peptide chains than any other constellation, most of the peptide chains will return to their original position when the denaturing action ceases.

Almost complete reversion to the native state is observed in a protein prepared from soybeans which has the properties of a trypsin inhibitor (166). In the temperature range of 35–50°C. the solution of this protein contains a mixture of native and denatured protein; the ratio "native protein: denatured protein" depends on the temperature and decreases when the system is heated; the denatured protein differs from the native protein by its insolubility at pH 4.5; since the mutual conversion of native and denatured proteins takes place very slowly, they can be separated by precipitation (166). Another reversible denaturation phenomenon is observed when an aqueous solution of Bence-Jones protein is heated; the solutions of the protein are transparent at room temperature and above 60°C., but are turbid between 45 and 60°.

It seems that in these cases the constellation of the peptide chains in the native state is so stable that almost complete reversion to the native state takes place at low temperatures. From the physicochemical point of view such behavior is comparable to the tautomerism of organic molecules (167); it is well known that the equilibrium between two or more tautomeric forms frequently depends on the temperature of the system. Renaturation, according to this viewpoint, would be nothing but the re-establishment of an equilibrium after cessation of the disturbing action. If the native constellation of the peptide chains is unstable in comparison to other constellations, the peptide chains will retain the arrangement of the denatured molecule. Since each of the protein molecules contains many hundreds of amino acids, innumerable possibilities for partial denaturation and renaturation exist. In other words, the constellation of the peptide chains of denatured and also of renatured proteins varies between that of the native protein and those of numerous more or less denatured proteins.

The view has been advanced that denaturation is an "all-or-none" reaction, *i.e.*, that denaturation is always complete and never partial (168). It is difficult to test this assumption experimentally, because there are only a few properties of denatured proteins which can be measured quantitatively. The insolubility of denatured proteins cannot be used as a criterion, because native protein molecules are adsorbed by the denatured coagulate and, furthermore, coagulation is inhibited by the protective action of the soluble protein. Since we have no simple reliable methods for deciding whether a partly denatured protein solution contains partly denatured protein molecules or whether it is a mixture of native and fully denatured molecules, this question is still under discussion (117).

It is evident from the foregoing that denaturation can be considered from the viewpoint of statistics or energetics. The energetics of denaturation can be treated quantitatively by applying the principles of *thermodynamics*. According to the second law of thermodynamics, for each reaction we can write the equation:

$$\Delta H = \Delta F + T\Delta S \tag{1}$$

where ΔH is the heat of reaction, *i.e.*, the difference between the heat content of the system before and after the reaction. If we call the heat content of the native protein H_N, and that of the denatured protein H_D, the heat of denaturation is $\Delta H = H_D - H_N$. It is customary to represent ΔH by a positive value when energy is taken up by the reacting system, and to write negative ΔH values when heat is given off during the reaction. A positive ΔH value, accordingly, indicates an endothermic reaction, while negative ΔH values represent exothermic reactions.

The heat content of a substance at the absolute temperature $T = t°K$ is the heat required to bring the substance from the temperature $T = 0°K$ to the temperature $T = t°K$. Obviously this difference in heat content cannot be measured directly. We can calculate, however, the heat of denaturation, ΔH, from the equilibrium constants K_1 and K_2 measured at two different temperatures, T_1 and T_2. If the concentrations of native and denatured protein at equilibrium are $[N]$ and $[D]$, respectively, the equilibrium constant of the denaturation is $K = [D]/[N]$. If, at the two temperatures T_1 and T_2, the equilibrium constants are K_1 and

K_2, ΔH can be calculated from van't Hoff's equation:

$$\Delta H = R \ln (K_1/K_2) \left(\frac{T_1 \times T_2}{T_1 - T_2}\right) = 2.3R \log (K_1/K_2) \left(\frac{T_1 \times T_2}{T_1 - T_2}\right) \quad (2)$$

Obviously, such a procedure is possible only in those cases in which a reversible equilibrium between native and denatured protein is established. Kunitz (166) has applied this method to the reversible denaturation of the trypsin inhibitor, and has found that ΔH is +57,000 cal. per mole protein.

Another method, used by Kistiakowsky (169), consists of measuring calorimetrically the heat of the reactions (A) and (B):

$$\text{Native protein} + \text{KOH} \rightarrow \text{denatured alkali proteinate} \quad (A)$$
$$\text{Denatured protein} + \text{KOH} \rightarrow \text{denatured alkali proteinate} \quad (B)$$

If the heat produced by the first reaction is ΔH_A, and that produced by the reaction B is ΔH_B, the difference, $\Delta H_B - \Delta H_A$, is equal to the heat of denaturation. The value found for the denaturation of crystalline pepsin was +15 cal. per gram nitrogen; this corresponds to +85,000 cal. per mole pepsin, when a molecular weight of 35,000 is assumed for pepsin. The heat of denaturation of methemoglobin was of the same order of magnitude (170).

The important result of these investigations is that the *denaturation* of proteins is an *endothermic reaction* and that it is necessary to increase the energy content of the protein in the native state in order to cause denaturation. This is somewhat surprising since one should expect that the oriented labile state of the peptide chains in the native protein corresponds to a higher energy content than the disoriented stable state of the same peptide chains in the denatured protein. In order to understand this discrepancy, it is necessary to discuss the changes of the two other thermodynamic constants, ΔF and ΔS, indicated in equation (1). According to this equation the total change in energy is the arithmetic sum of two other energy differences, ΔF and $T\Delta S$. In analogy to the procedure applied for ΔH, we can write $\Delta F = F_D - F_N$ and $\Delta S = S_D - S_N$, where F is the "free energy" and S the entropy of denaturation, respectively.

It is well known that the molecules of each substance are continuously in motion and that the intensity of this motion depends on the temperature. At a given temperature T, the energy represented by this motion is equal to $T \times S$. If the system contains an excess of energy, this excess, F, can be used to produce work. F is called the *free energy* of the system; it can be converted into electrical, mechanical, or other forms of energy.

The second term in equation (1), corresponding to $T \times S$, cannot be used to produce work because it is the minimum of energy required for the thermal motion of the molecules. If this motion is reduced owing to the mechanism of the reaction taking place, the energy $T \times S$ decreases by $T \times \Delta S$; such a decrease in entropy occurs, for instance, at the freezing point, when a liquid passes into the solid state; conversely energy has to be supplied to a crystalline solid in order to convert it into a liquid at the same temperature; thus, 79 cal. are necessary for the conversion of ice at 0° into water at the same temperature. Since the free energy, F, is the same in both ice and water at 0°, all the energy is consumed in increasing the entropy of the system.

It was believed for a long time that the course of a chemical reaction depends on the sign of ΔH, and that only exothermic reactions could take place without a supply of energy from outside. We know at present that this view is not correct. The direction of chemical reactions depends on the sign of ΔF. Only reactions with a negative ΔF value can proceed spontaneously. We call them exergonic reactions. Since ΔH, according to equation (1) is equal to the sum of ΔF and $T\Delta S$, we also can write:

$$\Delta F = \Delta H - T\Delta S \tag{3}$$

ΔF will be negative if either ΔH is negative and ΔS positive or slightly negative, or if ΔH is positive and ΔS has a high positive value. The latter case is of particular significance in connection with the denaturation of proteins. It was shown above that denaturation is an endothermic reaction, requiring a supply of approximately 10^5 cal. per mole protein. On the other hand, we know that denaturation is brought about very easily, even at room temperature, by a variety of agents such as urea or the detergents. We have to assume that ΔF in these cases is negative because of an increase in entropy and a positive value of the term $T\Delta S$ in equation (3). The process of denaturation would then be of the same type as the melting of ice, namely, an energy-consuming endothermic process which takes place spontaneously because of the increase in entropy.

The change in free energy, ΔF, can be calculated from the equilibrium constant, K, according to equation (4):

$$\Delta F = -RT \ln K = -2.3RT \log K \tag{4}$$

If ΔF and ΔH are known, ΔS can be computed from equation (3). The complete thermodynamic analysis of the reversible denaturation of the crystalline trypsin inhibitor gave for ΔH the value +57,300 cal. per mole and the following values for K and ΔF (166):

Temperature, °C.	30	35	40	45	47	50
$K = [D]/[N]$	0.010	0.042	0.220	0.870	2.03	4.35
$\Delta F = -4.58T \log K$	2780	1920	950	87.5	−450	−950
$\Delta S = \dfrac{\Delta H - \Delta F}{T}$	180	180	180	180	180	180

The table shows that native and denatured protein, in this case, are in a state of complete equilibrium ($\Delta F = 0$) between 45 and 47°C. At lower temperatures the equilibrium is shifted toward the native state, at higher temperatures toward the denatured state. The table also shows that the reaction "native protein → denatured protein" is accompanied by an increase in entropy amounting to 180 cal. per degree per mole. This large increase in entropy is, apparently, the driving force in denaturation, causing ΔF to become negative at higher temperatures, so that denaturation takes place at an increased rate.

If an attempt is made to interpret these results of thermodynamic analysis in terms of molecular kinetics, the process of denaturation can again be compared with the melting of ice. Upon an increase of the temperature the cross-linking hydrogen bonds between peptide chains "melt" so that the released peptide chains acquire a higher thermal motility.

The finding of high values of ΔH, which vary from 10^4 to 10^5, in protein denaturation came as a surprise to the first observers because this large amount of energy corresponds to that required for the splitting of strong covalent bonds and is higher than the heat of reaction observed in many chemical reactions. Thus ΔH for the formation of a peptide bond or an ester bond is approximately 2000–5000 cal. per mole; values of a higher order of magnitude are observed when stable compounds are split into their components; thus, 94,380 cal. are required for the cleavage of one mole of carbon dioxide into carbon and oxygen, and 115,660 cal. for the cleavage of water into hydrogen and oxygen. In order to understand the high values of ΔH resulting in protein denaturation one has to bear in mind that the structure of the native protein molecule is due to a large number of hydrogen bonds (171) between peptide groups, —CO·NH— (see page 117), and to a smaller number of salt bridges between anionic and cationic groups.

The amino acid analysis of pepsin (172) shows that the molecule contains about 300 peptide bonds and that the number of basic amino acids is six per molecule; hence the maximum number of hydrogen bonds between adjacent peptide groups is about 150. The maximum number of salt bridges (six), is so small that it can be neglected in this case. Since the heat of denaturation of pepsin is +85000 cal. per mole, it is approximately 85000/150 cal. per hydrogen bond; if all of the hydrogen bonds were cleaved upon denaturation, this would correspond to an expenditure of 570 cal. per hydrogen bond split. This is much less than the total bond energy of a hydrogen bond, which is approximately 5000 cal. We must not forget, however, that the splitting of a hydrogen bond of the type N—H · · · O═C is followed immediately by the formation of new hydrogen bonds with other parts of the peptide chain or with molecules of the solvent. In the latter case one or more water molecules can be inserted between the imino and the keto group, so that structural arrangements such as that shown in formula (5) result:

```
            H           H
            |           |
N—H · · · O—H · · · O—H · · · O═C        (5)
```

ΔH, in such a case, is the difference of two values ΔH_a and ΔH_b, the first of them representing the energy required for the splitting of the original hydrogen bonds N—H · · · O═C and of hydrogen bonds between solvent molecules, while ΔH_b is the energy released by the formation of the hydrogen bonds shown in formula (5) (173). Most probably denaturation does not involve the cleavage of all the hydrogen bonds present in the native protein molecule; the heat of denaturation will, therefore, be higher than 570 cal. per hydrogen bond.

From the standpoint of kinetics, the equilibrium between native and denatured protein can be considered the over-all result of the forward reaction "$N \rightarrow D$" and the reverse reaction "$D \rightarrow N$." If the velocity constant of the first reaction is k_1, and that of the second reaction, k_2, the equilibrium is represented by the equation $k_1[N] = k_2[D]$, where $[N]$ and $[D]$ are the concentrations of native and denatured protein, respectively, at equilibrium. The equilibrium constant K is $K = k_1/k_2$. The ratio $[D]/[N]$ and the magnitude of K depend on the temperature of the protein solution; at higher temperatures k_1 increases greatly, whereas k_2 increases only slightly; the result is an increase in the ratio k_1/k_2 and a shift of the equilibrium "$N \rightarrow D$" to the right side.

The great influence of the temperature on the velocity of slow reactions is ascribed to the fact that only "activated" molecules are able to react. The "activation energy" can be computed from the classical Arrhenius equation or according to the theory of absolute reaction rates. According to the latter view it is assumed that chemical reactions usually take place in a manner represented diagrammatically in Figure 31. In Figure 31 the energy content of the initial system is H_i, that of the final system, H_f, and that of the activated state, H_a. The heat of activation for the forward reaction, $H_1{}^*$, is obviously $H_a - H_i$; the heat of activation for the reverse reaction, H_2^*, is $H_a - H_f$. Since H_a is certainly larger than both H_i and H_f, the heat of activation will be positive in both cases. In other words, heat must be supplied for both the forward and the reverse reaction. Thus, while we have to heat an ester in order to split it into acid and alcohol, we have also to heat the mixture of acid and alcohol when it is desired to produce an ester. The over-all heat of the reaction, ΔH, is $H_f - H_i$.

The magnitude of the heat of activation is related to the velocity constant and can be computed according to the classical Arrhenius equation:

$$k = Ae^{-E/RT} \tag{6}$$

where k is the velocity constant, A a constant, e, the base of the natural logarithms, E the activation energy, R the gas constant (1.98 cal.), and

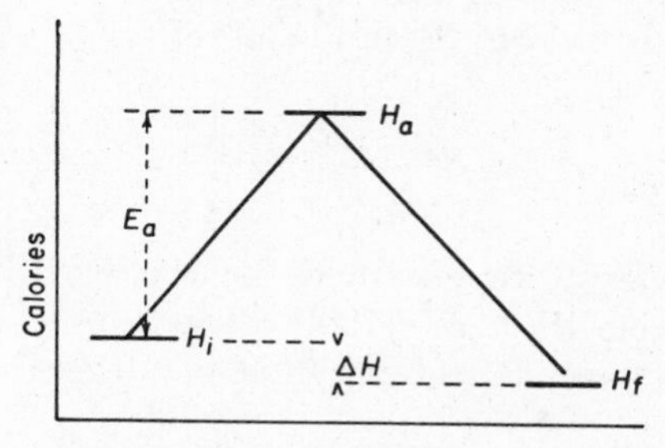

FIG. 31. Diagram of an exothermic reaction.

T, the absolute temperature. By determining the velocity constants, k_m and k_n, at two temperatures, T_m and T_n, the term A can be eliminated:

$$\ln (k_m/k_n) = \frac{E}{R}\left(\frac{1}{T_n} - \frac{1}{T_m}\right) = \frac{E}{R}\left(\frac{T_m - T_n}{T_m \times T_n}\right) \tag{7}$$

$$E = \ln (k_m/k_n) \times R \times \left(\frac{T_m \times T_n}{T_m - T_n}\right) = 2.3R \log (k_m/k_n) \left(\frac{T_m \times T_n}{T_m - T_n}\right) \tag{8}$$

The heat of activation, H^*, is:

$$H^* = E - RT \tag{9}$$

Equation (1), the fundamental equation of thermodynamics, can be applied to each of the activation processes "$N \rightarrow P^*$" and "$D \rightarrow P^*$," where P^* is the activated state of the protein, so that the equations (10) and (11) result:

$$H_1^* = F_1^* + TS_1^* \tag{10}$$

$$H_2^* = F_2^* + TS_2^* \tag{11}$$

where H^*, F^*, and S^* are the heat of activation, the free energy of activation, and the entropy of activation, respectively. Since activation in reactions of the type shown in Figure 31 does not occur spontaneously, H^* and F^* are positive values, while S^* is usually slightly positive or slightly negative.

The magnitude of H^*, F^*, and S^* has been determined by Kunitz (166) for the reversible denaturation of trypsin inhibitor protein. While H^* was determined according to equation (8) and (9), F^* was evaluated from equation (12):

$$F^* = RT\left(\ln \frac{K}{h} + \ln T - \ln k\right) = 4.58T\left(10.318 + \log T - \log k\right) \quad (12)$$

where K is the Boltzmann constant (1.38×10^{-16} erg per degree), h the Planck constant (6.62×10^{-27} erg sec.) and k the velocity constant per second. If F^* is known, S^* can be determined according to equation (13):

$$S^* = \frac{H^* - F^*}{T} \quad (13)$$

The following values were obtained for the trypsin inhibitor: $H_1^* = +55000$ cal. per mole, $H_2^* = -1900$ cal. per mole, $S_1^* = +95$ cal. per mole per degree, $S_2^* = -84$ cal. per mole per degree. From the negative

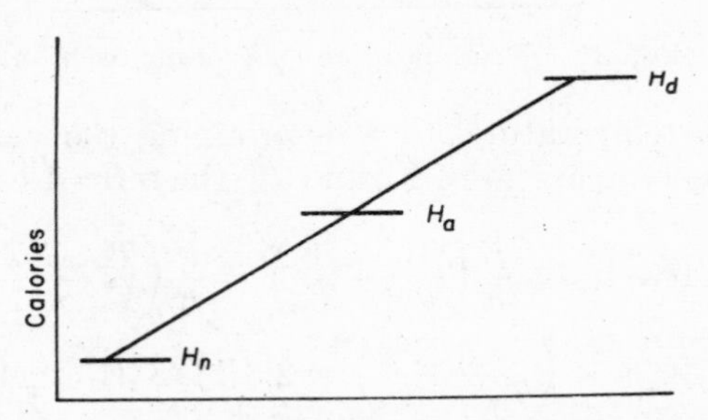

FIG. 32. Thermodynamic changes during protein denaturation.

value of H_2^* it is evident that the denaturation is essentially different from reactions of the type shown in Figure 31, and that it corresponds to the diagram of Figure 32 (174), where H_n, H_a, and H_d are energy contents of native, activated, and denatured protein, respectively. The negative heat of activation, $H_2^* = H_a - H_d$, corresponds thermodynamically to the fact that the conversion of denatured into native protein is more rapid at lower temperatures. The positive value S_1^* is a measure of the increase in disorientation accompanying denaturation.

The denaturation of the trypsin inhibitor has been discussed so extensively because it is the first, and hitherto only, example of protein denaturation which is almost completely reversible. In most other proteins we can neither measure the rate of renaturation nor the magnitude of the equilibrium constant, K. We must content ourselves with measuring k_1, the velocity constant of denaturation. By determining k_1 at two different temperatures we can evaluate E from equation (8), H_1^* from (9), F_1^* from (12), and S^* from (13). The heat of activation for the reaction "native protein $\rightarrow$ denatured protein" found in this way is of the same order of magnitude as the value H_1^* found by Kunitz (166). It varies for different proteins from 10^4 to 10^5 cal., which seems at first sight to be a high value. If we consider, however, the high molecular weight of the proteins, it becomes evident that a value of 100,000 cal. per mole is negligibly small.

Let us assume, for the sake of simplification, that the molecular weight of a protein is 100,000 and that the heat of denaturation is 100,000 cal. per mole. Then the difference between the energy content of 1 g. of the native protein, and 1 g. of the denatured protein will be 1 cal. On the other hand, the complete oxidation of 1 g. glucose to carbon dioxide and water furnishes 3900 cal. Evidently the heat of denaturation is so small that it does not play any role in the energy balances.

Since the state of the peptide chains in the native protein is one of high orientation, while that of the denatured protein is one of random disorientation, the entropy content of denatured protein is higher than that of native protein. The difference between the entropy content of the native and the denatured protein has been called the configurational entropy (175). It is related to the logarithm of the probability and can be calculated if some simplifying assumptions are made. Thus, values of -4.3 to -6.1 entropy units per amino acid residue are obtained for a protein molecule formed by 300–30,000 amino acids of 10–20 different types, when it is assumed that the number of each of the amino acids present is the same. If different numbers of amino acids are present, the entropy value per amino acid residue may increase to about -8 cal. per degree per amino acid residue. For pepsin, whose molecular weight, 35,000, is relatively small, this calculation furnishes an entropy of -5 cal. per degree per amino acid residue, and at $T = 300°$ a value of $300 \times -5 = -1500$ cal. per residue (175). ΔH, on the other hand, is 85,000 cal. per mole, or 300 cal. per amino acid residue. Evidently the term $T\Delta S$ is much larger than ΔH, demonstrating the large increase in entropy which accompanies denaturation.

M. Summary. It is evident from the foregoing sections that our knowledge concerning the internal structure of proteins does not go far beyond the hypotheses advanced by Hofmeister (176) and Fischer (177) as far back as 1902. Both men had proposed the peptide structure of proteins. There is no doubt that fibrous as well as globular proteins consist essentially of peptide chains. While some protein molecules may be formed by a single long peptide chain, proteins containing more than one terminal amino group and carboxyl group have been found. Apparently the molecules of such proteins are formed by more than one peptide chain; we do not yet know, however, whether these chains are linked to each other by dithio bonds of cystine, by means of peptide or ester bonds formed by the carboxyl groups of aspartic or glutamic acid, or by other, unknown linkages. While cyclopeptides formed by 10 or more amino acids have been isolated, it is not yet clear whether such polypeptide rings exist as such in protein molecules.

Physicochemical and serological investigations provide abundant evidence that the molecules of globular proteins have a rigid structure, which remains unaltered when the protein is salted out, crystallized, or dissolved. Proteins are unique in this respect. Rubber, starch, and many of the synthetic macromolecules unfold in solutions and thereby lose the structure of the macromolecule which existed originally in the solid state. The unfolded chain molecules of these substances assume in their solutions an endless number of constellations of approximately the same energy content. They are, therefore, without specificity. The specificity of proteins is due to the maintenance of their internal structure, and this in turn is due to the cross links between the folded peptide chains. It has been shown in the preceding sections that there are three main types of cross links: (*1*) dithio bridges formed by cystine molecules, (*2*) salt bridges formed by the carboxyl groups of aspartic or glutamic acid and by amino groups of lysine or guanido groups of arginine, and (*3*) hydrogen bonds between peptide linkages and between polar groups of the amino acids. If some or all of these cross links are split, the specific internal structure of the protein is lost and denaturation is said to occur (1*a*).

REFERENCES

1*a*. F. Haurowitz, *Experientia* **5,** 347 (1949).
1*b*. T. Boyes-Watson, E. Davidson, M. F. Perutz, *Proc. Roy. Soc. London* **A191,** 83 (1947).
2. H. B. Bull, *Advances in Protein Chem.* **3,** 93 (1947).
3. S. W. Fox, *Advances in Protein Chem.* **2,** 156 (1945).
4. A. C. Chibnall, *Proc. Roy. Soc. London* **B131,** 136 (1942).
5. H. Theorell, Å. Åkeson, *J. Am. Chem. Soc.* **63,** 1804 (1941).
6. H. Neurath, J. P. Greenstein, *Arch. Biochem.* **13,** 117 (1944).
7. R. K. Cannan, *Chem. Revs.* **30,** 395 (1942).

8. S. Edlbacher, *Z. physiol. Chem.* **112,** 80 (1920).
9. J. Herzig and K. Landsteiner, *Biochem. Z.* **61,** 458 (1914).
10. R. M. Herriott, *J. Gen. Physiol.* **19,** 283 (1936).
11. H. K. Barrenscheen, L. Messiner, *Biochem. Z.* **209,** 251 (1929).
12. C. Rimington, *Biochem. J.* **21,** 272 (1927).
12*a*. M. Heidelberger, B. D. Davis, H. P. Treffers, *J. Am. Chem. Soc.* **63,** 498 (1941).
13. S. Goldschmidt, *Z. physiol. Chem.* **183,** 244 (1929).
13*a*. W. L. Hughes, H. A. Saroff, A. L. Carney, *J. Am. Chem. Soc.* **71,** 2476 (1949).
14. F. Sanger and R. R. Porter, *Biochem. J.* **42,** 287 (1948).
15. F. Sanger, *Biochem. J.* **39,** 507 (1946).
15*a*. D. W. Woolley, *J. Biol. Chem.* **179,** 593 (1949).
16. P. Desnuelle, A. Casal, *Biochim. et Biophys. Acta* **2,** 64 (1948).
16*a*. F. Sanger, *Biochemical Society Symposia,* No. 3, p. 28 (1949).
17. H. Jensen and E. Evans, *J. Biol. Chem.* **108,** 1 (1935).
18. J. Roche, M. Reymond, T. Schiller, *Compt. rend.* **219,** 38 (1944).
19. A. H. Tracy, W. F. Ross, *J. Biol. Chem.* **142,** 871 (1942).
20. A. Wormall *et al., Biochem. J.* **40,** 730 (1946).
21. S. Moore, W. H. Stein, J. S. Fruton, *J. Org. Chem.* **11,** 675 (1946).
22. V. Du Vigneaud *et al., J. Am. Chem. Soc.* **70,** 2547 (1948).
23. F. Haurowitz, unpublished experiments.
24. S. Blackburn, H. Philipps, *Biochem. J.* **38,** 171 (1944).
25. S. Goldschmidt, *Ann.* **471,** 1 (1929).
26. J. Roche, M. Mourgue, *Compt. rend.* **218,** 86 (1944).
27. D. W. Woolley, *J. Biol. Chem.* **171,** 443 (1947).
28. F. Haurowitz, M. Tunca, *Biochem. J.* **39,** 443 (1945). F. Haurowitz, S. Tekman, *Bull. faculté mèd. Istanbul* **9,** 225 (1946).
29. H. Fraenkel-Conradt, H. S. Olcott, *J. Biol. Chem.* **161,** 259 (1945).
30. T. B. Johnson, B. H. Nicolet, *J. Am. Chem. Soc.* **33,** 1973 (1911).
31. P. Schlack, W. Kumpf, *Z. physiol. Chem.* **154,** 125 (1926).
32. F. Haurowitz M. Vardar, *Compt. rend. ann. et arch. soc. turq. sci. phys. et Nat.* **11,** 7 (1944).
33. F. Haurowitz, S. Lisie, unpublished experiments; F. Haurowitz *et al.,* Abstracts 112th meeting Am. Chem. Soc. 29C (1947).
34. R. M. Herriott, *Advances in Protein Chem.* **3,** 170 (1947).
35. H. Fraenkel-Conradt, H. S. Olcott, *Chem. Revs.,* **41,** 151 (1947).
36. D. French, J. T. Edsall, *Advances in Protein Chem.* **2,** 277 (1945).
37. E. H. Frieden *et al., J. phys. Chem.* **47,** 10 (1943).
38. E. R. Theis, *J. Biol. Chem.* **157,** 7 (1945).
39. H. Fraenkel-Conradt, H. S. Olcott, *J. Biol. Chem.* **168,** 99 (1947); **174,** 827 (1948); *J. Am. Chem. Soc.* **70,** 2673 (1948).
40. H. Nitschmann, H. Hadorn, *Helv. Chim. Acta* **27,** 299 (1944).
41. K. H. Gustavson, *Kolloid-Z.* **103,** 43 (1943).
42. H. S. Olcott, H. Fraenkel-Conrat, *J. Am. Chem. Soc.* **68,** 1024 (1946); **70,** 2101 (1948).
43. W. H. Mears, H. Sobotka, *J. Am. Chem. Soc.* **61,** 880 (1939).
44. A. Wormall, *J. exptl. med.* **51,** 195 (1930).
45. H. Bauer, E. Strauss, *Biochem. Z.* **211,** 163 (1929).
46. A. Kossell, F. Weiss, *Z. physiol. Chem.* **84,** 1 (1913).
47. K. Landsteiner, H. Lampl, *Biochem. Z.* **86,** 343 (1918).

48. F. Haurowitz, *Z. physiol. Chem.* **248,** 23 (1936).
49. M. Heidelberger, F. E. Kendall, *Proc. Soc. Exptl. Biol. Med.* **26,** 482 (1929).
50. H. Pauly, *Z. physiol. Chem.* **94,** 284 (1915).
51. R. Kapeller-Adler, G. Boxer, *Biochem. Z.* **285,** 55 (1936).
52. H. Eagle, P. Vickers, *J. Biol. Chem.* **114,** 193 (1936).
53. W. C. Boyd, S. B. Hooker, *J. Biol. Chem.* **104,** 329 (1934).
54. E. Abderhalden, *Z. physiol. Chem.* **277,** 248 (1943); **265,** 23 (1940).
55. A. H. Gordon, A. J. P. Martin, R. L. M. Synge, *Biochem. J.* **37,** 92 (1943).
56. E. Waldschmidt-Leitz, G. von Schuckmann, *Ber.* **62,** 1891 (1929).
57. J. P. Greenstein, *J. Biol. Chem.* **112,** 517 (1936).
58. A. Fodor, S. Kuk-Meiri, *Enzymologia* **12,** 101 (1947).
59. R. J. Block, D. B. Jones, C. E. F. Gersdorff, *J. Biol. Chem.* **105,** 667 (1934).
60. M. Pader, D. Melnick, B. L. Oser, *J. Biol. Chem.* **172,** 763 (1948).
61. G. Schramm, G. Thumm, *Z. Naturforsch.* **3, b,** 218 (1948).
62. A. Fodor, N. Lichtenstein, *Enzymologia* **6,** 201 (1939).
63. J. E. Tietzman, D. G. Doherty, M. Bergmann, *J. Biol. Chem.* **151,** 387 (1943).
64. R. L. M. Synge, *Bull. soc. chim. biol.* **27,** 286 (1945).
65. E. Fredericq, V. Desreux, *Bull. soc. chim. biol.* **29,** 100 (1947).
66. N. Troensegaard, The Structure of the Protein Molecule. Munksgaard, Copenhagen 1944.
67. D. Wrinch, *Proc. Roy. Soc. London* **A160,** 59 (1937); **161,** 505 (1937); *Science* **107,** 445 (1948).
68. D. Crowfoot, *Nature* **135,** 591, 891 (1935).
69. F. Haurowitz, *Z. physiol. Chem.* **256,** 28 (1938).
70. H. Neurath, *J. Phys. Chem.* **44,** 296 (1940).
71. L. Pauling, C. Niemann, *J. Am. Chem. Soc.* **61,** 1860 (1939).
71*a*. F. Arndt, *Z. angew. Chem.* **61,** 397 (1949).
72. F. Haurowitz, F. Münzberg, *Z. physiol. Chem.* **256,** 271 (1938).
73. M. L. Anson, *J. Gen. Physiol.* **25,** 355 (1942).
74. P. Desnuelle, A. Casal, S. Antonin, *Bull. soc. chim. biol.* **29,** 694 (1947).
75. F. Haurowitz, F. Bursa, A. Tümer, unpublished experiments.
76. W. B. Hanby, H. N. Rydon, *Biochem. J.* **40,** 297 (1946).
77. H. Mosimann, R. Signer, in The Svedberg. Almqvist and Wiksalls, Upsala, 1944, p. 464.
78. F. Haurowitz, F. Bursa, *Biochem. J.* **44,** 509 (1949).
79. A. J. P. Martin, R. L. M. Synge, *Advances in Protein Chem.* **2,** 4 (1945).
80. A. H. Corwin, C. I. Damarel, *J. Am. Chem. Soc.* **65,** 1974 (1943).
81. F. Haurowitz, M. Bilen, unpublished experiments.
82. R. Consden, A. H. Gordon, A. J. P. Martin, R. L. M. Synge, *Biochem. J.* **41,** 596 (1947).
83. F. Sanger, *Nature* **162,** 491 (1948).
84. M. Bergmann, C. Niemann, *J. Biol. Chem.* **118,** 301 (1937); **122,** 577 (1938).
85. H. B. Bull, J. Hahn, *J. Am. Chem. Soc.* **70,** 2128, 2132 (1948).
86. J. Roche, M. Mourgue, *Compt. rend.* **218,** 86 (1944); *Bull. soc. chim. biol.* **26,** 1010 (1946).
87. A. H. Gordon, A. J. P. Martin, R. L. M. Synge, *Biochem. J.* **35,** 1369 (1941).
87*a*. R. Consden, H. H. Gordon, A. J. P. Martin, *Biochem. J.* **44,** 548 (1949).
87*b*. J. Bateman, in P. Hoeber, Physical Chemistry of Cells. Blakiston, Philadelphia 1946, p. 97.
88. E. N. Lassettre, *Chem. Revs.* **20,** 259 (1937).

88*a*. W. M. Latimer, W. H. Rodebush, *J. Am. Chem. Soc.* **42,** 1419 (1920).
89. G. Briegleb, *Z. Elektrochem.* **50,** 35 (1944).
90. J. L. Crammer, A. Neuberger, *Biochem. J.* **37,** 302 (1943).
91. M. Davies, *Ann. Repts. Progress in Chem. Chem. Soc. London* **43,** 1 (1947).
92. J. D. Bernal, *Trans. Faraday Soc.* **36,** 886 (1940).
93. M. L. Huggins, *Ann. Rev. Biochem.* **11,** 28 (1943).
94. K. Wirtz, *Z. Naturforsch.* **2a,** 264 (1947).
95. H. Lundgren, A. Stein, W. Koorn, R. A. O'Connell, *J. Phys. Chem.* **52,** 180 (1948).
96. A. E. Mirsky, L. Pauling, *Proc. Natl. Acad. Sci. U. S.* **22,** 439 (1936).
97. G. E. Perlmann, L. G. Longsworth, *J. Am. Chem. Soc.* **70,** 2719 (1948).
97*a*. S. H. Armstrong *et al.*, *J. Am. Chem. Soc.* **69,** 1747 (1947).
98. W. Pauli, E. Valko, Kolloidchemie der Proteine. T. Steinkopff, Dresden, 1933.
99. H. J. Almquist, D. M. Greenberg, *J. Biol. Chem.* **93,** 167 (1931); **105,** 519 (1934).
100. C. R. Smith, *J. Am. Chem. Soc.* **41,** 135 (1919).
101. G. Gróh, L. Szélyes, M. Weltner, *Biochem. Z.* **290,** 24 (1937).
102. F. C. Smith, *Proc. Roy. Soc. London* **B104,** 198 (1929).
103. F. Haurowitz, T. Astrup, *Nature* **143,** 118 (1939).
103*a*. I. M. Klotz *et al.*, *J. Am. Chem. Soc.* **71,** 1615 (1949).
103*b*. E. J. Ambrose *et al.*, *Nature* **163,** 859 (1949).
104. A. M. Buswell, R. C. Gore, *J. Phys. Chem.* **46,** 575 (1942).
105. J. D. Bath, J. W. Ellis, *J. Phys. Chem.* **45,** 204 (1941).
106. J. L. Oncley, *Chem. Revs.* **30,** 433 (1942).
107. J. Wyman, Jr., *J. Biol. Chem.* **90,** 443 (1931). J. Wyman, Jr., E. N. Ingalls *ibid.* **147,** 297 (1943).
108. J. T. Edsall, in E. J. Cohn and J. T. Edsall, Proteins, Amino Acids and Peptides. Reinhold, New York, 1943, p. 140.
109. J. L. Oncley, in E. J. Cohn and J. T. Edsall, Proteins, Amino Acids and Peptides. Reinhold, New York, 1943, p. 543.
110. J. Wyman, Jr., T. L. McMeekin, *J. Am. Chem. Soc.* **55,** 908 (1933).
111. J. L. Oncley, *J. Phys. Chem.* **44,** 1103 (1940).
112. S. Arrhenius, *Nova Acta Regiae Soc. Sci. Upsaliensis* [4], **12,** (5) (1940).
113. E. J. Cohn, W. L. Hughes, J. H. Weare, *J. Am. Chem. Soc.* **59,** 1753 (1947).
113*a*. J. T. Edsall, *Fortschr. chem. Forsch.* **1,** 119 (1949).
114. W. Kuhn, *Helv. Chim. Acta* **31,** 1259 (1948).
115. J. F. Danielli, *Biochem. J.* **35,** 470 (1941).
116. F. Haurowitz, F. Marx, *Kolloid-Z.* **74,** 65, 208 (1936).
117. H. Neurath, J. P. Greenstein, F. W. Putnam, J. O. Ericksson, *Chem. Revs.* **34,** 158 (1944).
118. W. D. Loughlin, W. C. M. Lewis, *Biochem. J.* **26,** 476 (1932); **27,** 99, 106 (1933).
119. F. Haurowitz, *Kolloid-Z.* **71,** 198 (1935).
120. H. Neurath, H. B. Bull, *J. Biol. Chem.* **115,** 519 (1936).
121. H. Wu, *Chinese J. Physiol.* **5,** 321 (1931).
121*a*. H. P. Lundgren, W. H. Ward, *Ann. Rev. Biochem.* **18,** 134 (1949).
122. A. E. Mirsky, M. L. Anson, *J. Gen. Physiol.* **19,** 427 (1936).
123. P. Desnuelle, M. Rovery, *Biochim. et Biophys. Acta* **1,** 497 (1947).
124. R. Brdička, J. Klumpar, *Časopis Českosloven. Lékárnictva* **17,** 243 (1937).
125. M. L. Anson, *J. Gen. Physiol.* **24,** 399 (1941).
126. G. L. Miller, *J. Biol. Chem.* **146,** 339, 345 (1942).
127. F. Haurowitz, S. Tekman, *Biochim. et Biophys. Acta* **1,** 484 (1947).

128. J. Roche, M. Mourgue, *Bull. soc. chim. biol.* **30,** 322 (1948).
129. C. H. Li, *J. Am. Chem. Soc.* **67,** 1065 (1945).
130. R. Porter, *Biochim. et Biophys. Acta* **2,** 105 (1948).
131. M. L. Anson, A. E. Mirsky, *J. Gen. Physiol.* **17,** 399 (1934).
132. F. Haurowitz, M. Tunca, P. Schwerin, V. Göksu, *J. Biol. Chem.* **157,** 621 (1945).
132*a*. F. Bernheim, H. Neurath, J. O. Erickson, *J. Biol. Chem.* **144,** 259 (1942).
133. K. Linderstrøm-Lang *et al.*, *Nature* **142,** 996 (1938).
133*a*. E. Fredericq, *Bull. soc. chim. Belge* **56,** 223 (1947).
134. K. Bailey, *Biochem. J.* **36,** 140 (1942).
135. I. M. Klotz, H. Triwush, F. Walker, *J. Am. Chem. Soc.* **70,** 2935 (1948).
135*a*. F. Haurowitz, S. Tekman *et al.*, Abstracts 112th Meeting Am. Chem. Soc., p. 29C (1947); also unpublished experiments of F. Haurowitz and F. DiMoia.
135*b*. N. Burk, *J. Biol. Chem.* **87,** 197 (1930); **98,** 353 (1932); **121,** 373 (1937).
136. C. F. C. MacPherson, M. Heidelberger, *J. Am. Chem. Soc.* **67,** 574, 578 (1945).
136*a*. S. Brohult, *J. Phys. Chem.* **51,** 206 (1947).
137. T. Svedberg, S. Brohult, *Nature* **142,** 830 (1938).
138. H. B. Bull, *J. Am. Chem. Soc.* **68,** 742, 745 (1946).
138*a*. H. A. Dieu, H. B. Bull, *J. Am. Chem. Soc.* **71,** 450 (1949).
139. F. Haurowitz, F. Bursa, *Rev. faculté sci. univ. Istanbul,* **B10,** 283 (1945).
140. A. E. Mirsky, *Science,* **93,** 285 (1941).
141. A. E. Mirsky, *J. Gen. Physiol.* **24,** 725 (1941).
142. H. B. Bull, H. Neurath, *J. Biol. Chem.* **118,** 163 (1937).
143. E. Gorter, in Un Symposium sur les Proteines. Desoir, Liége, 1946.
144. H. Cohen, *Arch. Biochem.* **2,** 1 (1948).
145. C. H. J. van den Broeck, personal communication. D. B. Finn, *Proc. Roy. Soc. London,* **B111,** 396 (1942).
146. J. S. Mitchell, E. K. Rideal, *Proc. Roy. Soc. London* **A167,** 342 (1939).
146*a*. A. D. McLaren, S. Pearson, *J. Polymer Sci.* **4,** 45 (1949).
147. S. Fiala, *Biochem. Z.* **318,** 67 (1947).
148. P. Grabar, R. Prudhomme, *J. chim. phys.* **44,** 145 (1948); *Bull. soc. chim. biol.* **29,** 122 (1947).
148*a*. R. Pohlman, C. Wolpers, *Kolloid-Z.* **109,** 106 (1944).
149. E. J. Cohn, J. T. Edsall, Proteins, Amino Acids and Peptides. Reinhold, New York, 1943, p. 144.
150. J. Steinhardt, *J. Biol. Chem.* **123,** 543 (1938).
151. C. F. Jacobsen, L. Koorsgaard, *Nature* **161,** 30 (1948).
152. K. Thomas, J. Kapfhammer, *Ber. Verhandl. sächs. Akad. Wiss. Leipzig Math.-phys. Klasse* **77,** 181 (1925).
153. F. W. Putnam, H. Neurath, *J. Biol. Chem.* **160,** 239 (1945).
154. G. Sandor, *Bull. soc. chim. biol.* **26,** 48 (1946).
155. T. Brosteaux, B. Erickson-Quensel, *Arch. phys. biol.* **12,** 209 (1935).
156. P. D. Boyer, F. G. Lum, G. A. Ballon, T. M. Luck, R. G. Rice, *J. Biol. Chem.* **162,** 181 (1946).
157. F. H. Johnson, D. H. Campbell, *J. Biol. Chem.* **163,** 689 (1946).
158. F. Haurowitz, *Z. physiol. Chem.* **183,** 78 (1929).
159. F. Haurowitz, S. Tunc, unpublished experiments.
160. F. Haurowitz, N. Yurd, N. Eryol, L. Uzman, *Istanbul Seririyati* **26,** No. 6 (1944).
161. M. Kunitz, J. H. Northrop, *J. Gen. Physiol.* **17,** 591 (1934); **18,** 433 (1935).

162. M. L. Anson, A. E. Mirsky, *J. Gen. Physiol.* **14,** 597 (1931).
163. H. Neurath, G. R. Cooper, T. O. Erickson, *J. Phys. & Colloid Chem.* **46,** 203 (1942).
164. H. Neurath, G. R. Cooper, T. C. Erickson, *J. Biol. Chem.* **142,** 249, 265 (1942).
165. J. Roche, M. Chouaiech, *Bull. soc. chim. biol.* **22,** 283 (1946).
166. M. Kunitz, *J. Gen. Physiol.* **32,** 241 (1948).
167. M. Levy, personal communication; see also M. Levy, E. Slobodiansky, *Cold Spring Harbor Symposia Quant. Biol.* **14,** 113 (1950).
168. M. L. Anson, *Advances in Protein Chem.* **2,** 361 (1945).
169. J. B. Conn, C. D. Gregg, G. E. Kistiakowsky, R. M. Roberts, *J. Am. Chem. Soc.* **63,** 2080 (1941).
170. J. Conn, G. Kistiakowsky, R. Roberts, *J. Am. Chem. Soc.* **62,** 1895 (1940).
171. J. Steinhardt, *Kgl. Danske Videnskab. Selskab., Biol. Medd.* **14,** No. 2 (1937).
172. E. Brand, *Ann. Rev. Biochem.* **16,** 224 (1947).
173. A. Alten, C. Dippel, K. Keuning and J. van Dreven, *J. Colloid Sci.* **3,** 65 (1948).
174. A. E. Stearn, *Advances in Enzymol.* **9,** 25 (1949).
175. J. A. V. Butler, *Nature* **158,** 153 (1946).
176. F. Hofmeister, *Ergeb. Physiol.* **1,** 758 (1902).
177. E. Fischer, *Ber.* **35,** 1095 (1902).

CHAPTER VIII

Albumins, Globulins, and Other Soluble Proteins

A. Classification of Soluble Proteins. Although the solubility of proteins in different solvents has been used as a criterion for their classification, none of the many schemes so founded is entirely satisfactory. The first fractionation of soluble proteins was achieved by salting-out with ammonium sulfate (1). The fraction precipitated by 50% saturation was called *globulin,* and that precipitated by more than 50% saturation with ammonium sulfate called *albumin.* Later it was found that the globulin fraction gave a precipitate upon dialysis while the albumin fraction remained in solution even in the absence of salts. Globulins were accordingly defined as proteins which are insoluble in salt-free water, but soluble in neutral salts (2). Today we know that only one portion of the globulins, the *euglobulins,* is insoluble in pure water, while another portion, the *pseudoglobulins,* dissolves easily. Globulinlike proteins have been extracted not only from animal tissues, but also from cereals; some of them dissolve in ethanol–water mixtures and have been called *prolamins.* They are considered by some authors to be a separate group of proteins, and by others to be a subgroup of the globulins.

It is evident from these few examples that none of the classifications of soluble proteins is quite adequate. We are not yet able to correlate the solubility of proteins with a definite composition or with a definite arrangement of the amino acids in the protein molecule. It is preferable, therefore, to renounce a more or less unsatisfactory classification and to discuss the more important types of proteins according to their biological occurrence.

B. Proteins of Blood Serum (3–6). These proteins will be discussed first because they have been investigated exhaustively by a large number of workers. They were the first proteins to be fractionated by the salting-out method. The neutral salts used were ammonium sulfate (7) and magnesium sulfate (8). Later sodium sulfate (9) and phosphate mixtures of different pH values were used for the same purpose (10). If the amount of protein precipitated by one of these salts is plotted against the amount of salt added, curves such as that shown in Figure 33 are obtained. The figure reveals that the amount of protein precipitated increases sharply at certain salt concentrations, proving that the plasma contains more than one type of protein. The first protein precipitated from blood plasma by the addition of a neutral salt is *fibrinogen* (F). Since this protein has the specific property of clotting it will be treated in another section. The next part of the curve corresponds to the precipitation of serum globulins (G) and the last part to the precipitation of serum albumin (A). If magnesium sulfate is used as a precipitant the globulins are precipitated by the saturation of the solution, the albumins by adjustment of the pH to 4.6, their isoelectric point.

In discussing electrophoresis it was mentioned (Chapter V) that the serum globulin fraction is a mixture of at least three components called α-, β-, and γ-globulin (11). If ammonium sulfate is added cautiously

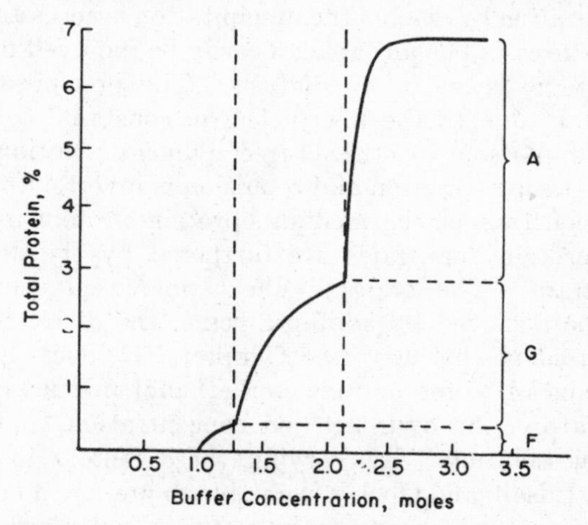

FIG. 33. Salting-out of human blood plasma by phosphate buffer solutions, pH 6.5.

to horse blood serum, the γ-globulins are precipitated at a concentration of 1.34 moles of ammonium sulfate per liter of solution; β- and α-globulins are precipitated by 1.64 and 2.05 moles, respectively, and albumins by 2.57 moles (12). Although this method is more convenient than electrophoresis for the preparation of large amounts of the globulins, the fractions obtained are somewhat impure; each of them is contaminated with small amounts of the other neighboring fractions. Ammonium sulfate has the disadvantage of containing nitrogen, so that direct Kjeldahl analyses of the protein fractions are rendered impossible. It has been replaced by sodium sulfate in the clinical determination of albumins and globulins (9).

Globulins are precipitated by 21.5% sodium sulfate, while albumins are determined in the filtrate; the precipitation and filtration are carried out at 37°, because the solubility of sodium sulfate at room temperature is not sufficiently high. Recently it has been discovered, however, that the albumin fraction contains considerable amounts of the α-globulins; it has been proposed, therefore, to precipitate the α-globulins by increasing the concentration of the sodium sulfate to 26.8%; β- and γ-globulins are precipitated by 19.6% sodium sulfate (13).

The salting-out methods, although very convenient for the preparation of the protein fractions in the laboratory, are not suited for large-scale preparations, it being difficult to remove large amounts of salts by dialysis. It was a contribution of great importance, therefore, when Cohn and coworkers (14) developed a procedure for separating the plasma proteins using *ethanol* (15) as the precipitating agent. In order to avoid denaturation by alcohol the precipitation is necessarily performed at low temperatures. The alcohol can easily be removed by drying from the frozen state *in vacuo* or by dialysis. The precipitating action of ethanol is mainly due to the low dielectric constant of ethanol–water mixtures in comparison to ethanol-free aqueous solutions. Since the force of electrostatic attraction and repulsion is inversely proportional to the dielectric constant of the medium, protein–protein interaction and formation of protein aggregates are furthered by the decrease of the dielectric constant. The opposite effect, increased solubility of the proteins, can be achieved by adding glycine; the dielectric constant of water is increased in this way (see Chapter VII, Sect. K). The solubility of proteins in water or in water–ethanol mixtures depends also on the temperature, the hydrogen ion concentration, and on the ionic strength of the solution. By varying these factors in a systematic manner, Cohn, Edsall, and Oncley were able to prepare a large number of protein fractions, and to separate from the blood plasma biologically active fractions such as enzymes and antibodies. The most important results of this procedure are shown by Figure 34 and by the following survey of one of the methods applied in the Harvard laboratory (4,16).

Fraction I. This fraction which is precipitated between 0 and −3° by adding 8–10% ethanol at pH 7, contains 60–65% fibrinogen (see below, Sect. C) and has been used for the preparation of fibrin films.

Fraction II + III. Precipitated by raising the ethanol concentration to 25% and lowering the temperature to −5°; further fractionation is achieved by treatment with 20% ethanol; the supernatant solution (Fraction III-0) contains the β_1-globulin and β_1-lipoprotein (see Chapter XI, Sect. A), while the precipitate contains γ-globulin, proteolytic enzymes, the midpiece of complement (page 296); prothrombin (Sect. C, below), and isoagglutinins; at a pH of 5.2 and with 17% alcohol only the last-named proteins are precipitated (Fraction III), while γ-globulin remains dissolved (Fraction II); it is precipitated by raising the ionic strength to 0.05. The proteolytic enzymes of Fraction II are those which cause the dissolution of fibrin clots. The enzymes plasmin and plasminogen (Fraction III-3) and prothrombin (Fraction III-2) are precipitated by 1% ethanol at pH 5.4 and ionic strength 0.08. The isoagglutinins (Fraction III-1) remain in solution; they comprise the anti-A and anti-B substances reacting with the blood groups A and B, and also the anti-Rh agglutinins. Fraction III-1 also contains the typhoid O-agglutinins and a portion of the diphtheria antitoxins. The most important subfraction of Fraction II + III is the γ-globulin of Fraction II. Since this fraction contains antibodies against measles, infectious hepatitis, and other diseases, it is used clinically. The bulk of the diphtheria antitoxins is found in Fractions II-1 and II-2 (16).

Fraction IV-1 is obtained by lowering the ethanol content to 18% and the pH to 5.2. The fraction contains a portion of the α-globulins; it includes a lipoprotein (17)

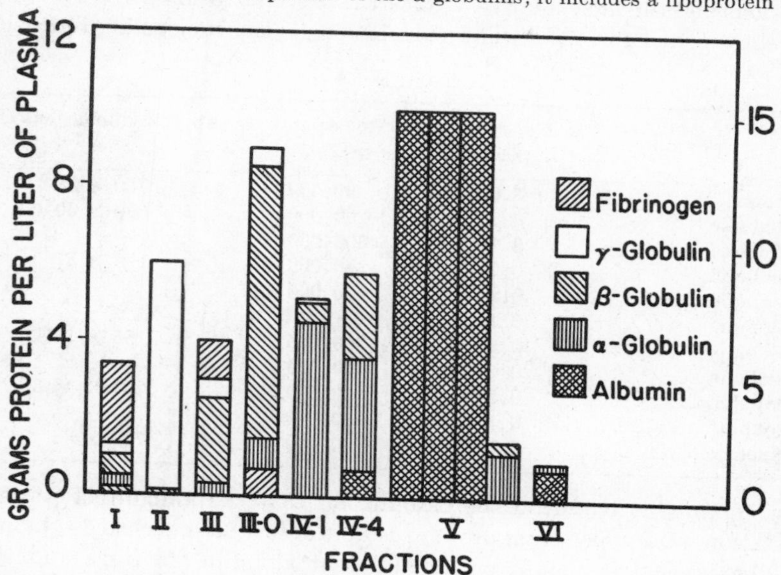

FIG. 34. Distribution of electrophoretic components in fractions of human plasma. The scale at the right side indicates the amount of the fractions in per cent of the total plasma protein (23).

containing about 35% cholesterol, fatty acids, and phospholipids (see Chapter XI, Sect. A) and a blue-green pigment.

Fraction IV-4 is precipitated by raising the ethanol concentration to 40% and adjusting the pH to 5.8. The fraction contains lipid-free α- and β-globulins and some of the albumin (IV-8). Among the globulins are some biologically active substances such as an esterase, a peptidase, phosphatase, and the thyrotropic hormone; Fraction IV includes also some globulins containing carbohydrates such as α_2-glucopseudoglobulin and α_2-mucoglobulin. Moreover, a β-globulin which combines readily with heavy metals has been found in this fraction and resolved into iron-binding and copper-binding components (18). The iron-binding protein, called transferrin or siderophilin, is probably responsible for the transport of iron in the organism (see Chapter XI, Sect. D); its molecular weight is 90,000 (18*a*), that of the copper-binding ceruloplasmin is 150,000 (18*a*).

Fraction V is precipitated by lowering the pH to 4.8 with acetate buffer, the ethanol concentration being maintained at 40%. It consists mainly of serum albumin, which can be obtained in crystals (19). The supernatant of Fraction V, designated Fraction VI, contains small amounts of albumin and α-globulin.

The total amount of protein in human plasma is about 6.5–7.0%; approximately 50% of the total protein consists of serum albumin, 15%, 19%, and 11% of α-, β-, and γ-globulin, respectively, and 5% of fibrinogen (4,20,21). The results obtained by ultracentrifugation differ, however, from those obtained electrophoretically in that they furnish much higher values for albumin (22). The amounts of the most important protein fractions and the molecular weights of the proteins forming these fractions are shown in Table XI. The calculation of the molecular dimensions

TABLE XI

Fraction	Per cent in plasma	Molecular weight	Approx. dimensions (23) Å
Albumin	3.2	69,000	150 × 38
α_1-Globulin	0.2	200,000	300 × 50
α_2-Globulin	0.1	300,000	—
β_1-Globulin	0.2	90,000	190 × 37
β_1-Globulin	0.2	150,000	—
β_1-Globulin	0.1	500,000–1 million	—
β_1-Globulin	0.2	1,300,000	185 × 185
β_2-Globulin	0.2	150,000	—
γ-Globulin	0.5	156,000	235 × 44
γ-Globulin	0.1	300,000	—
Fibrinogen	0.3	400,000	700 × 38

(last column) is based on the assumption that the amount of water of hydration is 0.2 g. per gram protein, but 0.6 g. for the spherical β_1-globulin.

The isoelectric points of the different globulin fractions and their electrophoretic mobilities are shown in Table XII (11). The last column

TABLE XII

Protein	Isoelectric point, pH	Mobility[a] at pH 6.87	Mobility[a] at pH 7.7
Albumin	4.64	5.90	5.1
α-Globulin	5.06	4.48	3.8
β-Globulin	5.12	3.58	2.7
γ-Globulin (24)	6.85–7.3	0.99	0.9
Fibrinogen	—	—	1.9

[a] $Cm.^2$ per volt per sec. × 10^5.

shows the mobility of 1% solutions of the purified fractions at 0°C. and at an ionic strength of 0.2 (20).

The proteins obtained either by fractional precipitation or by electrophoresis are not quite homogeneous substances. Thus crystalline horse serum albumin has been found to contain about 10% of a glucoprotein called seroglycoid and of a globulin called globoglycoid (25,26). The purified albumin has been called crystalbumin. γ_1-Globulin and γ_2-globulin, subfractions of γ-globulin, are electrophoretically uniform (27), but are not homogeneous in the ultracentrifuge (28); γ_1-globulin is identical with the β_1-globulin of some authors and with the T-component of certain immune sera (29). The isoelectric points of the two γ-globulin fractions from human sera are 6.85 and 7.3 (24), while bovine serum furnished two analogous fractions whose isoelectric points were pH 5.85 and 7.35 (29*a*); by a combination of electrophoresis with electrodecantation the bovine γ-globulins were resolved into eight fractions (29*b*).

It may be mentioned that ethanol can be replaced by other organic solvents and that a fractionation of blood plasma has also been achieved by using methanol (30) or a mixture of methanol and methylal, CH_3-OCH_2OCH_3 (31).

Recently heavy metal salts, such as zinc salts, have been used as precipitating agents in the fractionation of blood plasma proteins (31*a*). While proteins are irreversibly denatured by large amounts of heavy metal salts, small amounts of the metal ions combine reversibly with the proteins, probably with their sulfhydryl groups, forming precipitates from which the native protein can be recovered (31*a*).

It is difficult at present to interpret the results of fractional precipitation and to say with certainty whether the fractions characterized exist as such in the blood plasma and whether a further fractionation is possible. Most probably the plasma proteins can combine with lipids, with carbohydrates, and also with other proteins. Thus one can expect that γ-globulins, the isoelectric point of which is near to pH 7, will combine to form saltlike compounds with albumins, whose isoelectric point is close to pH 4.7. Possibly the protein moieties of the lipoproteins and glucoproteins found in the plasma are identical with some of the proteins isolated by fractional precipitation. Differences in the electrophoretic behavior and in precipitability may also be due to the combination of proteins with bicarbonate (32), with calcium, or with other ions. Finally, we have to consider alterations in the physicochemical state of the proteins brought about by the action of alcohol or salts. New complexes may be formed or compounds may be split by the addition of alcohol or of concentrated salt solutions.

From time to time it had been reported that albumins can be converted into globulins by treatment with an ethanol–diethyl ether mixture, with heparin or with other agents. A true conversion of serum albumin into globulin is certainly impossible because the amino acid composition of the globulins is different from that of albumins (see Table I, page 32). It is evident, however, from these reports that under the experimental conditions albumins suffer profound alterations in their solubility and that their physicochemical behavior becomes similar to that of globulins. One cannot exclude the possibility, therefore, that the native blood plasma contains only a small number of proteins and that many of the fractions found are formed by combination of these basic proteins with lipids, carbohydrates, other proteins, or certain ions.

On the other hand, we must be aware of the fact that successive refinements in technique have revealed the presence of more and more protein fractions. The original conclusion that there was but one albumin and one globulin in the protein fractions of blood serum had to be abandoned in favor of α-, β-, and γ-globulins, each of which has in turn been resolved into two or more subfractions. Further improvements in our methods have furnished additional protein fractions, and there may be no limit to fractionation. We might well have to forego the conclusion that such a thing as a uniform, pure protein even exists. The study of immunological reactions has shown that the injection of an antigen leads to the formation of a family of serum globulins (antibodies) of differing degrees of complementary adaptation to the polar groups of the antigen (33). It is possible that the same thing is valid for the normal serum globulins, that they belong to different types between which intermediates exist and that it would be hopeless to undertake the isolation of homogeneous proteins.

Many of the investigations of the plasma proteins have centered about the fact that their concentration undergoes typical alterations in certain diseases (5). A decrease, which is due to the loss of serum albumin through the kidneys, is frequently observed in renal disturbances. Not only the total protein, but also the albumin:globulin ratio in the blood serum decreases in such cases. Since the osmotic pressure of albumins, owing to their low molecular weight, is much higher than that of the globulins, the osmotic pressure of the serum proteins decreases considerably when the albumin level decreases. Extreme hyperproteinemia, a much rarer phenomenon, is observed in patients with myeloma and is characterized by an increase in the globulin fraction. In the urine of some of the patients suffering from myeloma a specific protein, the so-called Bence-Jones protein is found; it is coagulated by heating the urine to 50–58° but dissolves on further heating. The phenomenon is reversible since, if the boiling urine is cooled down, a precipitate appears which dissolves on further cooling. A similar protein which becomes insoluble on cooling has been detected in the blood plasma of patients suffering from lymphosarcoma (34); it has been called cryoglobulin. The Bence-Jones protein shares with virus proteins the property of being devoid of methionine (34*a*). However, its molecular weight,

35,000 (35), is much lower than that of virus proteins. Possibly it is a split product of a virus protein. Lower degrees of hyperglobulinemia than those observed in myeloma are seen in patients suffering from infectious diseases. An increase in antibodies in infected and sensitized organisms is generally accompanied by an increase in serum globulin.

Obviously all these changes are reflected in electrophoresis diagrams. The diagrams also reveal those changes which are not accompanied by an increase in total protein or in total albumin or globulin, but are due to the decrease of one component and the simultaneous increase of another, or to the appearance of abnormal types of proteins (36).

Deviations from the normal ratio of the plasma proteins (5) are revealed by several simple clinical tests. One of them is the Takata-Ara reaction, in which the serum is tested for its protective action on the precipitation of mercuric chloride by sodium carbonate; the higher the albumin: globulin ratio the higher is the protective capacity of the serum. The test is positive in certain diseases of the liver. Another similar test is the thymol turbidity test (37), in which the serum is mixed with a saturated solution of thymol in barbiturate buffer at pH 7.8. While normal serum remains clear, serum of patients with liver diseases frequently gives a distinct turbidity. It is due to an increase in γ-globulins, phospholipids, and cholesterol and is inhibited in normal serum by the albumins (38,39).

In all these clinical tests use is made of the fact that the formation of floccules and/or the appearance of turbidity is inhibited by albumins but not by the globulins. This "protective action" of the albumins is due to their higher negative charge and also to their high capacity of combining with anions (see page 189). Since the isoelectric point of serum albumin is near pH 4.7, its molecules have a large excess of negatively charged groups at pH 7. The number of ionic groups in globulin molecules is much smaller because their isoelectric point is near pH 6.

Extensive generalizations should not be made on the basis of the results obtained with human sera. The sera of the different species of the animal kingdom differ widely in their content of albumins and of the different types of globulins (40). Differences are also found in individuals of different ages. The plasma of newborn animals is, as a rule, poor in globulins; while the plasma of a newborn horse contained 3.7% protein that of a 10 year old horse contained 7% total protein. The content of albumin, α-, β-, and γ-globulin was 65, 32, 3, and 0% in the newborn horse and 30, 11, 12, and 47% in the adult horse, respectively. It is evident from these figures that the plasma of the newborn animal was free of γ-globulins and very poor in the other globulins (41). Similarly, the plasma of newborn rabbits contained only 0.2% globulins and 4.8% albumin (41*a*). On the other hand, a specific globulin of low molecular weight, called fetuin, was discovered in the serum of newborn calves where it composes about 90% of the globulins (20). Its molecular weight is 50,000 and it is salted out by 35–45% ammonium sulfate. Another globulin of low molecular weight, 34,000, was found in the plasma of *Petromyzon marinus* L. (41*b*).

C. Fibrinogen and Fibrin (Clotting of Blood) (42,42*a*). The clotting of blood is due to the conversion of fibrinogen, a soluble protein of the plasma, into fibrin, an insoluble protein. Since the formation of the clot is one of the most striking of all biological phenomena it has been investigated by a large number of workers. Nevertheless, the mystery of clotting has still to be solved. The conversion of fibrinogen into fibrin is promoted by an enzyme called thrombin. Prothrombin, the immediate precursor of thrombin, is present in the blood plasma and, by means of a thromboplastic substance, it is transformed into active thrombin. Hence the phenomenon of clotting consists of two phases:

$$\text{Prothrombin} \xrightarrow{\text{thromboplastin}} \text{thrombin}$$

$$\text{Fibrinogen} \xrightarrow{\text{thrombin}} \text{fibrin}$$

Prothrombin is a globulin present in the III-2 fraction of the blood serum obtained by ethanol fractionation. It has been purified by adsorption on colloidal tricalcium phosphate (43), aluminum hydroxide (44), or magnesium hydroxide (45). It is eluted from the adsorbate by phosphate buffer, pH 8, or by treatment of the magnesium hydroxide with carbon dioxide. The purest preparations contain 2000–2500 units per mg. (45).

Prothrombin is converted to the active enzyme thrombin by *thromboplastin*, a substance present in blood platelets which has been prepared from lung, brain, and other organs (46). Rabbit brain is used as thromboplastin source in the clinical prothrombin test. Thromboplastin is, apparently, present in cellular granules, for it is precipitated by high-speed centrifugation (46). Consisting of a specific protein combined with ribonucleic acid and an acetal phosphatide (47) in the form of a loose complex, thromboplastin can be split to yield the water-soluble thromboplastic protein and the water-insoluble thromboplastic lipid. The latter, although it resembles the cephalins, cannot, however, be replaced by synthetic cephalin in the conversion of prothrombin to thrombin (47).

The mechanism of the action of thromboplastin has not yet been thoroughly explained. Most authors believe that thromboplastin is an enzyme, a view which is supported by the fact that trypsin is also able to convert prothrombin into thrombin (48); accordingly, the old name, thrombokinase, is quite justified (47). On the other hand, however, it has been stated that thromboplastin and calcium react with prothrombin in stoichiometric amounts and not as catalysts (49). It has long been realized that *calcium* is indispensable for the clotting of blood, since this process may be prevented by adding to the blood oxalate, citrate, or fluoride, all of which form complexes with calcium ions. Decalcification of the plasma can also be accomplished by removing the calcium by adsorption to Amberlite IR 100; addition of calcium salts to the decalcified plasma restores the capacity to form a clot (50).

It is generally assumed that calcium is necessary for the first phase of clotting, that is to say, for the *formation of thrombin* from prothrombin (51,52). The conversion of fibrinogen to fibrin has been achieved by calcium-free thrombin. Although the role of calcium ions or of calcium complexes (53) in the first phase of clotting is not entirely clear, the effect is due to either activation of thromboplastin or to inactivation of an antiprothrombin (54). Calcium is not necessary in the clotting reaction of snake venom since clotting here occurs in the presence of oxalate (55).

The conversion of prothrombin to thrombin is considered by some authors to be an autocatalytic process, a chain reaction, which is initiated by calcium and thromboplastin, but which is then catalyzed by the *thrombin* formed. According to this concept, thrombin catalyzes the conversion of prothrombin to thrombin (52) in a manner analogous to the action of pepsin, which, as is well known, catalyzes the conversion of pepsinogen into pepsin (see Chapter XII, Sect. H). The physicochemical properties of thrombin are similar to those of prothrombin. It is extracted from fibrin clots by saline solutions and is precipitated from blood serum by ethanol. Purer thrombin preparations are obtained by treating prothrombin with thromboplastin in the presence of calcium salts (56). The molecular weight of thrombin is about 77,000, that of prothrombin 140,000; it is not yet known whether one molecule of prothrombin furnishes one or two thrombin molecules (42*a*). Dry preparations of pure thrombin are very stable and can be kept in an active state at room temperature for many months (42*a*).

Pure prothrombin and thromboplastin react very slowly to give thrombin; this first phase of the clotting process can, however, be accelerated considerably by a new protein discovered in blood plasma; it has been called Ac-globulin (Ac = accelerator) and has been purified by adsorption methods (57). It is evident from all these observations that the first phase of clotting, the formation of thrombin from prothrombin, is a very complicated process and that it is at present poorly understood.

The second phase, the formation of fibrin from fibrinogen, is also catalyzed by an enzyme, by thrombin. Neither fibrinogen nor fibrin are enzymatically active. *Fibrinogen*, which is a globulin present in the blood plasma in amounts of 0.2–0.4%, is precipitated from plasma by low concentrations of ethanol or by half-saturation with sodium chloride (58,58*a*). Fibrinogen molecules, solutions of which are highly viscous and show flow birefringence, are prolate ellipsoids, about 700 Å long, with an axial ratio of 18:1 (59). Very pure fibrinogen is precipitated from plasma by freezing and thawing (59*a*).

While it is generally agreed that the *conversion of fibrinogen to fibrin* is a catalyzed reaction, the sort of alteration which the fibrinogen molecule might undergo remains obscure. Most probably the clotting of fibrinogen is similar to the denaturation of native proteins and consists of an unfolding of the peptide chains of fibrinogen molecules. In the course of this unfolding positively and negatively charged groups of the fibrinogen molecule become mutually accessible, so that a network of fibrin molecules, linked to each other by salt links, is formed (60). This view is supported by the finding that the formation of fibrin clots is inhibited by all those reagents which combine with the positively or negatively charged groups of proteins; reagents of this type include heparin and formaldehyde, both of which combine with amino groups (60), and basic dyes, which combine with the acidic groups of fibrinogen (61). It is also possible that heparin affects the first phase of clotting by acting as an anti-prothrombin. If the conversion of fibrinogen into fibrin is fundamentally a process of denaturation, thrombin must be designated a denaturase (62), which is somehow designed to catalyze the cleavage of the weak bonds between folded peptide chains. The view that fibrinogen undergoes some mode of denaturation was supported by the finding that sulfhydryl groups are liberated during the action of thrombin on fibrinogen (63). However, clotting is not prevented by substances, such as chloromercuribenzoate, which react specifically with sulfhydryl groups (42*a*). Some evidence in favor of the view that clotting involves denaturation is provided by the inhibiting action of high pressures, in the neighborhood of 800 atmospheres (64); high pressures are known to inhibit the formation of salt bridges between ionized groups, because this process is accompanied by a release of water molecules from the hydrated ionized groups, *i.e.*, by an increase in volume.

If thrombin is allowed to act on fibrinogen at pH 5.1 no visible clotting occurs; but fibrinogen is converted into a substance, called profibrin, which easily clots at neutral reaction (65). All these observations are in accord with the contention that the peptide chains of fibrinogen first undergo an unfolding, and then polymerize to form the extensive network of fibrin fibers.

It is a well-known fact that blood plasma, while it readily shows the reaction in glass vessels, does not clot in paraffinized vessels, thus indicating that clotting is catalyzed by a glass surface. This is reminiscent of the analogous catalytic effects of the glass wall observed in certain chain reactions, and suggests that the formation of the clot may indeed be a reaction of this type. The formation of an insoluble clot from fibrinogen is also promoted by catalytic amounts of ninhydrin (66).

Electron micrographs of the fibrin clot reveal a periodic cross striation of the fibers, the distance between the bands being approximately 250 Å (67). The beaded character of the fibers suggests that they are formed by the longitudinal association of globular particles. The primary polymerization of fibrinogen to fibrin occurs probably by an end-

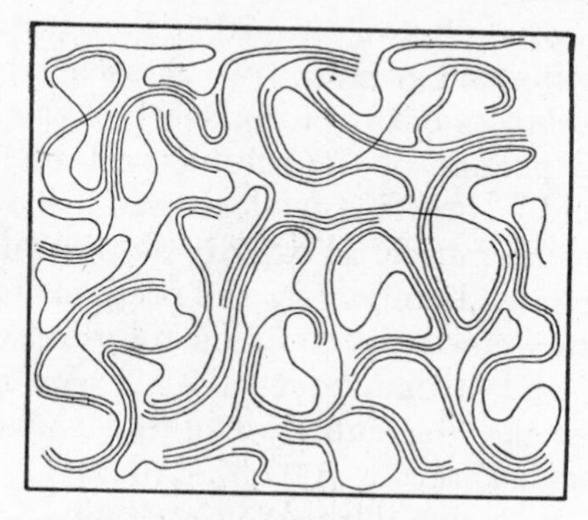

FIG. 35. Fibrin clot (69*a*).

to-end linkage of the fibrinogen molecules. Otherwise it would not be possible to account for the formation of the voluminous clot from the small amounts of fibrinogen required (68). Probably 10 to 14 fibrinogen molecules, attached in a head-to-tail arrangement to one another form the structural unit of the fibrin clot. Only a small number of lateral cross links may be present in the original loose clot.

The formation of the fibrin clot has been compared with the formation of a protein gel from a protein solution. However, the consistency and the structure of the clot differ markedly from those of typical gels. The fibrin gel, which contains only 0.2–0.4% fibrin, is much looser than a gelatin gel; on stirring with a glass rod, it is wound around the rod and in so doing collapses to a very small fraction of its initial volume. A fibrin clot which originally occupied a volume of 100 ml. is reduced in this way to a fibrin particle whose size is less than 1 ml. Use is made of this phenomenon for the quantitative isolation and determination of fibrinogen and fibrin in the blood plasma. The ease with which the network of fibrin threads collapses to form a small particle shows that the fibers stick together laterally, as soon as they are brought into contact with each other. This mutual adhesion of the fibrin threads leads to the formation of crystallike aggregates of parallel fibers (68,69) (Fig. 35). The nature of the end-to-end links and of the lateral cross links is not yet elucidated. However, the adhesion of fibrin clots to the silicate ion lattice on the surface of glass and the inhibition of clotting in paraffin vessels both indicate that ion–ion bonds serve an important function in the formation of the clot. By the action of thrombin the ionic groups, apparently, become reactive. We are not certain, however, whether the reacting ionic groups originate from a salt link, from the cleavage of a peptide bond, or from some other reaction.

D. Muscle Proteins (Contractile Proteins) (70–73*a*). The muscles of vertebrates contain approximately 15–20% protein, most of which can be extracted by treating the ground, fresh muscle with dilute salt solutions. If some time elapses between the death of the animal and extraction of the muscle, a portion of the soluble proteins becomes insoluble, and the yield of soluble proteins is decreased. To prevent this it is necessary to prepare the muscle as rapidly as possible and to extract it at low temperatures immediately after the preparation.

The aqueous extract contains the following *protein fractions:* myogen, myosin, globulin X, and stroma protein. Myogen is the most soluble of these; myosin becomes insoluble when the extract is diluted to a potassium chloride concentration of 0.03 *M* (0.22%); on further dilution with water to 0.005 *M* a globulin, called globulin X, becomes insoluble (74). Myosin forms approximately 40% of the total protein of the muscle; the remaining 60% is formed by approximately equal amounts of myogen, globulin X, and stroma protein (74).

Myogen, which had been regarded as a uniform protein, is a mixture of at least three myogens, A, B, and C (75). These have been prepared in the crystalline state by fractional salting-out with ammonium sulfate at 60, 80, and 96% saturation (75,76). The average molecular weight of the myogens, which has been found to be 81,000, is reduced by treatment with urea to 34,000 (74). On the basis of the large amount of ammonium sulfate required to salt them out, myogens have to be classified as albumins. On standing at room temperature one portion of the myogen solution clots to form an insoluble product which has been called myogenfibrin. The myogen fraction contains many of the enzymes of the muscle. Phosphorylase, phosphoglucomutase, aldolase, and glyceraldehyde phosphate dehydrogenase are present in this fraction (77). These enzymes make up at least 20–25% of the myogen.

Myosin, the most important of the muscle proteins, is considered to be the contractile substance of the muscle. Myosin is extracted from the muscle by Weber's solution (0.6 *M* KCl, 0.04 *M* $NaHCO_3$, 0.01 *M* Na_2CO_3). Myosin solutions are highly viscous and display a very intense flow birefringence (see page 47) (78). On standing they form a gel which is liquefied on shaking; this phenomenon of thixotropy is shown even by solutions of myosin as dilute as 0.3% (78). The flow birefringence is reduced by the addition of calcium chloride, potassium iodide, guanidine, and certain other substances, all of which also lower the viscosity of the solutions (79). When solutions of myosin are extruded through a narrow orifice into salt-free water, fine threads of myosin are formed (80). .

From what has been said it would seem that the myosin molecules in solution are elongated threadlike particles. This is confirmed by the physicochemical analysis of dry myosin. Electron micrographs of myosin show threads about 1000 mμ long and 5–10 mμ thick (81). X-ray analysis reveals a spacing of 726 Å along the axis of the fibers, and transverse spacings of 200–325 Å (82). Other transverse interferences observed are 66, 42, and 33 Å; 66 Å is regarded as the diameter of a single myosin fibril (83). Short periods of 2.82 Å along the axis of the fibers led to the proposal that the peptide chains of the myosin molecules form helices around the longitudinal axis and that the side chains are interlinked (84). The molecular weight of myosin is very high, values ranging from 0.6 to 3.9 million having been found (74,85) for myosin prepared by different methods.

By means of electrophoresis and by salting-out with varying concentrations of ammonium sulfate, it has been possible to obtain three different fractions of myosin, called α-, β-, and γ-myosin. The first of these, α-myosin, is precipitated by 23–27% saturation with ammonium sulfate, and the β-myosin by 35–39% saturation (86). Only solutions of α-myosin exhibit flow birefringence (86).

When muscle is extracted with Weber's solution for a prolonged period of time a myosinlike protein is obtained which is much more viscous than the myosin obtained on brief extraction (87). The viscous protein is actually a compound of myosin and a second protein, called *actin*. To prepare actin, muscle is extracted for a short time with water, then with acetone; the aqueous extract of the dry residue contains actin (88). One gram of fresh muscle furnishes approximately 80 mg. myosin and 20–30 mg. actin. Actin combines readily with myosin to form actomyosin (myosin B), the resultant myosin:actin ratio being approximately 5:2 (89,90). Actomyosin is identical with the myosin of the older literature. It has been suggested, therefore, that the term myosin be applied to Szent-Györgyi's actomyosin and that his myosin be designated as myosin (w.s.), *i.e.*, water soluble (90).

Actin occurs as F-actin (fibrous actin) or as G-actin (globular actin) (87). Only F-actin, which is formed from G-actin when the latter is treated with potassium chloride, combines with myosin to form actomyosin (87,91). Threads of F-actin are also depolymerized to G-actin by the action of ultrasonic waves (92,92*a*).

Actin will combine with α-myosin, but not with β- or γ-myosin (86). Since the formation of actomyosin from its components is inhibited by iodoacetate and by other sulfhydryl reagents, it has been inferred that actin combines with the sulfhydryl groups of the myosin molecules (93). Actomyosin displays a strong flow birefringence similar to that of myosin; actin solutions do not possess this property (94).

In addition to myosin the muscle contains 0.5% of a similar protein called tropomyosin (95). In order to prepare tropomyosin the muscle is first extracted with water, 50% aqueous ethanol, 97% ethanol, and diethyl ether; tropomyosin is extracted from the dry fibrous material by a molar solution of potassium chloride. The amino acid composition of tropomyosin is very similar to that of myosin (see Table I, p. 32). Both proteins contain about 17% lysine, an unusually large amount of this basic amino acid. Tropomyosin forms highly viscous solutions; its molecular weight is 135,000 in phosphate solution; upon the addition of sodium chloride tropomyosin is split into particles of molecular weight 65,000 (100). Since these values are much lower than those of myosin it is believed that myosin is in all probability the polymeric form of tropomyosin (95). The high viscosity of tropomyosin solutions is due to the asymmetric shape of the molecules as shown by electron micrographs (96); the frictional ratio, f/f_0, is 3 (97).

Myosin and actomyosin react in a peculiar manner with adenosine triphosphate (ATP), a mononucleotide present in the muscular fluid. If ATP is added to a solution of myosin or actomyosin, these solutions lose both their high viscosity and their property of flow birefringence (98,99). This is due to a coiling of the elongated actomyosin threads and their conversion into globular particles of the actomyosin-ATP complex (91,106). In this complex the molecular ratio actin:myosin:ATP is 1:1:1 (101). Artificial threads of actomyosin-ATP have been prepared by forcing solutions of this compound through narrow apertures into salt-free water. These threads contract to about 50–60% of their length when they are treated with 0.01 *M* solutions of potassium chloride (99).

Electron micrographs show that the actomyosin fibers pass without interruption through the isotropic and anisotropic discs of the striated muscle (90). They are thought to be the contractile substance of the resting muscle (101,101*a*).

In 1939 Engel'hardt and Lyubimova (102) discovered that ATP is hydrolyzed by myosin or by a protein occurring in close combination with myosin. In this reaction adenosine triphosphate is converted to adenosinediphosphate (ADP) (92*a*). By means of ultraviolet microscopy (see page 222) the nucleotide ADP was found to be present mainly in the isotropic discs (103). It has since been ascertained that the adenosinetriphosphatase can be separated from the bulk of the myosin (104,105).

It is at present generally agreed that *muscular contraction* consists essentially of a deformation of the myosin molecules. This is evident from the decrease in birefringence during the isotonic contraction of muscle (72). Since the birefringence of resting muscle is due to the parallel orientation of the myosin molecules, the decrease in birefringence indicates a disorientation of the myosin chains. X-ray analyses fail to reveal any marked alteration upon contraction of the muscle; the master period of 725 Å remains unchanged (106). Possibly, the myosin

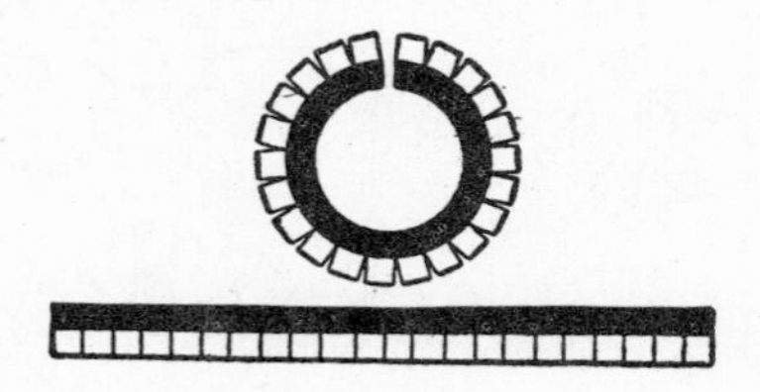

FIG. 36. Actomyosin (71).

molecules undergo reorientation by folding transversely (107) or by supercontracting in a manner analogous to the supercontraction of keratin fibers (108) (see Chapter IX, p. 179).

The hypothesis has been advanced that the actomyosin molecule consists of a myosin and an actin thread attached to each other laterally; while myosin can shrink, actin cannot and therefore contraction of the myosin molecule would result in a distortion of the whole actomyosin fiber (110*a*) (see Fig. 36). According to another view (109,110) muscular contraction is ascribed to the end-to-end combination of small actin globules of the molecular weight 70,000 to big units of molecular weight 1,500,000; the actin fibers formed would then combine with the myosin threads (109). Actomyosin would be split into its components on stimulation (109*a*).

It is evident from all these hypotheses that the structure of the contractile elements is not yet clear. Likewise, the immediate cause for the contraction has not yet been elucidated. Since the contraction takes place a few thousandths of a second after the electrical or the nervous excitation, a very rapid chemical reaction must be directly responsible for the deformation of the myosin molecules. Most probably it is a reaction between ions (111), since only these reactions take place at a sufficiently rapid rate; enzymatic reactions require a much longer time.

There are only a few experimental findings which permit some conclusions to be drawn concerning the nature of the ionic reaction underlying muscular contraction. One of them is the fact that a large portion of the potassium ions of resting muscle are not dialyzable before, but become dialyzable immediately after, the contraction. The potassium ions apparently become detached from negatively charged carboxyl groups of myosin or of other muscle proteins. A second important finding is that the contraction is accompanied by a slight decrease of the total

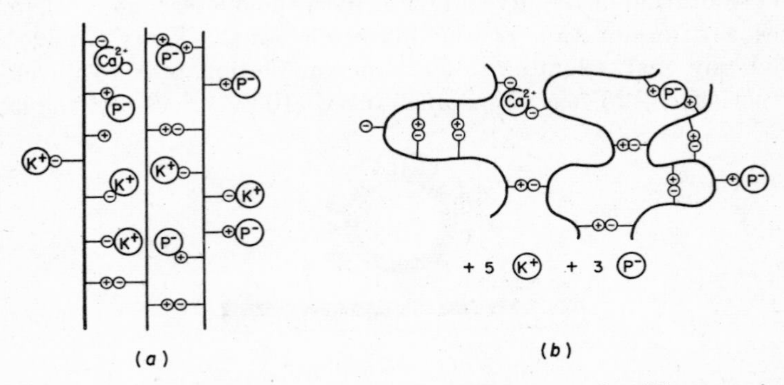

FIG. 37. Myosin molecules. (*a*) resting, (*b*) contracted. K^+, potassium ions; P^-, phosphate ions; Ca^{2+}, calcium ions. Plus signs in circles, $\overset{+}{N}H_3$ groups; minus signs in circles, $CO\overset{\cdot}{O}^-$ groups.

volume of the muscle amounting to 0.02 mm.³ per g. muscle (112). Decrease in volume must be attributed to the decrease of free water molecules, either by hydrolysis or by hydration of proteins or of other ions. The most likely explanation is that both the liberated potassium ions and the carboxyl groups undergo hydration (112):

$$R\cdot COO^-K^+ \xrightarrow{+H_2O} R\cdot COO^-(H_2O)_x + K^+(H_2O)_y$$

The deformation of myosin molecules is possibly due to this translocation of water molecules (113).

In addition to potassium ions, calcium (114) and phosphate ions (115) appear to be released during the muscular contraction. The shortening of myosin molecules may well be due to the intramolecular neutralization of those positive and negative groups of the peptide chain which have lost their inorganic counterions (116,117) (see Fig. 37).

On the other hand, however, one has to consider the possibility that bivalent ions such as the calcium or the phosphate ions form bridges between positively charged groups of the peptide chains and, in this way, cause contraction (117*a*). A similar contraction is observed when keratin fibers are exposed to solutions of copper salts in ammonia (118); if the copper ions are split off by acidification the contracted keratin fibers extend again (118).

Although we are not yet able to explain satisfactorily the action of the different ions on the contractile protein fibers, there is no doubt that the spatial arrangement of the fibers is closely related to their electrical charge. This is also evident from the fact that the reaction of the muscle is shifted toward higher pH values by passive extension (119,120).

The difficulty encountered by all hypotheses proposed to explain muscular contraction is the very strong contraction of certain muscles such as is observed in the holothuria *Thyone,* which contracts to about 8–9% of its original length (73). This can hardly be explained in terms of a folding according to the fashion shown in Figure 36 (121). No satisfactory explanation for this phenomenon has yet been advanced. Probably we are dealing here with the breaking of many transverse ionic cross links between extended parallel myosin fibers and the subsequent conversion of fibrous particles into more globular particles.

The problems presented by muscular energetics are far from being solved. It is not even certain whether the relaxation is a spontaneous or an active process, although the latter in all probability is the case (122). If it is assumed that the muscle consists of rigid rods connected end-to-end by flexible links, and that these rods are suspended in a fluid material, the modulus of elasticity, E, can be calculated (123):

$$E = 9RTW/5M$$

where R is the gas constant, T the absolute temperature, W the weight of the elastic material per milliliter, and M the molecular weight of each chain. Increase in the electric charge of the rods causes a drop of the modulus of elasticity and, consequently, relaxation; for the same reason a decrease in the free charge causes contraction (124). The connection between the number of charged groups, n, and ΔE, the increment in elastic modulus, is represented (124) by the equation:

$$\Delta E = -\frac{8}{3}\frac{N\rho}{M}\frac{n^2e^2}{D_eL}$$

where D_e is the effective dielectric constant (~ 100), N the Avogadro number, M the molecular weight (about 10^6), ρ the density, L the average distance between terminal groups (about 10^4 Å), and n the number of charges of magnitude e. From $\Delta E = 10^5$ dynes per cm.^{2} the value $n = \sim 100$ has been calculated (124).

The energy transformation occurring during the muscular contraction is that of the direct conversion of chemical energy into mechanical energy. The thermodynamic data for this reaction can be computed, when "extended myosin" and "contracted myosin" are considered to be two modifications of the same protein, and the extent of the reaction:

$$\text{extended myosin} \rightleftharpoons \text{contracted myosin}$$

is determined at different temperatures (see page 135). Such measurements show that the change in free energy, ΔF, is 7000–8500 cal. per mole and the change in heat content 53,500–56,000 cal. per mole (125).

E. Other Albumins and Globulins of Animal Origin. Only a few proteins have been investigated as thoroughly as those of the blood plasma. One of these is *ovalbumin*, the albumin of hens' eggs. It was crystallized for the first time by Hofmeister (126), who used ammonium sulfate for the preparation. The method was improved by Hopkins (127) and by Sørensen (128), who removed globulins by half-saturation with ammonium sulfate and precipitated the ovalbumin by acidifying the filtrate. For the reasons discussed in the preceding section it is advantageous to substitute sodium sulfate for ammonium sulfate (129). Fresh egg white is mixed with an equal volume of a 36.7% solution of sodium sulfate and the precipitated globulins are filtered off; the filtrate is brought to pH 4.7 by dilute sulfuric acid and anhydrous sodium sulfate is added to bring about a slight opalescence. On standing crystalline ovalbumin forms and settles out. The ease with which ovalbumin can be prepared in crystals has made it one of the favorite subjects of investigation in protein chemistry. Its properties have been mentioned repeatedly in the preceding chapters; its amino acid composition is shown in Table I (p. 32).

In spite of its beautiful crystals, ovalbumin is not a homogeneous substance. Electrophoretic analysis has shown that it consists of at least two fractions (130,131). Ovalbumin forms about 50% of the proteins of hens' egg white, while 15% is formed by *conalbumin*, a protein present in the filtrate of the ovalbumin crystals (132). Conalbumin is prepared directly from egg white by fractionation with aqueous ethanol (133) and has been found to be a flavoprotein of molecular weight 87,000; the isoelectric point of conalbumin is pH 6.1; it forms a red complex with iron salts (see page 204). A globulin called ovoglobulin may be prepared from egg white, but not much is known about its properties (134).

Egg white also contains *avidin*, a basic protein, responsible for the "egg white injury" produced in animals by feeding raw egg white. Avidin has been prepared in crystals (135). It is a basic glucoprotein, whose isoelectric point is near pH 10 (136). The injury is due to biotin deficiency caused by the combination of avidin with biotin (137). The avidin-bioti complex is very similar to and possibly identical with lysozyme (138,139).

The principal protein of *milk* (139*a*) is casein, a phosphoprotein (see p. 202), which is precipitated by acidification of the milk. The filtrate (whey) contains lactalbumin and lactoglobulin. The molecular weight of lactalbumin is 17,400 (140). When the albumin fraction, precipitated by ammonium sulfate, is dissolved in water and dialyzed at a slightly acid reaction a crystalline protein, which has been called *β-lactoglobulin*, precipitates (141). Since this protein can be obtained easily and in large amounts, it has been investigated extensively. Its molecular weight and the shape of its molecules are shown in Tables IV and V (pp. 53 and 54).

Proteins of the albumin and globulin types have been prepared not only from the body fluids, but from various organs as well. It is advisable to remove all the blood by perfusion of the organ with isotonic sodium chloride solution. The blood-free organ is then minced and ground and the pulp extracted with solutions of sodium chloride or of buffers. The proteins prepared in this way from muscle have been described in Section D. Many of the proteins extracted from organs are enzymatically active; these will be discussed in Chapter XII. The active protein hormones prepared from endocrine glands are treated in Chapter XIV. The organ extracts contain proteins chiefly of the globulin type which are precipitated by acidification, by salting-out, or by dialysis against distilled water. Proteins of the albumin type are rare in organ extracts. Thus, the protein of the crystalline lens of the eye contains 51.5% globulin and only 0.5% albumin; 48% of the total protein is an insoluble scleroprotein. From the globulin fraction two globulins, called α- and β-crystallin, have been isolated (142).

F. Vegetable Proteins (143). Vegetable proteins have been obtained principally from the seeds of grain and of leguminous plants. The seeds are ground and, if necessary, freed from lipids by extraction with diethyl ether or petroleum ether. The proteins are extracted from the fat-free residue by means of aqueous solutions of salts or of buffers, or by ethanol. Most of the proteins extracted from seeds have the properties of globulins; only 0.1–0.5% of albumins are present in the seeds. Those globulins which are soluble in aqueous ethanol have been called prolamins; globulins which dissolve neither in salt solutions nor in alcohol, but are extracted by dilute acids or alkali hydroxides, have been called glutelins (2). Neither the prolamins nor the glutelins are uniform proteins; they are mixtures of various similar proteins (144,145).

Among the salt-soluble *globulins* edestin from hemp seed has received the most attention. Other, similar proteins are excelsin from brazil nuts, amandin from almonds, legumin from peas and lentils, phaseolin from beans, glycinin from soybeans, canavalin and concanavalin from jack beans, and globulins from cotton seed, pumpkin seed, and other seeds. These globulins are extracted from the ground seeds by 2–10% sodium chloride solutions. The organic acids present in seeds are neutralized by adding baryta to the sodium chloride solution. Upon dialysis edestin and some of the other globulins precipitate as crystals. Edestin can be recrystallized from 10% sodium chloride solution. Its amino acid composition is shown in Table I (p. 32). The following molecular weights have been found for some of the globulins (146,147):

Edestin	310,000	Concanavallin B	42,000
Excelsin	295,000	Concanavallin A	96,000
Amandin	330,000	Canavalin	113,000

Not all the vegetable globulins correspond strictly to the definition of a globulin insofar as some of them are not precipitated by half-saturation with ammonium sulfate.

The ethanol-soluble seed globulins have been called *prolamins* because of their high content of proline and amide nitrogen. Table I (p. 32) shows that they contain only very small amounts of basic amino acids but very high amounts of glutamic acid. Thus more than 40% of the protein gliadin is formed by glutamic acid. In spite of this high content of glutamic acid the prolamins are not acidic proteins, because the carboxyl groups of all of the glutamic acid molecules are substituted by ammonia (see Table I). Some of the prolamins are devoid of lysine, a fact which is important in nutritional problems.

The most extensively investigated prolamins are gliadin from wheat or rye kernel, hordein from barley (*Hordeum vulgare*), and zein from maize (*Zea mays*). They may be extracted by 70–80% ethanol from the flour of their respective grains and precipitated by the addition of diethyl ether (148,149). Another procedure is to extract with alcohol the starch-free gluten (150) prepared from flour by kneading it with water. The prolamins, although insoluble in water and in absolute ethanol, are soluble in 50–80% ethanol. Zein was also found to be soluble in anionic and cationic detergents (151). The molecular weight of gliadin and of hordein is approximately 27,500, that of zein 40,000 (152). However, the prolamins were found electrophoretically to be mixtures of two or more components (144). Gliadin contains two fractions with isoelectric points of pH 5 and 7 (153).

Since zein contains no lysine all the free amino groups are considered to be α-amino groups; a thorough investigation revealed that zein contains only one or two free amino groups (154), which shows that the molecule consists of only one or two peptide chains. It contains only one molecule of cystine (154). If zein is hydrolyzed by the action of pepsin, peptides are produced, whose terminal amino group is formed by glutamic acid molecules. Hydrolysis with trypsin furnishes peptides with terminal alanine molecules (154).

Approximately half the gluten obtained from wheat flour by washing with water is made up of gliadin, the other half of *glutenin*. The latter protein is insoluble in ethanol and in neutral salt solutions. It is soluble in 0.2% potassium hydroxide solution and is precipitated by neutralization with hydrochloric acid. It is probable not a homogeneous substance, but a mixture of proteins and lipoproteins (144,145).

G. Protamines and Histones (155,156). The *protamines*, which are strongly basic proteins of low molecular weight, were first discovered by Miescher (1874) in the ripe sperm of the salmon and have since been identified in the sperm of other fishes. They are present in the sperm as nucleic acid salts and are set free from the dried, fat-free sperm by acidification with sulfuric acid or by treatment with copper chloride (157). They are precipitated as picrates from their solutions in sulfuric acid. The most thoroughly investigated protamines are salmine from the sperm of salmon, clupein from herring (*Clupea harengus*), sturin from sturgeon (*Acipenser sturio*), and scombrin from the mackerel (*Scomber scomber*).

Salmine is quite simple in composition, containing only seven different types of amino acids, among which arginine predominates. The molecular weight of salmine is 8000; the molecule contains 40 molecules of arginine, 7 serine, 4 proline, 3 glycine, 2 valine, 1 isoleucine, and 1 alanine (158). Since salmine has no free amino group it is either a cyclopeptide or a peptide whose terminal group is formed by proline, an imino acid (158). The structure of other protamines is more complicated than that of salmine. The protamine of sardine sperm contains only 15.8% arginine, but 15.7% histidine, 1.09% tyrosine, and 0.87% tryptophan (159).

The high basicity of the protamines is due to their high content of arginine. Kossel found that approximately two thirds of the amino acids of the protamines is arginine (160). This was later confirmed by other investigators (161–163). Protamines are so strongly basic that they combine with carbon dioxide of the air to form carbonates. Their sulfates are neutral salts which are soluble in hot water; on cooling they separate from water as an oily layer. While there is no free amino group in salmine and in clupein (164), the terminal carboxyl group is formed by an arginine molecule (163).

The *histones* are also basic proteins. They were discovered by Kossel (165) in cell nuclei, where they are combined with nucleic acids. They are less basic than protamines and are, therefore, not precipitated by alkaline solutions of picrates. The histones are possibly precursors of the protamines, since they have been found in the testes of immature fishes before the formation of the sperm. Owing to their basic character, the histones are precipitated by the addition of ammonia at their isoelectric point near pH 8.5. Use is made of this property for their preparation. The best known histone is that of the thymus gland; the nucleohistone is precipitated from aqueous extracts of the glands by acetic acid and dissolved in alkali; the nucleic acids are removed by precipitation with sulfuric acid and histone sulfate is precipitated by ethanol (166). The molecular weight of histones is higher than that of the protamines and their composition more similar to that of true proteins. They contain phenylalanine and tyrosine as well as small amounts of histidine and lysine. The histones can be differentiated from protamines on the basis of their tyrosine content. For the differentiation of nucleohistones from true nucleoproteins use is made of the tryptophan reaction; Kossel found small amounts of tryptophan in histones; according to the more recent analyses of Stedman, however, thymus histone and histone from cod sperm are completely devoid of tryptophan (167).

Globin, the protein component of hemoglobin was at one time regarded as a histone because preparations of globin were precipitated by ammonia; later it was found, however, that these preparations contained denatured globin. Native globin is not precipitated by ammonia. It also differs from the typical histones in its amino acid composition.

Basic proteins with properties intermediate between those of protamines and histones were isolated from the sperm of invertebrates; from 28 to 83% of their nitrogen is arginine nitrogen (168).

References

1. F. Hofmeister, *Arch. exptl. Path. Pharmakol.* **24,** 247 (1887).
2. Committee on Nomenclature, *J. Biol. Chem.* **4,** 142 (1908).
3. F. Wuhrmann, C. Wunderly, Die Bluteiweisskörper des Menschens. Schwabe and Co. Basel, 1947.
4. J. T. Edsall, *Advances in Protein Chem.* **3,** 383 (1947).
5. A. B. Gutmann, *Advances in Protein Chem.* **4,** 155 (1948).
6. E. J. Cohn, *Chem. Revs.* **28,** 395 (1941).
7. F. Pohl, *Arch. exptl. Path. Pharmakol.* **20,** 426 (1886).
8. O. Hammarsten, *Z. physiol. Chem.* **8,** 467 (1897).
9. P. E. Howe, *J. Biol. Chem.* **49,** 93, 109 (1921).
10. A. M. Butler, H. Montgomery, *J. Biol. Chem.* **99,** 173 (1933).
11. A. Tiselius, *Biochem. J.* **31,** 1464 (1937).

12. E. J. Cohn, T. L. McMeekin, J. L. Oncley, J. M. Newell, W. L. Hughes, Jr., *J. Am. Chem. Soc.* **62,** 3386 (1940).
13. M. L. Petermann, N. F. Young, K. R. Hogness, *J. Biol. Chem.* **169,** 579 (1947).
14. E. J. Cohn, J. A. Luetscher, Jr., J. L. Oncley, S. H. Armstrong, Jr., B. D. Davis, *J. Am. Chem. Soc.* **62,** 3396 (1940).
15. H. Wu, *Chinese J. Physiol.* **7,** 125 (1933).
16. J. L. Oncley *et al.*, *J. Am. Chem. Soc.*, **71,** 541 (1949); D. M. Surgenor *et al.*, *ibid.* **71,** 1223 (1949).
17. G. Blix, A. Tiselius, H. Svensson, *J. Biol. Chem.* **137,** 485 (1941).
18. C. Holmberg, C. B. Laurell, *Acta Physiol. Scand.* **1,** 944 (1947).
18*a*. J. T. Edsall, personal communication.
19. E. J. Cohn, W. L. Hughes, Jr., T. H. Weare, *J. Am. Chem. Soc.* **69,** 1753 (1947).
20. K. O. Pedersen, *Nature* **154,** 575, 642 (1944).
21. D. H. Moore, J. G. Lynn, *J. Biol. Chem.* **141,** 819 (1941).
22. R. A. Kekwick, *Biochem. J.* **33,** 1122 (1939).
23. J. L. Oncley, G. Scatchard, A. Brown, *J. Phys. Chem.* **51,** 184 (1947).
24. B. V. Jager, E. L. Smith, M. Nickerson, D. M. Brown, *J. Biol. Chem.* **176,** 1177 (1948).
25. L. F. Hewitt, *Biochem. J.* **32,** 1540 (1938); **31,** 360, 1534 (1937).
26. D. G. Sharp, G. R. Cooper, J. O. Erickson, H. Neurath, *J. Biol. Chem.* **144,** 139 (1942).
27. H. F. Deutsch, R. A. Alberty, L. J. Gosting, *J. Biol. Chem.* **165,** 21 (1946).
28. K. O. Pedersen, *Ann. Rev. Biochem.* **17,** 179 (1948).
29. J. Van der Scheer, R. W. G. Wyckoff, F. H. Clarke, *J. Immunol.* **39,** 65 (1940).
29*a*. E. L. Hess, H. F. Deutsch, *J. Am. Chem. Soc.* **71,** 1376 (1949).
29*b*. C. R. Cann, R. A. Brown, and J. G. Kirkwood, *J. Biol. Chem.* **181,** 161 (1949).
30. L. Pillemer, M. C. Hutchinson, *J. Biol. Chem.* **158,** 299 (1945).
31. J. L. Delsal, *Bull. soc. chim. biol.* **29,** 690 (1947).
31*a*. E. J. Cohn *et al.*, *J. Am. Chem. Soc.* **72,** 465 (1950).
32. W. Pauli, *Helv. Chim. Acta* **30,** 77 (1946).
33. F. Haurowitz, *J. Immunol.* **43,** 331 (1942).
34. A. Abrams, P. P. Cohen, O. O. Meyer, *J. Biol. Chem.* **181,** 237 (1949).
34*a*. C. E. Dent, G. Rose, *Biochem. J.* **43,** LIV (1948).
35. T. Svedberg, *J. Am. Chem. Soc.* **51,** 3594 (1929).
36. J. A. Luetscher, *Physiol. Rev.* **27,** 621 (1947).
37. N. F. Maclagan, *Brit. J. Exptl. Path.* **25,** 234 (1944).
38. P. P. Cohen, F. L. Thompson, *J. Lab. Clin. Med.* **32,** 475 (1947).
39. N. F. Maclagan, D. Bunn, *Biochem. J.* **41,** 580 (1947).
40. D. H. Moore, *J. Biol. Chem.* **161,** 21 (1945).
41. A. Polson, *Nature* **152,** 413 (1943).
41*a*. F. Haurowitz, P. Schwerin, unpublished experiments.
41*b*. J. Roche, Y. Derrien, M. Fontaine, *Bull. soc. chim. biol.* **22,** 395 (1940).
42. H. P. Smith, J. E. Flynn, *Ann. Rev. Physiol.* **10,** 417 (1948).
42*a*. J. T. Edsall, *Ergeb. Physiol. Exptl. Path.* 000, 000 (1950).
43. T. Astrup, S. Darling, *Acta Physiol. Scand.* **4,** 45 (1942).
44. F. L. Munro, M. P. Munro, *Arch. Biochem.* **15,** 295 (1947).
45. W. H. Seegers, E. C. Loomis, J. M. Vandenbelt, *Arch. Biochem.* **6,** 85 (1945).
46. E. Chargaff, R. West, *J. Biol. Chem.* **166,** 189 (1946); E. Chargaff, *Advances in Enzymol.* **5,** 31 (1935).
47. E. Chargaff, A. Bendich, S. S. Cohen, *J. Biol. Chem.* **156,** 161 (1945); **172,** 253

(1948). E. Chargaff, F. W. Bancroft, M. Stanley-Brown, *J. Biol. Chem.* **116,** 237 (1936).
48. H. Eagle, T. N. Harris, *J. Gen. Physiol.* **20,** 543 (1937).
49. A. J. Quick, *Science* **106,** 591 (1947).
50. M. Stefanini, *Proc. Soc. Exptl. Biol. Med.* **67,** 22 (1948).
51. H. Weitnauer, E. Wöhlisch, *Biochem. Z.* **288,** 137 (1936).
52. T. Astrup, *Enzymologia* **5,** 119 (1938).
53. A. J. Quick, M. Stefanini, *J. Gen. Physiol.* **32,** 191 (1948).
54. W. H. Howell, *Physiol. Revs.* **15,** 435 (1935).
55. J. Mellanby, in J. Needham and D. W. Green, Jr., Perspectives in Biochemistry. Cambridge Univ. Press, 1937, p. 286.
56. J. T. Edsall, *Advances in Protein Chem.* **3,** 383, 448 (1947).
57. A. G. Ware, W. H. Seegers, *J. Biol. Chem.* **172,** 699 (1948).
58. O. Hammarsten, *Z. physiol. Chem.* **22,** 333 (1897).
58*a*. P. R. Morrison, J. T. Edsall, S. G. Miller, *J. Am. Chem. Soc.* **70,** 3103 (1948).
59. J. T. Edsall, J. Foster, H. Scheinberg, *J. Am. Chem. Soc.* **69,** 2731 (1947).
59*a*. A. G. Ware, M. M. Guest, W. H. Seegers, *Arch. Biochem.* **13,** 231 (1947).
60. A. Fischer, *Biochem. Z.* **278,** 133 (1935); *Enzymologia* **1,** 81, 85 (1936).
61. H. Hermann, *Skand. Arch. Physiol.* **76,** 125 (1937).
62. E. Wöhlisch, L. Jühling, *Biochem. Z.* **297,** 353 (1938).
63. R. H. Lyons, *Nature* **155,** 633 (1945).
64. U. Ebbeke, *Arch. ges. Physiol. (Pflügers)* **243,** 43 (1941).
65. K. Laki, W. F. H. M. Mommaerts, *Nature* **156,** 664 (1945).
66. E. Chargaff, M. Ziff, *J. Biol. Chem.* **138,** 787 (1941).
67. C. van Z. Hawn, K. Porter, *J. Exptl. Med.* **86,** 285 (1947); **90,** 225 (1949).
68. J. D. Ferry, P. R. Morrison, *J. Am. Chem. Soc.* **69,** 386 (1947).
69. E. C. Hall, *J. Biol. Chem.* **179,** 857 (1949).
69*a*. J. D. Ferry, *Advances in Protein Chem.* **4,** 1 (1948).
70. A. Szent-Györgyi, Chemistry of Muscular Contraction. Academic, New York, 1947.
71. A. Szent-Györgyi, Nature of Life. Academic, New York, 1948.
72. W. O. Fenn, in R. Hoeber, Physical Chemistry of Cells and Tissues. Blakiston, Philadelphia, 1945, p. 445.
73. K. Bailey, *Advances in Protein Chem.* **1,** 312 (1944).
73*a*. O. Snellman, B. Gelotte, *Exptl. Cell Research* **1,** 234 (1950).
74. H. H. Weber, *Biochem. Z.* **266,** 137 (1933); **259,** 269 (1933).
75. T. Baranowski, *Biokhimiya* **4,** 179 (1940); *Compt. rend. acad. sci. U. R. S. S.* **31,** 129 (1941).
76. A. Distèche, *Biochim. et Biophys. Acta* **2,** 265 (1948).
77. G. T. Cori, Abstracts 114th Meeting Am. Chem. Soc. 27C (1948).
78. A. von Muralt, J. T. Edsall, *J. Biol. Chem.* **89,** 289 (1930).
79. J. T. Edsall, J. W. Mehl, *J. Biol. Chem.* **133,** 409 (1940).
80. H. H. Weber, *Ergeb. Physiol. exptl. Pharmakol.* **36,** 109 (1934).
81. M. von Ardenne, H. H. Weber, *Kolloid-Z.* **97,** 322 (1941).
82. R. Baer, *J. Am. Chem. Soc.* **66,** 2043 (1944).
83. O. Kratky, A. Sekora, H. H. Weber, *Naturwissenschaften* **31,** 91 (1943).
84. W. Lotmar, L. E. R. Picken, *Helv. Chim. Acta* **25,** 538 (1942).
85. M. Ziff, D. H. Moore, *J. Biol. Chem.* **153,** 653 (1944).
86. M. Dubuisson, *Experientia* **2,** 258, 421 (1946).
87. A. Szent-Györgyi, *Acta Physiol. Scand.* **9,** Suppl. 25 (1945).

88. F. Straub, *Studies Inst. Med. Chem. Univ. Szeged* **2,** 3 (1942); **3,** 23 (1943).
89. O. Snellman, T. Erdos, *Biochem. et Biophys. Acta* **3,** 523 (1949).
90. M. A. Jakus, C. E. Hall, *J. Biol. Chem.* **167,** 705 (1947).
91. S. Perry, R. Reed, *Biochim. et Biophys. Acta* **1,** 379 (1947).
92. G. Rózsa, M. Staudinger, *J. Makromol. Chem.* **2,** 66 (1947).
92*a*. F. G. Straub, G. Feuer, *Biochim. et Biophys. Acta*, **4,** 255 (1950).
93. K. Bailey, *Ann. Repts. on Progress Chem. (Chem. Soc. London)* **43,** 280 (1947).
94. F. Binkley, *J. Biol. Chem.* **174,** 385 (1948).
95. K. Bailey, *Biochem. J.* **43,** 271 (1948).
96. W. T. Astbury, R. Reed, L. Spark, *Biochem. J.* **43,** 282 (1948).
97. K. Bailey, H. Gutfreund, A. Ogston, *Biochem. J.* **43,** 279 (1948).
98. J. Needham, A. Kleinzeller, M. Miall, M. Dainty, D. M. Needham, A. S. C. Lawrence, *Nature* **150,** 46 (1942).
99. A. Szent-Györgyi, *Studies Inst. Med. Chem. Univ. Szeged* **1,** 1 (1942).
100. G. S. Adair, K. Bailey, T. C. Tsao, *Biochem. J.* **45,** 5 (1949).
100*a*. W. K. Jordan, G. Oster, *Science* **108,** 188 (1948).
101. A. Szent-Györgyi, *Acta Physiol. Hungary* **1,** 28 (1946).
101*a*. G. Rozsa, A. Szent-Györgyi, R. W. G. Wyckoff, *Exptl. Cell Research*, **1,** 194 (1950).
102. V. A. Engel'hardt, M. N. Lyubimova, *Nature* **144,** 668 (1939).
103. T. Caspersson, B. Thorell, *Acta Physiol. Scand.* **4,** 97 (1942).
104. H. O. Singher, A. Meister, *J. Biol. Chem.* **159,** 491 (1945).
105. B. D. Polis, O. Meyerhof, *J. Biol. Chem.* **169,** 389 (1947).
106. F. O. Schmitt, R. S. Bear, C. E. Hall, M. A. Jakus, *Ann. N. Y. Acad. Sci.* **47,** 799 (1947).
107. W. T. Astbury, *Proc. Roy. Soc. London* **B134,** 303 (1947).
108. W. T. Astbury, S. Dickinson, *Proc. Roy. Soc. London* **B129,** 307 (1940).
109. A. Szent-Györgyi, *Science* **110,** 411 (1949).
109*a*. M. Dubuisson, *Biochim. et Biophys. Acta* **4,** 25 (1950).
110. A. E. Mirsky, *J. Gen. Physiol.* **20,** 461 (1936).
110*a*. A. Szent-Györgyi, *J. Colloid Sci.* **1,** 1 (1946).
111. W. O. Fenn, *Physiol. Revs.* **16,** 450 (1936).
112. E. Ernst, J. Koczkas, *Arch. ges. Physiol. (Pflügers)* **239,** 691 (1938). E. Ernst, *Klin. Wochschr.* **15,** 1641 (1936).
113. A. Szent-Györgyi, *Enzymologia* **9,** 98 (1942).
114. K. Bailey, *Biochem. J.* **36,** 121 (1942).
115. H. M. Kalckar, *Chem. Revs.* **28,** 71 (1941).
116. K. H. Meyer, *Biochem. Z.* **214,** 253 (1929).
117. F. Verzar, *Schweiz. Med. Wochenschr.* **72,** 661 (1942).
117*a*. D. Needham, *Biochim. et Biophys. Acta* **4,** 42 (1950).
118. C. S. Whewell, H. J. Woods, *Nature* **154,** 546 (1944).
119. R. Margaria, *J. Physiol.* **82,** 496 (1933).
120. M. Dubuisson, *Arch. intern. physiol.* **50,** 203 (1940).
121. H. H. Weber, *Biochem. Z.* **217,** 470 (1930).
122. M. Dubuisson, *Experientia* **3,** 213 (1947).
123. H. B. Bull, *J. Am. Chem. Soc.* **67,** 2047 (1945).
124. J. Riseman, J. G. Kirkwood, *J. Am. Chem. Soc.* **70,** 2820 (1948).
125. L. Varga, *Acta Physiol. Hungary* **1,** 1 (1947).
126. F. Hofmeister, *Z. physiol. Chem.* **14,** 165 (1889).
127. F. G. Hopkins, *J. Physiol.* **25,** 306 (1900).

128. S. P. L. Sørensen, *Z. physiol. Chem.* **103,** 15 (1918).
129. R. A. Kekwick, R. K. Cannan, *Biochem. J.* **30,** 227 (1936).
130. A. Tiselius, B. Erickson-Quensel, *Biochem. J.* **33,** 1752 (1939).
131. L. G. Longsworth, R. K. Cannan, D. A. McInnes, *J. Am. Chem. Soc.* **62,** 2580 (1940).
132. H. Wu, *Chinese J. Physiol.* **1,** 131 (1927).
133. J. H. Bain, H. F. Deutsch, *J. Biol. Chem.* **172,** 547 (1948).
134. T. Osborne, G. Campbell, *J. Am. Chem. Soc.* **22,** 422 (1900).
135. D. Pennington, E. E. Snell, R. E. Eakin, *J. Am. Chem. Soc.* **64,** 469 (1942).
136. D. W. Woolley, L. G. Longsworth, *J. Biol. Chem.* **142,** 285 (1942).
137. R. E. Eakin, E. E. Snell, R. J. Williams, *J. Biol. Chem.* **140,** 535 (1941).
138. G. Alderton, J. C. Lewis, H. L. Fevold, *Science* **101,** 151 (1945).
139. K. Meyer, *Science* **99,** 391 (1944); W. L. Lawrence, *ibid.* **99,** 392 (1944).
139*a*. T. L. McMeekin, *Advances in Protein Chem.* **5,** 202 (1949).
140. T. Svedberg, *Nature* **139,** 1051 (1937).
141. A. H. Palmer, *J. Biol. Chem.* **104,** 359 (1934).
142. T. Mörner, *Z. physiol. Chem.* **18,** 61 (1894).
143. T. B. Osborne, Vegetable Proteins. Longmans, Green, New York, 1924; J. H. W. Lugg, *Advances in Protein Chem.* **5,** 230 (1949).
144. A. G. McCalla, *Ann. Rev. Biochem.* **18,** 617 (1949).
145. H. S. Olcott, D. K. Meecham, *Cereal Chem.* **24,** 407 (1947).
146. T. Svedberg, *Tabulae Biologicae* **11,** 351 (1936).
147. J. B. Sumner, N. Gralén, B. Erickson-Quensel, *Science* **87,** 395 (1938).
148. T. B. Osborne, C. Vorhees, *Am. Chem. J.* **15,** 392 (1893); *J. Am. Chem. Soc.* **17,** 539 (1895).
149. R. Chittenden, T. B. Osborne, *Am. Chem. J.* **13,** 453 (1891); **14,** 20 (1892).
150. G. Blix, *Advances in Protein Chem.* **2,** 337 (1945).
151. J. F. Foster, *J. Phys. Colloid Chem.* **53,** 175 (1949).
152. O. Lamm, A. Polson, *Biochem. J.* **30,** 528 (1937).
153. G. W. Schwert, F. W. Putnam, D. R. Briggs, *Arch. Biochem.* **4,** 371 (1944).
154. T. Laine, *Ann. Acad. Sci. Fennicae, Ser. A. II* No. 11 (1944).
155. A. Kossel, Protamines and Histones. Longmans, New York, 1928.
156. J. P. Greenstein, *Advances in Protein Chem.* **1,** 209 (1944).
157. A. Kossel, *Z. physiol. Chem.* **173,** 278 (1928).
158. G. R. Tristram, *Nature* **160,** 637 (1947).
159. M. Dunn, *J. Biol. Chem.* **70,** 697 (1926).
160. A. Kossel, H. Dakin, *Z. physiol. Chem.* **41,** 407 (1904).
161. K. Felix, K. Inouye, K. Dirr, *Z. physiol. Chem.* **211,** 187 (1932).
162. E. Waldschmidt-Leitz, E. Kofranyi, *Z. physiol. Chem.* **236,** 181 (1935).
163. R. J. Block, D. Bolling, *Arch. Biochem.* **6,** 419 (1945).
164. K. Felix, K. Dirr, *Z. physiol. Chem.* **184,** 111 (1929).
165. A. Kossel, *Z. physiol. Chem.* **8,** 511 (1884); **171,** 156 (1927).
166. K. Felix, *Z. physiol. Chem.* **200,** 26 (1931).
167. E. Stedman, E. Stedman, *Symposia Soc. Exptl. Biol.* **1,** 240 (1947).
168. T. Hultin, R. Herne, *Arkiv. Kemi Mineral. Geol.* **26A,** No. 20 (1949).

CHAPTER IX

Insoluble Proteins (Scleroproteins)

A. General Remarks. The proteins to be discussed in this section have in common the property of being insoluble in water, aqueous solutions of neutral salts, and organic solvents. Although they are easily separated from the soluble substances which also occur in tissues, such as salts, carbohydrates, lipids, and water-soluble proteins, no methods are available for the further purification of these insoluble, structural proteins. We can neither reprecipitate, nor recrystallize them and hence have no criteria to test conclusively whether they are uniform or consist of mixtures of various similar substances. The two most important classes of structural proteins are the keratins and the collagens. While keratins resist the action of both proteolytic enzymes and boiling water, collagens are hydrolyzed by the enzymes and are converted by the prolonged action of boiling water into gelatin (glue). Keratins and collagens further differ from each other in amino acid composition (see Table I page 32), distribution throughout animal organisms, and in certain other characteristics to be discussed in the following sections.

While keratin, collagen, and other similar proteins forming the skeletal structure of animals are classified as scleroproteins, this class does not include the insoluble proteins of the mitochondria and of other cellular granules. Many of these insoluble proteins are conjugated with lipids and will be discussed in the section on lipoproteins (page 194). Other insoluble proteins are enzymatically active and are, therefore, treated in the chapter on enzymes (Chapter XII). It must be admitted, however, that we are not always able to draw a sharp line between these insoluble proteins and the scleroproteins of the keratin and collagen type.

B. Keratins. Keratins are formed in the outermost living cells of the skin; they are the structural proteins of hair, wool, feathers, horn, nails, and hoofs. Keratin is prepared from these materials by pulverizing them, extracting first with hot organic solvents, then with water, and finally digesting with pepsin and trypsin. If the skin, the nervous tissue, and certain other organs are treated in this way, a small amount of keratinlike substances called *pseudokeratins* is obtained. Pseudokeratins are less resistant to enzyme action than are the true *eukeratins* (1). To the pseudokeratins belong the neurokeratin from nerve sheaths (2), the ovokeratin from hens' eggs (3), and possibly coilin, the keratinlike substance occurring in the gizzards of birds.

The eukeratins have a notably high content of cystine, the keratin from human hair and from wool containing approximately 11–12%, which corresponds to 3% sulfur. Other eukeratins contain from 3 to 5% sulfur, while the pseudokeratins contain 1–3% (4). Eukeratins and pseudokeratins also differ in their content of basic amino acids. In eukeratins the ratio histidine: lysine: arginine is approximately 1:4:12, while in pseudokeratins the ratio lysine/arginine is 1:1 (4). The typical, disagreeable odor of burned wool, which is probably due to the formation of mercaptans, is attributed to the high cystine content of keratin. When wool is boiled with a 2% solution of sodium carbonate and then hydrolyzed with boiling hydrochloric acid, lanthionine, $COOH{\cdot}CHNH_2{\cdot}CH_2{\cdot}S{\cdot}CH_2{\cdot}CHNH_2{\cdot}COOH$, is obtained rather than cystine (5).

The cystine molecules seem to be fundamentally involved in the insolubility of keratin and in its great resistance to enzymes. It has long been known that hair is dissolved by the action of sulfides. Use is made of the depilatory action of sulfides for cosmetic purposes and also for the preparation of laboratory animals prior to surgical operations. The action of the sulfides is apparently due to their reducing power, by which the dithio bond of cystine is reduced to two sulfhydryl groups. A somewhat similar effect is brought about by the action of thioglycolic acid or of cyanides (6):

$$R{-}S{-}S{-}R + HCN \rightarrow RSH + NCS{-}R$$

If the reduction is performed in the presence of alkylene dibromides, an alkylene group is inserted between the two sulfur atoms (53):

$$R{-}S{-}S{-}R \rightarrow R{-}S{-}CH_2{-}S{-}R$$

Reduced keratin, which has been termed keratein, is subject to hydrolysis by proteolytic enzymes (6). The dithio bond, —S—S—, can be cleaved as well by oxidizing agents such as bromine or hydrogen peroxide. When the oxidation is performed cautiously, the hair maintains its original shape and remains insoluble in water, but it becomes susceptible to proteolytic enzymes (7). It would appear that different types of keratins are present in hair, feathers, tortoise shells, and in other related substances, since different amounts of amino acids have been found in the keratins isolated from these organs (8,9). It is not yet known whether the keratins and pseudokeratins are species-specific. Since they are insoluble in water it is impossible to apply to them the serological tests for species specificity.

The resistance of keratin to solvents and enzymes is lowered not only by exposure to these chemical agents, but also by mechanical treatment. Wool is split by enzymes if it is finely ground (10) and pulverized horn is partly soluble in water (11).

Hair and wool fibers are extensible and possess *elastic* properties. That the extension of hair depends on its water content is the principle underlying hair hygrometers, which are used to determine the humidity of the air. X-ray analyses of normal and extended hair reveal that the stretching of the hair is accompanied by a typical alteration of the X-ray pattern. The unextended and the extended keratin fibers have been considered two modifications of keratin and have been designated α- and β-keratin, respectively. While the X-ray diagram of α-keratin shows periods of 5.1 Å along the fiber axis, that of β-keratin indicates periods of 3.4 Å (12). It has been assumed that the structure of β-keratin corresponds to an extended arrangement of the peptide chains (*A*), whereas the peptide chains of α-keratin are folded, forming regular loops of a diameter of 5.1 Å according to diagram (*B*) (50):

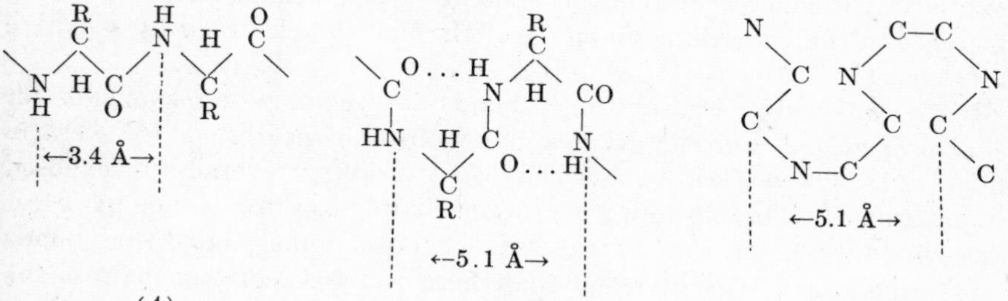

```
    R      H       O
    C      N   H   C
 \ / \   / :  \  /  \
  N  H C   :   C
  H    O   :   R
  :        :
  :←3.4 Å→:
  :        :

     (A)
```

```
                  R
                  C
  \  O...H     /   \
    C       N  H   CO
    |       |       |
    HN   H  C       N
    :    \ /  O...H: \
    :     C        :
    :     R        :
    :              :
    :   ←5.1 Å→    :
    :              :

         (B)
```

```
  N                 C—C
    \             /     \
      C    N            N
    /        \        /
  C            C    C
  : \        /      : \
  :   N—C           :   C
  :                 :
  :    ←5.1 Å→      :
  :                 :

                (C)
```

Folding of the peptide chains according to (*C*) (12) is irreconcilable with the presence of large side chains in the amino acids (13,13*a*). One has also to consider the possibility that the X-ray pattern of keratin is due to a parallel orientation in a definite direction of the central axis of the threads, without any regularity in other dimensions. This parallel orientation of the peptide chains is partly maintained by the *dithio bonds* —S—S— of cystine molecules. Cystine, a diaminodicarboxylic acid, can form bridges between parallel peptide chains:

```
—HN·CHR·CO—HN·CH·CO—HN·CHR·CO—
               ·
              CH2
               ·
               S
               ·
               S
               ·
              CH2
               ·
—OC·CHR·NH—OC·CH·NH—OC·CHR·NH—
```

The dithio bonds cannot be split, however, by water molecules at room temperature. The swelling of hair and of wool in humid air has, rather, been attributed to another phenomenon, that of the splitting of salt bridges (*D*) between positively and negatively charged side chains of the amino acids (14) and/or to the cleavage of *hydrogen bonds* between NH and CO groups of a peptide chain (*B*) or of two adjacent peptide chains (*E*) (15):

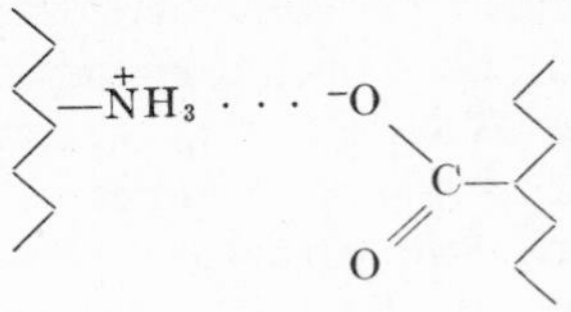

$$-\overset{+}{N}H_3 \cdots {}^{-}O-\overset{O}{\overset{\|}{C}}-$$

(*D*) Salt bridge

$$\begin{array}{ccc} C=O & & HCR \\ RCH & & NH \\ N-H & \cdots & O=C \\ OC & & HCR \end{array}$$

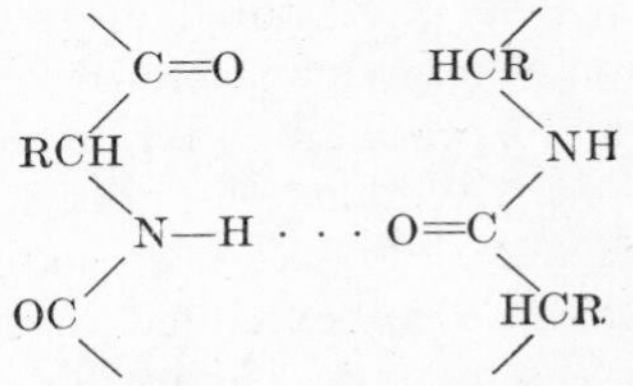

(*E*) Hydrogen bond

While only the increase in length of the wet hair is visible, a corresponding increase in the transverse diameter of the fiber is registered by sensitive measuring instruments (16).

The salt bridges and hydrogen bonds also seem to be responsible for *supercontraction*, another typical phenomenon exhibited by keratin fibers. It is a well known fact that wool shrinks irreversibly if exposed to hot water. This shrinking is apparently due to the cleavage by water at elevated temperature of the weaker cross links, the dithio bonds remaining intact with the result that there occurs a rearrangement of the peptide chains, a sort of crumbling accompanied by an increased randomness, *i.e.*, by a gain in entropy (17). While the distortion by stretching of salt bridges and/or hydrogen bonds is reversible, their cleavage by hot water, which results in supercontraction (Fig. 38) is irreversible.

The great importance of the electrovalent bonds between positively and negatively charged groups for the extensibility and the supercontraction of keratin is substantiated by the fact that both phenomena are affected by the deamination of keratin (18,19) and that wool is made unshrinkable if acid or basic polymers are anchored to the ionic groups (20).

While only the short regular spacings of 5.1 and 3.4 Å were detected by means of X-ray analysis, a periodicity of a higher order, about 110 Å, was revealed by the investigation of keratin fibers with the electron microscope (21). In view of this finding one must consider the possibility that the keratin fiber actually consists of a string of globular particles, each of which occupies a distance of 110 Å along the fiber axis.

By boiling with a neutral solution of dodecylbenzene sulfonate and sodium bisulfite, feather keratin is dissolved; osmometric and sedimentation analyses of the soluble particles show that their size corresponds to a molecular weight of 75,000. The particles contain about 40% of the detergent (dodecylbenzenesulfonic acid) and 60% of keratin. Supposing that each of the particles contained only one molecule of keratin, the molecular weight of the soluble keratin particles would be close to 40,000 (22). Attempts to determine the terminal amino groups of this unit by means of dinitrofluorobenzene (see page 107) led to an unexpected result; it was found that seven different amino acids formed dinitrophenyl compounds (22*a*). The molecular ratio of the dinitrophenylamino acids obtained was 18 glycine, 8 threonine, 4 valine, 2 alanine, 2 serine, 2 glutamic acid, and 1 aspartic acid; it is concluded, therefore, that the

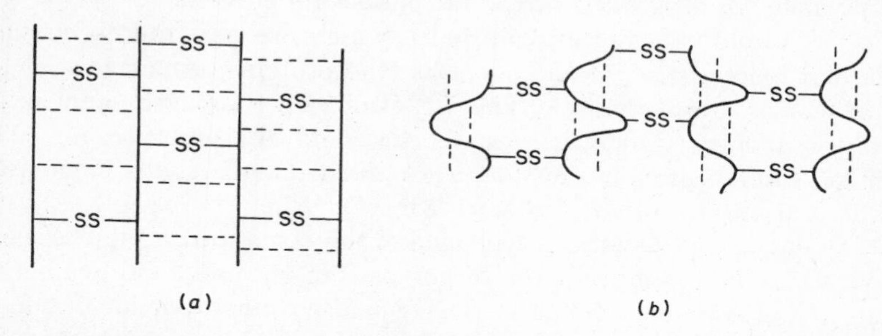

FIG. 38. Keratin fibers. (*a*) native state; (*b*) supercontracted. Broken lines represent hydrogen bonds.

keratin molecule has a minimum molecular weight of two million and that it is formed by 37 chains of the average molecular weight 55,000 (22*a*).

C. Fibroin and Other Keratinlike Proteins. *Fibroin* is the insoluble protein of silk, forming about two thirds of the natural product. The other third is composed of sericin, a protein which is soluble in hot water (23). The amino acid composition of fibroin is very simple (23*a*) and quite different from that of keratin (see Table I, page 32). The bulk of fibroin is formed by the four amino acids glycine, alanine, serine, and tyrosine. The tyrosine content of fibroin is so high that fibroin is commonly used as a source for the preparation of this amino acid. Partial hydrolysis of fibroin by concentrated hydrochloric acid at 37° furnished mainly alanylglycine, but no glycylglycine (23*b*).

The composition of fibroin is unique in that it is practically free of the aminodicarboxylic acids and of the basic amino acids. As a consequence it cannot contain more than a few anionic (negatively charged) or cationic (positively charged) groups. The X-ray pattern of fibroin is very similar to that of β-keratin, and the short-range spacings of 3.4 Å which it shows have been interpreted to mean that the peptide chains of fibroin occur extended (12). On the other hand, silk is reversibly extensible, indicating that large parts of the fibroin consist of disordered material (24) and that the peptide chains of the unstretched fibroin are not extended to their theoretical maximum. Fibroin is dissolved by an aqueous solution of ethylenediamine–copper and if the copper complex is later removed by dialysis an aqueous solution of pure fibroin is obtained. The molecular weight of the soluble fibroin particles is about 30,000 (25). The solubility-promoting action of the copper complex is reminiscent of the analogous action of ammoniacal copper sulfate on cellulose. In both these instances it seems that hydrogen bonds occurring between the closely packed and parallel, threadlike chains are cleaved.

To the insoluble structural proteins, which are resistant to enzyme action also belong *spongin* and *gorgonin*, the proteins of marine sponges and of corals, respectively. They contain 1–2% iodine, and upon hydrolysis furnish diiodotyrosine (26–28) and dibromotyrosine (29). Other keratinlike proteins include *conchiolin* from the shells of mussels and the structural protein of *Byssus* (3).

D. Collagen and Gelatin. Collagen is the structural protein of connective tissue and composes the larger part of the tendons, ligaments, fasciae, and other similar tissues. Collagen also forms a portion of bones, cartilage, and skin. Since native collagen is only slowly attacked by dilute acids and bases and by enzymes, other proteins can be removed by treating the tissues with these hydrolytic agents. The prolonged action of acids, alkali, and enzymes, however, results in the irreversible alteration of collagen. The preparation of leather consists of purifying and tanning the collagen of the animal hide. The tanning is achieved by the action of precipitating agents such as tannic acid and the salts of heavy metals. Low pH values are favorable for tanning; at high pH values the tanning agent is partly removed from the hide(29*a*).

In its composition, collagen differs essentially from keratin and fibroin in that it contains no cystine, cysteine, or tryptophan and only very small amounts of tyrosine and methionine. It is extremely rich in glycine, proline, and hydroxyproline, glycine having been isolated from collagen as early as 1820 by Braconnot (30). The composition of a collagen prepared from ox hide corresponds to the formula: gly_{136}, ala_{41}, $leu\text{-}iso_{17}$, val_{11}, phe_{10}, tyr_{3}, ser_{13}, thr_{8}, met_{2}, pro_{51}, $hydroxypro_{41}$, lys_{12}, $hydroxylys_{3}$, arg_{20}, his_{2}, asp_{19}, glu_{30}, $ammonia_{18}$ (31). The minimum molecular weight calculated is 39,000.

When collagen is heated with water at a temperature of 63–64°C., an irreversible supercontraction to one third of the original length occurs. The shrinking of leather in hot water demonstrates that the supercontraction also takes place in tanned collagen. If the heating of collagen in water is continued for a long time, the collagen finally dissolves and is transformed irreversibly into a water-soluble substance called *gelatin.* Solutions of gelatin are very viscous and form stiff gels at room temperature in concentrations at or above 2–3%. The formation of gels depends not only on the concentration of gelatin, but also on the kind and concentration of any salts present and on the pH of the gelatin solution (32). The same factors influence the swelling of gelatin gels in water (33).

X-ray analyses of collagen show that its structure is different from that of keratin or of fibroin. The short spacings correspond to regular periods of 2.86 Å along the fiber axis (12,34). Since this 2.86 Å is less than the length of one amino acid residue in the extended peptide chain (3.4 Å) one must assume that there is a distortion of the peptide chain. Such an effect has been ascribed to the presence of numerous proline and hydroxyproline residues (35), which render impossible an extended *trans*-configuration of the peptide chain.

3.4 Å

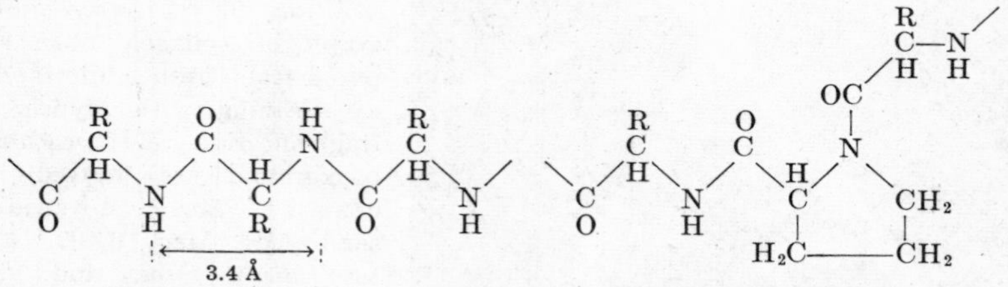

Trans-peptide chain

Proline-containing peptide chain

That collagen consists essentially of threadlike particles is proved by the birefringence shown by the fibers in polarized light. The positive sign of the birefringence indicates that the anisotropic particles are submicroscopic rodlets, arranged parallel to the longitudinal axis of the fiber (36). Collagen, unlike keratin, is not extensible and its peptide chains are thought to be maximally extended. Since the X-ray interferences are hardly altered by the supercontraction, this phenomenon has been attributed to the transverse folding of the longitudinally oriented peptide chains (35).

The conversion of collagen into gelatin was at one time thought to be due to a slight hydrolysis of the peptide bonds and to the reverse of this reaction, the condensation of amino and carboxyl groups. However, since collagen is slowly dissolved by hot water and since its dissolution is enhanced by *m*-cresol, formamide, or lactic acid (37), it is assumed that the structure of native collagen is maintained by salt bridges and by hydrogen bonds (see Chapter VII, p. 116). If only some of these bonds are ruptured, reorientation with supercontraction will take place, while rupture of all the cross linkages results in the complete dissolution and the conversion to gelatin (37).

The formation of gelatin gels is due to the mutual entangling of the long filamentous molecules; the weak forces involved are overcome by heating, so that these gels dissolve at 45–50°C. If formaldehyde is added to gelatin there are formed between the amino groups of adjacent molecules —CH_2— bridges which do not rupture on the addition of more water or on cautious heating, so that gels of formolized gelatin, contrary to those of untreated gelatin, swell only to a limited extent (38,39).

Examination of collagen by low-angle X-ray analysis reveals long spacing periods of approximately 640 Å (40,41) in the direction of the longitudinal fiber axis. When the relative humidity of the air is raised to 100%, the X-ray spacings increase to 672 Å (44). The same periodicity has been found by electron microscopy (42). According to the electronmicrographs collagen is cross-striated (43). The interband dis-

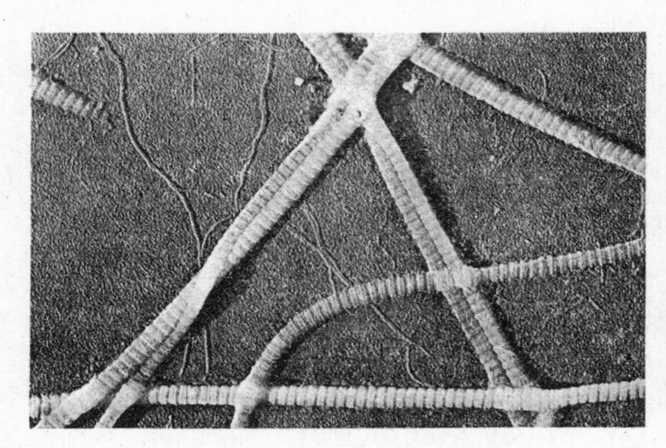

FIG. 39. Electron micrograph of collagen fiber. Prepared from fresh adult rat skin by cleaning with trypsin and fragmentation. Filaments in background are derived from elastic fibers. Chromium shadowed. Mag. 16,400. Courtesy of I. Gross and F. O. Schmitt, Massachusetts Institute of Technology.

tance of different collagens varies from 522 to 902 Å and depends to a certain extent on the water content of the collagen (44).

The long spacing periods may be due to a periodic distribution of the amino acids along the longitudinal peptide threads (35), to regular occurrence of loops along the long axis of the fiber (42), or, finally, to the linear aggregation of globular protein particles as essential constituents of the collagen fiber (45). It has so far been impossible to decisively establish which one of these assumptions gives the best picture of the situation which actually exists.

E. Elastin. Elastin, the structural protein of elastic fibers, has been prepared from the cervical ligament of beef. It is similar to collagen but more resistant to the action of proteolytic enzymes, acids, and bases. The glycine content of elastin is just as high as that of collagen, but the content of proline and hydroxyproline is much lower (46) (see Table I, p. 32).

F. Polyglutamic Acid. The insoluble capsular substance of *Bacillus anthracis* and of *B. mesentericus* is a protein which on hydrolysis furnishes only L-glutamic acid (47). The molecular weight is more than 50,000; the molecule consists of α-peptide chains of glutamic acid, held together by a few γ-glutamyl bonds (48,49). The substance is extracted from the bacteria by hydrochloric acid–ethanol and precipitated from the extract by sodium hydroxide (48). A similar poly-α-glutamic acid has been prepared synthetically (50).

G. Biological Importance of Structural Proteins. The insolubility of the scleroproteins might lead one to expect that they are lifeless substances with none other than passive, protective functions. This is certainly true for hair and wool or for the fibroin of silk. The typical eukeratins of hair, nails, and horn may be considered as being excreted from the surface of the organism and sooner or later they are removed by detrition. On the other hand, a much greater importance must be attributed to those scleroproteins which form the insoluble, spongelike framework of the cell and cellular membranes. The permeability and the metabolism of the cells depend to a great degree on the properties of the structural proteins and in particular on their electrochemical behavior. If a membrane protein has an excess of positively or negatively charged groups, the membrane will be permeable only to ions of opposite charge, while ions of the same charge will be repelled.

The ultramicroscopic organization of the cellular skeleton varies from tissue to tissue and from species to species. It seems, however, that all these insoluble structures consist of long, filamentous protein molecules which are frequently arranged in a regular manner so that birefringence is observed when the cells are examined in polarized light. Conclusions concerning the structure of the membranes can be drawn from the sign of the birefringence; and it has been concluded that the protein of the nervous sheaths forms concentric cylindrical layers, in which the protein fibers are oriented tangentially to the cross section of the cylinder (36).

While protein membranes are frequently anisotropic (birefringent), *gelatin gels* are isotropic. It has been mentioned above that the protein content required for the formation of a gel is astonishingly low, and that firm gelatin gels containing 97–98% water and only 2–3% gelatin can be prepared. A similar high water content is found in the structural substance of the jelly-fishes. The high water content of these protein gels cannot be ascribed to the hydration of their protein molecules. It has been shown in Chapter VI that true hydration, *i.e.*, the linkage of water molecules to the protein does not exceed 30–60% of the weight of the protein. The much higher amount of water present in the gels consists not of water molecules linked to the protein, but of free water molecules which are immobilized in the loops of the network of hydrated gelatin fibers. This *immobilized water* behaves in the same way as free water, having the same freezing point and the same capacity to dissolve other molecules or ions, whereas the true water of hydration has a lower freezing point and is marked by its inability to serve as a solvent (51). If gelatin

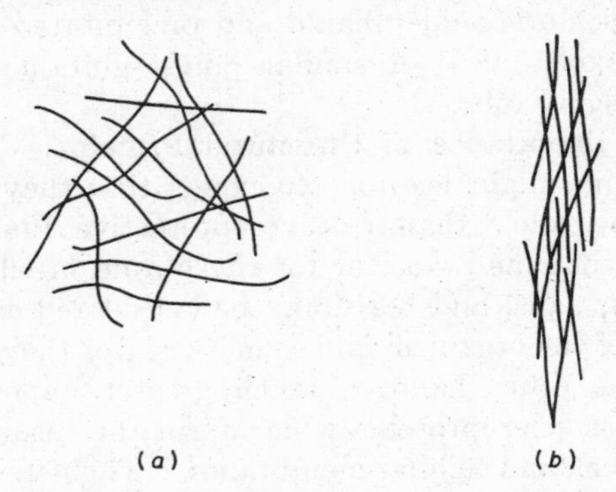

FIG. 40. Network of gelatin fibers. (a) unoriented, isotropic fibers; (b) extended, birefringent fibers.

gels are subjected to mechanical tension so that their protein threads are regularly oriented (Fig. 40), they become birefringent (52). This phenomenon of "birefringence by stress" is analogous to flow birefringence and is explained in terms of a similar mechanism.

REFERENCES

1. R. J. Block, H. B. Vickery, *J. Biol. Chem.* **121,** 761 (1937).
2. W. Kuehne, R. H. Chittenden, *Z. Biol.* **26,** 291 (1890).
3. Z. Stary, *Z. physiol. Chem.* **148,** 83 (1926).
4. R. J. Block, D. Bolling, *J. Biol. Chem.* **127,** 685 (1939).
5. M. J. Horn, D. B. Jones, S. J. Ringel, *J. Biol. Chem.* **138,** 141 (1941).
6. D. R. Goddard, L. Michaelis, *J. Biol. Chem.* **106,** 605 (1934); **112,** 361 (1935).
7. Z. Stary, *Z. physiol. Chem.* **136,** 160 (1924); **144,** 147 (1925).
8. E. Abderhalden *et al.*, *Z. physiol. Chem.* **46,** 1 (1905); **52,** 348 (1907).
9. H. Buchtala, *Z. physiol. Chem.* **52,** 474 (1907); **74,** 212 (1911); **85,** 241 (1913).
10. J. I. Routh, *J. Biol. Chem.* **123,** CIV (1938).
11. H. Cohen, *Arch. Biochem.* **4,** 145 (1944).
12. W. T. Astbury, *Advances in Enzymol.* **3,** 63 (1943).
13. H. B. Bull, M. Gutmann, *J. Am. Chem. Soc.* **66,** 1253 (1941).
13*a*. H. Neurath, *J. Phys. Chem.* **44,** 296 (1940).
14. J. B. Speakman, F. Townend, *Nature* **139,** 411 (1937).
15. D. Crowfoot, *Ann. Rev. Biochem.* **17,** 115 (1948).
16. T. Lochte, H. Brauckhoff, *Biochem. Z.* **318,** 384 (1948).
17. D. J. Lloyd, M. Dempsey, M. Garrod, *Trans. Faraday Soc.* **B42,** 228 (1946).
18. R. Cochburn, B. Drucker, L. Lindley, *Biochem. J.* **43,** 438 (1948).
19. J. B. Speakman, E. Stott, *Nature* **141,** 1138 (1938).
20. J. B. Speakman, *Intern. Congr. Chem., 11th Congr.*, p. 135/2 (1947).

21. J. L. Farrant, A. L. G. Rees, E. H. Mercer, *Nature* **159**, 535 (1947).
22. W. H. Ward, L. M. High, P. Lundgren, *J. Polymer Sci.* **1**, 22 (1946).
22*a*. W. R. Middlebrook, *Abstracts 1st Intern. Congr. Biochem.* p. 141 (1949).
23. K. Kodama, *Biochem. J.* **20**, 1208 (1926).
23*a*. A. Polson, V. M. Mosley, R. W. G. Wyckoff, *Science* **105**, 603 (1947).
23*b*. M. Levi, *Cold Spring Harbor Symposia Quant. Biol.* **14**, 113 (1949).
24. H. Mark, *Chem. Eng. News.* **27**, 138 (1949).
25. D. Coleman, F. O. Howitt, *Proc. Roy. Soc. London* **A190**, 145 (1947).
26. E. Drechsel, *Z. Biol.* **33**, 84 (1896).
27. M. Henze, *Z. physiol. Chem.* **51**, 64 (1907).
28. H. L. Wheeler, C. O. Johns, *J. Am. Chem. Soc.* **43**, 11 (1910).
29. D. Ackermann, E. Müller, *Z. physiol. Chem.* **269**, 146 (1941).
29*a*. K. H. Gustavson, *Advances in Protein Chem.* **5**, 354 (1949).
30. H. Braconnot, *Ann. chim. phys.* **13**, 113 (1820).
31. J. Bowes, R. Kenten, *Biochem. J.* **43**, 358, 365 (1948).
32. D. J. Lloyd, *Biochem. J.* **16**, 531 (1922).
33. J. Loeb, M. Kunitz, *J. Gen. Physiol.* **5**, 665 (1923).
34. W. Lotmar, L. E. R. Picken, *Helv. Chim. Acta* **25**, 538 (1942).
35. W. T. Astbury, *Proc. Roy. Soc. London* **B134**, 303 (1947).
36. F. O. Schmitt, *Advances in Protein Chem.* **1**, 25 (1944).
37. D. J. Lloyd, M. Garrod, *Trans. Faraday Soc.* **44**, 441 (1948).
38. H. Staudinger, *Ber.* **68**, 1682 (1935).
39. J. D. Ferry, *Advances in Protein Chem.* **4**, 2 (1948).
40. R. S. Baer, *J. Am. Chem. Soc.* **64**, 727 (1942).
41. O. Kratky, *J. makromol. and Chem.* **1**, 113 (1943); *J. Polymer. Sci.* **3**, 195 (1948).
42. F. O. Schmitt, C. E. Hall, M. A. Jakus, *J. Cellular Comp. Physiol.* **20**, 11 (1942).
43. C. E. Hall, M. A. Jakus, F. O. Schmitt, *J. Am. Chem. Soc.* **64**, 1234 (1943).
44. B. Wright, *Nature* **162**, 23 (1948).
45. R. W. G. Wyckoff, R. B. Corey, *Science* **82**, 175 (1935).
46. C. E. Graham, H. K. Waitkoff, S. W. Hier, *J. Biol. Chem.* **177**, 529 (1949).
47. G. Ivanovics, V. G. Bruckner, Jr., *Naturwissenschaften* **25**, 250 (1937).
48. W. E. Hanby, H. N. Rydon, *Biochem. J.* **40**, 297 (1946).
49. F. Haurowitz, F. Bursa, *Biochem. J.* **44**, 509 (1949).
50. E. J. Ambros *et al.*, *Nature* **163**, 483, 859 (1949).
51. H. H. Weber, *Biochem. Z.* **234**, 62 (1931).
52. M. Kunitz, *J. Gen. Physiol.* **13**, 565 (1930).
53. A. E. Brown *et al.*, *Abstracts 114th Meeting Am. Chem. Soc., p. 21C (1948).*

CHAPTER X

Combination of Proteins with Other Substances

A. Intermolecular Forces. Proteins combine with nonprotein substances to form more or less stable compounds which have been called conjugated proteins, symplexes (1) or cenapses (2). Some of these compounds exist as such in the organism (see Chapter XI). Hemoglobin is an example of a more stable conjugated protein. In other cases it is not clear whether the conjugated protein exists in the organism or is formed during the procedure used for its preparation.

While some of the conjugated proteins are compounds of one protein molecule with a single nonprotein molecule, other complexes contain more than one nonprotein group. The nonprotein portion of the conjugated proteins has been called its *prosthetic group*. Different forces bind the prosthetic group to the protein in the different types of conjugated proteins. In the phosphoproteins the partners are attached to one another by true ester linkages, *i.e.*, by true covalent bonds. In other cases the two components are held together by weak intermolecular forces. These forces operate principally between (*a*) ionic groups, (*b*) polar nonionic groups, and (*c*) nonpolar groups. Bonds of type (*a*) are formed between proteins and organic or inorganic ions. It is well known that proteins combine very firmly with certain organic acids such as picric, trichloroacetic, or sulfosalicylic acid, forming insoluble precipitates. The analysis of such a precipitate formed by metaphosphoric acid revealed that the amount of metaphosphate in the precipitate was equivalent to the number of amino groups of the precipitated protein (2*a*). Evidently, the negative metaphosphate ions combined with the positive ammonium groups of the protein.

The mutual attraction of positively and negatively charged *ionic groups* is due to the well known electrostatic forces. If the charges of the two groups are e_1 and e_2, respectively, the force of attraction is $f = \frac{e_1e_2}{Dr^2}$, where D is the dielectric constant and r the distance between the positive and negative charge. The electrostatic forces, the importance of which for the formation of intramolecular and intermolecular "salt links" was discussed in Chapter VII, p. 116 are able to hold together the two components of a conjugated protein. It is evident that such a bond will be destroyed by any agent which causes the ionic groups to lose their electric charge. Since the positive and the negative groups of proteins lose their charges by the addition of strong bases or acids, respectively, the saltlike bonds will be cleaved by these reagents. Complications arise, however, by the denaturing action of acids and alkalies. It is difficult, therefore, to decide whether the cleavage of a conjugated protein by acids or alkalis is due to denaturation of the protein moiety, or to the cleavage of the linkage between protein and prosthetic group; frequently both phenomena will occur simultaneously.

Salt links are to be considered highly localized links; the mutual attraction of the two components is restricted to the two atomic groups which carry the positive and the negative charge. Salt links are rather stable toward heat. Let us assume that the bond energy between two centers of electrical charge is 5000 cal. and that their distance apart is 3 Å; if this distance increases by thermal movement from 3 to 4 Å, the bond energy will decrease to $5000 \times (3/4)^2$, *i.e*, to 2800 cal. In other words, the two charged points will still be held together by 56% of the original force of attraction and will tend to resume their original position.

Bonds of the type (*b*), *i.e.*, *dipole–dipole bonds* are effective between OH, SH, NH_2 groups and include the hydrogen bond (see page 116). The dipole–dipole bonds are also due to electrostatic forces. If the two poles are close to each other, the force of attraction has the same order of magnitude as that between ions of an opposite charge. However the force of attraction decreases here in proportion to a very high power of the mutual distance r, probably in proportion to $1/r^6$ (2*b*). If we again assume a bond energy of 5000 cal. and an increase of the distance from 3 Å to 4 Å between the two poles, the bond energy decreases to $5000 \times (3/4)^6 = 900$ cal. *i.e.*, about one sixth of the original strength. Dipole–dipole bonds are therefore much more labile at elevated temperatures than are salt links, a fact which is also evident from the lower melting point of molecules held together by polar bonds. The striking difference in the melting points of the two isomeric substances glycolamide and glycine has been discussed on page 60.

In spite of their sensitivity to heat the dipole–dipole bonds are of great importance and are in many instances stronger than the saltlike bonds. This is due to the fact that frequently a great number of polar groups is present on a small part of the molecule and that two molecular surfaces of this kind are held together by several dipole–dipole linkages. This is obviously the case in compounds formed by carbohydrates; each of the sugar molecules has a large number of polar hydroxyl groups, so that each molecule is attached to adjacent polar molecules by multiple bonds. The attraction of sugar molecules to the surface of protein molecules is so strong that the coagulation of denatured proteins is prevented by high concentrations of sugars (see page 132).

The third type of bond to be discussed is the bond between *nonpolar groups* (type *c* above). We find this bond in solid and in liquid hydrocarbons. It has been attributed to short-period oscillations of the electrons and has been called dispersion effect (3). The attraction between nonpolar groups is weaker than that between ionic or polar groups (3*b*). This is evident from the low melting points and boiling points of the lower members of the paraffin series. The mutual attraction between nonpolar groups, which can be effective only between large, extended groups such as the long paraffin chains of the higher fatty acids, is enhanced by the deformability of the saturated paraffin chains. Owing to the free rotation of their carbon atoms around the carbon–carbon bonds the paraffin chains are flexible and can, therefore, come close enough to one another for attractive forces to result.

Having discussed the three main types of intermolecular bonds it must be emphasized that *intermediary types* exist. Electrostatic forces are effective not only between two ions or two dipoles but also between an ion and adjacent dipoles. The strength of the ion–dipole bond lies between that of the ion–ion and the dipole–dipole bond. Similarly, intermediary types of linkage may exist between polar and nonpolar groups.

B. Protein–Nonprotein Compounds. The nature of the forces operative in the conjugated proteins has been studied by combining proteins with different types of substances, particularly with anions and cations. The combination of the small *inorganic ions* with proteins has been discussed in Chapter V, p. 73. It was mentioned there that the ionic groups of proteins combine with calcium cations, phosphate anions, and with other inorganic ions through the formation of saltlike bonds. Similar bonds are formed *in vitro;* thus, insulin combines readily with thiocyanate ions (3*a*).

Organic anions or cations are bound to proteins by the same kind of electrovalent bond. While the combination of proteins with colorless ions can be proved only by tedious analytical methods, the combination of proteins with dyes can be measured spectrophotometrically since it is accompanied by changes in color and absorption spectra. In this way the combination of proteins with *methyl orange* and similar dyes (4,5), and with *nitrophenols* (6) has been investigated quantitatively. By dialyzing serum albumin against methyl orange it has been found that the maximum number of methyl orange molecules bound per protein molecule is 22. Methyl orange is an acid azo dye:

$$(CH_3)_2N-C_6H_4-N{=}N-C_6H_4-SO_3^-$$

whose sulfonate anion is bound to cationic groups of the protein, in particular to the ϵ-ammonium groups of the basic amino acid lysine (5). If the pH is raised above 12, the basic groups of lysine lose their positive charge (see page 65) and the amount of bound dye decreases. The color of the dye at a given pH is altered by the addition of protein, because the protein combines with dye anions and thereby disturbs the equilibrium between the dye anions and the undissociated dye molecules (5). A thermodynamic analysis shows that the change in free energy in the reversible reaction:

$$\text{protein} + \text{methyl orange} \rightleftharpoons \text{protein–methyl orange}$$

is $\Delta F = -6411$ cal. per mole of the dye at 25°C. (4,6*a*). ΔH was found to be -2100 cal. (6*a*). In a similar analysis it was found that one molecule of serum albumin combines with six molecules of *o*-nitrophenol, but with 24 molecules of *m*-nitrophenol or 25 of *p*-nitrophenol (6). Evidently the combination depends on steric factors. Not only aromatic dyes, but simple aliphatic anions such as butyrate, caproate, or caprylate also combine with proteins; this is proved by electrophoresis (7) as well as by the fact that the fatty acid anions prevent the coagulation of proteins denatured by heat or by other methods (8).

It is remarkable that methyl orange, which readily combines with serum albumin, does not combine with γ-globulin, insulin, pepsin, or trypsin (6*a*). Lactoglobulin is able to bind small amounts of methyl orange (6*a*). The different behavior of the various proteins indicates that the surfaces of their globular molecules are formed by different molecular groups.

Denatured ovalbumin combines very firmly with the azo dye *Congo red;* the heat coagulation of ovalbumin is prevented by Congo red (9). The dye anion is attached so firmly to the denatured protein that it remains in the anionic red form even at pH 2, whereas free Congo red anions are converted into Congo blue at pH values below pH 3–4. In salt-free solutions Congo red gives precipitates with proteins (10). Besides combining with proteins in solution Congo red also combines with the insoluble protein *amyloid,* which accumulates in certain chronic inflammations in the liver, spleen, and other organs. Use is made of this reaction in the diagnosis of amyloidosis; because it is bound to the amyloid the intravenously injected dye disappears from the blood much more rapidly in patients suffering from amyloidosis. The staining of amyloid by Congo red is especially interesting in view of the fact that the protein–dye compound is birefringent, while amyloid shows no birefringence (11).

Numerous investigations have been made of the combination of proteins with *anionic detergents.* These consists of long-chain alkylsulfonic acids, RSO_3H, or of alkyl sulfuric acid esters, $ROSO_3H$. In most of the investigations sodium dodecyl sulfate, $C_{12}H_{25}·OSO_3^-Na^+$, has been used. The anionic detergents form insoluble precipitates with proteins at pH values lower than the isoelectric pH value of the protein. Since the isoelectric point of most proteins is approximately pH 5–6, precipitation by anionic detergents occurs at distinctly acid reactions. Evidently the detergent anions combine with the cationic groups of the protein (12). β-Lactoglobulin combines with two molecules of dodecyl sulfate (13) to give a crystalline compound. If, however, the protein is mixed with a large excess of the detergent each protein molecule combines with a very large number of detergent anions; more than 1000 millimoles of dodecyl sulfate are bound to 100 g. gelatin, although this amount of gelatin contains only about 90 milliequivalents of cationic groups (14). To explain this unexpectedly high detergent: protein ratio it has been proposed that multimolecular micelles of the detergent combine with the protein (15) or that the detergent is linked to the protein molecule by forces operating between the paraffin chains of the detergent and hydrophobic groups of the protein as well as by the saltlike bonds (15*a*). The formation of insoluble compounds of proteins with anionic detergents has also been observed in monomolecular films on the water–air interface (16). The reaction is accompanied by a denaturation of the protein; by mixing 4% ovalbumin solutions with 5% solutions of the detergent in the presence of ammonium sulfate insoluble threads are formed (17). The precipitates consist possibly of alternate layers of protein and detergent (18). The protein–detergent compound is soluble in an excess of the detergent; this is apparently due to the formation, about the protein molecule as a center, of a complex whose surface is covered by the anionic groups of the detergent (19). Soluble compounds of protein and detergent are also formed in alkaline solutions (12,19). Their presence can be proved electrophoretically.

Similar compounds are formed between proteins and acid azo proteins. These also form precipitates in the *interisoelectric range, i.e.*, in the pH range between the isoelectric points of the protein and of the azoprotein (20). Acid azoproteins are prepared by coupling proteins with diazotized aminophenylsulfonic acids; they contain sulfonic acid groups and are present as anions above pH 2 (20). The protein–azoprotein precipitates dissolve above pH 8, because at these pH values both the azoprotein and the protein are present as anions. The protein–azoprotein precipitates are soluble in an excess of the azoprotein just as the protein–detergent precipitates dissolve in an excess of the detergent.

Other macromolecular anions which combine with proteins are the anions of *polysaccharidic acids* such as those present in pectin or in gum arabic; they also form precipitates in the interisoelectric range and dissolve in an excess of the anion (21). The precipitates of these fibrous anions have a loose, gel-like structure and form microscopic droplets instead of solid phases. This form of precipitation, which has been called *coacervation* (22), is due to the immobilization of large amounts of water between the fibrous anions of the polysaccharidic acids.

The reactions taking place between proteins and macromolecular anions are especially important insofar as they serve as models of the combination of proteins with *nucleic acids*, which are also anions of high molecular weight. Their reaction with proteins will be treated in Chapter XI, Sect. G, on nucleoproteins. It may be anticipated, however, that nucleic acids behave in the same way as the anions discussed above, combining with proteins through saltlike linkages and forming precipitates in the interisoelectric region (23,24). It is obvious that anions should combine most readily with those proteins which have basic properties. Lysozyme, a basic protein whose isoelectric point is 10.5–11.0, combines in neutral solutions with nucleic acids as well as with anionic detergents and methyl orange (25).

The combination of proteins with *organic cations* has been investigated much less thoroughly than that with anions. The strongly basic *protamines* give precipitates with globulins, and with denatured albumins, but not with native albumins; these precipitates are formed in the interisoelectric region, *i.e.*, at alkaline reactions; they are soluble in acid solutions (26). The precipitates are also soluble in concentrated solutions of neutral salts, because the ions of the salt compete with the ionic groups of the protein and of the protamine (27).

In recent years *cationic detergents* (invert soaps) have been prepared synthetically (28) and used very effectively as disinfectants. The invert soaps combine with proteins in the interisoelectric region, *i.e.*, in alkaline solutions. Most of the cationic detergents have the structure $RR'R''R'''N^+X^-$, where X^- is a halogen ion and R represents different aliphatic or cyclic groups. Zephirol (Zephiran), one of the cationic detergents, is a dodecyltrimethylammonium chloride; with proteins in the alkaline pH range it forms precipitates which dissolve at acid reactions, where the negative COO^- groups of the protein lose their charge (29,30). The precipitates are also soluble in an excess of the cationic detergent (31). An analysis of the precipitates obtained by the action of Desogen (tolyldodecyltrimethylammonium methosulfate) on hemoglobin shows that up to 300 cations of the detergent are bound per molecule of hemoglobin; since hemoglobin contains only 65 anionic groups it is assumed that micelles of the cationic detergent are bound to the protein molecule (32).

It is not established with certainty whether the disinfectant action of the invert soaps is due to their combination with the bacterial proteins. Since they also combine with neutral polysaccharides (33) their combination with the capsular polysaccharides of bacteria might play a significant role.

While there is no doubt that the anionic and cationic detergents are attached to the proteins by means of their ionic groups, it is highly probable that their nonpolar paraffin chains are involved in the combination with proteins. The *nonpolar hydrocarbon group* probably combines with the nonpolar groups of the proteins, *i.e.*, with the aliphatic side chains of alanine, valine, leucine, and isoleucine, with the benzyl group of phenylalanine and with the CH_2 groups of the pyrrolidine ring of proline. By means of these nonpolar groups proteins combine with fats and fatty acids (34) and also with simple hydrocarbons. Thus it has been found that a 2% solution of edestin in 10% sodium chloride is able to hold in solution 5000 molecules of pentane per protein molecule (35). The absorption from the intestine of nonpolar drugs of low molecular weight such as carbon tetrachloride is possibly due to the same phenomenon, to their loose combination with proteins.

Hydroxyl, sulfhydryl, amide, and other nonionic *polar* or polarizable groups of the protein molecules combine with polar groups or with ionic groups of other molecules by means of electrostatic forces. Many drugs such as the sulfonamides are bound to protein molecules by means of such bonds. The free energy change in the combination of proteins with sulfonamides has been found to be $\Delta F = 4000\text{–}5000$ cal. per mole (36). The steric arrangement of the binding polar groups has a great influence on the strength of the bonds. The closer the two bonding partners are adjusted to one another, the less the intermolecular distance will be, so that the mutual attraction between ionic or polar groups increases sharply (2*b*). The mutual attraction between antigens and their specific antibodies is due to this type of linkage, to the mutual attraction of complementarily shaped surfaces (see Chapter XIV, Section C).

Competitive inhibition is due to the same effect, to the competition of molecules of similar dimensions for a complementarily shaped surface of a protein molecule. The action of certain "antimetabolites" has been explained on this basis. A good example is the competition between *p*-aminobenzoic acid and the sulfonamides, which is attributed to the two- or three-dimensional similarity of both compounds:

$H_2N—C_6H_4—COOH$ *p*-Aminobenzoic acid

$H_2N—C_6H_4—SO_2NH_2$ Sulfanilamide

The similar competition between enzyme substrates and specific inhibitors and between antigens and haptens will be discussed in Chapters XII and XIV.

References

1. R. Willstätter, M. Rohdewald, *Z. physiol. Chem.* **225,** 103 (1934).
2. M. A. Macheboeuf, M. Januszkiewicz, *Bull. soc. chim. biol.* **19,** 694 (1937).
2a. G. E. Perlmann, H. Hermann, *Biochem. J.* **32,** 926, 931 (1938).
2b. D. Pressman, L. Pauling, *J. Am. Chem. Soc.* **71,** 2893 (1949).
3. F. London, *Z. physik. Chem.* **B11,** 222 (1930). J. C. Slater and J. G. Kirkwood, *Phys. Rev.* **31,** 682 (1931).
3a. E. Volkin, *J. Biol. Chem.* **175,** 675 (1948).
3b. W. D. Harkins, *Scientific Monthly* **70,** 220 (1950).
4. I. M. Klotz, F. M. Walker, *J. Am. Chem. Soc.* **69,** 1609 (1947).
5. I. M. Klotz, *Chem. Revs.* **41,** 373 (1947).
6. J. D. Teresi, J. M. Luck, *J. Biol. Chem.* **174,** 653 (1938).
6a. I. M. Klotz, J. M. Urquhart, *J. Phys. Colloid Chem.* **53,** 100 (1949); *J. Am. Chem. Soc.* **71,** 847 (1949).
7. G. A. Ballou, P. D. Boyer, J. M. Luck, *J. Biol. Chem.* **159,** 111 (1945).
8. R. G. Rice *et al.*, *J. Biol. Chem.* **158,** 609 (1945).
9. F. Haurowitz, S. Tekman, S. Lisie, F. Bursa, Abstracts 112th Meeting Am. Chem. Soc. P. 29C (1947) and unpublished experiments with F. Di Moia.
10. W. Pauli, P. Szarvas, *Helv. Chim. Acta* **26,** 1885 (1943).
11. P. Ladewig, *Nature* **156,** 81 (1945).
12. F. W. Putnam, *Advances in Protein Chem.* **4,** 80 (1948).
13. T. L. McMeekin *et al.*, *Federation Proc.* **7,** 172 (1948).
14. K. G. A. Pankhurst, R. C. M. Smith, *Trans. Faraday Soc.* **40,** 565 (1944).
15. H. Neurath, F. W. Putnam, *J. Biol. Chem.* **160,** 397 (1945).
15a. F. Karush, M. Sonenburg, *J. Am. Chem. Soc.* **71,** 1369 (1949).
16. H. B. Bull, *J. Am. Chem. Soc.* **67,** 4, 8, 10 (1945).
17. H. P. Lundgren, *J. Am. Chem. Soc.* **63,** 2854 (1941).
18. K. J. Palmer, *J. Phys. Chem.* **48,** 12 (1944).
19. F. W. Putnam, H. Neurath, *J. Am. Chem. Soc.* **66,** 692, 1992 (1944).
20. F. Haurowitz, P. Schwerin, S. Tunc, *Arch. Biochem.* **11,** 515 (1946).
21. D. Dervichian, C. Magnant, *Bull. soc. chim. biol.* **29,** 655, 660 (1947).
22. H. G. B. de Jong, P. Teunissen, *Kolloid-Beihefte* **47,** 254 (1938).
23. K. Bjørnesjø, T. Teorell, *Ark. Kemi Mineral. Geol.* 19A (1945).
24. A. Kleczkowski, *Biochem. J.* **40,** 677 (1946).
25. I. M. Klotz, F. M. Walker, *Arch. Biochem.* **18,** 319 (1948).
26. F. Haurowitz, *Kolloid-Z.* **74,** 208 (1936).
27. M. A. Lissitzin, N. S. Alexandrowskaja, *Z. physiol. Chem.* **221,** 156 (1933).
28. R. Kuhn, H. J. Bielig, *Ber.* **73,** 1080 (1940).
29. K. H. Schmidt, *Z. physiol. Chem.* **277,** 117 (1943).
30. W. G. Jaffé, *J. Biol. Chem.* **148,** 185 (1943).
31. J. Polonovski, M. Macheboeuf, *Ann. inst. Pasteur* **74,** 196, 203 (1948).
32. F. Haurowitz, L. Etili, P. Kara, *Bull. faculté med. Istanbul* **12,** 183 (1949); *Discuss. Faraday Soc.* **6,** 58 (1949).
34. S. J. Przylecki, H. Hofer, S. Frajberger-Grynberg, *Biochem. Z.* **282,** 362 (1935).
35. D. L. Talmud, *Acta Physicochimica. U.R.S.S.* **14,** 562 (1941).
36. I. M. Klotz, F. M. Walker, *J. Am. Chem. Soc.* **70,** 943 (1948).

CHAPTER XI

Conjugated Proteins

A. Lipoproteins (1,2). The complexes formed by proteins and lipids fall into two categories, the soluble and the insoluble lipoproteins. The first type is present in the blood plasma and in other body fluids. Even though the plasma is a clear, transparent fluid, it contains 0.5–0.7% of water-insoluble lipids. A considerable portion of these lipids cannot be extracted from the serum by the usual treatment with ether or similar nonpolar solvents; this was attributed by Macheboeuf to the presence of lipoprotein complexes, called by him "cenapses" (2*a*). Such lipoprotein complexes can be precipitated from the blood serum by the usual salting-out methods with ammonium sulfate (3). Lipids have also been found in protein fractions obtained electrophoretically (4). The lipoprotein complexes are split by the action of ethanol or acetone at room temperature; most of the lipid can be extracted by diethyl ether after the treatment with alcohol. In order to avoid denaturation by the organic solvents it has been recommended that the splitting of lipoproteins by alcohol and ether be performed at low temperatures (5) or by repeated freezing and thawing with ether (6).

If blood serum is extracted with ether at –70°C., all the cholesterol is extracted, while the phospholipids remain bound to the serum proteins (7). Similar results are achieved by the action of cationic detergents (see Chapter X, Sect. B) on serum proteins (8).

Fractionation of human blood serum with ethanol (see Chapter VIII, p. 150) furnished two principal lipoproteins, a β_1-lipoprotein from Fraction III-0, and a α_1-lipoprotein from Fraction IV-1; they form 5 and 3% of the total plasma proteins, respectively (9–11). The β_1-lipoprotein contains about 70% of the plasma lipids; its molecular weight is 1,300,000; it contains 25% protein, 30% phospholipid, and 45% cholesterol esters and cholesterol. The α_1-lipoprotein has a molecular weight of 200,000; it consists of 65% protein and 35% lipid (9–11).

The components forming the lipoprotein are apparently held together by more than one type of bond. It has not been possible to prepare analogous compounds by merely mixing proteins with lipids. Probably the lipoproteins arise in the organism during the formation of the protein macromolecule, in which process lipids may be occluded between the folded peptide chains, to be liberated only when the peptide chains unfold. Another possibility to be taken into consideration is that the lipids form the center of micelles which are coated by a protein envelope (12).

While it was long believed that the phospholipids of the blood plasma consist mainly of lecithins or of cephalins more recent investigations reveal that one portion of the phospholipids is formed by *sphingomyelins* (13,14). The manner in which the phospholipids are bound to the plasma proteins has not yet been established with certainty. Cephalins are acidic substances, because of their phosphoric acid groups and their serine residues. They combine with the basic protamines to give insolu-

```
CH₂O·OC·R             CH₂O·OCR                 CH₂O·OC·R
|                     |                        |
CHO·OC·R              CHO·OC·R                 CHO·OC·R
|                     |                        |
CH₂O·PO·O⁻            CH₂O·PO·O⁻               CH₂O·PO·O⁻
    |     COO⁻            |                        |      ˙.
    |     |               |                        |        ˙.
    OCH₂CHN⁺H₃            OCH₂CH₂NH₂               OCH₂CH₂N⁺(CH₃)₃
  Cephalin              Cephalin                 Lecithin
(phosphatidylserine)  (phosphatidylaminoethanol)
```

```
                                    R·CO
                                    |
CH₃(CH₂)₁₂CH=CH·CHOH·CHNH·CH₂O
                                          |
                                       ⁻OPO
                                      .·  |
                                    .·    |
                        (CH₃)₃N⁺CH₂CH₂O
```

Sphingomyelin

ble compounds and are also able to precipitate ovalbumin (15). The salmine:cephalin ratio in the precipitate of the protamine salmine is approximately 3:1. Lecithin and sphingomyelin are less acidic than cephalin because their phosphoric acid anion is to some extent neutralized by the basic quaternary ammonium group of the choline portion of the molecule. As a result neither protamines nor other proteins are precipitated by lecithin. Nevertheless, there exist ways by which lecithins and sphingomyelins could combine through electrovalent bonds with proteins; such bonds could form between the phosphoric acid anion and cationic groups of the protein, and between the quaternary ammonium group of choline and the acidic groups of the proteins:

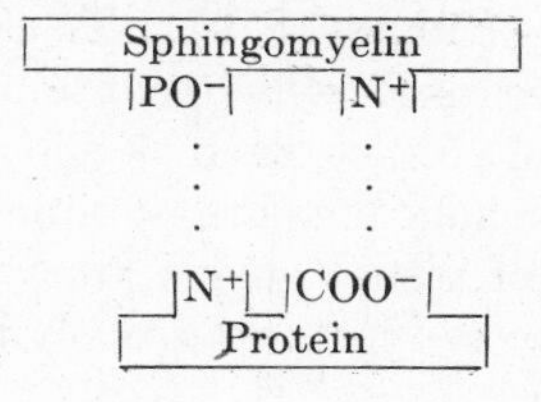

In addition to these electrovalent bonds (salt links), weaker bonds may be formed between polar groups of both partners or between nonpolar groups of the lipid and the protein. Nothing definite is known about the existence of such bonds in the soluble lipoproteins of the blood plasma.

A second group of lipoproteins includes those present in the cellular membranes and the structural elements of the cell such as the granules or mitochondria. While it is certain that there are lipids in cellular membranes and in granules, next to nothing is known about the linkages involved in these structural elements. In contrast to the lipids of the adipose tissue, which are stained by the common lipid stains (Sudan or Scarlet red, Nile blue), the lipids of the cellular structures are not stained by these dyes; they are called "masked lipids." Their failure to combine with the lipophilic dyes is a strong indication that they are linked to proteins. Mitochondria of the liver contain 15–20% lipids (16). Lipids have also been found in the submicroscopic particles prepared from liver or from pancreas by high-speed centrifugation (17). The particles contain 40–50% lipid bound to a ribonucleoprotein (see p. 221).

Some of the lipoproteins are biologically active. For example the thromboplastic lipoprotein of animal tissues is important in the process of clotting (Chapter VIII, p. 156). The endotoxins of *Shigella* and of other bacteria (see Chapter XV, Sect. B-*c*) also belong to the active lipoproteins.

Proteins also combine with *carotenes* to form colored lipoproteins. The color of crustaceans is due to crustacyanin (18), a lipoprotein containing the carotenoid astaxanthin, a 5,5′-dihydroxy-4,4′-diketo-β-carotene (19). Crustacyanin is extracted from lobster shells by citric acid (18). A similar lipoprotein is the green pigment of lobster eggs, ovoverdin; the molecular weight of this lipoprotein, which contains one molecule of astaxanthin per protein molecule, is about 300,000; its isoelectric point is pH 6.7 (20). While it exists combined with protein, the carotene is safeguarded against oxidation; on heating, the protein is denatured and the carotenoid is liberated as a red pigment. Lipoproteins containing carotenoids have also been found in green grasshoppers (21) and are probably present in other insects.

The most interesting carotenoid–protein compound is *visual purple* (22,23), which is present in the retinal rods, but not in the cones, and is necessary for night vision (Kühne, 1879). To extract visual purple from the retina, substances are used which contain hydrophilic as well as lipophilic groups in their molecules, such as bile acids, digitonin (24), and invert soaps (25). Stable solutions are obtained by using 75% aqueous glycerol (26). Solutions of visual purple must be prepared in the dark since the solutions are bleached instantaneously by light; the rose-colored solution first becomes yellow, then colorless. According to Wald (27) the yellow pigment contains retinene, an aldehyde, which has been prepared from vitamin A by oxidation with MnO_2 (28). The molecular weight of soluble visual purple is 240,000 as found by sedimentation (29), and 600,000–800,000 as found by diffusion measurements (30). The isoelectric point is 4.47–4.57 (26). Two different carotenoids have been found in the visual purple of animals. The visual purple of chicken, frog, and marine fish contains *rhodopsin,* which on irradiation furnishes retinene$_1$, a derivative of vitamin A_1; the retina of fresh-water fish contains the purple-colored *porphyropsin,* which when irradiated gives retinene$_2$, the analogous derivative of vitamin A_2 (23). The absorption maxima of rhodopsin and porphyropsin are 500 and 522 mμ, respectively (23).

The retinal rods contain 5–10% visual purple, corresponding to approximately 10^9 molecules of the substance per rod (26). The mechanism of the photoreaction taking place on irradiation is not yet fully understood. According to Wald (23,27), irradiation cleaves the visual purple into the protein component and retinene. In the retinal tissue this reaction is reversible so that the visual purple is regenerated in a dark reaction from the protein and retinene. The regeneration is an aerobic reaction; the oxygen consumption of retinas is higher in the dark (31). The photoreaction is considered to involve a denaturation of the protein component (25,32), an interpretation supported by the greater stability of visual purple in the dry state. The red residue obtained by drying visual purple *in vacuo* over calcium chloride is rather resistant to the action of light and can even be exposed to daylight (33).

The first irradiation product of the carotenoid component has been called "transient orange"; it is stable near 0°C. and is converted to "indicator yellow" at room temperature; in alkaline solution indicator yellow is colorless (34). Indicator yellow is a conjugated protein in which the aldehyde group of retinene is probably bound to an amino group of the protein moiety (35). Vitamin A is not formed as a split product of the photolysis of dry visual purple (33,36). Dry visual purple does not undergo decomposition when treated with benzene or with chloroform; however, treatment with ethanol or methanol decomposes it instantaneously, converting it into a yellow substance. Since retinene is yellow and vitamin A colorless, neither of these can constitute the prosthetic group of visual purple. No satisfactory explanation has yet been given for the intense color and for the extreme photosensitivity of visual purple. The color of carotenes depends mainly on their chain length and the number of double bonds in the chain; it seems very likely that two or more retinene molecules combine to form a red carotene derivative which is linked to the protein component (27,35). While visual purple is found in the retinal rods, the cones contain the pigments of daylight vision; these also are carotenoids, possibly linked to proteins (18).

B. Glucoproteins (**Mucoproteins**) (37). The terms glucoprotein and mucoprotein are used here to designate conjugated proteins containing glucose or other sugars and sugar derivatives. The glucoproteins include substances of very different composition and properties. They have been classified as *neutroglucoproteins* and as *acidoglucoproteins* according to the properties of the carbohydrate component (38). The first of these groups includes the proteins containing neutral carbohydrates built up from monosaccharides and from amino sugars. The acidoglucoproteins owe their acidic properties to hexuronic acids or to the esterification of their sugars with sulfuric acid. One must bear in mind, however, that most glucoproteins contain a mixture of neutral and acid carbohydrates, so that this classification is not very satisfactory. Another classification is based on the carbohydrate content of the glucoproteins. Substances containing more than 4% carbohydrate have been called *mucoids* or *mucoproteins*, while those containing less than 4% carbohydrate were designated *glycoproteins* (37).

Hitherto no glucoprotein has been obtained in pure, crystalline form. Some of the "glucoproteins" might well be mixtures of various substances; other glucoproteins are artifacts formed from proteins and carbohydrates during their preparation. The resistance to denaturation of the glucoproteins frequently serves as a basis for separating them from mixtures with proteins. Proteins are removed by heat-coagulation and the glucoproteins are precipitated from the filtrate by salting-out or by acidification.

Until recently there was some doubt as to whether the glucoproteins contain a few large polysaccharide molecules per protein molecule or many small sugar residues linked to different groups of the protein. It seems at present that the typical glucoproteins contain *polysaccharides* as their prosthetic group. Proteins combine with polysaccharides *in vitro* to form more or less stable symplexes (39). Among the amino acids, the tendency of tyrosine and arginine to combine with polysaccharides is outstanding (39). It has been suggested, therefore, that the polysaccharide is bound to these amino acids of the protein component. The linkage between polysaccharidic acids and proteins in the acidoglucoproteins is most probably a saltlike link formed by electrostatic forces between the acidic groups of the polysaccharide and basic groups of the protein (40). In addition to these salt links, dipole–dipole attraction is probably involved in the mutual linkage of the protein and its prosthetic group.

Cartilage consists mainly of collagen and of chondroitinsulfuric acid. The latter compound is a polysaccharidic acid containing equivalent amounts of glucuronic acid and of acetylchondrosaminesulfuric acid ester (41). The chondroitinsulfuric acid ester prepared from cartilage is a high-molecular polysaccharide which gives viscous solutions and shows flow birefringence (42). Its molecular weight is approximately 260,000; the length of the chain molecules is about 4700 Å (42). It is not yet clear whether the molecules of chondroitin sulfuric acid ester are straight long chains (43) or branched chains (44). They combine with proteins at pH values below pH 4.85, the isoelectric point of the proteins (45).

The main protein of the cartilage is collagen, an insoluble fibrous scleroprotein (see Chapter IX), built up of long peptide chains. The polyvalent chondroitinsulfuric acid anions apparently combine with basic groups of the protein threads, so that a network of fibrous polysaccharide anions and protein cations is formed (45). If cartilage is boiled with water, the collagen is converted to water-soluble gelatin; this combines with chondroitinsulfuric acid to give the so-called *chondromucoid;* it is evidently a degradation product of the native collagen compound (45). Since collagen at the pH of the body has an excess of negative groups it seems that not only saltlike bonds but also van der Waals' forces are involved in the linkage between collagen and chondroitinsulfuric acid (45). Collagen as well as chondroitinsulfuric acid has been found in the skin and in the organic substance of bones, which probably contain the same glucoprotein as cartilage. There remains some doubt as to whether or not *amyloid* belongs in the category of the glucoproteins containing chondroitinsulfuric acid. Amyloid is formed in the liver and in other organs in chronic inflammatory processes. It gives a purplish color with iodine. The name amyloid is derived from its resemblance to starch. Sulfuric acid esters have been identified in amyloid (46).

Mucins are the glucoproteins of saliva, gastric juice, intestinal juice, and other secretions. Highly viscous in solution, mucins apparently consist of long threadlike molecules. The carbohydrate component of the mucins, which are acidoglucoproteins contains a hexuronic acid, possibly glucuronic acid, COOH·CHOH·CHOH·CHOH·CHOH·COH (38); in the mucin of the submaxillary gland gluconic acid, CH_2OH·-CHOH·CHOH·CHOH·CHOH·COOH, has been discovered (37). Besides hexuronic acid, the mucins contain 5–8% mannose and 5–8% acetylated glucosamine (47) or chondrosamine (48). Since only traces of sulfuric acid are found in mucins, they cannot contain large amounts of mucoitin sulfuric acid, as had been assumed for some time (47). Owing to their content of hexonic or hexuronic acid the mucins are acidic substances with an isoelectric point between pH 3 and 5 (49); they are precipitated from the secretions by the addition of acetic acid and are dissolved again by adding alkali.

The glucoproteins extracted from various organs by water or by salt solutions and precipitated by acidification have been called *mucoids*. Large amounts of mucoids are found in cysts, chiefly in ovarian cysts. Mucoids also constitute the bulk of the vitreous humor of the eye. Different carbohydrates have been found in the different mucoids. The mucoid of the vitreous humor contains acetylglucosamine and glucuronic acid, while the mucoid of the cornea is formed by mucoitinsulfuric acid. The latter is a sulfuric acid ester of hyaluronic acid (50). In the mucoid prepared from tendons chondroitinsulfuric acid has been found (51); it seems that this mucoid is formed secondarily by the degradation of collagen and that the native tendon consists of collagen and chondroitinsulfuric acid without any mucoid. Urinary mucoid contains acetylglucosamine and galactose (52).

Hyaluronic acid, found in the mucoid of the vitreous humor, is a polysaccharidic acid consisting of equimolecular amounts of *N*-acetylglucosamine and glucuronic acid (53). It has also been isolated from the umbilical cord and from synovia (42). Its molecular weight is approximately 200,000; the length of its chain molecule is 4800–10,000 Å (42). The role of hyaluronic acid is to hold the cells together by forming a viscous barrier and thus to serve as a kind of cement (54). Hyaluronic acid is probably bound to the cellular proteins of soft tissues in the same manner as chondroitinsulfuric acid is bound to collagen in the cartilage and in bones. Hyaluronic acid is responsible for the typical gelatinous structure of the vitreous humor and of the umbilical cord.

Ovomucoid, a thoroughly investigated glucoprotein of egg white is present in the filtrate of the heat-coagulated proteins and is precipitated from this filtrate by ethanol. The carbohydrate portion of ovomucoid, constituting 20% of its substance, consists of three molecules of mannose, seven of acetylglucosamine, and one molecule of galactose, or a total of eleven monosaccharide residues. The remaining 80% of ovomucoid is formed by protein (55*a*,*b*). The structure of the carbohydrate component is probably the following (55*a*):

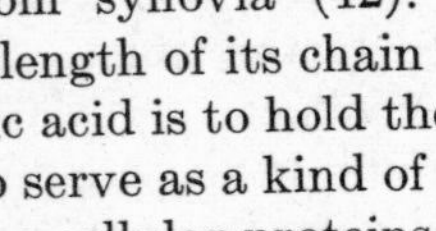

```
A   A   A   A
  \ |   | /
    M — M — M — G
  / |   |
A   A   A
```

where A is *N*-acetylglucosamine, M is mannopyranose, and G is galactopyranose (55). The carbohydrate seems to be bound to the protein by an ester linkage formed by a hydroxyl group of acetylglucosamine and a protein carboxyl group (55). In the egg, ovomucoid forms complexes with other proteins of egg white (56).

Glucoproteins have also been found in blood serum; if the serum is mixed with an equal volume of saturated ammonium sulfate solution, the bulk of the globulins is precipitated. The filtrate contains a mixture of serum albumin and glucoproteins which is precipitated by acidifying the filtrate to pH 4.7, the isoelectric point of serum albumin. By dissolving the precipitate in water and by mixing it with an equal volume of a saturated ammonium sulfate solution at pH 7.6, globoglycoid is precipitated (57). It is free of carbohydrates (58), and very similar to serum albumin. The serum albumin in the supernatant liquid is coagulated by heating; from the filtrate two glucoproteins, seroglycoid and seromucoid, have been prepared. *Seroglycoid,* which contains galactose, mannose, and glucosamine, is not a uniform protein, since it can be separated into several fractions by precipitation with concentrated buffer solutions (59). The second glucoprotein, *seromucoid,* contains 10.7% carbohydrate, consisting of *N*-acetylglucosamine, D-galactose, and D-mannose in the ratio 1:1:1 (58). Horse serum contains 0.5% globoglycoid, and approximately the same amount of seroglycoid and seromucoid (57). If the blood serum is treated with ethanol, the glucoproteins are found in Fraction IV (see Chapter VIII); the fraction contains a carbohydrate-rich α_2-globulin, and two other conjugated proteins called glycoprotein and mucoprotein (60). To the glucoproteins belongs also the *gonadotropic hormone* present in the urine of pregnant women; it contains 18% carbohydrate (see Chapter XIII).

The *blood group substances* also contain carbohydrates; they are responsible for the group specificity of human blood corpuscles. It is well known that four main groups of blood corpuscles exist; they are designated as A, B, AB, and O and contain the very similar substances A, B, and O; red blood corpuscles containing these substances are agglutinated by specific agglutinins present in blood sera (see Chapter XIV) of persons of different groups, a fact which results in agglutination if blood of a foreign type is used in transfusions. The blood group substances are glucoproteins or glucopolypeptides, containing carbohydrates as well as amino acids (68).

The red blood cells contain only small amounts of the blood group substances; larger amounts of very similar substances have been discovered in saliva, in the commercial peptone, in pepsin preparations, and in hog stomach (61–63,64). The A-substances prepared from different tissues are similar to, but not quite identical with, the A-substance

derived from red blood cells; they contain 40–70% carbohydrate consisting of D-galactose, D-mannose, D-glucosamine, and also D-fucose (63). The carbohydrate is present as a polymer with terminal fucose units (65). The A-substance from hog stomach contains 39% of its nitrogen as glucosamine and 27.1% as amino acid nitrogen; hydrolysis of the A-substance furnishes 1.6% glycine, 0.7% valine, 0.3% isoleucine, 3.3% proline, 1.9% histidine, 0.3% tyrosine, 0.1% phenylalanine, 0.2% tryptophan, and small amounts of other amino acids (66).

The substances B and O are very similar to the A substance. All three factors, A, B, and O, have been prepared from saliva and from ovarian cysts (67), and are found to contain 5.3–5.7% of total nitrogen, 2.3–2.9% of amino acid nitrogen, and 1.7–1.8% of hexosamine nitrogen (61). They display the arginine reaction (Sakaguchi), the diazo test, and the biuret reaction; none of them contains sulfur (61). The nature of the other nitrogenous substances present in the blood group factors and the manner in which the carbohydrate component is linked to the protein or peptide component have yet to be established. The blood group substances are very viscous in their native state and at pH 8.5 they form gels; the action of sodium hydroxide or of sodium carbonate causes them to lose their viscosity (68), apparently due to cleavage or denaturation in such alkaline solutions. By heat treatment the blood group substances are inactivated (65).

It is not quite clear whether the cuticula of insects is formed by a true conjugated protein containing carbohydrate, or whether the cuticula consists of two interpenetrating lattices of a protein and the carbohydrate chitin; both possibilities have been taken into consideration (69).

C. Phosphoproteins. The phosphoproteins, which differ from nucleoproteins in that they lack purine and pyrimidine bases, contain phosphoric acid ester groups. The most important and most thoroughly investigated phosphoprotein is *casein*, the phosphoprotein of milk. It contains approximately 0.9% phosphorus. If casein is hydrolyzed by acid or alkali, phosphoric acid is split off. Owing to its high content of phosphoric acid ester groups, casein is an acidic protein with an isoelectric point of pH 4.6–4.7. It is precipitated from milk by the addition of acetic acid, but it is soluble in an excess of strong acids.

Casein is far from being a uniform protein. It has been resolved into different fractions by fractional precipitation with aqueous or with alcoholic acids (70,71). The molecular weight of these fractions varies from 75,000 to 375,000 (72). The main fractions called α- and β-casein differ from each other by their amino acid composition (see Table I, page 32) (73), and their electrophoretical behavior (71).

The phosphoric acid is joined by an ester bond to the hydroxyl groups of serine molecules; enzymatic hydrolysis of casein with trypsin furnishes phosphoserylglutamic acid (74,75). On partial hydrolysis of casein with dilute hydrochloric acid the phosphoric acid ester of serine is obtained (76).

Phosphoproteins are prepared *in vitro* by phosphorylation of proteins with phosphorus oxychloride, $POCl_3$ (77,78). These synthetic phosphoproteins differ, however, from the natural phosphoproteins in that a considerable portion of their phosphoric acid groups is linked to amino groups and to the hydroxyl groups of tyrosine; furthermore, they are more resistant to the hydrolytic action of alkali than are the natural phosphoproteins.

Casein is precipitated from milk not only by acids, but also by the action of the enzyme chymosin (rennin, rennet), which is produced in the gastric mucosa (79). The clotting of milk in the stomach is a prerequisite for the digestion of the milk proteins by the gastric juice; if the milk did not clot, it would leave the stomach as rapidly as water or other liquids and its proteins would not be digested. The mechanism of the clotting process remains somewhat obscure. It has been proposed that the insoluble clot consists of dimerized or polymerized casein or that it is formed by calcium phosphate–casein complexes. The clotting has been described as a conversion of caseinogen into casein or of casein into paracasein. The terms caseinogen and paracasein are rarely used, however, because we know nothing about the process underlying the formation of the casein clot. It seems that the enzyme causes a slight unfolding of the peptide chains of casein, by which polar or ionic groups of the casein molecules are rendered mutually accessible to one another and are thereby able to form intermolecular saltlike bonds. Calcium ions seem to be indispensable for this process. The great tendency of casein molecules to unfold and to form a fibrous protein is made use of in the preparation of textile fibers. If alkaline solutions of casein are extruded through fine jets into an acid bath, threads are obtained which can be spun and hardened by treatment with formaldehyde.

While casein has been investigated rather extensively, very little is known about the phosphoproteins found in the eggs of birds, fish, and other animals. The phosphoproteins of the yolk of avian eggs are called *vitellins.* The vitellin from hens' eggs is prepared by extracting the yolk with 10% sodium chloride solution, removing the lipids (lecithin) with diethyl ether and precipitating the lipid-free protein solution by diluting with water (80). Vitellin contains 0.92% phosphorus (80). By the action of 12% ammonia vitellinic acid is split off from vitellin; hydrolysis of vitellinic acid with 2 *N* hydrochloric acid furnishes the phosphoric acid ester of serine (81). Evidently vitellin is very similar to casein. It seems to have much the same role as casein, namely that of furnishing phosphorus and the essential amino acids for the developing organism.

Two other phosphoproteins have been prepared from hens' eggs. One of them, called *livetin*, is prepared by heat coagulation of the supernatant solution obtained after the precipitation of vitellin (82). A second phosphoprotein, called *phosphovitin*, was precipitated by copper salts from the supernatant solution obtained by precipitation of egg yolk with sodium sulfate; phosphovitin contains 10% phosphorus and 12% nitrogen, and is free of sulfur. Having a molecular weight of 21,000, each molecule contains 31 phosphorus atoms and 33 molecules of hydroxyamino acids, mainly serine (83). Evidently, the phosphorus occurs linked to serine molecules (83).

D. Metalloproteins. *Ferritin* (84), a crystalline protein containing more than 20% iron, was isolated by Laufberger (85) from liver and spleen. Ferritin contains the iron as ferric iron, the high percentage of which corresponds to almost one iron atom per peptide bond (86). If the ferric iron is reduced to ferrous iron by the action of sodium dithionite ($Na_2S_2O_4$), the molecule is split into the iron-free *apoferritin* and a solution of ferrous salts (87). Apoferritin has been obtained in crystals (87) and is found to have a molecular weight of 465,000 (88). The prosthetic group of ferritin is an inorganic ferric compound of the composition $(FeO{\cdot}OH)_8(FeO{\cdot}OPO_3H_2)$ (89). It seems that ferritin is a storage form of iron; if ferric salts are injected intravenously, they are incorporated into ferritin (90).

Metal-combining proteins have also been isolated from blood plasma; when plasma is fractionated by ethanol, metal-combining β_1-globulins are found in Fraction IV (60) (see page 151). They consist of a copper-binding protein, and of siderophilin, an iron-binding protein (91,91*a*). Fe-siderophilin has the salmon-pink color displayed by iron compounds of hydroxamic acids; most likely its iron atom is bound to the grouping —N(OH)CO—, present in the protein moiety of siderophilin (91). The molecular weight of siderophilin is 90,000; each molecule is able to combine with two iron atoms.

Hemerythrin, a protein containing 1.01% iron, is the respiratory pigment of *Sipunculus nudus, Plaseolum vulgare, Plaseolum elongatum*, and of other marine worms (92,93). The molecular weight of hemerythrin is 66,000; each molecule contains three atoms of iron, but combines with only one molecule of O_2 (94). Hemerythrin is a yellowish ferrous compound, free of porphyrins and hemins, which on standing is oxidized to a brown ferric compound (93). The prosthetic group of hemerythrin is hemoferrin; its protein component is a globulin, which is insoluble in salt-free water and whose isoelectric point is at pH 5.85 (94). Although the composition of hemoferrin is not yet elucidated, it seems to be a polypeptide to which ferrous ions are bound.

Hemocyanin (95) is the respiratory pigment of many crustaceans and of certain mollusks (96) and is a porphyrin-free copper protein. The hemocyanins behave as globulins; they are obtained in crystalline form by precipitation with ammonium sulfate and/or by dialysis (97,98). The isoelectric point of the hemocyanins is between pH 4.5 and 5.0. Hemocyanin combines with molecular oxygen to form a blue oxygenated compound which contains one molecule of O_2 for every two copper atoms (99). Under reduced pressure oxygen is given off and the slightly yellowish oxygen-free compound is formed. The copper atom of hemocyanin is probably present in the cuprous state (100). It is split off by the action of hydrogen cyanide (100) or by hydrochloric acid (101).

The hemocyanins are species-specific, as might be concluded from the difference in the shapes of the crystals obtained from different animals (102). While the hemocyanins of lobster, crayfish, and other arthropods contain 0.17 to 0.18% copper, those of the snail *Helix pomatia*, the squid *Loligo*, and of other mollusks contain 0.24 to 0.26% copper (103,104).

All attempts to isolate a prosthetic group of hemocyanin have resulted in failure. Copper-containing polypeptides have been obtained by the action of alkali or of enzymes on hemocyanin, but it is not clear whether these correspond to that part of the hemocyanin molecule to which copper was originally bound, or whether they are fragmented products which combined secondarily with copper ions (105,106).

The molecular weight of the hemocyanins is extremely high. Sedimentation measurements made with the ultracentrifuge give values varying from 500,000 to 10,000,000 (107). These values, the highest ever observed for any protein, were confirmed by osmometry and by considerations of the scattering of light by the substance (see page 51). Electron micrographs of the hemocyanin isolated from the horseshoe crab, *Limulus polyphemus*, revealed it to consist of almost spherical particles with an average diameter of 200 Å (108). The hemocyanin of *Busycon caniculatum*, on the other hand, is formed by parallel bundles of four rodlike subunits (109).

In concentrated solutions of urea the hemocyanins undergo disaggregation into smaller particles (110); reversible disaggregation of hemocyanin molecules into subunits is brought about by acids or by alkaline solutions (see page 128). This splitting occurs under conditions which ordinarily are considered too mild to cause denaturation (111). The split products have the same shape as the native hemocyanin molecule (111) and recombine to form hemocyanin; it is a matter of definition whether the split products are to be designated denatured (111).

Since the equivalent weight of the hemocyanins of mollusks is approximately 25,000 per copper atom and that of arthropods 37,000, it is evident that each molecule contains a large number of copper atoms and is capable of combining with many oxygen molecules. Copper has also been found in the enzymes laccase, tyrosinase, ascorbic acid oxidase (95), and in hemocuprein and hepatocuprein, two proteins isolated from blood plasma and from ox liver, respectively. Both contain 0.34% copper (112). The biological function of these two copper proteins is not yet known.

E. Hemoglobin (113,114). The prosthetic group of hemoglobin and of some other proteins is a heme, *i.e.*, a ferroporphyrin complex. Hemoglobin, one of the most exhaustively studied of all proteins, has received so much attention because of its great importance as an oxygen carrier, because of the ease with which it can usually be crystallized, and because of its intense color, which lends itself to quantitative colorimetric determinations. Moreover, changes in the native state of hemoglobin are reflected by changes in its color and absorption spectrum. It is not our task to discuss here the chemistry of the heme compound and of the different porphyrins. It is necessary, however, to consider those properties of hemoglobin which are associated with its protein component.

In order to prepare hemoglobin, whole blood is centrifuged, the plasma removed, and the red cells washed with isotonic saline solution. The cells are hemolyzed by the addition of water, diethyl ether, or toluene (115–117). The stromata of the red cells are removed by centrifuging. If ether or toluene has been used, a considerable portion of the stromata remains suspended between the aqueous and the organic solvent layer from under which the hemoglobin solution can be removed by syphoning off. Hemoglobin is precipitated from this solution by cautiously adding ethanol at low temperatures; some hemoglobins are barely soluble in salt-free water and crystallize on dialysis; others are precipitated by passing a current of oxygen and carbon dioxide through the solution, the latter serving to keep the reaction slightly acidic. The prosthetic group of hemoglobin, which is split off by the action of acids, is the same for all hemoglobins and myoglobins; it is protoheme, the ferro compound of protoporphyrin:

```
                   CH3C ——— CCH=CH2
                       ||    ||
                   HC—C      C—CH
                       \    /  ||
          CH3C—C        N      C—CCH3
               ||  \    |    /   ||
               ||   N   Fe  N    ||
               ||  //   |    \\  ||
HOOCCH2CH2C—C           N        C—CCH=CH2
            |      /      \         |
            CH=C            C=CH
               |            |
       HOOCCH2CH2C=========CCH3
```

Protoheme

The protein component of hemoglobin is called *globin*. While pure hemoglobin was prepared as early as 1867, native globin was not known until 1926, when Hill and Holden (118) showed that the globins prepared before that time were denatured. Native globin was obtained by cautiously adding dilute hydrochloric acid (118) or oxalic acid (119) to hemoglobin and extracting the hemin with diethyl ether, or by precipitating the native protein with large amounts of acetone (119–121). While the denatured globin obtained by the older methods combines with reduced protohemin to form a hemochromogen, hemoglobin is regenerated when native globin is mixed with protohemin and a reducing agent at pH 8–9 (118). While most proteins contain 2–3% histidine, the globins contain 6–10% of this basic amino acid (see Table I, p. 32). Owing to this high content of histidine the isoelectric point of globin is at pH 6.8 to 7.0, that of denatured globin near pH 8.0. Native globin is soluble over a wide pH range; denatured globin is precipitated in slightly alkaline solutions and can thus be removed from solutions of the native globin.

Although heme by itself is extremely unstable and is instantaneously oxidized by air to hemin, hemoglobin combines with oxygen to form the ferrous compound oxyhemoglobin in a reaction which may be reversed *in vacuo*. Evidently globin serves to prevent the oxidation of the iron from ferrous to ferric (122), thus rendering possible the formation of the oxygenated compound HbO_2. Since no other protein is able to replace globin in this respect, globin presumably contains a special "hemaffinic" group or a special arrangement of molecular groups, which combine with heme to form hemoglobin (123,124).

The "synthetic" hemoglobin, prepared by coupling native globin with heme, differs from the original hemoglobin by a greater instability toward heat (125), and toward sodium hydroxide solutions (126). However, it combines reversibly with O_2 and behaves in many respects in the same way as native hemoglobin.

The molecular weight of the hemoglobin of mammals is 66,000–68,000. Since all hemoglobins contain 0.34% iron, this corresponds to 230 gr. iron per mole, *i.e.*, four iron atoms. Each of these iron atoms is afforded by a single heme residue, so that each hemoglobin molecule contains four heme molecules as its prosthetic group (127,128). By the action of urea (129), dilute hydrochloric acid (130), or salts (131) smaller units of the molecular weight of 34,000 are obtained. Disaggregation also takes place when native globin is prepared from hemoglobin by hydrochloric acid (132). Evidently the hemoglobin molecule consists of four subunits, each of which contains one heme molecule as its prosthetic group. Their reaction with large particles, such as ferricyanide ions, indicates that the hemes are fixed to the surface of the globin units (133). From the different absorption spectrum of hemoglobin crystals along different optical axes, it has been concluded that the planes of the four hemes in each hemoglobin molecule are parallel (134); the hemoglobin molecule has the shape of a cylinder with a height of 33.5 Å, and a diameter of 57 Å (135), the four hemes apparently being attached to the surface of the cylinder.

Red cells contain about 34% hemoglobin, the maximum possible concentration at which the hydrated hemoglobin cylinders are still able to rotate freely around their three axes (136).

The structure of hemoglobin and of its derivatives is represented by the following formulas (123), in which the porphyrin ring is shown by the four nitrogen atoms of the pyrrole rings:

```
      N  N                        N  N                      N  N
      | /                         | /                       | /
Globin--Fe—(H2O)          Globin—Fe—O2              Globin—Fe—OH
      / |                       / |                       / |
     N  N                      N  N                      N  N
   Hemoglobin               Oxyhemoglobin            Methemoglobin
```

The side chains of protoheme are not essential for the formation of hemoglobin; hemoglobins have also been obtained by coupling globin with mesohemin dimethyl ester, in which the vinyl groups of protoheme are saturated and the carboxyl groups substituted by methyl groups (125). Although it is not yet clear which group of the globin molecule combines with the heme iron, most authors assume them to be the imidazole rings of histidine molecules; this view is supported by the fact that hemin combines readily with imidazoles (137), that cobalt histidine combines reversibly with O_2 (138), and that the affinity of hemoglobin for O_2 is altered markedly in the pH range between 5 and 8, the region where imidazole groups are titrated (113). Moreover, the base-binding capacity of hemoglobin in this pH range is profoundly modified by the combination with oxygen (113,139). Upon oxygenation the pK values are shifted from 7.93 to 6.68 and from 5.25 to 5.75 (113), which means that in neutral solutions more base is bound by oxyhemoglobin than hemoglobin, while the reverse is true in acid solutions (140).

While all these facts are in agreement with the assumption that the heme iron is bound to imidazole groups, the instability of the absorption spectrum of hemoglobin and of oxyhemoglobin toward dilute acids and its resistance to concentrated alkali (141) tend more to support the view that the heme iron is bound to an acid group such as a carboxyl group (123) or a sulfhydryl group; sulfhydryl groups are not found in neutral solutions of native globin; they appear, however, on alkalinization (142) or on denaturation (143).

The nature of the linkage of the iron atoms in hemoglobin and its derivatives has been elucidated by measuring their magnetic moments. The ferrous ion has four, while the ferric ion has five, unpaired electrons; since each of these electrons has a "spin," there is a resultant magnetic moment which can be measured with magnetic balances. If the number of unpaired electrons in a molecule or an ion is n, the magnitude of the magnetic moment, measured in Bohr magnetons, is $\mu_B = \sqrt{n(n+2)}$. Accordingly a magnetic moment of 4.9 magnetons is characteristic for ionic ferrous compounds and 5.9 magnetons for ferric ions. Actually a moment of approximately 6 Bohr magnetons was found for hemin (144) and a moment of 4.7 magnetons in heme (145). Accordingly, both heme and hemin are ionic iron compounds. The same is true for hemoglobin (145); oxyhemoglobin and carbon monoxide hemoglobin, however, are diamagnetic, *i.e.*, devoid of any magnetic moment (145). This proves that the electron orbits of the iron ion undergo a great alteration when oxygen or carbon monoxide are bound; all the unpaired electrons present in hemoglobin are involved in the formation of the new diamagnetic compound which has no unpaired electrons. In addition to the bond between iron and O_2 or CO, the bonds between iron and globin and between iron and porphyrin also lose their ionic character and become covalent. Oxyhemoglobin and CO-hemoglobin in this respect resemble the diamagnetic iron compounds, whose typical representative is the ferrocyanide complex. The maximum magnetic moment calculated for hemoglobin is $\sqrt{4(4+2)} = 4.9$ magnetons; however, the measured magnetic moment is 5.43 Bohr magnetons (145). The reason for this significant divergence is not yet known. It cannot be due to the mutual interaction of the heme groups, because it has also been found in the monomeric myoglobin, whose molecular weight is 17,000 (146).

All changes in the state of the iron atom and in the bond between heme iron and globin are accompanied by changes in the intense absorption spectrum; two absorption bands in the green region of the visible spectrum are characteristic for the diamagnetic compounds oxyhemoglobin, carbon monoxide hemoglobin, and hemochromogen (147).

Partial hydrolysis of hemoglobin by trypsin yields a preparation containing all the hemin linked very firmly to a portion of the globin (148). Partial hydrolysis of globin with 70% sulfuric acid at 37°C. furnishes a basic peptide containing large amounts of histidine (149). Apparently the histidine residues form a more resistant core in the globin molecule.

The combination of hemoglobin with O_2 affects not only the prosthetic group, but also the physical and chemical behavior of the molecule as a whole. It has been mentioned above that the base-binding capacity of neutral hemoglobin increases on oxygenation. As a consequence of this significant reaction, the pH is almost the same in the arterial as in the venous blood; the higher amount of carbonic acid in the venous blood is compensated for by the higher acidity of oxyhemoglobin in the arterial blood. The combination of hemoglobin with oxygen proceeds according to a quite unusual sigmoid curve (Fig. 41) (150). Since it is not observed in the monomeric myoglobin, whose molecule contains only one iron atom, the $\sim$-shape of the dissociation curve is attributed to a mutual interaction of the four heme groups in the hemoglobin molecule.

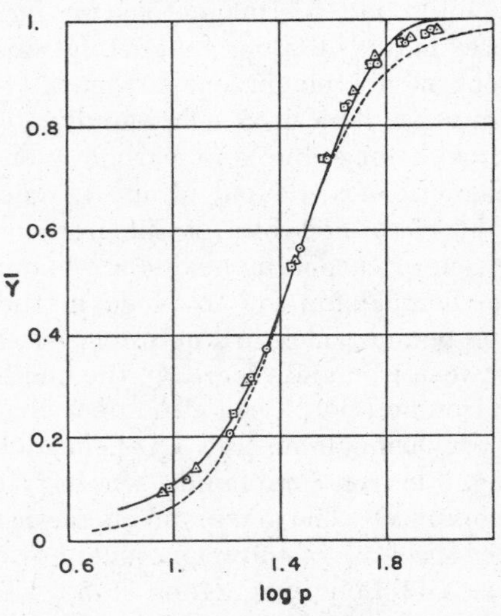

FIG. 41. Oxygen equilibrium of hemoglobin (113). Full curve, sheep hemoglobin (150); points, human blood (150*a*); broken curve is calculated according to Pauling's equation for an interaction constant of 12.

Oxygen always combines with all four hemes of a hemoglobin molecule; intermediates containing one, two, or three O_2 molecules per hemoglobin molecule give a hyperbolic curve (151). When the first oxygen molecule is bound to one of the four hemes, the affinity of the other three hemes for oxygen is enhanced and as a result they are saturated by oxygen in preference to other hemoglobin molecules.

The kinetics of this complicated reaction and its thermodynamics has been investigated by Roughton, who was able to describe the reaction satisfactorily by an equation (152):

$$\frac{y}{100} = \frac{K_1p\left(1 + \frac{K_1p}{4}\right)^3 + \lambda p^4}{4\left(1 + \frac{K_1p}{4}\right)^4 + \lambda p^4}$$

Here y is the percent saturation with oxygen, p the oxygen pressure, K_1 the equilibrium constant of the initial reaction $Hb_4 + O_2 = Hb_4O_2$, and λ is approximately $K_1^3(K_4/4)$, where K_4 is the equilibrium constant of the final reaction:

$$Hb_4(O_2)_3 + O_2 = Hb_4(O_2)_4$$

It is assumed, moreover, that the equilibrium constants K_1, K_2, and K_3 decrease statistically in this order, and that K_4 is much larger than K_1 (152). The high value of K_4 is a measure of the interaction between the four heme groups of each hemoglobin molecule.

FIG. 42. Crystals of horse hemoglobin and oxyhemoglobin (154).

It is obvious that some interrelationship must exist between the four heme groups linked to a globin molecule (153); most probably they are arranged in two pairs, so that the interaction between two hemes of one pair is stronger than that between two hemes of different pairs (113). That both the whole hemoglobin molecule and the heme groups are affected by the combination with oxygen is evident from the change in the shape of hemoglobin crystals on oxygenation (154) (Fig. 42). Oxygen diffuses from the air bubble at the top of the microphotograph to the six-sided platelets of reduced hemoglobin, transforming them into long oxyhemoglobin needles.

The drastic change in the shape of hemoglobin crystals upon oxygenation reveals a striking difference between the shape and the surface of hemoglobin and oxyhemoglobin molecules. This difference between hemoglobin and oxyhemoglobin is also responsible for the interesting phenomenon of "sickling" in the erythrocytes of negroes suffering from sickle cell anemia; at low oxygen pressures these erythrocytes display sickle forms (155).

The equilibrium between hemoglobin and oxygen is generally represented by $Hb + O_2 \rightleftharpoons HbO_2$. However, the equation:

$$Hb(H_2O) + O_2 \rightleftharpoons HbO_2 + H_2O$$

has been proposed in view of the fact that hemoglobin is an aquo compound (156). If hemoglobin is cautiously dried *in vacuo* the broad absorption band of "aquohemoglobin" is replaced by the two narrow hemochromogen bands of "anhydrohemoglobin"; on the addition of water, aquohemoglobin is regenerated (156,157).

The affinity of hemoglobin for oxygen is reduced by salts (158), but increases in concentrated solutions of urea, where the hemoglobin molecule undergoes disaggregation (113,159). Acidification by carbonic acid or by other acids reduces the affinity of hemoglobin for oxygen; this is a reversal of the phenomenon described above, namely, the increase in acidity (base-binding capacity) of hemoglobin on oxygenation (Bohr effect) (113). Both phenomena have been ascribed to the presence in globin of an ionic group which is in the vicinity of the iron-binding group and affects the affinity of the iron for oxygen.

It is well known that oxygen is displaced from its combination with hemoglobin by *carbon monoxide*, CO; the absorption spectrum, the crystalline shape, and various other properties of carbon monoxide hemoglobin are similar to those of oxyhemoglobin. The main differences are: (*1*) carbon monoxide hemoglobin is much more stable, than O_2Hb in that the dissociation into hemoglobin and carbon monoxide proceeds at a slower rate than the dissociation of oxyhemoglobin (160); (*2*) carbon monoxide hemoglobin is split into its components on irradiation with visible light (161); one quantum is required for each carbon monoxide molecule (162); (*3*) carbon monoxide hemoglobin, in contrast to hemoglobin and oxyhemoglobin, has no observable absorption band in the near-infrared region at 9000–10,000 Å (163). Carbon monoxide hemoglobin is differentiated from oxyhemoglobin by the bright red color of its solutions even after treatment with copper sulfate, sodium hydroxide, or tannin; oxyhemoglobin under the same conditions is converted to a brown compound. All these tests are based on the higher stability of COHb and on the formation of bright red CO-heme complexes, whereas the decomposition of oxyhemoglobin gives brown hemin derivatives.

While oxygen and carbon monoxide combine with the iron atoms of hemoglobin, *carbon dioxide* combines with the protein component. A considerable part of the carbonic acid in normal blood is present as "carbhemoglobin" (164). The nature of this carbhemoglobin is not quite clear. Since a large portion of the carbonic acid is not precipitated by barium salts, it has been concluded that carbhemoglobin is a carbamino compound, in which carbonic acid is bound according to the reaction (165):

$$R{\cdot}NH_2 + CO_2 \rightarrow R{\cdot}NH{\cdot}COOH$$

On the other hand, however, carbamino compounds are formed only at alkaline reactions and are not stable at the pH of normal blood (113,158,166). Possibly bicarbonate ions are bound so firmly to ammonium groups $^+NH_3$ of hemoglobin that they are inactivated in the same fashion as calcium or phosphate ions are inactivated by casein, and that, therefore, they are not precipitated by barium salts (see also Chapter V, Sect. C).

By the action of oxidizing agents the ferrous iron of hemoglobin is oxidized to ferric iron. The oxidation product is *methemoglobin*, which behaves like an indicator; it is brown in acid solution and red in alkaline solution (167). The two forms of methemoglobin correspond to an equilibrium between a ferric hydroxide and its cation (168):

$$\rangle FeOH \rightleftharpoons \rangle Fe^+ \, OH^-$$

acid alkaline

Methemoglobin combines with cyanides, fluorides, sulfides, and peroxides to form complex compounds, which have typical absorption spectra and which have been prepared in crystals (169,170). Normal human blood contains approximately 0.1% methemoglobin (171).

When hemoglobin solutions are treated with both hydrogen sulfide and oxygen gas or hydrogen peroxide, *sulfhemoglobin*, a green compound, is formed (172,173). Sulfhemoglobin is also formed when hemoglobin or blood undergoes putrefaction.

The *hemoglobins* of different animals are *species-specific*. While the specificity of many proteins is revealed only serologically, the specificity of hemoglobins is proved not only by their serological behavior (174), but also by differences in their crystalline shape (175,176), solubility, and amino acid content (see Table XIII, p. 214).

The globins of the different species also differ in the terminal amino groups of their peptide chains. These are provided by five valine molecules in human hemoglobin, six valine molecules in horse hemoglobin,

TABLE XIII (177–179)

Species of hemoglobin	Molecules per protein molecule (mol. wt 66,700) Histidine	Arginine	Isoleucine
Human	35	16	0
Horse	33	14	—
Sheep	32	15	—
Dog	—	—	6

and two valine and two methionine molecules in cow, sheep, and goat hemoglobin (180).

The hemoglobins of the different species are decomposed at very different rates by 0.05 *N* sodium hydroxide; with human hemoglobin the time required for 90% decomposition is about 1 min., with beef hemoglobin it is more than 24 hr. (Fig. 43) (181). By means of this reaction a specific hemoglobin was discovered in the blood of the human fetus (182). Its decomposition time is about 60 min. (182). Crystals of the hemoglobins of the human adult (183) and of the human fetus have different

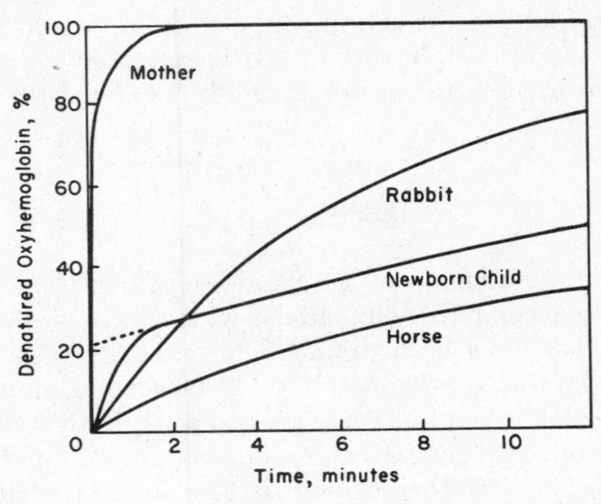

Fig. 43. Denaturation of different hemoglobins by 0.25 *N* sodium hydroxide (189).

shapes (Figs. 44 and 45) (182). The terminal amino groups of fetal human hemoglobin are formed by valine molecules; their number is 2.6 per 4 iron atoms (180). This ratio 2.6/4 indicates that fetal hemoglobin is not uniform; actually both fetal and adult hemoglobin have been found to be mixtures of at least three to five components (184). Fetal and adult human hemoglobin differ from each other not only in the shape of their crystals, but also in their X-ray interferences (185). However, the molecular weights of both hemoglobins are the same (186). A third type of human hemoglobin, more resistant to sodium hydroxide than normal adult hemoglobin, appears in the blood after the third year (187).

Although the absorption spectrum of hemoglobin and its affinity for oxygen are properties of the prosthetic group, both properties depend to a certain degree on the globin component. Small differences among

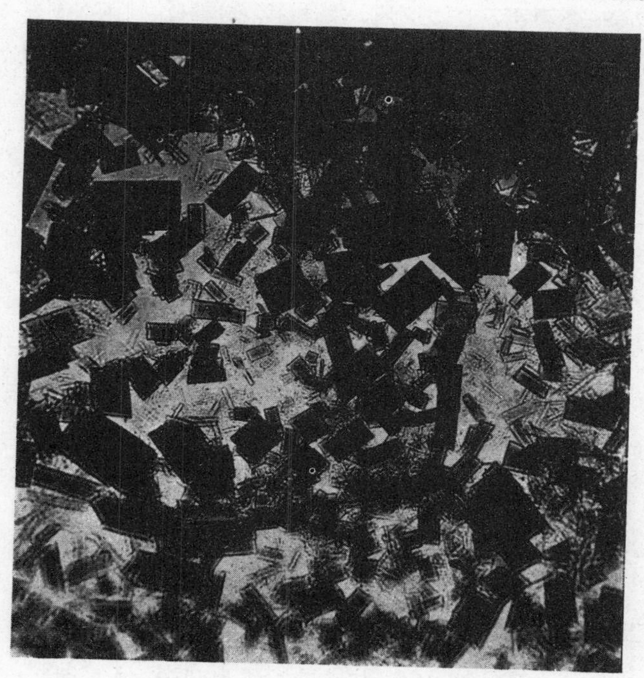

FIG. 44. Hemoglobin of an adult human (189).

various species in the "span," *i.e.*, the distance between the absorption maxima of oxyhemoglobin and CO-hemoglobin, varying from 53 to 62 Å as well as differences in the affinity for O_2 were found (188). The affinity of fetal red cells for oxygen is higher than that of adult red cells; on hemolysis the affinity of fetal hemoglobin remains unchanged, while that of adult hemoglobin increases (189,190). Evidently the affinity of hemoglobin for oxygen depends not only on its prosthetic group and on the protein component, but also on the conditions in the red blood cell. Although the great difference between fetal and maternal hemoglobins in humans is unique, differences in the affinity for oxygen have also been found in the blood of other animals such as the ox or the goat (191).

In pernicious anemia, when the regeneration of hemoglobin is increased, normal hemoglobin is formed, not the fetal type (167). In sickle cell anemia, however, a second type of hemoglobin has been discovered by electrophoresis; the sickle hemoglobin is more alkaline than normal human hemoglobin and has a positive charge at pH 6.9, whereas normal adult hemoglobin is negatively charged at this pH value (155).

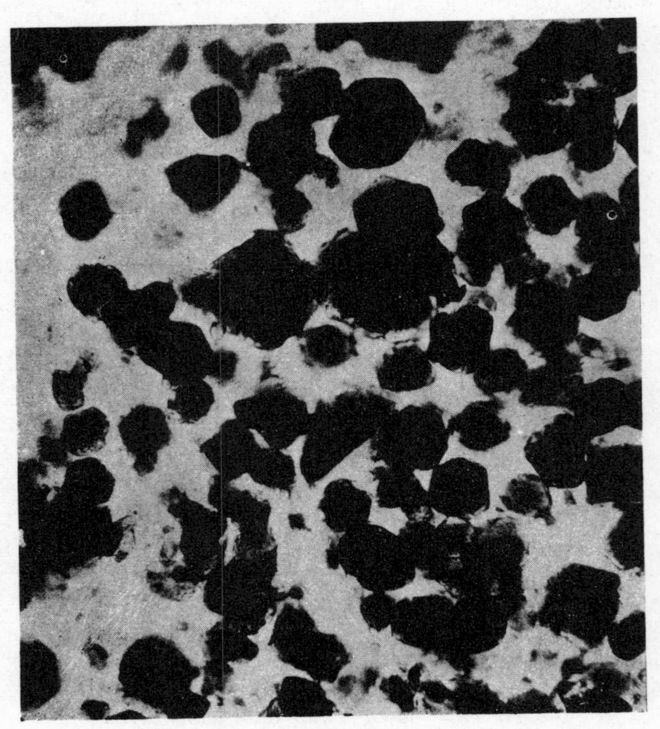

FIG. 45. Oxyhemoglobin of a newborn child (189).

While it is certain that the hemoglobins of the different species are specific, it is not clear whether they are uniform substances. Electrophoretic experiments (192,193) and fractional adsorption (194) have revealed the presence of more than one hemoglobin in beef and horse blood.

Hemoglobin has been also discovered in the root nodules of the legumes (195–197). It is not yet clear whether it serves some special function in the assimilation of nitrogen.

Myoglobin, the pigment of the red muscles, contains protoheme as its prosthetic group (198); the protein component is different from globin.

Crystalline myoglobin is obtained by dialyzing the muscle extract against concentrated ammonium sulfate solution (199). Crystalline myoglobin has also been obtained by resynthesis from its components (200). Myoglobin differs from hemoglobin by its greater tendency to combine with O_2 (201), by a shift of the absorption bands to longer wave lengths, by a higher resistance to sodium hydroxide solutions (189), and by its amino acid content (202). The molecular weight of myoglobin is 17,000; it contains one iron atom per molecule (199). Its terminal α-amino group is formed by glycine (180). Myoglobin has been found in the urine of persons whose muscles were severely crushed (203). It is interesting that myoglobin phylogenetically corresponds to the hemoglobin of the invertebrates (204).

Owing to its intense color the determination of hemoglobin and its derivatives is frequently made colorimetrically, especially in clinical laboratories. Since neither hemoglobin nor oxyhemoglobin are stable, they cannot be used as standard solutions. In many investigations hemoglobin has been determined by mixing the blood with dilute hydrochloric acid and by comparing colorimetrically the brown solution with a standard solution of "acid hematin." It must be emphasized that this method gives erroneous values, because the pigment slowly flocculates so that the incident light is not only absorbed, but also scattered (205). Turbidities are also caused by lipids (206) and by flocculated plasma proteins (207). Better results are obtained by colorimetric measurements in alkaline solutions. The best method is the colorimetric or photometric determination of cyanide-methemoglobin (208), obtained by mixing blood with hydrochloric acid and potassium cyanide (209). The method has been tested very thoroughly in several laboratories and found to be very satisfactory (210). The great advantage of this method is that cyanhematin is used as a stable standard; it has the same color and the same absorption spectrum as cyanide-methemoglobin.

The hemoglobin content of normal human blood has been found to be 15.7–16.1% (211). A reliable method for the determination of hemoglobin is also the gas-analytical method employing Van Slyke's volumetric or manometric apparatus; by saturating the blood with oxygen or with carbon monoxide before and after reduction with dithionite, $Na_2S_2O_4$, methemoglobin can be determined in the presence of hemoglobin (212). Dithionite is one of the few reducing agents which can be used for the conversion of oxyhemoglobin or methemoglobin to hemoglobin; most of the other reducing substances denature the globin component irreversibly; one has to take into account, however, that small amounts of "inactive pigment" which are not able to bind O_2, are converted to hemoglobin by dithionite (213). Very small amounts of molecular oxygen and oxyhemoglobin can be determined by polarography (214). Carbon monoxide hemoglobin and methemoglobin have been determined by infrared spectrophotometry (215). All these hemoglobin derivatives can be determined spectrophotometrically in their mixtures by a comparison with the absorption curves of the pure hemoglobin derivatives (167,216).

If large amounts of hematin are formed under pathological conditions by the decomposition of hemoglobin, a portion of the hematin combines with serum albumin; the hematin–albumin compound has been called methemalbumin (217). To the heme proteins also belong catalase, peroxidase, cytochrome, and cytochrome oxidase. They will be discussed in Chapter XII.

While some invertebrates such as *Sabella spallanzanii* and *Daphnia magna* contain true hemoglobins (218), two other hemoglobinlike pigments have been found in other invertebrates. One of them, erythrocruorin, has the typical red color of hemoglobin, while the other pigment, chlorocruorin, is green. *Erythrocruorin* contains the same protoheme as that found in hemoglobin. The protein component is, however, different; it contains much less histidine (219) and its isoelectric point is near pH 5. Erythrocruorins are found either in blood corpuscles or in the plasma of invertebrates. The intracorpuscular erythrocruorins of *Dasybranchus, Glycera, Thione briareus, Arca pescata,* and *Petromyzon fluvialis* have low molecular weights, varying from 16,700 to 56,500 (220,221). The extracellular erythrocruorins, which are dissolved in the blood plasma of *Arenicola, Planorbis, Lumbricus,* and other invertebrates, have molecular weights between 350,000 to 2,800,000 (221,222).

Chlorocruorin has been found by Fox (223) in the blood of *Spirographis* and *Serpula.* The crystalline protein contains 1.2% iron (224). Its molecular weight is very high, its isoelectric point pH 4.3 (225). Erythrocruorin as well as chlorocruorin combine with one molecule of oxygen per iron atom.

F. Combination of Proteins with Porphyrins and Bile Pigments. *Porphyrins* occur only in traces in the normal body fluids. Their amount increases under certain pathological conditions. They are bound to the albumin fraction of the plasma proteins (226). The green pigment of the chloromes, lymphatic tumors of the bone marrow, is protoporphyrin (227). It is bound to insoluble proteins and, therefore, is not extracted directly by diethyl ether.

Bilirubin, whose presence in the blood plasma is symptomatic of jaundice, is bound to serum albumin (228). Each molecule of serum albumin is able to fix three molecules of bilirubin (229). Electrophoresis shows that not only the direct bilirubin but also the so-called indirect bilirubin migrates with the albumin and the α-globulin fraction (230).

The indirect bilirubin reacts with diazobenzenesulfonic acid only after the previous addition of ethanol.

The dark-brown color of blood serum and of the feces in the rare cases of myodystrophia is caused by *myobilin,* a conjugated protein containing mesobilifuscin (231). The latter is a dipyrrylmethene, formed by the degradation of hemoglobin or of a hemoglobin derivative. Conjugated proteins containing bilirubin derivatives have also been found in the *Erythrophyceae,* the red algae; by treating them with alkaline methanol, mesobilirubin and mesobiliverdin are obtained (232).

Green chromoproteins are formed *in vivo* by the breakdown of hemoglobin. The first degradation product is *choleglobin,* whose protein component is globin, and the prosthetic group of which is the ferric salt of biliverdin (233). Bilirubin is a linear tetrapyrryl compound of the formula shown below, where M is methyl, $—CH_3$; V is vinyl, $—CH{=}CH_2$;

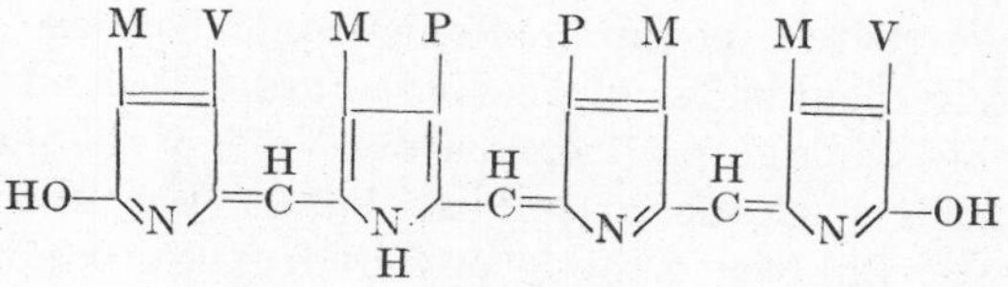

```
  M   V       M   P       P   M       M   V
  |===|       |===|       |===|       |===|
  |   |   H   |   |   H   |   |   H   |   |
HO—\N/=C—\N/—C=\N/—C=\N/—OH
                H
```

Biliverdin

and P is propionic acid, $—CH_2CH_2COOH$. Denaturation of choleglobin furnishes cholehemochromogen, a compound of denatured globin and ferri-biliverdin (233). By the action of acids biliverdin is split off. Similar green chromoproteins containing the open tetrapyrryl chain of the bile pigments are obtained when hemoglobin is treated with cyanides and hydrogen peroxide; they are also formed in the organisms of persons treated with sulfa drugs; they have been called *verdoglobins* or pseudohemoglobins (234). While the iron of heme proteins containing the closed porphin ring is bound so firmly that it is resistant to the action of hydrochloric acid, the iron of verdoglobins is split off very easily by dilute hydrochloric acid. The "inactive hemoglobin" present in small amounts in normal blood is possibly identical with verdoglobin; its concentration is approximately 1.3% (235). The concentration of verdoglobins in the blood can also be determined spectrophotometrically (236). Small amounts of a green pigment similar to or identical with choleglobin have been found in the root nodules of legumes (236b).

G. Nucleoproteins (237–240). While the nucleoproteins are the most important of the conjugated proteins, they nevertheless form the group about which the least is known. The great biological importance of nucleoproteins is evident in view of their occurrence in living cells and also in bacteria and viruses (241). Nucleoproteins consist of a protein component combined with a prosthetic group called nucleic acid. Since many authors regard the nucleic acids as templates for the *in vivo* synthesis of proteins, a brief discussion of their chemistry is necessary.

Complete hydrolysis of nucleic acids furnishes equivalent amounts of phosphoric acid, pentose, and purine or pyrimidine bases. By the enzymatic hydrolysis of nucleic acids, such as with gastric juice or pancreatic enzymes, mononucleotides are obtained; these are substances consisting of one molecule of phosphoric acid, one molecule of a pentose, and one molecule of a purine or pyrimidine base (242,243). Further cleavage is achieved by the use of enzymes from the intestine or the liver (244–246). More specifically, the products obtained by total hydrolytic cleavage are: (*1*) phosphoric acid, (*2*) ribose or desoxyribose, and (*3*) the purine bases, adenine, and guanine, and the pyrimidine bases thymine, cytosine, and uracil (247,248).

The general structure of the mononucleotides is: base–pentose–phosphoric acid. The pentosides of the bases are called nucleosides; their sugar component is linked to nitrogen atom No. 9 of the purine base or to nitrogen atom No. 3 of the pyrimidine base. The phosphoric acid is bound by an ester linkage to the 3- or 5-hydroxyl group of the pentose. A typical nucleoside and a mononucleotide are shown by the following formulae:

```
    NH2
    |
    C
  //  \
 N     CH
 |     ||
 OC    CH    ┌───────────O──────────┐
   \  /      │                      │
    N───────CH·CHOH·CHOH·CH·CH2OH
```

Cytidine
(cytosine riboside)

```
          NH2
          |       7
         6C       N
       //  \ 5  /  \\
    1N      C        \\ 8
     |      ||         CH
   2HC      C         /     ┌─────────────O──────────────┐
      \\   / 4 \     /      │                            │
        N        N ──────CH·CHOH·CHOH·CH·CH2OPO3H2
        3        9
```

Adenylic acid
(adenosine monophosphoric acid)

In the nucleic acids the mononucleotides are held together by phosphoric acid residues, so that chains of the following type are formed:

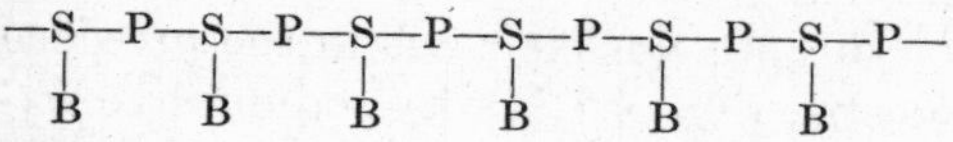

```
                                                         B      B      B
                                                         |      |      |
                                                        —S—P—S—P—S—P—
                                                         |
                                                         P
                                                         |
—S—P—S—P—S—P—S—P—S—P—S—P—                    —S—P—S—P—S—P—S—P—
 |     |     |     |     |     |                         |      |      |      |
 B     B     B     B     B     B                         B      B      B      B
               I                                                 II
```

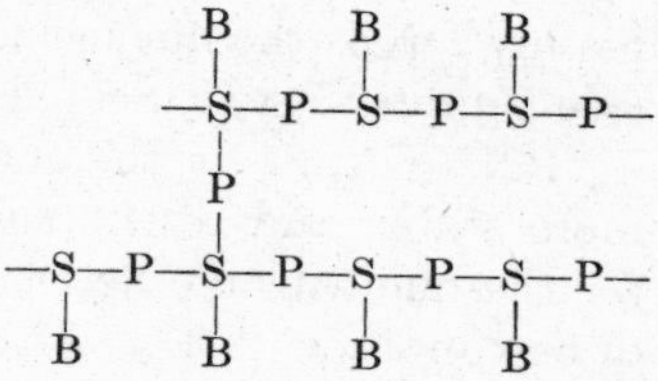

where S is sugar (ribose or desoxyribose), P is phosphoric acid, and B is purine or pyrimidine base (245). It remains to be established, however, whether the nucleotide chains are straight or branched, as indicated in the above diagrams I and II, respectively, whether they contain subunits such as tetranucleotides or pentanucleotides, whether the purine and pyrimidine bases are arranged in a regular periodic pattern, or whether they are distributed at random (249,250).

Nucleic acids were originally prepared by extraction of cells with alkali and precipitation with acid. However, through the action of alkali or acid, macromolecules of nucleic acid are altered so that their solutions at pH values below 5.6 or above 10.9 (251) lose their high viscosity. This effect is probably caused by disaggregation of the macromolecules. The highly viscous polymeric nucleic acid may also be disaggregated by the action of two enzymes called ribonuclease and desoxyribonuclease (252,253). Both enzymes have been isolated from pancreas in crystalline form by Kunitz (see Chapter XII).

The natural macromolecular nucleic acids are prepared from native nucleoproteins which have been extracted from tissues by neutral salt solutions or by water; if these nucleoproteins are cautiously dialyzed or shaken with chloroform (254) they are split into protein and polymeric nucleic acid. The protein can be removed by denaturation or by salting-out with sodium chloride (255). The molecular weight of the macromolecular native thymonucleic acid has been estimated to be 820,000 (256) or 1.5 or 3.7 million, respectively (257–259); the length of the threadlike molecule is about 5000 Å, and its transverse diameter is 18–20 Å (257–259).

Depending on the type of pentose found in the nucleic acids we classify them as *ribonucleic acids* (RNA) and *desoxyribonucleic acids* (DNA). There is no evidence for the occurrence of hybrid molecules which contain both these sugars (251). Ribonucleic acid is essentially identical with the "yeast nucleic acid" of the older literature, desoxyribonucleic acid with "thymonucleic acid" prepared from the thymus gland. The former designation was not justified, because yeast also contains small amounts of DNA. The ratio RNA:DNA varies from 30 to 50 in yeast (260). While the nuclei of animal and vegetable cells contain mainly DNA, the nucleic acid of the cytoplasm is chiefly RNA (261,262) (see Chapter XVII, Sect. D).

RNA is split by the action of *N* sodium hydroxide, whereas DNA is more stable and resists such treatment; use is made of this difference for the quantitative determination of both nucleic acids in the presence of one another (263). After the destruction of RNA by sodium hydroxide, DNA is precipitated by the addition of proteins in acid solution (263).

In tissues the two types of nucleic acid are differentiated by means of the Feulgen test (264); the tissue section or the cell suspension is treated with *N* hydrochloric acid and then with the aldehyde reagent fuchsin, which has previously been reduced by sulfurous acid. Desoxyribose, but not ribose, is converted by the action of hydrochloric acid into an aldehyde, probably ω-hydroxylevulinic aldehyde, $CH_2OH \cdot CO \cdot CH_2 \cdot CH_2 \cdot CHO$ (265), which gives a red color with the reduced fuchsin and is also responsible for Dische's diphenylamine test (266). A positive reaction for both tests is considered characteristic of DNA.

Another important method used for differentiating between RNA and DNA is to treat cells or tissue sections with solutions of the specific enzymes, ribonuclease and desoxyribonuclease, which hydrolyze only the respective nucleic acid; staining of the cells with basic dyes before and after the treatment with the respective enzymes reveals the sites of RNA and DNA in the untreated cells (267).

Purines and pyrimidines intensively absorb ultraviolet light; since the maximum of the absorption band is near 2600 Å, a region where proteins show no noticeable absorption, nucleic acids can be detected with quartz microscopes by ultraviolet micrography at this wave length (268). By combining this method with the enzymatic method, the two types of nucleic acid can be distinguished. If the tissue section is first treated with ribonuclease in order to dissolve RNA, any remaining regions of ultraviolet absorption indicate the sites of DNA. As has been pointed out, it is not yet known whether the nucleotide chains formed by the two types of nucleic acids are straight or branched. Although the existence of a branched structure would be more consistent with the postulate that nucleic acids are species-specific, no experimental evidence for the presence of branches has yet been brought forth (269).

Until recently it was believed that the macromolecular nucleic acids are polymers of tetra- or pentanucleotides, a view based on the fact that yeast nucleic acid contains *approximately* four moles of phosphoric acid for each mole of adenine, guanine, cystosine, and uracil, and that RNA from pancreas contains *approximately* five moles of phosphoric acid (270). Quantitative analyses employing chromatographic separation gave the following values (249,271):

Nucleic acid	Adenine	Guanine	Cytosine	Uracil	Thymine
	Moles per mole of phosphoric acid				
Yeast (RNA)	0.260	0.255	0.245	0.0825	—
Pancreas (RNA)	0.166	0.402	0.205	0.046	—
Thymus (DNA)	0.260	0.205	0.172	—	0.242
Pig liver (RNA)	0.31	0.17–0.18	0.26	0.13	—

These values do not agree with the hypothesized polymeric tetra- or pentanucleotides, although some of them are very close to the postulated values of 0.250 for a tetranucleotide and 0.200 or 0.400 for a pentanucleotide, respectively. It has been proposed that the macromolecular nucleic acids are "statistical tetranucleotides" with randomly arranged purine and pyrimidine bases (251). Enzymatic degradation indicates that the core of the nucleic acid molecule contains more purine bases than pyrimidine bases; the latter are split off more easily by enzymes (272–274). The amino groups of adenine and cytosine occur unbound in the nucleic acids and as such are subject to deamination (275). They can also react with mustard gas to form thiazane rings (276):

$$RNH_2 + (ClCH_2CH_2)_2S \rightarrow RN\begin{matrix} CH_2—CH_2 \\ \quad \\ CH_2—CH_2 \end{matrix}S$$

The present state of our knowledge does not permit us to say whether or not nucleic acids are species-specific. It is obvious that the biological importance of the nucleic acids depends on the answer to this question. If there exist for each species and for the different organs specific nucleic acids, these are possibly the ultimate carriers of hereditary traits. On the other hand, if they are nonspecific, their role in the reproduction of cells and in heredity can be of only secondary importance.

Owing to their high content of phosphoric acid residues, the nucleic acids are acidic substances. Like many other macromolecular anions, they combine with proteins to form saltlike compounds which are insoluble in the interisoelectric pH range. Thus, ovalbumin and other proteins are precipitated with nucleic acids at slightly acid reactions (277,278). There is no doubt but that we are dealing here with saltlike compounds linked to each other through electrovalent bonds; like other similar compounds they are soluble in concentrated solutions of neutral salts (278).

The main difficulty in nucleoprotein chemistry is our inability to determine whether the nucleoproteins prepared by the extractions of cells are saltlike compounds of nucleic acids and cellular proteins formed during the course of their preparation, or whether they are naturally pre-existent in the cells either as saltlike compounds or as substances made up of other types of bonds (239). Most of the nucleoproteins are found to contain either protamines or histones. Both groups of proteins are strongly basic substances (see Chapter VIII, p. 169), so that the formation of saltlike compounds with nucleic acids is entirely possible. Nucleoprotamines and nucleohistones are distinguished from other proteins by virtue of their deficiency in tyrosine and tryptophan, respectively (279). It seems that cells contain either nucleohistones or nucleo-

Substance	Tryptophan	Tyrosine
Proteins	+	+
Histones	0	+
Protamines	0	0

protamines but never mixtures of both (279). Nucleoprotamines have been prepared from fish sperm, nucleohistones from the thymus gland and from other mammalian cells. The nucleic acid content of these nucleoprotamines and nucleohistones varies from 31 to 66% (240). Nucleoproteins of plants or bacteria contain neither protamines nor histones, but true proteins (280). Similar true nucleo*proteins* have been found in animal cells (see Chapter XVII, Sect. D).

Extraction of the cells with 1% sodium chloride solution furnishes proteins, while the nucleoproteins are insoluble. The nucleoproteins containing DNA are obtained by a second extraction with 6–11% saline solution, and can be precipitated from this solution by dilution with water (281). The solutions of the nucleoproteins are highly viscous and display a strong flow birefringence; it is assumed, therefore, that the molecules of the nucleoproteins have a threadlike shape. Their axial ratio has been found to vary from 40:1 to 60:1 (282).

The DNA–histone complex obtained by extraction of thymus with sodium chloride solution is present in large amounts in the nuclear euchromatin (282). The heterochromatin of the nucleolus consists mainly of RNA. The question as to whether the chromatin contains a histone nucleinate or a specific nucleohistone has not yet been answered unequivocally. Extraction of thymus tissue with water and precipitation of the extract by high-speed centrifugation furnishes another nucleoprotein, called genoprotein T (for thymus), which is insoluble in isotonic saline solution (283). Both the salt-soluble nucleoprotein and genoprotein T have been claimed to be the original nucleoprotein present in the cells.

The difficulty of all experiments involving nucleoproteins is that we are unable to distinguish with certainty these compounds from the protein nucleinates which are formed *in vitro* by combining nucleic acids with basic proteins. The formation of such "synthetic" protein nucleinates is demonstrated by the fact that the heat coagulation of proteins is inhibited by small amounts of nucleic acid (284) and that the flow birefringence of the native macromolecular nucleic acids is abolished by the addition of proteins (285). We do not yet know whether the two components of these protein nucleinates are linked together by electrovalent bonds alone. Since proteins are known to combine with nonionic, polar compounds such as sugars (see p. 198), the same type of dipole–dipole bonds might be involved in the formation of protein nucleinates, this in addition to the electrovalent bonds between the anionic groups of nucleic acid and cationic groups of the protein compound. In the same way the "natural" nucleoproteins might contain nucleic acids linked to the protein moiety by electrovalent and also by dipole–dipole or ion–dipole bonds (286).

A certain differentiation between authentic nucleoproteins and artifacts seems to be possible by the use of calcium salts; while native nucleoproteins extracted from streptococci were not precipitated by calcium salts, precipitation took place after the action of acids on the nucleoprotein (287). This is interpreted to indicate either that the phosphoric acid groups of the native nucleoprotein are inaccessible to calcium ions, or that they form soluble calcium compounds. Nucleoproteins from the liver give precipitates with 0.03–0.06% solutions of calcium chloride; but it is not clear whether this is the true precipitation of an insoluble calcium compound or an agglutination of nucleoprotein granules by calcium ions (288).

Since it has been revealed that proteins, including even some crystalline proteins, are mixtures of two or more components, it is not surprising that nucleoproteins also have been found to be mixtures of several compounds; the molecular weight of these compounds extracted from liver cells varies from 1.6 to 2.3 million (282). X-ray analysis of the nucleoproteins indicates short-range periods of 3.3 Å (289); their length is almost the same as that of the short-range periods of peptides.

H. Melanins (290). It is not yet quite clear whether the melanins, the black and brown pigments of the skin, of the hair and of certain pathological tumors, are true conjugated proteins, possessing one colored prosthetic group, or whether they are partly oxidized proteins containing numerous oxidized rings. The melanin of melanotic tumors is attached to a globulin fraction. If the tumor is treated with pancreatin, the melanin dissolves and is precipitated by acetic acid (290). Melanin is free of sulfur and contains 8.8% nitrogen (290). The melanins of the hair do not dissolve in sodium hydroxide; they behave like keratins and have been designated melanokeratins (291).

The dark color of the melanins seems to be due to quinoid compounds formed upon the oxidation of their tyrosine residues. It is well known that tyrosine and dihydroxyphenylalanine are oxidized by enzymes to pigments containing the indole ring (292):

HO—C_6H_4—CH_2—$CH(NH_2)COOH$ (Tyrosine)

$(HO)_2C_6H_3$—CH_2—$CH(NH_2)COOH$ (Dihydroxyphenylalanine)

$(\text{indole quinone})_n$ (Pigment (?))

Tyrosine Dihydroxyphenylalanine Pigment (?)

Possibly a similar oxidation takes place in the tyrosine molecules of the peptide chains forming the protein, and the melanins are proteins containing such oxidized tyrosine rings. Another possibility is that the melanins are proteins which combine with the pigments formed by the oxidation of tyrosine. The latter view is supported by the finding that the "melanoid" portion of melanins forms 30–56% of the molecule and the protein portion only 44–70% (293).

References

1. E. Chargaff, *Advances in Protein Chem.* **1,** 1 (1944).
2. Discussion on Lipoproteins, *Discuss. Faraday Soc.*, vol. **6,** (1950).

2*a*. M. Macheboeuf, *Bull. soc. chim. biol.* **11,** 268 (1929).

3. M. Macheboeuf, *Expos. Ann. Biochim. Med.* **5,** 71 (1945). M. Macheboeuf and L. Dizerbo, *Compt. rend. soc. biol.* **132,** 268 (1939).
4. G. Blix, A. Tiselius, H. Svensson, *J. Biol. Chem.* **137,** 485 (1941).
5. W. B. Hardy, J. A. Gardiner, *J. Physiol.* **40,** LXVIII (1910).
6. A. S. McFarlane, *Nature* **149,** 439 (1942).
7. J. Delsal, *Bull. soc. chim. biol.* **31,** 122 (1949).
8. M. Macheboeuf J. Polonovski, *Bull. soc. chim. biol.* **31,** 125 (1949).
9. J. L. Oncley, F. R. N. Gurd, Abstracts 116. Meeting Am. Chem. Soc. 14C, (1949). E. J. Cohn, J. T. Edsall, *Discuss. Faraday Soc.* **6,** 70 (1950).
10. J. W. Gofman, F. T. Lindgren, H. Elliott, *J. Biol. Chem.* **179,** 973 (1949).
11. J. L. Oncley, F. R. N. Gurd, M. Melin, *J. Am. Chem. Soc.* **72,** 458 (1950).
12. A. S. McFarlane, *Discuss. Faraday Soc.* **6,** 74 (1950).
13. S. Thannhauser *et al.*, *J. Biol. Chem.* **116,** 527 (1936); **129,** 709 (1939); **135,** 1, 15 (1940).
14. A. Taurog, C. Entenman, J. L. Chaikoff, *J. Biol. Chem.* **156,** 385 (1944).
15. E. Chargaff, M. Ziff, *J. Biol. Chem.* **125,** 661 (1938); **131,** 25 (1939).
16. E. Chargaff, *J. Biol. Chem.* **142,** 491 (1942).
17. A. Claude, *Science* **97,** 451 (1943).
18. G. Wald *et al.*, *Biol. Bull.* **96,** 249 (1948); *Documenta Ophthalmol.* **3,** 94 (1949).
19. R. Kuhn, N. A. Sörensen, *Ber.* **71,** 1879 (1938).

20. K. G. Stern, K. Salomon, *J. Biol. Chem.* **122,** 461 (1938).
21. H. Junge, *Z. physiol. Chem.* **268,** 179 (1941).
22. S. Hecht, *Ann. Rev. Biochem.* **11,** 465 (1942).
23. G. Wald, *Harvey Lectures* **41,** 117 (1945); *Science* **111,** 179 (1950).
24. K. Tansley, *J. Physiol.* **71,** 442 (1931).
25. L. Busch, H. G. Neumann, G. von Studnitz, *Naturwissenschaften* **29,** 781 (1941).
26. E. E. Broda, C. F. Goodeve, *Proc. Roy. Soc. London* **A179,** 151 (1941).
27. G. Wald, *J. Gen. Physiol.* **20,** 45 (1936); **22,** 775 (1938); **31,** 489, **32,** 367 (1948).
28. R. A. Morton, *Biochem. J.* **40,** LIX (1946).
29. S. Hecht, E. G. Pickels, *Proc. Natl. Acad. Sci. U. S.* **24,** 172 (1938).
30. S. Hecht, *Science* **85,** 567 (1937).
31. J. Jongbloed, A. K. M. Noyons, *Z. Biol.* **97,** 399 (1936).
32. A. E. Mirsky, *Proc. Natl. Acad. Sci. U. S.* **22,** 147 (1936).
33. F. Haurowitz, *Med. Klin.* **29,** 1148 (1933).
34. A. F. Bliss, *J. Biol. Chem.* **172,** 165 (1947).
35. S. Ball *et al.*, *Biochem. J.* **45,** 304 (1949).
36. A. C. Krause, A. E. Sidwell, *Am. J. Physiol.* **121,** 215 (1938).
37. K. Meyer, *Advances in Protein Chem.* **2,** 249 (1945).
38. G. Blix, *Acta Physiol. Scand.* **1,** 29 (1940).
39. S. Przylecki, K. Kasprzyk, H. Rafalowska, *Biochem. Z.* **286,** 360 (1936).
40. K. Meyer, E. Chaffee, *J. Biol. Chem.* **138,** 491 (1941).
41. P. A. Levene, *J. Biol. Chem.* **36,** 73, 89 (1918).
42. G. Blix, O. Snellman, *Arkiv. Kemi Mineral. Geol.* **A19,** No. 32 (1945).
43. H. G. Bray, J. E. Gregory, M. Stacey, *Biochem. J.* **38,** 142 (1944).
44. K. H. Meyer, M. Odier, *Experientia* **2,** 311 (1946).
45. S. M. Partridge, *Biochem. J.* **43,** 387 (1948).
46. G. A. Johansson, F. Wahlgren, *Acta Path. Microbiol. Scand.* **15,** 358 (1939).
47. G. Blix, O. Karlberg, *Z. physiol. Chem.* **240,** 43, 55 (1936).
48. F. Hisamura, Y. Tanabe *et al.*, *J. Biochem. Japan* **28,** 217, 473 (1938).
49. J. Roche, *Compt. rend. soc. biol.* **121,** 71 (1936).
50. K. Meyer, E. Chaffee, *J. Biol. Chem.* **114,** 689 (1936).
51. M. Suzuki, *J. Biochem. Japan* **31,** 357 (1940).
52. T. Kobayashi, *J. Biochem. Japan* **30,** 451 (1939).
53. K. Meyer, E. M. Smyth, M. H. Dawson, *J. Biol. Chem.* **128,** 319 (1939).
54. K. Meyer, *Physiol. Revs.* **27,** 335 (1947).
55*a*. M. Stacey, J. M. Woolley, *J. Chem. Soc.* **1942,** 550.
55*b*. E. Fredericq, H. F. Deutsch, *J. Biol. Chem.* **181,** 499 (1949).
56. G. Young, *J. Biol. Chem.* **120,** 1 (1937).
57. L. F. Hewitt, *Biochem. J.* **32,** 26, 1281 (1938).
58. C. Rimington, M. Van den Ende, *Biochem. J.* **34,** 931, 941 (1940).
59. J. Roche, Y. Derrien, S. Mandel, *Compt. rend. soc. biol.* **138,** 515, 634, 651, 665, 676 (1944).
60. D. M. Surgenor *et al.*, *J. Am. Chem. Soc.* **71,** 1223 (1949).
61. K. Landsteiner, R. A. Harte, *J. Exptl. Med.* **71,** 551 (1940); *J. Biol. Chem.* **140,** 673 (1945).
62. K. Landsteiner, M. W. Chase, *J. Exptl. Med.* **63,** 185, 813 (1936).
63. H. G. Bray, H. Henry, M. Stacey, *Biochem. J.* **40,** 124, 130 (1946).
64. F. Schiff, *Zentr. Bakt. Parasitenk. Abt. I.* **98,** 94 (1930).
65. H. Baer *et al.*, *J. Exptl. Med.* **91,** 105 (1950).
66. E. Brand, L. J. Saidel, *J. Exptl. Med.* **83,** 477 (1946).
67. W. T. J. Morgan, *Biochem. J.* **40,** xv (1946).

68. W. T. J. Morgan, *Ann. Repts. on Progress Chem., Chem. Soc. London* **42,** 235 (1946); G. Holzman, C. Niemann, *J. Am. Chem. Soc.* **72,** 2044, 2048 (1950).
69. G. Fraenkel, K. M. Rudall, *Proc. Roy. Soc. London* **B134,** 111 (1947).
70. K. Linderstrøm-Lang, *Z. physiol. Chem.* **176,** 76 (1928).
71. R. C. Warner, *J. Am. Chem. Soc.* **66,** 1725 (1944).
72. T. Svedberg, L. Carpenter, D. Carpenter, *J. Am. Chem. Soc.* **52,** 241, 701 (1930).
73. W. G. Gordon *et al., J. Am. Chem. Soc.* **71,** 3293 (1949); T. L. McMeekin *et al., ibid.* **71,** 3298 (1949).
74. P. A. Levene, D. Hill, *J. Biol. Chem.* **101,** 711 (1933).
75. T. Posternak, H. Pollaczek, *Helv. Chim. Acta* **24,** 921 (1941).
76. F. Lipmann, *Biochem. Z.* **262,** 9 (1933).
77. C. Rimington, *Biochem. J.* **21,** 272 (1927).
78. M. Mayer, M. Heidelberger, *J. Am. Chem. Soc.* **68,** 18 (1946).
79. O. Hammarsten, *Z. physiol. Chem.* **22,** 103, 333 (1897).
80. H. O. Calvery, A. White, *J. Biol. Chem.* **94,** 635 (1931).
81. P. A. Levene, A. Schormüller, *J. Biol. Chem.* **103,** 537 (1933).
82. H. P. Kay, P. G. Marshall, *Biochem. J.* **22,** 1264 (1930).
83. D. A. Mecham, H. S. Olcott, *J. Am. Chem. Soc.* **71,** 3670 (1949).
84. L. Michaelis, *Advances in Protein Chem.* **3,** 53 (1947).
85. V. Laufberger, *Bull. soc. chim. biol.* **19,** 1575 (1938).
86. R. Kuhn, N. A. Sörensen, L. Birkhofer, *Berl* **73,** 823 (1940).
87. S. Granick, L. Michaelis, *Science* **95,** 439 (1942).
88. A. Rothen, *J. Biol. Chem.* **152,** 679 (1944).
89. S. Granick, P. F. Hahn, *J. Biol. Chem.* **155,** 661 (1944).
90. P. F. Hahn, S. Granick, W. F. Bale, L. Michaelis, *J. Biol. Chem.* **150,** 407 (1943).
91. S. Fiala, D. Burk, *Arch. Biochem.* **20,** 172 (1949); S. Fiala, *Coll. Czechoslov. Chem. Commun.* **14,** 287 (1949).
91*a*. C. G. Holmberg, C. B. Laurell, *Scand. Chim. Acta* **1,** 944 (1947).
92. A. Griffiths, *Compt. rend.* **115,** 669 (1892).
93. M. Florkin, *Arch. internat. physiol.* **36,** 247 (1933).
94. J. Roche, *Ann. Rev. Biochem.* **5,** 472 (1936); *Compt. rend. soc. biol.* **112,** 251, 683 (1933).
95. C. R. Dawson, M. F. Mallette, *Advances in Protein Chem.* **2,** 182 (1945).
96. A. Griffiths, *Compt. rend.* **114,** 496 (1892).
97. M. Henze, *Z. physiol. Chem.* **43,** 290 (1904).
98. C. Dhéré, *Compt. rend.* **157,** 309 (1913); *Compt. rend soc. biol.* **76,** 539 (1914).
99. A. Redfield, *Biol. Revs.* **9,** 175 (1934); *J. Biol. Chem.* **76,** 185, 191 (1928).
100. F. Kubowitz, *Biochem. Z.* **299,** 32 (1938).
101. J. Roche, *Arch. phys. biol.* **7,** 207 (1930).
102. C. Dhéré, *Compt. rend. soc. biol.* **101,** 759 (1929).
103. F. Hernler, E. Philippi, *Z. physiol. Chem.* **216,** 110 (1933).
104. J. Roche, *Skand. Arch. Physiol.* **69,** 87 (1934).
105. J. B. Conant, W. Humphreys, *Proc. Natl. Acad. Sci. U. S.* **16,** 543 (1930).
106. W. Rawlinson, *Australian J. Exptl. Biol. Med. Sci.* **18,** 131 (1940); **19,** 137 (1941).
107. B. Erickson-Quensel, T. Svedberg, *Biol. Bull.* **71,** 498 (1936).
108. W. M. Stanley, T. F. Anderson, *J. Biol. Chem.* **146,** 25 (1942).
109. A. Polson, R. W. G. Wyckoff, *Nature* **160,** 153 (1947).
110. N. F. Burk, *J. Biol. Chem.* **133,** 511 (1940).
111. H. Neurath *et al., Chem. Revs.* **34,** 158 (1944).
112. D. Keilin, T. Mann, *Nature* **141,** 870 (1938).

113. J. Wyman, Jr., *Advances in Protein Chem.* **4,** 410 (1948); *J. Biol. Chem.* **127,** 1 (1939).
114. F. Haurowitz, *Tabulae Biologicae.* **10,** 18 (1934).
115. F. Hoppe-Seyler, *Medizinisch-Chemische Untersuchungen* **2,** 181 (1867).
116. F. Haurowitz, *Z. physiol. Chem.* **136,** 147 (1924).
117. M. Heidelberger, *J. Biol. Chem.* **53,** 34 (1922).
118. R. Hill, H. F. Holden, *Biochem. J.* **20,** 1326 (1926).
119. A. Hamsik, *Z. physiol. Chem.* **187,** 229 (1930).
120. M. L. Anson, A. E. Mirsky, *J. Gen. Physiol.* **13,** 469 (1930).
121. M. Laporta, *Arch. Sci. Biol.* **16,** 575 (1931).
122. L. Michaelis, *Federation Proc.* **7,** 512 (1948).
123. F. Haurowitz, *Z. physiol. Chem.* **232,** 146 (1936).
124. F. Haurowitz, *Abstracts 1st Intern. Congr. Biochem.* p. 347 (1949).
125. F. Haurowitz, H. Waelsch, *Z. Physiol. Chem.* **182,** 82 (1929).
126. J. Roche, M. Chouaiech, *Bull. soc. chim. biol.* **22,** 263 (1940).
127. G. S. Adair, *Proc. Roy. Soc. London* **A109,** 292 (1925).
128. J. H. Northrop, M. L. Anson, *J. Gen. Physiol.* **12,** 543 (1929).
129. J. Steinhardt, *Nature* **138,** 800 (1936).
130. N. Gralén, *Biochem. J.* **33,** 1907 (1939).
131. T. Svedberg, K. O. Pedersen, Ultracentrifuge, Oxford Univ. Press, London, 1940.
132. G. S. Adair, M. E. Adair, J. Roche, A. Roche, *Compt. rend.* **195,** 1433 (1933).
133. S. Granick, *J. Gen. Physiol.* **25,** 571 (1942).
134. M. F. Perutz, *Nature* **143,** 731 (1939).
135. J. Boyes-Watson, E. Davidson, M. F. Perutz, *Proc. Roy. Soc. London* **A191,** 83 (1947).
136. M. F. Perutz, *Nature* **161,** 204 (1948).
137. W. Langenbeck, *Ber.* **65,** 842 (1932).
138. D. Burk, S. Fiala *et al.*, *Federation Proc.* **7,** 146 (1948).
139. H. Theorell, *Arkiv. Kemi Mineral. Geol.* **16A** No. 14 (1942).
140. B. German, J. Wyman, Jr., *J. Biol. Chem.* **117,** 533 (1937).
141. K. Philipp, *Z. vergleich. Physiol.* **18,** 459 (1933).
142. A. E. Mirsky, M. L. Anson, *J. Gen. Physiol.* **19,** 439 (1936).
143. J. P. Greenstein, *J. Biol. Chem.* **128,** 233 (1939).
144. F. Haurowitz, H. Kittel, *Ber.* **66,** 1047 (1933).
145. L. Pauling, C. D. Coryell, *Proc. Natl. Acad. Sci. U. S.* **22,** 159 (1936).
146. D. Taylor, *J. Am. Chem. Soc.* **61,** 2150 (1939).
147. H. Theorell, *Arkiv. Kemi Mineral. Geol.* **16A** No. 3 (1941).
148. F. Haurowitz, *Z. physiol. Chem.* **188,** 161 (1930).
149. F. Haurowitz, *Z. physiol. Chem.* **162,** 41 (1926).
150. W. H. Forbes, F. J. W. Roughton, *J. Physiol.* **71,** 229 (1931).
150*a*. F. E. Courtice, C. G. Douglas, *J. Physiol.* **105,** 345 (1947).
151. M. Kiese, G. Klingmüller, *Arch. exptl. Pathol. und Ther.* **207,** 655 (1949).
152. F. J. W. Roughton, in Hemoglobin. Interscience, New York, 1949, p. 83.
153. L. Pauling, *Proc. Natl. Acad. Sci. U. S.* **21,** 186 (1935).
154. F. Haurowitz, *Z. physiol. Chem.* **254,** 268 (1938).
155. L. Pauling, H. A. Itano, S. J. Singer, I. C. Wells, *Science* **110,** 543 (1949).
156. F. Haurowitz, in Hemoglobin. Interscience, New York, 1949, p. 53; F. Haurowitz, S. Tunc, R. Cindi, *Federation Proc.* **9,** 183 (1950).
157. R. von Zeynek, *Nowiny Lekarskie* **38,** 10 (1926).
158. A. E. Sidwell, Jr., R. H. Munch, E. S. G. Barron, T. T. Hogness, *J. Biol. Chem.* **123,** 335 (1938).

159. J. F. Taylor, A. B. Hastings, *J. Biol. Chem.* **144,** 1 (1942).
160. H. Hartridge, F. J. W. Roughton, *J. Physiol.* **64,** 405 (1928).
161. J. Haldane, J. B. Smith, *J. Physiol.* **20,** 405 (1896).
162. T. Bücher, E. Negelein, *Naturwissenschaften* **29,** 672 (1941).
163. B. L. Horecker, *J. Biol. Chem.* **148,** 173 (1943).
164. O. Henriques, *Ergeb. Physiol.* **28,** 625 (1929).
165. A. Ferguson, F. J. W. Roughton, *J. Physiol.* **83,** 68, 87 (1935).
166. W. C. Stadie, *Science* **81,** 207 (1935).
167. F. Haurowitz, *Z. physiol. Chem.* **138,** 68 (1924); **194,** 98 (1931).
168. C. D. Coryell, F. Stitt, L. Pauling, *J. Am. Chem. Soc.* **59,** 633 (1937).
169. F. Haurowitz, *Z. physiol. Chem.* **232,** 159 (1935).
170. D. Keilin, E. F. Hartree, *Proc. Roy. Soc. London* **B117,** 1 (1935).
171. W. Heubner, M. Kiese *et al., Arch. exptl. Path. Pharmakol.* **204,** 313 (1947).
172. F. Haurowitz, *J. Biol. Chem.* **137,** 771 (1941).
173. H. O. Michel, *J. Biol. Chem.* **126,** 323 (1938).
174. M. Heidelberger, K. Landsteiner, *J. Exptl. Med.* **38,** 561 (1923).
175. D. L. Drabkin, *J. Biol. Chem.* **164,** 703 (1946).
176. A. Reichert, A. Brown, Publ. No. 116 of the Carnegie Institute of Washington, 1909.
177. H. B. Vickery, *J. Biol. Chem.* **143,** 77 (1942).
178. E. Brand, J. Grantham, *J. Am. Chem. Soc.* **68,** 724 (1946).
179. J. Roche, Pigments Respiratoires. Masson and Co. Paris, 1935.
180. R. Porter, F. Sanger, *Biochem. J.* **42,** 287 (1948).
181. F. Haurowitz, *Z. physiol. Chem.* **183,** 78 (1929).
182. F. Haurowitz, *Z. physiol. Chem.* **186,** 141 (1930).
183. D. L. Drabkin, *Arch. Biochem.* **21,** 224 (1949).
184. Y. Derrien, J. Roche, *Abstracts 1st Intern. Congr. Biochem.*, p. 368 (1949).
185. J. C. Kendrew, M. F. Perutz, *Proc. Roy. Soc. London* **A194,** 375 (1948).
186. J. F. Taylor, R. L. Swarm, *Federation Proc.* **8,** 259 (1948).
187. R. Brinkman, T. H. P. Jonxis, *J. Physiol.* **85,** 117 (1935).
188. J. Barcroft, Respiratory Function of the Blood. Macmillan, New York, 1928.
189. F. Haurowitz, *Z. physiol. Chem.* **232,** 125 (1935).
190. E. McCarthy, *J. Physiol.* **102,** 55 (1943).
191. J. Barcroft, *Lancet* **225,** 1021 (1933).
192. M. P. Munro, F. L. Munro, *J. Biol. Chem.* **150,** 427 (1943).
193. L. Reiner, D. H. Moore, E. H. Lang, M. Green, *J. Biol. Chem.* **146,** 583 (1942).
194. A. M. Altschul, T. T. Hogness, A. E. Sidwell, Jr., *J. Biol. Chem* **127,** 123 (1939).
195. H. Kubo, *Acta Phytochim. Japan* **11,** 195 (1939).
196. D. Keilin, T. D. Smith, *Nature* **159,** 692 (1947).
197. A. I. Virtanen, T. Jorma, H. Linkola, A. Linnasalmi, *Acta Chem. Scand.* **1,** 90 (1947).
198. R. Schoenheimer, *Z. physiol. Chem.* **180,** 144 (1929).
199. H. Theorell, *Biochem. Z.* **252,** 1 (1932); H. Theorell, C. de Duve, *Arch. Biochem.* **12,** 113 (1947); A. Rossi, *Science* **108,** 15 (1948).
200. D. L. Drabkin, *J. Biol. Chem.* **158,** 721 (1945).
201. R. Hill, *Nature* **132,** 897 (1933).
202. G. R. Tristram, in Hemoglobin. Interscience, New York, 1949, p. 109.
203. E. G. L. Bywaters, G. E. Delory, C. Rimington, T. Smiles, *Biochem. J.* **35,** 1164 (1941).
204. F. Krüger, *Biol. Generalis* **15,** 456 (1941).

205. G. Barkan, J. Olesk, *Biochem. Z.* **289,** 251 (1937).
206. F. Haurowitz, M. Reiss, *Zs. physiol. Chem.* **198,** 191 (1931).
207. L. Heilmeyer, A. Sundermann, *Deut. Arch. klin. Med.* **178,** 397 (1936).
208. W. C. Stadie, *J. Biol. Chem.* **41,** 237 (1920).
209. R. Barnard, *J. Lab. Clin. Med.* **17,** 824 (1932).
210. E. King *et al.*, *Lancet* **254,** 478 (1948).
211. Q. H. Gibson, D. C. Harrison, *Biochem. J.* **40,** 247 (1946).
212. D. D. Van Slyke, A. Hiller, *J. Biol. Chem.* **84,** 205 (1929).
213. F. J. W. Roughton, R. C. Darling, W. S. Root, *Am. J. Physiol.* **142,** 708 (1944).
214. J. P. Baumberger, *Am. J. Physiol.* **129,** P308 (1940).
215. B. L. Horecker, F. S. Brackett, *J. Biol. Chem.* **152,** 669 (1944).
216. D. L. Drabkin, J. H. Austin, *J. Biol. Chem.* **112,** 51, 67, 89, 105 (1935).
217. N. H. Fairley, *Quart. J. Med.* **10,** 115 (1941); M. Rosenfeld, D. M. Surgenor, *J. Biol. Chem.* **183,** 663 (1950).
218. H. M. Fox, *Endeavour* **8,** 43 (1949); *Nature* **164,** 59 (1949).
219. J. Roche, G. Jean, *Bull. soc. chim. biol.* **16,** 769 (1934).
220. J. Roche, R. Combette, *Bull. soc. chim. biol.* **19,** 613 (1937).
221. T. Svedberg, B. Eriksson-Quensel, *J. Am. Chem. Soc.* **55,** 2834 (1933); **56,** 700 (1934).
222. J. Roche, M. Chouaiech, *Compt. rend. soc. biol.* **130,** 562 (1939).
223. M. Fox, *Proc. Roy. Soc. London* **B115,** 451 (1934).
224. M. Fox, J. Roche, *Compt. rend.* **197,** 874 (1933).
225. J. Roche, *Compt. rend. soc. biol.* **115,** 776 (1934).
226. H. Bennhold, *Kolloid-Z.* **85,** 171 (1938).
227. P. Thomas, *Bull. soc. chim. biol.* **20,** 1058 (1938).
228. W. M. Bendien, I. Snapper, *Biochem. Z.* **261,** 1 (1933).
229. E. J. Cohn, W. L. Hughes, Jr., and J. H. Weare, *J. Am. Chem. Soc.* **69,** 750 (1947).
230. C. Gray, R. Kekwick, *Nature* **161,** 274 (1948).
231. G. Meldolesi, W. Siedel, H. Möller, *Z. physiol. Chem.* **259,** 137 (1939).
232. R. Lemberg, G. Bader, *Naturwissenschaften* **21,** 206 (1933).
233. R. Lemberg, J. W. Legge, W. H. Lockwood, *Biochem. J.* **35,** 328, 339, 353, 363 (1941).
234. C. Liébecq, *Bull. soc. chim. biol.* **28,** 523 (1946); *Arch. intern. physiol.* **53,** 104 (1943).
235. D. D. Van Slyke, A. Hiller, J. R. Weiziger, W. O. Cruz, *J. Biol. Chem.* **166,** 121 (1946).
236. M. Kiese, *Klin. Wochschr.* **21,** 565 (1942).
236*b*. A. Virtanen, J. K. Miettinen, *Scand. Chim. Acta* **3,** 17 (1949).
237. Society for Experimental Biology, Nucleic Acids. Cambridge Univ. Press, Cambridge, 1947.
238. *Cold Spring Harbor Symposia Quant. Biol.* **12,** (1947).
239. J. P. Greenstein, *Advances in Protein Chem.* **1,** 209 (1944).
240. A. E. Mirsky, *Advances in Enzymol.* **3,** 1 (1943).
241. H. S. Loring, *J. Biol. Chem.* **130,** 251 (1939).
242. P. A. Levene, L. W. Bass, H. S. Simms, *J. Biol. Chem.* **70,** 229 (1926).
243. S. J. Thannhauser, W. Klein, *Z. physiol. Chem.* **218,** 164, 173 (1933).
244. P. A. Levene, L. A. Mikeska, T. Mori, *J. Biol. Chem.* **85,** 785 (1930).
245. P. A. Levene, E. S. London, *J. Biol. Chem.* **81,** 711; **83,** 793 (1929).
246. S. J. Thannhauser, *Z. physiol. Chem.* **91,** 329 (1914); **186,** 13 (1929).
247. P. A. Levene, S. A. Harris, *J. Biol. Chem.* **95,** 755 (1932).
248. P. A. Levene, R. S. Tipson, *J. Biol. Chem.* **97,** 491 (1932).

249. E. Visscher, E. Chargaff, *J. Biol. Chem.* **176,** 715 (1948); **177,** 405 (1948).
250. F. Schlenk, *Advances in Enzymol.* **9,** 455 (1949).
251. J. M. Gulland, Soc. Exptl. Biol. Nucleic Acids. Cambridge Univ. Press, 1947, pp. 1, 56.
252. R. Feulgen, *Z. physiol. Chem.* **237,** 261 (1937).
253. G. Schmidt, P. A. Levene, *Science* **88,** 172 (1938).
254. M. Sevag, D. B. Lackman, J. Smolens, *J. Biol. Chem.* **124,** 425 (1938).
255. R. Signer, H. Schwander, *Helv. Chim. Acta* **32,** 853 (1949).
256. R. Cecil, A. G. Ogston, *J. Chem. Soc.* **1948,** 1382.
257. H. Kahler, *J. Phys. Colloid Chem.* **52,** 207 (1948).
258. R. Signer, T. Caspersson, E. Hammarsten, *Nature* **141,** 122 (1938).
259. J. M. Gulland, *Cold Spring Harbor Symposia Quant. Biol.* **12,** 98 (1947).
260. E. Chargaff, S. Zamenhof, *J. Biol. Chem.* **173,** 327 (1948).
261. J. N. Davidson, C. Waymouth, *Nature* **152,** 47 (1943).
262. A. W. Pollister, A. E. Mirsky, *Nature* **152,** 692 (1943).
263. G. Schmidt, S. J. Thannhauser, *J. Biol. Chem.* **161,** 83 (1945).
264. R. Feulgen, K. Imhäuser, *Z. physiol. Chem.* **148,** 1 (1925).
265. M. Stacey *et al.*, *Nature* **157,** 740 (1946); **163,** 538 (1949).
266. Z. Dische, *Mikrochemie* **8,** 4 (1930).
267. J. Brachet, *Arch. biol. Liége* **53,** 151, 167 (1940).
268. T. Caspersson, *Naturwissenschaften* **28,** 514 (1940); Soc. Exptl. Biol., Nucleic Acids. Cambridge Univ. Press, 1947, p. 127.
269. J. M. Gulland, G. R. Barker, D. O. Jordan, *Ann. Rev. Biochem.* **14,** 175 (1945).
270. E. Jorpes, *Biochem. J.* **28,** 2102 (1934).
271. E. Chargaff, B. Magasanik, R. Doniger, E. Visscher, *J. Am. Chem. Soc.* **71,** 1513 (1949); see also *Nature* **165,** 765 (1950).
272. G. Schmidt, R. Cubiles, B. H. Swarts, S. J. Thannhauser, *J. Biol. Chem.* **170,** 759 (1948); see also *Federation Proc.* **9,** 224 (1950).
273. S. Zamenhof, E. Chargaff, *J. Biol. Chem.* **178,** 531 (1949).
274. H. S. Loring, F. H. Carpenter, P. M. Roll, *J. Biol. Chem.* **169,** 601 (1947).
275. W. E. Fletcher, J. M. Gulland, D. O. Jordan, H. E. Dibben, *Biochem. J.* **38,** 30 (1944).
276. G. Young, R. Campbell, *Can. J. Research* **25,** 37 (1947).
277. K. Bjørnesjø, T. Teorell, *Arkiv. Kemi Mineral. Geol.* **19A,** No. 34 (1945).
278. A. Kleczkowski, *Biochem. J.* **40,** 677 (1946).
279. E. Stedman, E. Stedman, Soc. Exptl. Biol., Nucleic Acids. Cambridge Univ. Press, Cambridge, 1949, p. 232.
280. A. N. Belozerskiĭ, *Cold Spring Harbor Symposia Quant. Biol.* **12,** 1 (1947).
281. A. E. Mirsky, A. W. Pollister, *Proc. Natl. Acad. Sci. U. S.* **28,** 344 (1942).
282. Q. Van Winkle, W. G. France, *J. Phys. Colloid Chem.* **52,** 207 (1948).
283. K. G. Stern, J. Wagman, J. Schryver, *Federation Proc.* **6,** 296 (1947).
284. C. E. Carter, J. P. Greenstein, *J. Natl. Cancer Inst.* **6,** 219 (1946).
285. J. P. Greenstein, M. L. Hoyer, *J. Biol. Chem.* **182,** 607 (1950).
286. C. A. Zittle, F. B. Seibert, *J. Immunol.* **43,** 47 (1942).
287. M. Sevag, J. Smolens, *J. Biol. Chem.* **140,** 833 (1941).
288. W. Schneider, *J. Biol. Chem.* **166,** 595 (1946).
289. W. T. Astbury, F. O. Bell, *Nature* **141,** 747 (1938).
290. J. P. Greenstein, *Ann. N. Y. Acad. Sci.* **4,** 433 (1948).
291. Z. Stary, R. Richter, *Z. physiol. Chem.* **253,** 159 (1938).
292. H. S. Mason, *J. Biol. Chem.* **172,** 83 (1948).
293. J. A. Serra, *Nature* **157,** 771 (1946).

CHAPTER XII

Proteins with Enzymatic Properties

A. The Function of Proteins as Enzymes and Apoenzymes. It is not within the scope of this book to present a complete survey of all enzymes or to discuss fully the mechanism of catalysis and the kinetics of enzymatic reactions. On the other hand, however, we are faced with the fact that all enzymes are proteins. This was long ascribed to a contamination of "true" enzymes with proteins. Willstätter and his school tried in vain to remove the protein portion of enzymes by different methods of purification. It was finally proved by Sumner (1) and Northrop (2) that urease and pepsin, two typical enzymes, were proteins; both were prepared in the crystalline state and it was shown that their protein substance is inseparably connected with their enzymatic activity. Since that time, many other enzymes have been obtained as crystals and all have been found to be proteins (2*a*).

Enzymes are macromolecular catalysts of biological origin. This definition does not include any statement concerning the protein nature of enzymes and it is certainly imaginable that one or another of the enzymes not yet isolated in a pure form could be of a nonprotein nature. Up to this time, however, protein-free enzymes have not been found, and hence enzymes can also be defined as catalytically active proteins.

It has been realized for many years that some of the enzymes possess catalytically active prosthetic groups. In these enzymes, too, the protein component is essential. This is evident from the fact that the enzymatic activity is destroyed when the protein is denatured by heat or by other denaturing agents. Some enzymes such as ribonuclease are, however, relatively resistant to heat, since their protein component does not easily undergo denaturation (3). The great thermal stability of ribonuclease and some of the other enzymes indicates that the structure of these enzymes is very stable and more rigid than that of most globular proteins. It is sometimes very difficult to assert whether or not a protein has been denatured. Although most denatured proteins are insoluble, it is well known that flocculation of the denatured protein is sometimes inhibited by other native proteins, by soluble protective colloids such as gelatin, and also by certain organic anions. On the other hand, some proteins can be rendered insoluble without any loss of enzymatic activity by the cautious addition of ethanol; urease treated with alcohol becomes irreversibly insoluble but remains enzymatically active (4). Similarly proteolytic enzymes (5), urease (6), and saccharase (7) remain active when spread in monomolecular films. Apparently the catalytically active groups of the enzymes are not affected by spreading on the water surface. Since enzymes are proteins themselves, it is understandable that the enzymatic activity of pepsin (8), urease (9), and other enzymes decreases when they are exposed to the action of proteolytic enzymes. Only the uncleaved fraction of the enzyme remains enzymatically active.

The inhibition of some enzymes by monohalogen acetates has been considered to be proof of the catalytic function of sulfhydryl groups of the protein moiety, because these are substituted by monohalogen acetate. It must be borne in mind, however, that amino groups and possibly hydroxyl groups also react with monohalogen acetate (10). Therefore, an unequivocal interpretation of these experiments is not possible.

B. Physicochemical Properties of Enzymes. Some of the enzyme proteins are dissolved in the gastric juice, the intestinal juice, the blood serum, and other body fluids. They are typical globulins soluble in dilute solutions of neutral salts. Similar soluble enzymes are extracted from the cells by the same methods by which other cellular proteins are extracted. Most of these extracts are more or less turbid; a brief centrifugation at high speed removes mitochondria or other granular particles containing some of the enzymes. Another portion of the enzymes occurs in the microsomes, which are sedimented only upon prolonged centrifugation at high speed. Finally, some of the enzymes are found in the insoluble structural proteins of the cell. While most of the hydrolyzing enzymes, such as pepsin, trypsin, or urease, are soluble enzymes of the globulin type, succinoxidase and cytochrome oxidase are found in the granular particles (11). The cleavage of ATP by myosin shows that enzymatic activity may also be displayed by fibrous proteins such as myosin (12).

The *colloidal or insoluble state* of the enzymes seems to be essential for their action in the cells. If the catalytically active small groups were present in the cell as free molecules, they could diffuse through the cellular membranes and would in this way be lost by the cell. Such a loss is prevented by the combination of the smaller molecules, such as riboflavin or heme, with protein.

A further consequence of the insoluble or colloidal state of the enzymes is the presence of an *interface* between the aqueous solution and the colloidal or insoluble protein phase. This heterogeneous character of the enzyme system in some instances favors the action of the enzyme. Hemin, which can be regarded as a simple, typical representative of the heme protein group of enzymes, is a very active lipoxidase in heterogeneous water–oil emulsions, but is quite inefficient when the same system is made homogeneous by the addition of ethanol or of bile salts (13).

While some enzymes have no prosthetic groups, others contain *catalytically active nonprotein groups* such as heme, riboflavin, copper, or thiamine pyrophosphate. The enzymes involved in oxidoreduction belong, in general, to the second type of enzymes, while the enzymes catalyzing hydrolyses are apparently free of prosthetic groups. Obviously one has to be very cautious in making a definitive negative statement in this respect, although in some cases amino acid analyses of enzymes have revealed that they contain at least 99% amino acids. Evidently the prosthetic group of these enzymes, if present at all, cannot comprise more than 1% of the total enzyme molecule. However, 1% of a molecule of molecular weight 50,000 is 500; this could account for prosthetic groups of an unknown type. The view that even the apparently pure protein enzymes contain some kind of prosthetic group is supported by peptidase investigation in which it has been shown that the activity of some of these enzymes depends on the presence of certain metal ions (14) such as cobalt, zinc, manganese, magnesium, or calcium. Thus, carboxypeptidase (15) and alkaline kidney phosphatase (15*a*) are magnesium complexes.

The two components of a conjugated enzyme have been called *coenzyme* and *apoenzyme*. The apoenzyme is the protein moiety; the coenzyme can frequently be split off from the apoenzyme, *e.g.*, by dialysis against acids. The apoenzymes share with other proteins the property of being denatured by heat; it is a familiar fact that the apoenzymes are much more labile than are the total enzymes, and hence one must conclude that the coenzyme exerts a protective action on the apoenzyme as long as it is bound to the latter. The coenzymes are thermostable when split off from the apoenzyme; their solutions can be boiled without any loss of activity; on recombination with the apoenzyme the activity of the whole enzyme is restored.

Although the reacting group of the *conjugated enzymes* is certainly their prosthetic group, the *protein moiety is essential* for the full activity of these enzymes. The isolated prosthetic group has in many cases a slight catalytic activity. Combination with the apoenzyme increases the activity considerably, sometimes by more than a thousand fold over the action of the free prosthetic group. This is partly due to the high molecular weight of the complex so formed, and partly to a specific action of the apoenzyme which cannot be replaced by other proteins. All apoenzymes are specific in that they combine only with a certain type of coenzyme and in that they confer on the coenzyme the property of catalyzing specific reactions.

While each of the apoenzymes combines only with one definite coenzyme, each of the coenzymes can combine with different similar apoenzymes. Thus hemoglobin, catalase, peroxidase, and cytochrome c, while they contain the same protoheme as their prosthetic group, have different protein components. Likewise, lactic dehydrogenase, phosphoglyceraldehyde dehydrogenase, and other dehydrogenases contain the same pyridine nucleotide linked to different apoenzymes (16).

The mode of linkage between coenzyme and apoenzyme differs in various enzymes. In some enzymes covalent bonds are involved, in other enzymes electrovalent bonds or van der Waals' forces. The specificity of these bonds and the fact that each of the apoenzymes confers on the prosthetic group a specific catalytic activity cannot yet be explained satisfactorily.

C. Function of Apoenzymes. It seems that the apoenzyme molecule has two important functions, (*1*) to activate the prosthetic group and (*2*) to bind the substrate. In order to explain the activation of the prosthetic group (coenzyme) it is assumed that the coenzyme is fixed by the apoenzyme in a spatial position which is particularly favorable for the reaction with the substrate. We can very well imagine that collisions between substrate and active group are facilitated in this way.

On the other hand, it seems that some apoenzymes combine not only with the coenzyme but also, temporarily, with molecules of the substrate. This is the mode of action of the metal-containing peptidases; their metal atom forms the coordination center of a complex in which substrate as well as apoenzyme are bound to the metal (15). By the action of the substrate–coenzyme–apoenzyme complex, the substrate is brought so close to the apoenzyme that the reaction can take place more easily.

At present we know nothing concerning the chemical nature of those groups of the apoenzyme which combine with the coenzyme or with the substrate. The elucidation of this problem is a prerequisite for our understanding of enzyme action. Our best guess for the present is that the bonding groups of the apoenzyme are polar groups which form a kind of a negative print of the coenzyme or of the substrate so that these fit into the negative molds and are fixed there by numerous dipole–dipole bonds (see page 187) between the complementarily shaped surfaces (15,16*a*,16*b*).

D. Specificity of Enzymes. In discussing the nature of enzymes and of their components it must be recalled that we have no other indication for the presence of an enzyme than its action on a suitable substrate. If no substrate is known we cannot prove the presence of the enzyme. Moreover, if we want to get some information on the specificity of an enzyme we have to use substrates differing in one or the other of their molecular groups. In this respect the work of Bergmann on the substrates of proteolytic enzymes was of the utmost importance. Until recently it was not known what peptide bonds are split by pepsin, trypsin, and other proteolytic enzymes. By means of the carbobenzoxy method, Bergmann and coworkers (17) were able to synthesize a large number of different peptides and to use them to test the specificity of the proteolytic enzymes. In this way it was found that trypsin splits mainly peptides containing the basic amino acids arginine or lysine, while pepsin attacks chiefly peptides containing the aromatic amino acid tyrosine (18). Obviously, it is to be concluded that the basic side chains of arginine or lysine combine specifically with the surface of the trypsin molecule, while the aromatic ring of tyrosine fits into the surface pattern of pepsin.

Since the enzymes hydrolyze only the natural L-peptides, not D-peptides, it is evident that the stereochemical configuration of the substrate is of great importance for the formation of the enzyme–substrate compound. In order to explain the sterical specificity of the enzymes one must postulate that enzyme and substrate are linked to one another by three or more different atoms or molecular groups (19). Obviously, this can take place only if the surfaces of enzyme and substrate can approach each other very closely, *e.g.*, by the mutual complementariness of their surfaces.

It had been considered obvious that one of the combining groups of the proteolytic enzymes is the peptide group —CONH—; recently however it was shown by Neurath, Schwert, and coworkers that the peptide bond can be replaced by the ester bond —CO—O—. Actually benzoyl-

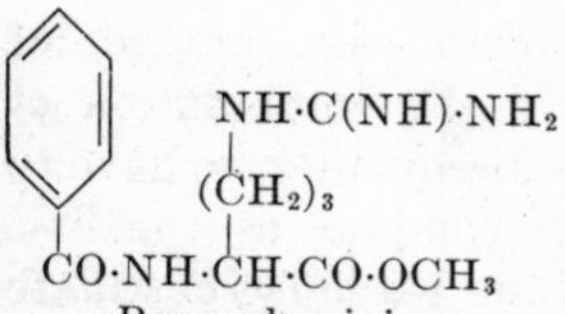

C_6H_5—CO·NH·CH(—$(CH_2)_3$·NH·C(NH)·NH_2)·CO·OCH_3

Benzoylarginine methyl ester

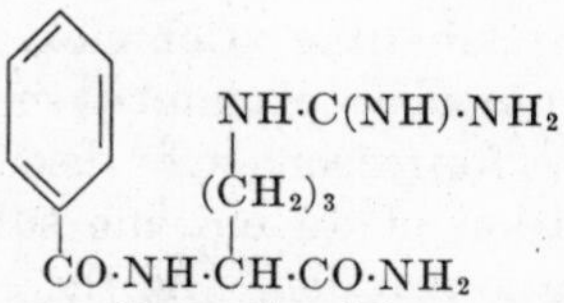

C_6H_5—CO·NH·CH(—$(CH_2)_3$·NH·C(NH)·NH_2)·CO·NH_2

Benzoylarginine amide

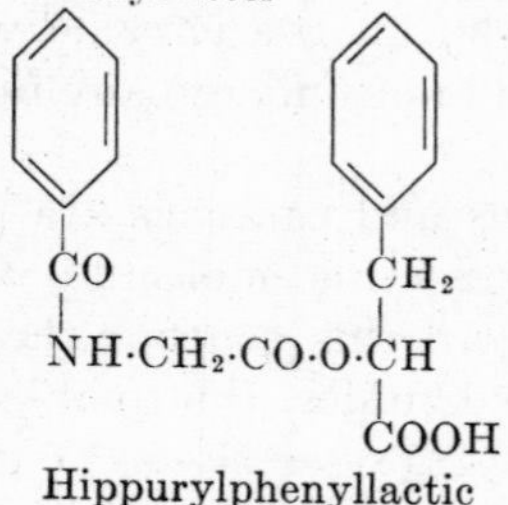

C_6H_5—CO—NH·CH_2·CO·O·CH(—CH_2—C_6H_5)—COOH

Hippurylphenyllactic acid

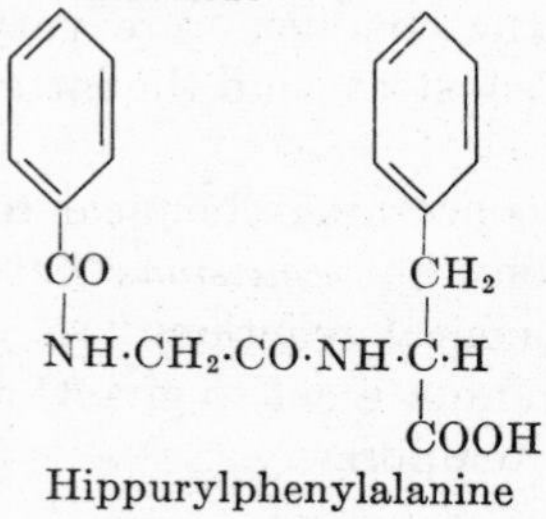

C_6H_5—CO—NH·CH_2·CO·NH·C·H(—CH_2—C_6H_5)—COOH

Hippurylphenylalanine

arginine methyl ester is split by trypsin more rapidly than benzoylarginine amide (20), and hippurylphenyllactic acid is split by carboxypeptidase just as readily as the peptide hippurylphenylalanine (21).

These experiments have severely shaken the basis of enzyme classification. Since we have no means by which to differentiate enzymes other than by their action on definite substrates, enzymes have been classified as proteases, esterases, carbohydrases, etc., according to the substrates attacked. However, since trypsin and carboxypeptidase are able to split ester bonds and since this action takes place more rapidly than the splitting of the corresponding peptides, we must abandon the idea that the specificity of an enzyme is determined only by the type of the bond to be split.

Likewise we have to abandon the classification of proteolytic enzymes as endo- and exopeptidases; the latter were assumed to attack only peptides with a free amino or carboxyl group and were subdivided as aminopeptidases and carboxypeptidases, respectively. Recently, however, it was shown that leucineaminopeptidase is able to hydrolyze glycylleucinamide, although the leucine residue of this substrate has no free amino group (21*a*).

From the formulae of the substrates of trypsin and carboxypeptidase (see above) it is evident that the action of these enzymes depends mainly on the steric arrangement of the molecular groups of the substrate, on their shape, and their mutual position; the chemical nature of the bond undergoing hydrolysis is, apparently, of secondary importance. This viewpoint is in agreement with the contention that the combination of enzyme and substrate takes place by the mutual bonding of complementarily adapted surfaces.

E. The Enzyme–Substrate Complex. Although the nature of enzymatic action cannot be explained simply by the combination of enzyme and substrate, for reasons to be discussed subsequently we have to postulate the formation of an enzyme–substrate complex as the first phase of the enzymatic reaction. At the same time we must postulate that the enzyme–substrate complex is unstable, so that it is formed only temporarily. If the complex were very stable, all the enzyme would combine with the substrate and the latter would not undergo any further reaction.

Our concepts concerning chemical reactions and catalysis are based on the supposition that *collisions* between reacting molecules are a prerequisite of chemical reaction. According to this concept the substances A and B cannot react to give C and/or D unless the complex AB is formed at least temporarily.

While this concept is generally accepted, it has been reported that trypsin acts on serum albumin over distances of more than 100 Å. In these experiments the enzyme and substrate were separated from one another by plastic sheets more than 100 Å thick (22). It has been concluded on the basis of these experiments that enzymes are able to act by long-range forces. However, there is at present no method available by which inhomogeneity of the film could be completely ruled out (23). Therefore, the results obtained cannot be considered sufficient evidence for the existence of long-range forces between enzyme and substrate. It is hardly necessary to emphasize that the law of mass action as well as all other fundamental laws of chemical kinetics are founded on the concept of molecular collisions. The theory of long-range forces as responsible for chemical reactions is irreconcilable with the overwhelming evidence in favor of molecular collisions.

The important fact that the first phase of the enzymatic action is the combination of the enzyme with its substrate had originally been proved by an analysis of the reaction kinetics in the presence of substances which are bound preferentially by the enzyme and thus compete with the substrate. We are aware of two groups of competing substances: reaction products and specific enzyme poisons.

The competing action of the reaction products is evident from the fact that the action of hydrolytic enzymes is often inhibited by the products formed (24–26). If we represent the hydrolytic cleavage of the substance AB by the equation:

$$AB + H_2O \rightleftharpoons AOH + BH$$

the enzyme–substrate complex is represented by the symbol E(AB), where E is the free enzyme. If the hydrolysis is inhibited by addition of an excess of AOH, but not by an excess of BH, we may safely say that E combines with the A moiety of AB and not with the B moiety. It was found in this way that the hydrolysis of sucrose by yeast invertase is inhibited by fructose, but not by glucose; accordingly, it is inferred that the enzyme combines with the fructose moiety of sucrose (24,26) and that the first phase of the enzymatic reaction is represented by:

$$E + AB \rightarrow E(-AB)$$

where E is the enzyme molecule, A the fructose, and B the glucose moiety of sucrose (24–26).

The combination of the enzyme with the substrate is also inhibited by substances which, though different from the reaction products, form stable compounds with the enzyme. The very well known example is the inhibition by cyanide of enzymes containing heme as an active group. We know that the cyanide ion combines with the iron atom of the heme forming a stable heme–cyanide complex and preventing in this way the combination of the iron atom with substrate molecules.

While the assumption of an enzyme–substrate complex until recently was mainly based on kinetic experiments concerned with the rate of catalysis under different conditions, the existence of enzyme–substrate complexes of catalase and peroxidase was recently proved by spectrophotometric measurements. Both catalase and peroxidase are colored compounds possessing typical absorption spectra. The color and absorption spectra of both enzymes undergo typical changes when they combine with their substrates; at first a green primary complex is formed, which later is converted into a red complex (27). By measuring the velocity of these transformations it was found that the primary green complex is formed very rapidly (k_1 = about 10^7), that it slowly passes into the red secondary complex ($k_2 = 4.0$ for peroxidase), and that only the green complex is an intermediate in the reaction between enzyme and substrate. The green complex decomposes slowly into the free enzyme and the reaction products (28). Most probably the heme iron of catalase and peroxidase is bound to the protein moiety by an ionic bond in the reactive green complexes, but by covalence in the red complexes (27,28). If we represent the enzyme by the symbol $>FeOH$, where $>Fe^+$ is the ferric iron of the heme group, the enzyme–hydrogen peroxide complex, formulated as $>FeOOH$ (27,28), is formed according to the equation:

$$>FeOH + HOOH \rightarrow >FeOOH + HOH$$

F. Kinetics of Enzyme Reactions. It will be recalled that the velocity of reactions of the type $A \rightarrow B + C$ depends on [A], the concentration of substance A, and that the velocity of the reverse reaction, $B + C \rightarrow A$, depends on the product, $[B] \times [C]$. Moreover, if the equilibrium $B + C \rightleftharpoons A$ is attained, the velocity of the forward reaction will be equal to that of the reverse reaction. We can write, therefore:

$$\text{Velocity of forward reaction, } v_f = k_1[B][C]$$
$$\text{Velocity of reverse reaction, } v_r = k_2[A]$$
$$\text{Equilibrium constant, } K = k_2/k_1 = [B][C]/[A]$$

The same procedure can be applied to the formation of the enzyme–substrate complex, represented by the equation $E + S \rightarrow ES$, where E and S are molecules of the enzyme and the substrate, respectively. The enzyme–substrate complex, ES, is unstable and is decomposed either by the reverse reaction, $ES \rightarrow E + S$, or by the reaction $ES \rightarrow E + P$, where P is the reaction product. The velocity of the catalyzed reaction depends mainly on [ES], the concentration of the enzyme–substrate complex. In analogy to the formula given for the equilibrium constant, we can write here also:

$$K = \frac{[E] \times [S]}{[ES]} \tag{1a}$$

where K is the equilibrium constant of the reversible reaction $E + S \rightleftharpoons ES$. However this reaction never proceeds reversibly because ES undergoes further decomposition into the free enzyme, E, and the reaction products, P, according to the reaction $ES \rightarrow E + P$. The velocity of this reaction is proportional to the concentration of ES, so that we can write $v_d = k_3[ES]$, where v_d is the velocity of decomposition of the enzyme–substrate complex. Since ES can be decomposed either to E + S, or to E + P, a steady state will result (29). The equilibrium constant for this state is represented by:

$$K_m = \frac{k_2 + k_3}{k_1} \tag{1b}$$

Owing to the lability of ES, its concentration and that of E cannot as a rule be determined. If we designate the total amount of the enzyme by E_t, its concentration, $[E_t]$, is equal to the sum of [E] and [ES] and we can replace [E] by $[E_t] - [ES]$, so that

$$K_m = \frac{[E_t] - [ES]}{[ES]} [S] = \frac{[E_t]\,[S]}{[ES]} - [S] \tag{2}$$

$$[ES] = [E_t]\left(\frac{[S]}{K_m + [S]}\right) \quad \text{and} \quad K_m + [S] = \frac{[E_t] \times [S]}{[ES]} \tag{3}$$

According to Michaelis and Menten (30) the rate of the reaction is proportional to [ES], the concentration of ES. As shown by the last equation [ES] is in turn proportional to $[E_t]$, the concentration of the total enzyme. Actually the velocity of most enzymatic reactions has been found to be proportional to the concentration of the total enzyme used.

The constant K_m is called the Michaelis constant. When K_m is equal to [S], $[ES] = [E_t]/2$ and the velocity of the reaction is 50% of the maximal velocity, the maximal velocity being that developed in the presence of a large excess of the substrate so that $[ES] \simeq [E_t]$. Use is made of this relation for the determination of K_m by measuring the reaction rate at different concentrations of S. The Michaelis constant, K_m, is equal to that concentration of S at which the reaction velocity is half of its maximal value.

From equation (*3*) it is evident that [ES] depends on K_m and on [S]. If at equilibrium [ES] is negligibly small in comparison to [S] and to [E_t], the velocity of the reaction will depend on [S] and the reaction will proceed as a first-order reaction at low substrate concentrations. If, however, practically all the enzyme combines with the substrate to form ES, and if [S] is sufficiently high, the concentration of ES will remain unchanged and the velocity of the reaction will remain constant. We are then dealing with a zero-order reaction (31). Most of the enzyme reactions are neither strictly first-order reactions, nor strictly zero-order, but proceed according to some intermediary order (29,31,32). This is also due to the fact that the concentration of the substrate decreases during the reaction, and that different types of enzyme–substrate compounds are formed. Thus, catalase and peroxidase, as was shown above, form green and red enzyme–substrate complexes; the decomposition of the green and the red complexes proceeds at different velocities (27,28). Further complications arise by the combination of the enzyme–substrate complex with *hydrogen ions* (33) or with other ions or molecules. Thus, the velocity of the hydrolysis of ovalbumin by pepsin depends on the hydrogen ion concentration of the solution; the reactive intermediate is here not ES, but H^+ES (33). If ions are involved in the formation of the enzyme–substrate complex, the velocity of the catalyzed reaction depends on the *dielectric constant* of the solvent; organic solvents such as methanol or ethanol reduce the dielectric constant and the extent of ionization, so that the velocity of the catalyzed reaction decreases (34).

The foregoing discussion was based on the assumption that the velocity of enzymatically catalyzed reactions depends on [ES], the concentration of the enzyme–substrate complex. This assumption, however, does not seem to be quite justified. We have to make the additional assumption that the enzyme–substrate complex undergoes activation before it can be converted into enzyme and reaction products (29,33). If we represent the activated complex by ES*, the catalyzed reaction proceeds in the following phases:

$$E + S \rightleftharpoons ES \rightarrow ES^* \rightarrow E + P$$

If the solution contains substances which are able to combine with the enzyme, a competition for the enzyme ensues between these substances and the substrate. Accordingly these substances will act as *inhibitors.* The kinetics of the enzyme reaction in the presence of inhibitors has been calculated in the same way as the kinetics of the enzyme–substrate reaction (35). It will be recalled that the enzymatic hydrolysis of sucrose by invertase is inhibited by one of the reaction products, fructose (see page 239); evidently the reaction products of the enzymatic hydrolysis act as inhibitors.

Owing to the interference of ions, solvent, reaction products, and other inhibitors with the enzyme–substrate reaction, we frequently find deviations of the reaction rate from the theoretical values derived from equation (*3*).

G. Mechanism of Enzymatic Hydrolysis. The second phase of the enzymatic hydrolysis is, evidently, the hydrolytic cleavage of the substrate AB into AOH and BH. Since AB in the absence of the enzyme is not hydrolyzed to any appreciable extent, we have to assume that the cleavage occurs while AB is bound to E in the complex E(AB). In this complex the bond between A and B is loosened so that hydrolysis proceeds more readily. We do not yet know in what way the loosening of the bond between A and B is accomplished. Most probably the molecule AB is distorted as a result of its combination with the enzyme so that the A-B bond is weakened and elongated either mechanically or by electrostatic forces of adjacent polar groups. We call this state of the molecule the *activated* state.

It is possible to convert normal molecules AB into activated molecules AB* by supplying energy, such as heat energy. The energy required for the conversion of normal molecules into activated molecules is called the *activation energy*. It can be determined as shown on page 138. There it also was emphasized that the activation energy, ΔH^*, is the sum of the free energy of activation, ΔF^*, and of the product of T and ΔS^*. If we assume that the enzyme–substrate complex is decomposed very rapidly into the free enzyme and the reaction products, the velocity of the catalytic reaction will depend mainly on the velocity of the activation process. This, in turn, depends on ΔF^*, the free energy of activation (see page 140). The free energy of activation required for the hydrolysis of esters by hydrogen ions is about 10,000–13,000 cal. per mole; the activation energy required for the hydrolysis of peptide bonds is about 20,000 cal. per mole. By the action of the enzyme the activation energy is reduced to about 4000 cal. per mole for ester hydrolysis and to 12,000–14,000 cal. mole for peptide hydrolysis (36). We can represent this action of the enzyme by the following equations:

$$\text{without enzyme} \qquad AB \xrightarrow{10{,}000 \text{ cal.}} AB^* \rightarrow AOH + BH$$

$$\text{with enzyme} \qquad E(AB) \xrightarrow{4{,}000 \text{ cal.}} E(AB)^* \rightarrow E + AOH + BH$$

We define, accordingly, enzymes and other catalysts as substances which increase the velocity of reactions or which render reactions possible *by lowering the free energy of activation.* This is a definition of enzymes from the standpoint of thermodynamics, and, as are all statements of thermodynamics, it is concerned only with the energy balance of the reaction and is of general validity. However, it gives no hint as to the mechanism of the enzyme action, *i.e.*, as to the reacting groups of the enzyme and the substrate, or the intermediary products.

In order to gain some insight into the mechanism of these intermediary reactions it is necessary to divert our attention from the complicated molecules of the natural enzymes to simpler substances possessing catalytic activity and to use these simpler molecules as models for the more complicated enzyme proteins.

Until recently no simple catalysts of hydrolysis other than strong acids and bases were known. The action of these is due to the high concentration of hydrogen and hydroxyl ions, respectively. Most enzymes are effective near pH 7, where the concentration of these ions is very small, so that the mechanism of the enzymatic hydrolysis seemed to be quite different from that of the catalytic hydrolysis by strong acids or bases. In recent years, however, a new group of hydrolyzing catalysts has been discovered. It was found by Steinhardt (37) that various organic sulfonic acids such as dodecylsulfonic acid or orange II are able to hydrolyze amide groups, $RCONH_2$, to $RCOOH + NH_3$ even when very low concentrations of the sulfonic acid are used. Similarly the hydrolysis of proteins is catalyzed by 0.1–0.01 M solutions of dodecyl sulfonate at 65°C., although much higher concentrations of hydrochloric or sulfuric acid are generally required (38); the hydrolysis of proteins by these sulfonic acids is not complete, the process coming to a standstill when about 50% of the amino acids have been split off (38).

Not only water-soluble sulfonic acids but also insoluble resins containing sulfonic acid groups are catalytically active. Ethyl acetate is hydrolyzed at 25°C. by Amberlite IR 100, a resin containing one gram equivalent of SO_3H groups in 500 g. of the resin (39). Similarly the esterification of oleic acid with butanol is catalyzed by resins of the phenolformaldehydesulfonic acid type (40). Evidently, the sulfonic acid group of organic compounds is catalytically much more active than sulfuric acid, when used in the same concentration. Since the dissociation constant of the organic acids is certainly not higher than that of sulfuric acid, their superiority cannot be ascribed to a higher concentration of hydrogen ions. It is, evidently, due to the structure of the organic portion of their molecules. This organic skeleton acts as a kind of apoenzyme, while the sulfonic acid group is comparable to a coenzyme.

Another possibility which has to be taken into consideration is the accumulation of many ionic groups within a restricted space of the protein enzyme molecule. It is a well known, but hitherto inexplicable, fact that the activity of ions in concentrated solutions of alkali or of mineral acids is more than 100 times higher than the calculated activity. Similarly one could imagine that the accumulation of many polar groups in a restricted portion of the protein molecule would result in extremely high activities and, accordingly, in a high catalytic efficiency. Actually the tetravalent lanthanum ions are able to catalyze the hydrolysis of meta- or pyrophosphates to orthophosphates (41). Moreover, many of the peptidases (15) and some phosphatases (15*a*) contain metal ions such as Mg^{2+} or Mn^{2+}. In the enzyme–substrate complex the metal ion is linked to the polar groups of the enzyme on the one hand, and to polar groups of the peptide on the other. In this manner a chelate ring may be formed in which the electronic structure of the peptide bond is loosened to such an extent that hydrolysis takes place (14,15,21*a*,42).

The mechanism of the enzyme–substrate combination is particularly clear in reactions catalyzed by phosphomutases or kinases. One of these enzymes is phosphoglucomutase, which catalyzes the equilibrium between glucose-1-phosphate and glucose-6-phosphate. The enzyme contains firmly bound phosphorus which cannot be removed by dialysis. However, when glucose-1-phosphate containing radioactive P^{32} is added to the enzyme, exchange of phosphorus atoms between enzyme and glucose-1-phosphate occurs (43). The catalytic reaction takes place as shown by the following formulas (44,45):

$$\begin{matrix} C_1\text{—P} \\ | \\ C_6 \end{matrix} + \begin{matrix} C_1\text{—P} \\ | \\ C_6\text{—P} \end{matrix} \rightleftharpoons \begin{matrix} C_1\text{—P} \\ | \\ C_6\text{—P} \end{matrix} + \begin{matrix} C_1 \\ | \\ C_6\text{—P} \end{matrix}$$

Glucose-1-phosphate — Glucose-1,6-diphosphate — Glucose-1,6-diphosphate — Glucose-6-phosphate

The formulas demonstrate clearly that the phosphate residue is transferred by the enzyme from the carbon atom 1 of glucose-1,6-diphosphate to carbon atom 1 of glucose-6-phosphate, and from the carbon atom 6 of the diphosphate to carbon atom 6 of glucose-1-phosphate. This was proved by using glucose phosphate labeled with C^{14}. Evidently the reaction can take place only in the presence of glucose-1,6-diphosphate; since the diphosphate is continuously regenerated, only traces of this substance are required (44,45). Similar results were obtained with phosphoglyceric mutase, which catalyzes the interconversion of 2-phosphoglyceric acid and 3-phosphoglyceric acid (45). The enzyme acts in both cases as a phosphate transferase, which temporarily combines with phosphoric acid residues and transfers them from one molecule to another. Likewise myokinase and hexokinase act as phosphotransferases (see below, Sect. L). If the phosphate residue is transferred to a water molecule, hydrolysis of the organic phosphoric acid compound results. Phosphatases, accordingly, can be considered as phosphotransferases which catalyze the transfer of phosphate residues from organic compounds to water, or from inorganic phosphates to organic compounds. Similarly, proteolytic enzymes can act as aminoacyl transferases, combining with an aminoacyl residue and transferring it to another amino acid, a peptide, or a water molecule. While new peptides will be formed in the first case, amino acids will be liberated when the amino acid residue combines with water.

It is evident from these considerations that the combination of the enzyme with its substrate will depend mainly on the *configuration* and the *structural arrangement of the reacting groups* of the enzyme and the substrate. If these reacting groups of the enzyme and the substrate can come close enough to one another, the enzyme–substrate complex will be formed and the catalytic reaction can take place.

While we do not yet know much about the combining groups of the hydrolyzing enzymes, some information on the binding groups of the substrate can be obtained by measuring the velocity of the catalytic reaction in the presence of competitive inhibitors (45*a*). These are substances of the same molecular type as the substrate, but they differ from the substrate in details of molecular structure. Molecules of this kind combine with the enzyme and compete in this way with the substrate, thus reducing the velocity of the catalytic reaction.

By experiments of this type it was found that the aromatic ring of tyrosine or phenylalanine is essential for the action of chymotrypsin or of carboxypeptidase on polypeptides (16*b*,46). Evidently the mesomeric electron system of the aromatic ring is involved in the combination of chymotrypsin or carboxypeptidase with their substrates. Since the benzene ring is neither ionized nor a dipole, we have no reason to assume that it combines with polar groups of the enzymes. Possibly the aromatic ring of the substrate combines with a similar aromatic ring of the enzyme.

The foregoing discussion shows that the details of the mechanism of the enzyme–substrate combination are obscure, but that several groups of the substrate and also a multiplicity of groups of the enzyme are involved in the combination of enzyme and substrate. This agrees well with the great specificity of enzymatic reactions, and also with the view that the reacting areas of the substrate and the enzyme molecule are complementarily shaped.

H. Hydrolases. The term hydrolase is generally used to embrace three different groups of enzymes: esterases, carbohydrases, and proteases. Esterases catalyze the ester hydrolysis:

$$RCOOR + H_2O \rightarrow RCOOH + HOR$$

and the reverse reaction as well. Carbohydrases catalyze the cleavage of the ether bond, ROR, present in disaccharides and polysaccharides. Proteases catalyze splitting of peptides, RCONHR, to yield RCOOH and H_2NR.

Esterases which split esters of phosphoric or sulfuric acid are called phosphatases and sulfatases, respectively; lipase is the term employed to designate those esterases which split neutral fats. A crystalline lipase has been obtained from liver (47).

The phosphoric acid ester bonds present in nucleic acids (see Chapter XI, page 221) are cleaved by ribonuclease and desoxyribonuclease. *Ribonuclease* has been obtained in crystalline form by fractionating the aqueous extract of beef pancreas with ammonium sulfate at slightly acid reaction (48). The enzyme withstands heating (3); although no enzymatic activity is observed at temperatures above 85°, the activity is restored on cooling. The stability of ribonuclease is probably due to a very rigid structure of its small molecule; its molecular weight has been found to be 12,700 (49). Beef pancreas has also been used for the preparation of crystalline *desoxyribonuclease* (50).

Carbohydrases. Although many of these enzymes have been known for a long time, only one of them, amylase, has as yet been obtained in crystals. The enzyme was prepared from potatoes (51), barley (52), pancreas, and saliva (53). The amylases from human saliva and human pancreas are identical, but differ from the amylase of pig pancreas (53). The molecular weight was found to be 20,000. As has been known for many years, amylase loses its activity on dialysis, but acquires it again on the addition of sodium chloride; the presence of sodium chloride prevents the formation of an inactive amylase–mucin complex (54).

Although preparations of yeast *invertase* have been thoroughly investigated, it has not yet been possible to prepare the enzyme in crystalline state. The best preparations have been obtained by adsorption to calcium phosphate. They contain only 5% nitrogen (55).

An enzyme which hydrolyzes polysaccharidic acids has been isolated from egg white, nasal mucus, and cartilage. It is a basic protein, called *lysozyme.* Its isoelectric point is pH 10.5–11.0, its molecular weight 17,000 (56–58). Lysozyme is very similar to hyaluronidase, the "spreading factor" prepared from testes. Lysozyme forms about 3% of the proteins of egg white (see page 166).

Pepsin. This enzyme has been prepared in crystals from gastric mucosa and from commercial pepsin preparations by fractional addition of magnesium sulfate or ethanol (59). The pepsins prepared from different animals are species-specific (60). The molecular weight of crystalline pepsin is 33,000–38,000 (59,61). X-ray analyses of crystalline pepsin reveal the presence of units consisting of 12 molecules (62). Pepsin is a strongly acidic protein having an isoelectric point below pH ~ 2.7; analysis of its component amino acids reveals that it is poor in basic amino acids and rich in aspartic and glutamic acid (see Table I, p. 32). Pepsin contains small amounts, probably one mole per mole, of phosphoric acid. In spite of its ability to crystallize, pepsin has proven to be a mixture of two or more different proteins.

The gastric mucosa contains an inactive precursor of pepsin, called *pepsinogen*, which has also been isolated in crystalline form (63). Pepsinogen is converted into active pepsin, by the action of hydrochloric acid, 15–20% of the nitrogen being split off in the process (63). Most probably some inhibiting peptide having a molecular weight of 2500 is removed during this activation of pepsinogen. The peptide bonds most easily attacked by pepsin are those formed between an aminodicarboxylic acid and tyrosine; one of the simplest substrates of pepsin is carbobenzoxyglutamyltyrosine (64):

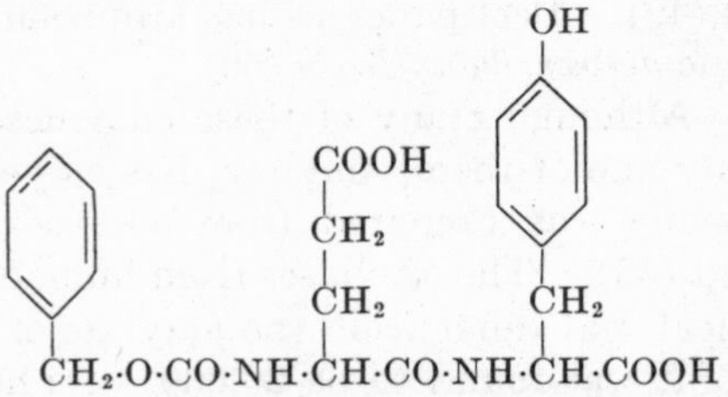

```
                                        OH
                                        |
                                     (ring)
   (ring)              COOH             |
     |                 |                |
     |                 CH2              |
     |                 |                |
     |                 CH2              CH2
     |                 |                |
     CH2·O·CO·NH·CH·CO·NH·CH·COOH
```

Carbobenzoxyglutamyltyrosine

Apparently the functional binding group of the pepsin molecule is structurally adapted to the combination of both the negatively charged side chain and the phenolic side chain present in this dipeptide. This view is supported by the fact that proteins are not split by pepsin following iodination of their phenolic groups, but that they become susceptible to the enzyme when iodine is split off again (65).

Trypsin. This enzyme has been obtained in crystals from pancreas (66). It is best isolated by first preparing *trypsinogen*, its inactive precursor, which is accomplished by mixing the ground pancreas with dilute sulfuric acid and then fractionating by the addition of ammonium sulfate; the first fractions contain chymotrypsinogen, while trypsinogen is precipitated by further addition of ammonium sulfate (67). After standing for several days, the trypsinogen is converted to trypsin by the addition of magnesium sulfate or enterokinase. Pancreas also contains a specific trypsin inhibitor which has been prepared in crystals (68). Another inhibitor isolated from egg white has been found to be identical with ovomucoid (69).

Trypsin is rather resistant to hot dilute acids. Its molecular weight is 34,000 (70). The peptide bonds attacked by trypsin are those whose carbonyl groups are furnished by arginine or lysine; evidently the basic side chains of these amino acids are essential for the action of trypsin (71). The NH group of the peptide bond is not required for the hydrolytic action of the enzyme; arginine esters are also split by trypsin (20).

Chymotrypsin is a second proteolytic enzyme of the pancreas. It also has the property of catalyzing the clotting of milk. Fresh pancreas gland contains chymotrypsinogen which has been isolated in the crystalline state (72). Chymotrypsinogen is converted to the active enzyme, chymotrypsin, by small amounts of trypsin; 1 mg. trypsin is able to activate 3 g. chymotrypsinogen, whose activity increases about 1000 times in the process. The activation seems to be a very complicated process, proceeding through two intermediates, called π-chymotrypsin and δ-chymotrypsin, and furnishing a mixture of several chymotrypsins designated by the letters α, β and γ (73,74). The essential reaction appears to consist of the liberation of four to six free amino groups per chymotrypsinogen molecule (76). If α-chymotrypsin is allowed to stand in aqueous solution at pH 7.6 it is irreversibly changed to β- and γ-chymotrypsin, which differ from the α-enzyme in crystalline shape and solubility (74). γ-Chymotrypsin is a dimer of α-chymotrypsin (75). The peptide bonds split by chymotrypsin are those whose carbonyl groups are furnished by tyrosine, phenylalanine, tryptophan, or methionine (16*b*,77). However, tyrosine esters are also hydrolyzed (78).

Papain, the protease of the milk juice of *Carica papaya*, has been prepared in crystals (79). Its action depends on the presence of sulfhydryl groups, since the enzyme is inactivated if the sulfhydryl groups are oxidized; the inactivated enzyme is reactivated by reducing agents such as glutathione (80,81). Similar behavior has been noted in other vegetable enzymes such as bromelin from pineapple and ficin from the fig tree and also in cathepsin, a protease present in most animal cells; all these enzymes are activated by reducing agents and also by cyanides (82). The simplest peptide split by papain is hippuryl amide (79).

Abderhalden and coworkers report that the injection of foreign proteins into rabbits leads to the formation of specific proteases which split only the injected protein. Albumin, globulin, and fibrinogen furnished different "*protective enzymes*" (83). Likewise, different protective enzymes were produced by injecting plasma proteins of young and old individuals (84). The "protective enzymes" were found both in the blood serum and urine (85). It has since been reported that these protective proteases can be obtained in crystals, although the pure preparations were devoid of specific proteolytic activity (86). They were reactivated by trypsin (87,88). The author and coworkers (89) were unable to produce protective enzymes by the injection of serum globulin or substituted globulins.

Carboxypolypeptidase is the only peptidase so far obtained in crystalline form. It is prepared from frozen pancreas by precipitation of the exuded fluid with ammonium sulfate in a slightly acid solution (90). The molecular weight of carboxypolypeptidase is 33,800 (42). The enzyme splits peptides containing free carboxyl groups, but free amino groups are not necessary for its action (91). Not only peptide bonds, but also ester bonds are split by carboxypolypeptidase (21,46).

Rennin (rennet, chymosin), the milk-coagulating enzyme of the gastric juice, has been prepared in crystalline form (93,94). One part of the pure enzyme is able to coagulate 10^7 parts of milk.

Urease, the first enzyme ever to be crystallized, is obtained from jack bean meal by extraction with 32% acetone (1). Although the molecular weight of the pure protein is 483,000 (95), a depolymerized urease, which has a molecular weight of 17,000, is also active (96). Crystalline urease is inactivated by treatment with trypsin (97).

I. Catalysis of Oxidoreductions by Enzymes. The mechanism of enzymatic oxidoreduction is somewhat different from the mechanism of hydrolysis, since the former always involves two substrates, one of which undergoes oxidation, the other being reduced. The role of the latter substrate is frequently filled by oxygen, which is reduced to hydrogen peroxide and water.

It was originally thought that the active prosthetic group of the enzymes catalyzing oxidoreductions combines with both substrates, accepting electrons (and hydrogen atoms) from one of them and transferring them to the substance to be reduced. However, the specificity of dehydrogenases is frequently determined by their apoenzymes, suggesting that at least one of the substrates is linked to the apoenzyme (97*a*).

Many of the oxidoreductions are irreversible reactions. This is particularly true for those reactions in which oxygen is reduced. The reversal of this reaction, the formation of oxygen from water, would require large amounts of energy. It must be recalled that enzymes do not alter the equilibrium of the catalyzed reaction, but that they only facilitate and accelerate those reactions which lead to the equilibrium state. In the reaction:

$$O_2 + 2\ H_2 \rightleftharpoons 2\ H_2O$$

the equilibrium is shifted far to the right side of the equation. Therefore, enzymes catalyze practically only the forward direction of this reaction, not the reverse reaction.

The prosthetic groups of many of the enzymes catalyzing oxidoreductions have been elucidated. Some of them contain metals which can exist in either of two different valence states. Other enzymes contain prosthetic groups consisting of organic molecules which may exist in reduced or oxidized form. It is believed, therefore, by many authors that the prosthetic group of the oxidoreductases acts by oscillating between the oxidized and the reduced state, and that in this manner electrons are transferred from one substrate to the other. If DH_2 is the hydrogen and electron donor, A the acceptor, and E the enzyme, the over-all scheme can be represented by the following reactions:

$$DH_2 + E \rightarrow EH_2 + D \qquad (1)$$
$$EH_2 + A \rightarrow AH_2 + E \qquad (2)$$

It is also possible that intermediary enzyme–substrate complexes of the forms:

$$(DH_2)E \rightarrow D(EH_2) \rightarrow (EH_2)A \rightarrow E(AH_2),$$

may be formed and have a transitory existence.

In the opinion of the author (98,99) the assumption of a true oxidoreduction of the enzyme is in many cases unnecessary; more likely the enzyme catalyzes oxidoreductions without actually suffering oxidation and reduction itself (100). In other words, E is not reduced to EH_2 by the hydrogen donor, but catalyzes the reaction $DH_2 + A \rightarrow D + AH_2$ by linking some of these compounds, *e.g.*, in the following way (27,28,-100,101):

$$DH_2 + E \rightarrow E(DH_2) \qquad (1)$$
$$E(DH_2) + A \rightarrow E(DH_2{\cdot}A) \rightarrow E(D{\cdot}H_2A) \rightarrow E + D + AH_2 \qquad (2)$$

According to this view the enzyme acts by binding both substrates, the hydrogen donor and the hydrogen acceptor, in such a way that these come into close contact and react with one another.

If one of the substrates is an electron, the enzyme will combine with the electron and will thus be reduced. If the enzymatic group to which the electron is bound is an organic group, it will generally combine with two electrons and two protons, so that the enzyme undergoes a bivalent reduction. This reaction is reversible; otherwise the enzyme would not be able to transfer the electrons to the oxidizing substrate. Commonly, the enzyme–electron or enzyme–hydrogen compound is not called an enzyme–substrate complex, but is designated a dihydroenzyme.

If the electron-accepting group of the enzyme is a metal ion which can undergo univalent reduction, only one electron will be bound; in this way ferric or cupric enzymes are reduced to ferrous or cuprous enzymes, respectively. Michaelis (102) has found that the *reversible* reduction of enzymes always proceeds as a *univalent* reduction; if the enzyme combines with two or more electrons, they are bound stepwise. The intermediary products of this stepwise reduction are radicals as indicated by their intense color and their paramagnetic susceptibility (103).

It is not always possible to decide whether the metal atom of a metal-containing enzyme undergoes oxidation and reduction, or whether it only combines with one of the substrates to form an enzyme–substrate complex. The difference between these two reactions is not very great as shown by the following formulas, where the reactive ferric atom of an iron-containing enzyme is represented by $\rangle Fe^{+}$ and the electron donor by (: D).

$$\rangle Fe^{+}(\,:D) \qquad\qquad \rangle Fe \quad (\cdot D)$$

(I) (II)

In formula I the substrate forms a complex with the ferric ion of the enzyme, while in II the iron combines with one electron to give ferrous iron and the radical (·D). One can very well imagine the existence of intermediates between I and II such as Fe(·D) or $Fe^{+}\cdot(\cdot D)$. In these complexes the valence of the iron atom would be intermediate between bivalence and trivalence (99). The idea of intermediary valences deviating from the usual integers has been advanced by Pauling (104) in order to explain some properties of the metallic state. Possibly we have to assume a similar state of the metal atoms in metal-containing enzymes in the presence of their substrate, *i.e.*, during the catalytic action of the enzyme.

In the following sections those oxidation-reduction enzymes will be discussed which have been either isolated or purified to a certain extent. The active groups of these enzymes are well known so that the classification of these enzymes is based on the composition of their prosthetic groups.

J. Enzymes Containing Iron or Copper. The iron-containing enzymes are very important catalysts of oxidoreductions in the animal organism; their prosthetic groups are iron porphyrin complexes.

One of these enzymes is *catalase*, isolated from beef liver in crystals by Sumner and Dounce (105). The enzyme is extracted from the liver by aqueous dioxane, and precipitated from the extract by increasing the concentration of dioxane; it is recrystallized by fractional addition of ammonium sulfate to an aqueous solution. Catalase has also been prepared from red blood cells (106). The molecular weight of pure catalase is 225,000–248,000 (95,106). Catalase contains 0.09% iron, corresponding to four iron atoms per molecule (95,106). All these iron atoms are bound to protoporphyrin residues (107). By the action of hydrochloric acid one portion of the protoheme groups is converted to biliverdin–iron complexes (107). The active group of catalase can be split off by dialyzing the enzyme against dilute hydrochloric acid; the colorless apoenzyme is inactive, but is reactivated by combining it with protohemin (108).

While catalase catalyzes the oxidoreduction of hydrogen peroxide to water and oxygen (equation 1), *peroxidase* catalyzes a very similar reaction, the coupled oxidoreduction of hydrogen peroxide and a hydrogen donor (equation 2):

$$H_2O_2 + H_2O_2 \rightarrow 2\ H_2O + O_2 \tag{1}$$

$$H_2O_2 + \text{dihydrosubstrate} \rightarrow 2\ H_2O + \text{substrate} \tag{2}$$

A sharp line of distinction between these two very similar reactions cannot be drawn. In the presence of certain substrates such as alcohols, catalase acts as a peroxidase (109). A crystalline peroxidase has been isolated from horse radish by Theorell (110). The enzyme was purified by adsorption on alumina, precipitation with picric acid, electrophoresis, and fractionation with ammonium sulfate. The molecular weight is 44,000 (110). Another peroxidase, called lactoperoxidase, has been isolated from milk; its molecular weight is 93,000 (111). The peroxidase molecule is highly asymmetric; its axial ratio is 7/1 (110). The prosthetic group has been split off by acetone and hydrochloric acid at −15°C. From electrometric titrations and from the dependence of the catalytic activity on pH it has been concluded that the prosthetic group of peroxidase is linked to the apoenzyme not only by the iron atom, but also by the two carboxyl groups of the protohemin moiety. The enzyme–substrate complexes of catalase and peroxidase have been discussed above (Sect. E).

A third catalyst containing protohemin as the active group is *cytochrome*. This substance was first found in muscles by McMunn (112) but was long regarded as a decomposition product of hemoglobin or myoglobin. Keilin and Hartree (113) purified cytochrome by precipitating the trichloroacetic acid extract with ammonium sulfate, dissolving the precipitate, removing the trichloroacetic acid by dialysis, and reprecipitating the cytochrome with ammonium sulfate. The preparation thus obtained is cytochrome c. Two other cytochromes, a and b, have been identified spectroscopically, but have not as yet been purified.

Cytochrome c has a molecular weight of 13,000 and contains 0.43% iron (114,109), *i.e.*, one atom of iron per molecule. The protein component of cytochrome has an unusually high lysine content, 24.7% of the molecule being formed by this strongly basic amino acid (114). The isoelectric point of cytochrome c is, therefore, in the alkaline region at pH 9.8. The histidine content of cytochrome is much lower than that of hemoglobin. The prosthetic group of cytochrome c is protohemin (116), which is linked to the protein component by one or two thioether bonds between thio groups of the protein moiety and the vinyl side chains of the porphyrin (114,117):

$$-SH + \underset{\overset{\|}{CH_2}}{CH}- \rightarrow -S-\underset{\overset{|}{CH_3}}{CH}-.$$

Possibly imidazole groups of the protein component are also involved in the fixation of the prosthetic group (114). The iron atom is present in the ferrous state and is not oxidized to the ferric form by oxygen (114). Cytochrome cannot catalyze the oxidation of organic substances by molecular oxygen. The stability of the ferrous state of the iron in cytochrome is probably due to the covalent linkage of the protein moiety, which prevents the oxidizing action of molecular oxygen. The absorption spectrum of cytochrome is that of a typical hemochromogen, *i.e.*, of a ferroporphyrin complex. The amount of cytochrome c in the organism is much smaller than that of hemoglobin or myoglobin. In the body of a rat weighing 250 g., 3.19 g. hemoglobin, 0.101 g. myoglobin, but only 0.0144 g. cytochrome c were found (118). Helicorubin isolated from snails is very similar to cytochrome c and seems to replace cytochrome in these organisms (119,120).

Neither cytochrome, catalase, nor peroxidase are able to catalyze the oxidation of organic substrates by molecular oxygen. Warburg (121) found, however, that a heme-containing protein is involved in this reaction, in the reduction of molecular oxygen in the cell. The molecular weight of this enzyme, which he called the *respiratory enzyme,* is 75,000 (122). The enzyme, according to Keilin, catalyzes the reaction:

$$O_2 + \text{ferrocytochrome} \rightarrow H_2O_2 + \text{ferricytochrome}$$

The name *cytochrome oxidase* was, therefore, proposed for this enzyme (123). It is not yet quite clear whether the respiratory enzyme and cytochrome oxidase are identical. The enzyme is extracted from cells at pH 7 with phosphate and is precipitated by adding acid to pH 4.5. Cytochrome oxidase is present in small granules which pass into the aqueous extract of the cell, but can be separated from the solution by centrifugation. True solutions of the enzyme have been obtained by means of desoxycholate (124), suggesting that lipids are involved in the fixation of the enzyme to the granules. Cytochrome oxidase has not yet been prepared in a pure state; its prosthetic group is a hemin, which differs from protohemin, and whose formula is not yet known.

The decided influence of the protein component on the specificity of catalytic action is well illustrated by a comparison of hemoglobin, cytochrome c, catalase, and peroxidase. All four compounds contain protoheme as a prosthetic group, and in all of them heme is linked to the protein component through its iron atom. The binding group of the protein moiety is not yet known, although it has been suggested that the iron atom is bound to imidazole or to carboxyl groups of the protein component (see page 208). It is assumed that in peroxidase the acidic side chains of heme and in cytochrome the vinyl groups are involved in the bond between protein and heme. The different composition of the proteins and the different mode of linkage with heme must therefore be responsible for the great difference in the properties of hemoglobin, cytochrome, catalase, and peroxidase. Hemoglobin and hemin have slight catalatic, and distinct peroxidatic activity (92,125), their activity amounting to about 0.1% that of catalase or peroxidase. The great dependence of catalytic activity on the protein component of these enzymes is evident from these facts and from those shown in Table XIV.

TABLE XIV

Compound	Prosthetic group	Isoelectric point, pH	Groups of heme linked to protein	Reaction with oxygen
Hemoglobin	Protoheme	6.9–7.0	Fe	Oxygenation
Cytochrome c	Protoheme	9.8	Fe and vinyl groups	No reaction
Catalase	Protohemin	5.7	Fe and unknown	No reaction
Peroxidase	Protohemin	—	Fe and COOH groups	No reaction
Respiratory enzyme	Unknown heme	—	—	Oxidation to ferric compound

The *enzymes containing copper* as the active group (126) resemble cytochrome oxidase in that they are able to catalyze the reduction of molecular oxygen by organic substrates. The well known browning of apples, potatoes, and other vegetable material on exposure of sections to air is due to the formation of quinoid dyes from tyrosine or dihydroxyphenylalanine through the mediation of copper–protein catalysts. The copper-containing enzyme of potatoes is extracted by water and has been precipitated by acetone or by ammonium sulfate; it contains 0.165% copper (127). The metal is split off by dialysis against hydrogen cyanide; it recombines with the protein in the absence of cyanide (127). A tyrosinase containing copper as active group (128) and a copper-containing ascorbic acid oxidase (129) have been prepared in the crystalline state. The molecular weight of the tyrosinase is 100,000 (130). Ascorbic acid oxidase has also been extracted from squash using 30% ethanol and precipitated by the addition of acetone (131). Tyrosinase has been prepared from animal tissue too, *e.g.*, from grasshoppers (115). This enzyme also loses its copper when dialyzed against cyanide. The properties of the copper-free apoenzymes have not yet been examined and we are not as yet aware of the groups to which the copper ion is bound.

K. Flavoproteins and Pyridine Nucleotides. The first "yellow enzyme" was discovered in yeast by Warburg and Christian (132) and obtained in crystals by Theorell (133). It is extracted from yeast by water and precipitated by acetone or methanol. By the action of methanol or on dialysis against dilute hydrochloric acid the yellow active group is split off. The apoenzyme is denatured by hydrochloric acid, as shown by the increase of reactive sulfhydryl groups; on dialysis against distilled water the apoenzyme passes again into the original native state and is able to combine with the yellow active group (133). This group had originally been considered to be riboflavin phosphate.

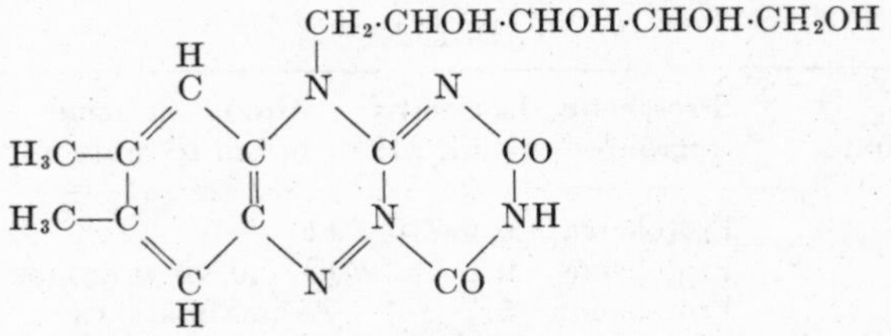

```
                    CH2·CHOH·CHOH·CHOH·CH2OH
           H             |
           C             N          N
         //  \         /   \      //  \
H3C—C        C        C        CO
        |         ||       |        |
H3C—C        C        N        NH
         \\  /         \   //     \  /
           C             N          CO
           H
```

Riboflavin

Later it was found that the prosthetic group of the flavoproteins is a flavin adenine dinucleotide, the structure of which is represented by the scheme: Fl—P—P—R—Ad, where Fl is riboflavin, P, phosphoric acid; R ribose; and Ad adenine (132). While the flavoproteins are rather stable enzymes, the colorless apoenzymes are extremely unstable substances which are, however, rendered more stable by combination with the prosthetic group (134). The molecular weight of the yellow enzyme is about 80,000 (135). It contains one flavin adenine dinucleotide per molecule. Most probably the phosphoric acid residues of the dinucleotide combine with basic groups of the protein moiety.

```
          NH2
          |
          C     N
        //  \  / \\
       N     C      CH
       |     ||     /
       HC    C     /
        \\  / \  /|______O______|
          N    N—CH·CHOH·CHOH·CH·CH2OH
```

Adenosine (Adenine riboside)

The catalytic action of the flavoproteins is based on the capacity of their prosthetic group to accept electrons and to pass them on to other substrates. The reduced form of the prosthetic group, called leucoflavin, is colorless and is converted once again into the oxidized yellow form by giving up two electrons. The great modifying influence of the apoenzyme on the catalytic action of the prosthetic group is indicated by a con-

```
                     CH2·CHOH·CHOH·CHOH·CH2OH
            H        |
            C        N        NH
         //   \    /   \    /    \
  H3C—C         C        C         CO
      |         ||       ||        |
  H3C—C         C        C         NH
         \\   /    \   /    \    /
            C        N         CO
            H        H
```

Leucoflavin

siderable shift in the oxidoreduction potential; while that of equivalent concentrations of the oxidized and the reduced flavin is -0.060 volt at pH 7, that of equivalent concentrations of the oxidized and the reduced flavoprotein is approximately -0.185 volt (136).

The great importance of the protein component of the flavoproteins is also manifested in the pronounced specificity of these enzymes. At present at least ten different flavoproteins are known, all of which contain either riboflavin phosphate or the flavin adenine dinucleotide; they differ in the nature of their protein components. The most important flavoproteins are: D-amino acid oxidase (137), L-amino acid oxidase, glycine oxidase (138), glucose oxidase from molds (139), xanthine oxidase (140), fumaric hydrogenase (140a), cytochrome c reductase (141), histaminase (142), and diaphorase (143). The latter enzyme catalyzes the oxidation of the reduced pyridine nucleotides (see below) in the presence of methylene blue. While it is well established that the protein components of the various flavoproteins are not the same, the way in which they differ from one another remains obscure. As yet it is impossible to say in what manner the apoenzymes direct the action of the flavin adenine dinucleotide so that the oxidation of only a definite class of substances is catalyzed.

A similar situation is found in the enzymes whose prosthetic group is a *diphosphopyridine nucleotide* (*DPN*) or a *triphosphopyridine nucleotide* (*TPN*) (144). There is, however, an important difference between this group of enzymes on the one hand, and the flavoproteins on the other. While the flavoproteins are well defined conjugated proteins which do not dissociate markedly into their components unless they are split by acid or methanol, the apoenzymes of DPN and TPN are less firmly bound to their coenzymes (145). Even in neutral aqueous solutions most of the nucleotide is free. The chemical structure of DPN is represented by N—R—P—P—R—Ad, that of TPN by N—R—P—P—P—R—Ad, where N is nicotinic acid amide, R is ribose, P is phosphoric acid, and Ad is adenine. DPN, also called cozymase or coenzyme I, is extracted from yeast by hydrochloric acid (146); the proteins are precipitated by lead acetate, and from the supernatant solution the nucleotide, after the removal of lead, is adsorbed on Norite and eluted with amyl alcohol and water (147). TPN was isolated from red blood cells by extraction with acetone and precipitation with mercury acetate (148). The two coenzymes combine with different proteins to form enzymes of different specificity (146).

The most important of the substrates whose oxidation is catalyzed by enzymes containing DPN or TPN are lactic acid, triose phosphate, glucose, alcohol, glucose-6-phosphate, glycerophosphate, malic acid, isocitric acid, phosphogluconic acid, glutamic acid, and formic acid. Each of these substrates requires a specific apoenzyme. Some of the apoenzymes have been obtained in the crystalline state.

Crystals of *alcohol dehydrogenase* were obtained by the cautious addition of acetone or ethanol to yeast extracts (149). *Lactic acid dehydrogenase* was extracted from heart muscle, adsorbed to tertiary calcium phosphate, and eluted at pH 7.2 (150). A crystalline preparation was also obtained by precipitation with mercury salts and removal of mercury by dialysis against cyanide (151). *1,3-Diphosphoglyceraldehyde dehydrogenase*, which catalyzes the oxidation of the substrate to phosphoglyceric acid, was extracted from yeast and precipitated with nucleic acid, the latter being removed by precipitation with the protamine sturin; the crystalline enzyme was then obtained by the cautious addition of ammonium sulfate (152). Crystalline *3-phosphoglyceraldehyde dehydrogenase* was obtained from muscle by extraction with 0.03 *N* potassium hydroxide and precipitation with ammonium sulfate (153). The enzyme is found in the myogen fraction of muscle (see Chapter VIII, p. 160). Approximately 10% of the soluble proteins of muscle are formed by phosphoglyceraldehyde dehydrogenase (154). The apoenzymes of the phosphoglyceraldehyde dehydrogenases isolated from yeast and from muscle are different (155). Apparently the protein components of the pyridine nucleotides are not only substrate-specific, but also species-specific. To the enzymes containing pyridine nucleotides also belong the cytochrome c reductases; they are oxidized by the ferric form of cytochrome c. Cytochrome c reductase from yeast contains DPN, while the enzyme from liver is a TPN enzyme (156).

L. Other Enzymes. The myogen fraction of muscles contains *enolase,* an enzyme prepared in the crystalline state; it is precipitated from the muscle extract by lower concentrations of ammonium sulfate than those required for the precipitation of phosphoglyceraldehyde dehydrogenase (157). Enolase, which has also been prepared from yeast, catalyzes the reversible reaction:

$$\text{2-phosphoglyceric acid} \rightleftharpoons \text{phosphopyruvic acid} + H_2O$$

The enzyme was precipitated from yeast extract by nucleic acid and with mercuric salts; a crystalline mercury compound of enolase was obtained (158). The molecular weight of the pure enzyme is 66,000 (159). The enzyme contains one magnesium atom per molecule.

Zymohexase is an enzyme complex formed by *aldolase* and *isomerase;* aldolase catalyzes the reversible reaction:

$$\text{fructose-1,6-diphosphate} \rightleftharpoons \text{2 triosephosphates}$$

Aldolase from yeast seems to require metals for its action, while aldolase from muscle is active even in the presence of metal poisons (161). From the muscles of 20–30 rats, 1 g. of the crystalline enzyme was obtained (161). Aldolase and phosphoglyceraldehyde dehydrogenase have been analyzed for their amino acid content (157). The result of these analyses is shown in Table I, page 32.

As the last of the crystalline oxidizing enzymes, mention must be made of *lipoxidase,* which has been extracted from soybeans, precipitated by ammonia, and recrystallized from ammonium sulfate (160). The enzyme catalyzes the oxidation of unsaturated fatty acids by oxygen; its molecular weight is 90,000–100,000 (160). It is not yet known whether lipoxidase has a nonprotein active group.

Yeast and animal tissues also contain several enzymes which catalyze the phosphorylation or dephosphorylation of organic substances. Since this *phosphorylation* is coupled with oxidoreductions, these enzymes are generally discussed with the oxidoreduction enzymes. *Hexokinase,* the enzyme which catalyzes the conversion of glucose into glucose-6-phosphate, has been obtained in crystals by fractionation with ammonium sulfate (162,163). The molecular weight of hexokinase is 96,000. *Transphosphorylase*, one of the most active enzymes in yeast fermentation, has also been obtained in crystals (164). The enzyme, which catalyzes the equilibrium:

$$\text{1,3-diphosphoglycerate} + \text{ADP} \rightleftharpoons \text{3-phosphoglycerate} + \text{ATP}$$

is a nucleoprotein. It is not yet known whether hexokinase and transphosphorylase contain prosthetic groups of nonprotein nature. The mechanism of their action has been discussed in Section H, above.

The protein component of *carboxylase*, another enzyme important in fermentation, is obtained by splitting the enzyme by means of dilute alkaline solutions; the prosthetic group of yeast carboxylase is thiamine pyrophosphate (165); it seems to be linked to the apoenzyme by means of a magnesium ion bound to the protein moiety and to the phosphoric acid groups of the prosthetic group. It has also been suggested that the quaternary ammonium group of thiamine is the point of attachment to the protein (166). *Bacterial decarboxylases*, which split carbon dioxide from tyrosine and from other amino acids, contain pyridoxal phosphate as their prosthetic group (167). The protein component of these decarboxylases is not yet known.

Proteins also take part in the photochemical reaction by which oxygen is produced in green plants. The biological formation of oxygen has been imitated in the laboratory by irradiating a suspension of *chloroplasts* in solutions containing ferric oxalate and ferricyanide (168) or quinone (169). In both experiments oxygen was formed. The chloroplasts, which contain proteins and lipids, cannot be replaced by protein-free chlorophyll.

M. Summary. It is evident from the numerous findings reported in the preceding sections that a great number of proteins act as enzymes or as apoenzymes. Although this property is undoubtedly due to some particular chemical structure, we do not yet know what the nature of this structural configuration might be. Whether it is the possession of larger amounts of certain of the amino acids, a particular arrangement of the amino acids in the protein molecule, or some other set of conditions are questions which remain to be answered.

Comparing the properties of the enzyme proteins with those of other proteins, we find that many of the enzymes have surprisingly small molecular weights and are highly resistant to heating in slightly acid solutions. The low molecular weight of many enzymes, their resistance to heat and their great tendency to form crystals indicate that the enzyme proteins consist of units which have a very rigid internal structure, and which do not tend to form extensive aggregates. The great rigidity of the internal structure must be due to the presence of numerous cross links between the peptide chains. Analyses of the amino acid content of pepsin and of chymotrypsin show that these enzyme proteins contain an unusually large number of the hydroxyamino acids, serine and threonine (see Table I, p. 32); since each of the hydroxyl groups is able to form a hydrogen bond, a large number of cross links can be formed by means of these amino acids. The relative abundance of hydroxyl groups will also facilitate the combination with substrate molecules and will give rise to strong intermolecular attraction, and to distortion of the bound substrate molecule.

It is not yet possible to generalize these assumptions, because only a few enzymes have been analyzed for their amino acid content. We are not able, therefore, to give a satisfactory explanation for the enzymatic activity of proteins. We can only guess that a preponderance of polar groups might cause a certain rigidity of the protein enzyme molecules and give rise, at the same time, to intense forces of attraction at the surface of the enzyme molecule.

References

1. J. B. Sumner, *J. Biol. Chem.* **69,** 435 (1926).
2. J. H. Northrop, *J. Gen. Physiol.* **13,** 739 (1929–1930).
2*a*. J. B. Sumner, G. F. Somers, Chemistry and Methods of Enzymes, Academic Press, New York (1947).
3. R. J. Dubos, R. H. S. Thompson, *J. Biol. Chem.* **124,** 501 (1938).
4. J. B. Sumner, *Science* **108,** 410 (1948).
5. E. Gorter, *Nature* **142,** 1024 (1938).
6. I. Langmuir, V. J. Schaefer, *J. Am. Chem. Soc.* **60,** 1351 (1938).
7. H. Sobotka and E. Bloch, *J. Phys. Chem.* **45,** 9 (1941).
8. J. H. Northrop, *J. Gen. Physiol.* **16,** 33 (1932).
9. J. B. Sumner, J. S. Kirk, S. F. Howell, *J. Biol. Chem.* **98,** 543 (1932).
10. L. Michaelis, M. P. Schubert, *J. Biol. Chem.* **106,** 331 (1934).
11. G. H. Hogeboom, A. Claude, R. D. Hotchkiss, *J. Biol. Chem.* **165,** 615 (1946).
12. V. A. Engel'hardt, M. N. Lyubimova, *Nature* **144,** 668 (1939).
13. F. Haurowitz, P. Schwerin, *Enzymologia* **9,** 193 (1940).
14. E. L. Smith, *Proc. Natl. Acad. Sci. U. S.* **35,** 80 (1949).
15. E. L. Smith, L. T. Hanson, *J. Biol. Chem.* **176,** 997 (1948); **179,** 803 (1949).
15*a*. H. Abul Fadl, E. J. King, *Biochem. J.* **44,** 435 (1949).
16. H. von Euler, E. Adler, G. Günther, *Z. physiol. Chem.* **249,** 1 (1937).
16*a*. F. Haurowitz, *Abstracts 1st Intern. Congr. Biochem.*, p. 347 (1949).
16*b*. S. Kaufman, H. Neurath, *J. Biol. Chem.* **181,** 623 (1949).
17. M. Bergmann, *Naturwissenschaften* **20,** 420 (1932).
18. J. S. Fruton, M. Bergmann, *J. Biol. Chem.* **145,** 253 (1942).
19. M. Bergmann, L. Zervas, J. S. Fruton, *Science* **81,** 180 (1935).
20. G. W. Schwerdt, H. Neurath, S. Kaufman, J. E. Snoke, *J. Biol. Chem.* **172,** 221 (1948).
21. J. E. Snoke, G. W. Schwerdt, H. Neurath, *J. Biol. Chem.* **175,** 893 (1948).

21*a*. E. L. Smith, *Ann. Rev. Biochem.* **18,** 35 (1949); *Federation Proc.* **8,** 581 (1949).
22. A. Rothen, *J. Biol. Chem.* **167,** 299 (1947).
23. F. Karush and B. M. Siegel, *Science* **108,** 107 (1948); H. J. Trurnit, *Science* **111,** 1 (1950).
24. R. Kuhn, *Z. physiol. Chem.* **135,** 1 (1924).
25. L. Michaelis, H. Pechstein, *Ber.* **60,** 79 (1914).
26. L. Michaelis, P. Rona, *Ber.* **60,** 62 (1914).
27. B. Chance, *J. Biol. Chem.* **179,** 1299, 1311, 1331, 1341; **180,** 865, 947 (1949).
28. B. Chance, *Arch. Biochem.* **21,** 416; **22,** 224 (1949) *Biochem. J.* **46,** 387, 402 (1950).
29. H. Neurath, G. W. Schwerdt, *Chem. Revs.* **46,** 88 (1950).
30. L. Michaelis, M. Menten, *Biochem. Z.* **49,** 333 (1913).
31. E. Elkins-Kaufman, H. Neurath, *J. Biol. Chem.* **175,** 893 (1948).
32. H. Neurath, G. W. Schwerdt, *Chem Revs.* **46,** 69 (1950).
33. H. B. Bull, B. T. Currie, *J. Am. Chem. Soc.* **71,** 2758 (1949).
34. S. Kaufman, H. Neurath, *J. Biol. Chem.* **180,** 181 (1949).
35. H. Lineweaver, D. Burk, *J. Am. Chem. Soc.* **56,** 658 (1934).
36. H. Lineweaver, *J. Am. Chem. Soc.* **61,** 403 (1939).
37. J. Steinhardt, *J. Biol. Chem.* **141,** 681 (1941).
38. G. Schramm, J. Primosigh, *Z. physiol. Chem.* **283,** 34 (1948).
39. G. Thomas, C. Davies, *Nature* **159,** 373 (1947).
40. C. Levesque, A. Craig, *Ind. Eng. Chem.* **40,** 96 (1948).
41. E. Bamann, E. Nowotny, *Ber.* **81,** 442, 455 (1949).
42. E. Smith *et al.*, *J. Biol. Chem.* **180,** 33 (1948).
43. V. Jagannathan, J. M. Luck, *J. Biol. Chem.* **179,** 569 (1949).
44. L. F. Leloir, R. Caputto *et al.*, *Arch. Biochem.* **18,** 201; **19,** 339 (1948); **23,** 55 (1949).
45. E. W. Sutherland, T. Posternak, C. F. Cori, *J. Biol. Chem.* **179,** 501 (1949); **181,** 153 (1949); **180,** 1285 (1949).
45*a*. H. Neurath *et al.*, *Arch. Biochem.* **21,** 351, 437 (1949).
46. E. Elkins-Kaufman, H. Neurath, G. DeMaria, *J. Biol. Chem.* **178,** 645 (1949).
47. M. S. Mohammed, *Acta Chem. Scand.* **2,** 49 (1948); W. M. Connors *et al.*, *J. Biol. Chem.* **184,** 29 (1950).
48. M. Kunitz, *J. Gen. Physiol.* **24,** 15 (1940).
49. A. Rothen, *J. Gen. Physiol.* **24,** 203 (1940).
50. M. Kunitz, *Science* **107,** 19 (1948).
51. A. K. Balls, R. R. Thompson, M. K. Walden, *J. Biol. Chem.* **163,** 571 (1946).
52. S. Schwimmer, A. K. Balls, *J. Biol. Chem.* **179,** 1063 (1949).
53. K. H. Meyer, E. Fischer, P. Bernfeld, F. Duckert, *Arch. Bioch.* **18,** 203 (1948).
54. Ya. P. Barmenkov, *Biokhimiya* **4,** 160 (1939).
55. J. B. Sumner, J. O'Kane, *Enzymologia* **12,** 251 (1948).
56. G. Alderton, J. C. Lewis, H. L. Fevold, *J. Biol. Chem.* **157,** 43 (1945).
57. E. P. Abraham, R. Robinson, *Nature* **140,** 24 (1937).
58. K. Meyer, E. Hahnel, *J. Biol. Chem.* **163,** 723 (1946).
59. J. H. Northrop, *J. Gen. Physiol.* **13,** 767 (1930); **14,** 713 (1931); **30,** 177 (1946).
60. J. H. Northrop, *J. Gen. Physiol.* **16,** 615 (1933).
61. J. S. L. Philpot, B. Erickson-Quensel, *Nature* **132,** 932 (1933).
62. J. D. Bernal, D. Crowfoot, *Nature* **133,** 794 (1934).
63. R. M. Herriott, *J. Gen. Physiol.* **21,** 501 (1938).
64. J. S. Fruton, N. Bergmann, *Science* **87,** 557 (1938).
65. H. Bauer, E. Strauss, *Biochem. Z.* **211,** 163 (1929).

66. J. H. Northrop, M. Kunitz, *Science* **73**, 262 (1931).
67. M. Kunitz, J. H. Northrop, *Science* **80**, 505 (1934).
68. M. Kunitz, J. H. Northrop, *J. Gen. Physiol.* **19**, 991 (1936).
69. H. Lineweaver, C. W. Murray, *J. Biol. Chem.* **171**, 565 (1947).
70. J. H. Northrop, Crystalline Enzymes. Columbia Univ. Press, New York, 1939.
71. M. Bergmann, W. F. Ross, *J. Am. Chem. Soc.* **58**, 1503 (1936). M. Bergmann, C. Niemann, *Ann. Rev. Biochem.* **7**, 102 (1938).
72. J. H. Northrop, M. Kunitz, *J. Gen. Physiol.* **18**, 433 (1935).
73. C. Jacobsen, *Compt. rend. trav. lab. Carlsberg Sér. chim.* **25**, 325 (1947).
74. M. Kunitz, *J. Gen. Physiol.* **22**, 207 (1938).
75. G. W. Schwert, *J. Biol. Chem.* **159**, 655 (1949).
76. J. A. V. Butler, *J. Am. Chem. Soc.* **63**, 2968 (1941).
77. M. Bergmann, J. S. Fruton, *J. Biol. Chem.* **117**, 189; **118**, 405 (1937).
78. S. Kaufmann, H. Neurath, G. W. Schwerdt, *J. Biol. Chem.* **177**, 793 (1949).
79. A. K. Balls, H. Lineweaver, *J. Biol. Chem.* **130**, 669 (1939).
80. E. Waldschmidt-Leitz, A. Purr, A. K. Balls, *Naturwissenschaften* **18**, 645 (1930).
81. T. Bersin, W. Logemann, *Z. physiol. Chem.* **220**, 209 (1933).
82. M. Bergmann, J. S. Fruton, *Science* **84**, 89 (1936).
83. E. Abderhalden, S. Buadze, *Fermentforschung* **14**, 215 (1934).
84. E. Abderhalden, R. Abderhalden, *Z. Altersforchung* **3**, 109 (1941).
85. E. Abderhalden, S. Buadze, *Fermentforschung* **13**, 305 (1933); **14**, 283 (1934).
86. G. Mall, T. Bersin, *Z. physiol. Chem.* **268**, 129 (1941).
87. R. Abderhalden, *Schweiz. med. Wochschr.* **76**, 671 (1946).
88. M. Winkler, *Z. exptl. med.* **109**, 670 (1941).
89. F. Haurowitz, M. Bilen, F. Marx, V. Göksu, *Bull. faculté med. Istanbul* **11**, 30 (1948).
90. M. L. Anson, *J. Gen. Physiol.* **20**, 663 (1936).
91. E. Waldschmidt-Leitz, A. Purr, *Ber.* **62**, 2217 (1929).
92. R. Willstätter, A. Pollinger, *Ann.* **430**, 269 (1923).
93. L. C. Hankinson, *J. Dairy Sci.* **26**, 53 (1943).
94. N. J. Berridge, *Biochem. J.* **39**, 179 (1943).
95. J. B. Sumner, N. Gralèn, B. Erickson-Quensel, *J. Biol. Chem.* **125**, 33, 37, 45 (1938).
96. D. B. Hand, *J. Am. Chem. Soc.* **61**, 3180 (1939).
97. H. Tauber, *J. Biol. Chem.* **87**, 625 (1930).
97*a*. I. M .Soquet, K. J. Laidler, *Arch. Biochem.* **25**, 171 (1950).
98. F. Haurowitz, P. Schwerin, *Enzymologia* **9**, 193 (1940).
99. F. Haurowitz, Progress in Biochemistry. Interscience, New York, 1950.
100. F. Haurowitz, *Enzymologia* **2**, 9 (1937).
101. F. Haurowitz, *Enzymologia* **10**, 141 (1941).
102. L. Michaelis, *Federation Proc.* **7**, 513 (1948).
103. L. Michaelis, C. Smythe, *Ann. Rev. Biochem.* **7**, 1 (1938); **16**, 1 (1947).
104. L. Pauling, *Nature* **161**, 1019 (1948).
105. J. B. Sumner, A. L. Dounce, *J. Biol. Chem.* **121**, 417 (1937).
106. K. Agner, *Arkiv Kemi Mineral. Geol.* **17B** No. 9 (1943).
107. R. K. Bonnichsen, *Acta Chem. Scand.* **2**, 561 (1948).
108. K. Agner, *Z. physiol. Chem.* **235**, II (1935).
109. D. Keilin, E. F. Hartree, *Biochem. J.* **39**, 283, 289 (1945).
110. H. Theorell, *Arkiv Kemi Mineral. Geol.* **15B**, No. 24; **16A**, No. 2 (1942).
111. H. Theorell, K. O. Pedersen, in The Svedberg. Almqvist and Wiksells, Upsala, 1945, p. 523.

112. C. McMunn, *J. Physiol.* **8,** 57 (1887).
113. D. Keilin, E. F. Hartree, *Proc. Roy. Soc. London* **B122,** 298 (1937).
114. H. Theorell, Å. Åkeson, *Science* **90,** 67 (1939); *J. Am. Chem. Soc.* **63,** 1809 (1941).
115. T. H. Allen, J. H. Bodine, *Science* **94,** 443 (1941).
116. R. Hill, D. Keilin, *Proc. Roy. Soc. London* **B107,** 896 (1930–1931).
117. K. Zeile, H. Meyer, *Naturwissenschaften* **27,** 596 (1939).
118. M. W. Crandall, D. L. Drabkin, *J. Biol. Chem.* **166,** 653 (1946); **182,** 317 (1950).
119. J. Roche, J. Morena, *Compt. rend. soc. biol.* **123,** 1215, 1218 (1936).
120. E. Baldwin, *Biochem. J.* **32,** 1225 (1938).
121. O. Warburg, E. Negelein, *Biochem. Z.* **202,** 202 (1929).
122. O. Warburg, *Naturwissenschaften* **33,** 94 (1947).
123. D. Keilin, E. F. Hartree, *Proc. Roy. Soc. London* **B125,** 171 (1938).
124. W. Wainio, *Science* **106,** 471 (1947).
125. F. Haurowitz, *Z. physiol. Chem.* **198,** 9 (1931).
126. J. M. Nelson, C. R. Dawson, *Advances in Enzymol.* **4,** 99 (1944).
127. F. Kubowitz, *Biochem. Z.* **292,** 221 (1937); **296,** 463 (1938).
128. H. R. Dalton, J. M. Nelson, *J. Am. Chem. Soc.* **60,** 3085 (1938)
129. T. Tadokoro, N. Takasugi, *J. Chem. Soc. Japan* **60,** 188 (1939), cited by J. B. Sumner, G. F. Somers, Chemistry and Methods of Enzymes; Academic, New York.
130. M. F. Mallette, C. R. Dawson, *Arch. Biochem.* **23,** 29 (1949).
131. H. Tauber, *Ergeb. Enzymforsch.* **7,** 301 (1938).
132. O. Warburg, W. Christian, *Biochem. Z.* **266,** 377 (1933); **298,** 150 (1938).
133. H. Theorell, *Biochem. Z.* **272,** 155 (1934).
134. H. Theorell, *Biochem. Z.* **278,** 263 (1938).
135. R. A. Kekwick, K. O. Pedersen, *Biochem. J.* **30,** 2201 (1936).
136. K. Laki, *Z. physiol. Chem.* **249,** 61, 63 (1937).
137. H. A. Krebs, *Enzymologia* **7,** 53 (1939).
138. S. Ratner, V. Nocito, D. E. Green, *J. Biol. Chem.* **152,** 114 (1944).
139. D. Müller, *Biochem. Z.* **232,** 423 (1931).
140. E. G. Ball, P. A. Ramsdell, *J. Biol. Chem.* **131,** 767 (1939).
140*a*. F. G. Fischer, *et al.*, *Naturwissenschaften* **27,** 197 (1939).
141. E. Haas, C. J. Harrer, T. R. Hogness, *J. Biol. Chem.* **143,** 344 (1942).
142. R. Kapeller-Adler, *Biochem. J.* **44,** 70 (1949).
143. J. G. Dewan, D. Green, *Nature* **140,** 1097 (1937).
144. O. Warburg, W. Christian, *Biochem. Z.* **287,** 291 (1936).
145. E. Negelein, E. Haas, *Biochem. Z.* **282,** 206 (1935).
146. H. von Euler *et al.*, *Z. physiol. Chem.* **233,** 120 (1935).
147. B. J. Jandorf, *J. Biol. Chem.* **138,** 305 (1941).
148. O. Warburg, W. C. Christian, A. Griese, *Biochem. Z.* **282,** 157 (1935)
149. E. Negelein, H. J. Wulff, *Biochem. Z.* **293,** 251 (1937).
150. F. Straub, *Biochem. J.* **34,** 483 (1940).
151. F. Kubowitz, P. Ott, *Naturwissenschaften* **29,** 590 (1941).
152. O. Warburg, W. Christian, *Biochem. Z.* **301,** 221 (1939); **303,** 40 (1939).
153. G. T. Cori, M. W. Slein, C. F. Cori, *J. Biol. Chem.* **159,** 565 (1944).
154. R. Caputto, M. Dixon, *Nature* **156,** 630 (1945).
155. E. G. Krebs, V. A. Najjar, *Federation Proc.* **7,** 166 (1948).
156. L. A. Heppel, B. L. Horecker, *Federation Proc.* **8,** 205, 207 (1949); *J. Biol. Chem.* **183,** 593 (1950).

157. C. F. Cori, G. T. Cori, J. F. Taylor, A. A. Green, M. W. Slein, S. Velick, E. Ronzone, *J. Biol. Chem.* **173,** 591, 605, 619 (1948).
158. O. Warburg, W. Christian, *Biochem. Z.* **310,** 384 (1942).
159. T. Bücher, *Biochim. et Biophys. Acta* **1,** 467 (1947).
160. H. Theorell, R. T. Holmann, Å. Åkeson, *Arch. Biochem.* **14,** 250 (1947), R. T. Holman *et al.*, *Arch. Biochem.* **26,** 199 (1950).
161. O. Warburg, W. Christian, *Biochem. Z.* **314,** 149 (1943).
162. L. Berger, M. W. Slein, S. P. Colowick, C. F. Cori, *J. Gen. Physiol.* **29,** 141 (1946).
163. M. McDonald, M. Kunitz, *J. Gen. Physiol.* **29,** 143 (1946).
164. T. Bücher, *Naturwissenschaften* **30,** 756 (1942).
165. K. Lohmann, P. Schuster, *Biochem. Z.* **294,** 188 (1937).
166. D. E. Green, D. Herbert, V. Subrahmanyan, *J. Biol. Chem.* **138,** 327 (1941).
167. I. C. Gunsalus, W. D. Bellamy, W. W. Umbreit, *J. Biol. Chem.* **155,** 685 (1944).
168. R. Hill, R. Scarisbrick, *Nature* **146,** 61 (1941).
169. O. Warburg, W. Lüttgens, *Naturwissenschaften* **32,** 161 (1944).

Chapter XIII

Proteins with Hormone Activity

A. General Remarks. Hormones arise in the endocrine glands, and pass from these directly into the blood stream, by which they are transported to the site of their action. The chemical structure of those hormones which are steroid derivatives has been elucidated in the last few years. The formula of adrenaline, the hormone of the medullar part of the adrenal gland, has been known for a long time. While these hormones are small molecules, the hormones of the thyroid gland, the parathyroids, the pancreas, and the hypophysis are proteins or protein derivatives of higher molecular weights. They differ from the smaller hormone molecules not only in their molecular size but also in their instability to heat and their mode of action. Analyses of these hormones, which are prepared by applying the techniques of protein chemistry, reveal that they are built up of the well known amino acids. We do not yet know, however, to what molecular groups they owe their great physiological activity. The situation resembles that of the hydrolytic enzymes There, also, we could not explain satisfactorily the structure responsible for the catalytic activity, although a tentative explanation of enzymatic action and of its mechanism was advanced. In the field of hormone chemistry the state of our knowledge is still less satisfactory. We cannot even advance a reasonable speculation as to the mode of action of the hormones. We must for the present be content with a description of their properties, wherein emphasis will be given to those properties which are characteristic of each and which serve to distinguish them from other proteins.

Since the hormones to be discussed in this chapter are proteins, the question of whether or not they are species-specific must be examined. Species specificity of proteins is usually proved serologically, *i.e.*, by the formation of antibodies. Actually, some of the hormones such as the gonadotropic hormone of the pituitary gland or the hormone of the thyroid gland give rise to the formation of antibodies if injected parenterally into species other than that of their origin. The term antihormone is sometimes used for these antibodies (1–3). Their formation, which has been observed after prolonged administration of the hormones, is the cause for a decline in the hormonal activity (4). It seems that antibodies are produced only by those hormones whose molecules are very large. The smaller peptide-like hormones exert no antigenic effect, so that most of them are effectual in other species, even when administered repeatedly over long periods.

B. Thyroid Hormone (Thyroglobulin) (5,5*a*). The hormonal activity of the thyroid gland has been known for a very long time. It was also noted very early that the gland contained iodine and that this element was essential for its hormonal activity. Oswald (6) in Hofmeister's laboratory succeeded in extracting an iodoglobulin from the gland, which he precipitated by half-saturation with ammonium sulfate. A better method for the preparation of this protein, called thyroglobulin, is to extract the gland with 1% sodium acetate, precipitate the hormone with acetic acid at pH 5, and reprecipitate the dissolved hormones by half-saturation with sodium sulfate (7).

Thyroglobulin is the only hormone to be discussed whose active groups are known. They are the thyroxine groups of its peptide chain. Thyroxine is the diiodophenyl ether of diiodotyrosine. Its formula is:

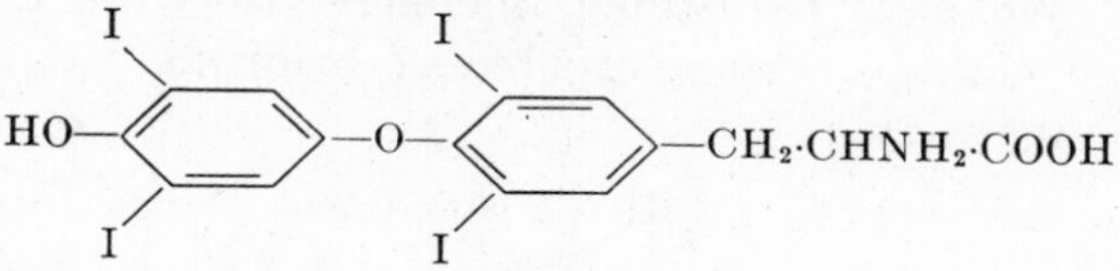

$$HO-C_6H_2I_2-O-C_6H_2I_2-CH_2\cdot CHNH_2\cdot COOH$$

Harington (5*a*), who proved this formula, isolated thyroxine after hydrolyzing thyroglobulin with baryta. Not all the iodine is present in thyroglobulin as thyroxine; a portion of it occurs as diiodotyrosine (iodogorgoic acid) (8,9). If thyroglobulin is hydrolyzed by proteolytic enzymes, 16% of the iodine is obtained as diiodotyrosine.

Thyroglobulin contains 0.6% iodine (9). Its molecular weight is 700,000 (10), so that each molecule contains 32 iodine atoms belonging to 2–3 thyroxine groups and 8–12 diiodotyrosine units (10). Outside its pH stability region the molecule is split into smaller subunits (10*a*). Thyroglobulin does not combine with antibodies against iodinated proteins (11), indicating that the thyroxine residues are in the interior of the large thyroglobulin molecule, not at its surface, so that they are not accessible to the specific anti-iodo groups of the antibody molecules.

Thyroxine is easily formed *in vitro* when proteins are exposed to the action of iodine in slightly alkaline solution (12). Thus 0.4 g. crystalline thyroxine is obtained by treating 100 g. casein with iodine (13,14). Thyroxine is also obtained when diiodotyrosine is oxidized by hydrogen peroxide in alkaline solutions (15). It is evident from all these observations that the first step in the formation of thyroxine is the iodination of tyrosine:

$$4\,I + HO\text{-}C_6H_4\text{-}CH_2\cdot CHNH_2\cdot COOH \rightarrow 2\,HI + HO\text{-}C_6H_2I_2\text{-}CH_2\cdot CHNH_2\cdot COOH$$

Subsequently a portion of the diiodotyrosine is split by the oxidizing action of the alkaline iodine solution and the iodinated aromatic residue combines with diiodotyrosine to give thyroxine. While these *in vitro* reactions are understandable, we do not yet know why administered iodine combines preferentially with a specific globulin and why the thyroglobulin formed accumulates in the thyroid gland. That this is indeed the normal metabolic pathway of iodine is demonstrated very convincingly by injecting radioiodine (16).

Proteins *in vitro* combine with iodine, but not with iodide ions. On the other hand, iodine administered is rapidly reduced to iodide in the body fluids. We have to assume, therefore, that the thyroid gland contains some enzyme system capable of oxidizing iodide to iodine, according to the reaction:

$$O_2 + 4\,HI \rightarrow 2\,H_2O + 2\,I_2$$

and that the iodine formed combines with a globulin to form thyroglobulin. The formation of thyroglobulin is inhibited by the "goitrogens," a recently discovered class of important drugs (17). The goitrogens are derivatives of thiourea, which, although exhibiting distinct goitrogenic activity, is less powerful than thiouracil and other similar substances.

The reactions induced by the thyroid hormone are no less mysterious than the process of its formation. They are certainly due to the thyroxine residues, for similar effects are brought about by administering pure thyroxine. The hormone increases the basal metabolic rate, and the rate at which tadpoles and other organisms mature. We do not yet know the site of action of the hormone or the mechanism of this acceleration of metabolism and development. Deficiency of the hormone has the opposite effects and results in a slowing down of the metabolic rate and the rate of development.

C. Insulin (17*a*). Insulin, the hormone of the pancreas, is rapidly destroyed by the proteolytic enzymes of the pancreas if the gland or its extracts are stored for a period of time. This loss of insulin from extracts of the pancreas is the reason why previous workers failed to obtain active solutions of the hormone. Effectual extracts were obtained by Banting and Best (18), who inhibited the action of trypsin by using acidified ethanol as a solvent. The action of trypsin can also be prevented by adding picric acid to the extracts (19). Insulin is resistant to dilute acids.

Crystals of insulin were prepared by dissolving crude preparations in acetic acid and by the subsequent cautious neutralization with ammonia and pyridine (20,21). Crystallization is facilitated by adding saponin (22). One milligram of the purified crystalline preparation contains about 20 International Units of insulin. In certain classes of fish the islets of Langerhans of the pancreas form a separate organ; in these fishes insulin is found in these large islets and not in the hepatopancreas (23).

The molecular weight of insulin in solution is approximately 48,000 (24,25). The exact figure depends, however, on the concentration of the solution and on its hydrogen ion concentration; at pH under 4 and more than 7.5 dissociation into smaller units occurs (24). The molecular weight of the subunits is approximately 12,000; X-ray analysis reveals that crystalline insulin consists of unit cells formed by three subunits, so that the equivalent weight of the crystal unit is 36,000. In electrophoresis experiments insulin migrates as a uniform substance (25*a*). The isoelectric point of insulin is near pH 5.3–5.8 (25).

The amino acid analysis of insulin reveals an unusually high sulfur content. About 12% of the molecule is formed by cystine and cysteine, 10% by leucine, and 12% by tyrosine (26) (see Table I page 32). Another peculiarity is the large number of free amino groups, which is considerably in excess of the number of lysine molecules. The complete analysis of insulin furnished the following formula: arg_2, his_4, lys_2, glu_{15}, asp_6, gly_7, ala_7, val_8, leu_{12}, $ileu_3$, pro_3, tyr_9, phe_6, ser_6, thr_2, $cys(SS/2)_{12}$, $ammonia_{12}$ (26*a*). The amino groups seem to be involved in the physiological activity of insulin, for insulin is inactivated by formaldehyde (27).

Inactivation is also accomplished by reducing agents such as cysteine (28), thioglycolic acid (27*a*), or leucomethylene blue (29). This is possibly due to the cleavage of dithio bonds; each of them is converted into two sulfhydryl groups (27*a*). The dithio bonds of insulin are also split by the action of periodic acid through which they are converted into sulfonic acid groups, $—SO_3H$ (30). Esterification of insulin with sulfuric acid furnishes a sulfuric acid ester, which displays most of the hormonal activity of insulin (31). If crystalline insulin is exposed to the action of crystalline trypsin its activity decreases only slightly; at the same time only one or two peptide bonds per molecule are hydrolyzed (32). Both pepsin and chymotrypsin readily split insulin (32*a*).

When insulin is alkylated by coupling with dinitrofluorobenzene (see page 108) and hydrolyzed, two molecules of dinitrophenylglycine and two of dinitrophenylphenylalanine per unit of the mol. wt. 12,000 are obtained; this shows that each of these units consists of four peptide chains, whose terminal amino groups are furnished by glycine and phenylalanine (33). Sanger (34) succeeded in isolating from insulin two peptides (A) containing terminal glycine residues, and two peptides (B) with terminal phenylalanine groups. From the peptides A the following lower peptides were obtained by treatment with dinitrofluorobenzene: DNP-glycyl-isoleucine (DNP = dinitrophenyl-), DNP-isoleucyl-valine, DNP-glycyl-isoleucyl-valyl-glycine, and DNP-tyrosine; peptide A was free of arginine, histidine, phenylalanine, threonine; peptide B furnished DNP-phenylalanyl-valine, DNP-phenylalanyl-valyl-aspartic acid, DNP-phenylalanyl-valyl-aspartyl-glutamic acid, DNP-lysyl-alanine, and threonyl-DNP-lysyl-alanine. These results prove convincingly that the insulin molecule is built up of different peptides linked to each other by dithio groups of cystine molecules, and that arginine and histidine, which form the bulk of the basic amino acids (see Table I, p. 32) are found only in some of these peptides (34*a*).

Insulin combines readily with bivalent metals, chiefly with zinc, cobalt or cadmium; the zinc compound is more easily crystallized than pure insulin (35). The formation of complexes of insulin with protamines is of great clinical importance, because the hormonal action of protamine-insulin does not decline as rapidly as that of pure insulin (36).

Although insulin is a protein, it is rather resistant to denaturing agents. It is not denatured by organic solvents, by dilute acids, or by spreading in monomolecular films (37). If insulin is heated in weakly acid solution, inactive fibrils are formed, which, secondarily, aggregate to insoluble spherites (37*a*). It is remarkable that these phenomena are reversible and that insulin is reactivated by alkali (37*a*). Insulin does not act as an antigen when injected into animals of other species; it does not seem to be species-specific (38).

Injection of insulin lowers the blood sugar and prevents the loss of glucose from the systems of diabetic persons; it also prevents the dangerous acidosis in diabetic patients. Insulin increases the utilization of glucose and of pyruvate by the surviving rat diaphragm (38*a*); if the diaphragm is replaced by a diaphragm extract insulin is inefficient (38*b*); this suggests that insulin modifies the permeability of the cells for one of the substances involved in carbohydrate metabolism (38*b*).

When working with commercial insulin preparations, it should be borne in mind that these are not always pure insulin; some of them contain glycogenolytic factors, which cause an initial hyperglycemia, *i.e.*, an increase in the blood sugar level (39).

D. Hormones of the Posterior Pituitary Lobe. Three different hormonal actions are attributed to the posterior lobe of the hypophysis: (*1*) excitation of uterine muscle contractions, (*2*) increase of the blood pressure, and (*3*) diuresis, *i.e.*, increase in the volume of urine produced by the kidney. Attempts to purify the respective hormones resulted in the preparation of proteinlike active substances. The substance causing uterine contractions is called oxytocin, while that which raises the blood pressure is termed pitressin or vasopressin. Some authors (40) are of the opinion that both hormonal effects are due to a single substance, which can secondarily be split into substances having either oxytocic or pressor activity. Such a substance actually has been prepared (41*a*) and found to have a molecular weight of 30,000; its isoelectric point is 4.8, its sulfur content 4.89%.

The two active hormones were separated by other authors, who made use of the fact that pitressin is adsorbed on permutite (42) or bentonite (43), and that it is precipitated by ethyl acetate from an ethanolic solution of both hormones (44). The separation of the two hormones has also been accomplished by extracting the gland with acetic acid and fractionally precipitating the extracts with diethyl ether (45).

Preparations of oxytocin and pitressin contain 3.06 and 3.10% sulfur, and 14.3 and 10.5% tyrosine, respectively (46). The high sulfur and tyrosine contents recall similar high values of insulin. Actually the physicochemical behavior of the posterior pituitary hormones is similar to that of insulin. They are split by proteolytic enzymes into amino acids (47) and are inactivated by reducing agents such as cysteine (48). They are reactivated, however, by treatment with methylene blue. Recent analyses of the oxytocic hormone revealed that it contains only one molecule of each of the following amino acids: leucine, isoleucine, tyrosine, proline, glutamic acid, aspartic acid, glycine, cystine, and three molecules ammonia (41). It is not yet known whether similar simple amino acid combinations are present in other hormones. While the oxytocic and the pressor hormone of the posterior lobe have been obtained in purified preparations, not much is known about the diuretic hormone of the hypophysis; it seems to be associated with the fraction which has both oxytocic and pressor activity (41*a*).

The pars intermedia of the hypophysis, situated between the anterior and the posterior lobe, contains a hormone called intermedin or melanophore hormone. It causes expansion of the pigmented melanophores of the skin, so that the skin assumes a darker color (49). The hormone is tested on frogs (50). It is not clear whether it is identical with the substance which causes the appearance of bright colors in certain fishes at the time of mating (51,52).

E. Hormones of the Anterior Pituitary Lobe. Although the hypophysis is a very small organ, weighing about 0.7 g. in man, it contains many significant hormones. The hormones of the anterior lobe differ from those of the posterior lobe by their mode of action. Oxytocin and pitressin act very rapidly, producing noticeable effects within a few minutes after their injection. The hormones of the anterior lobe act very slowly, their effects being manifested only after many hours or days. The action of many of these hormones is indirect in that they act by means of other endocrine glands. Thus the gonadotropic hormone of the hypophysis causes increased activity of the sexual glands; likewise, the thyrotropic hormone of the hypophysis enhances the activity of the thyroid hormone. It is understandable that the result of these actions is not seen immediately, but only after a long period of time.

The presence of 10–15 different hormones in the small anterior lobe of the hypophysis has been claimed. Most of these claims are based on the observation of a specific physiological action and not on the isolation of a definite chemical substance. To date, the following hormones have been isolated and separated from each other (53,54):

Growth hormone.
Thyrotropic hormone.
Adrenocorticotropic hormone.
Lactogenic hormone (prolactin).
Two gonadotropic hormones, one of them follicle-stimulating (FSH), the other stimulating the interstitial cells (ICSH).

Most of these hormones can be separated from each other by fractionation with ammonium sulfate (55). The diabetogenic hormone of the hypophysis (55*a*) is identical with the growth hormone or with a mixture of growth hormone and adrenocorticotropic hormone (56,56*a*). It is not yet clear whether a ketogenic hormone, a parathyrotropic hormone, and other factors are identical with one of the six isolated hormones.

The growth hormone is prepared from the hypophysis by extraction with alkaline solvents (57–59) such as lime water (54). From these extracts the hormone is precipitated by addition of 30% acetone (60), by ammonium sulfate (59), sodium sulfate (61), or by adjusting the reaction of the solution to the isoelectric pH 6.85 (54). The hormone, accordingly, has the properties of a typical globulin. It is thermolabile, but is not denatured by the action of urea (62). The hormone has been obtained in crystals from 15% ethanolic solutions (63,64). Its amino acid content is shown in Table I (page 32). The molecular weight is 49,200 (64*a*).

The alkaline extracts of the anterior pituitary lobe also contain the *thyrotropic hormone.* It is more soluble than the growth hormone and is not precipitated by 30% acetone (60). It is soluble in 50% acetone and also in 50% pyridine (65). In contrast to true proteins, the hormone is not precipitated by trichloroacetic acid (66,67). It has been purified about 100 times, but has not yet been obtained in pure form. The molecular weight has been estimated at 10,000 (68). The best preparations are free of growth activity and gonadotropic activity (67). The action of the thyrotropic hormone on the thyroid gland is demonstrated by an increase in the size of the thyroid gland, which is measured by weighing the gland (65). Upon administration of thyrotropic hormone the iodine content of the thyroid gland decreases, while that of the blood increases (66). The thyrotropic hormone raises the respiration of thyroid tissue, not that of other tissues (69). This can also be demonstrated in thyroid sections (70). Evidently the thyrotropic hormone has a specific affinity for thyroid tissue and stimulates the action of the thyroid gland in an unknown manner.

The *adrenotropic hormone* (adrenocorticotropic hormone) of the anterior pituitary gland is the most stable of the anterior pituitary hormones. It is stable against boiling 0.25% hydrochloric acid. It is prepared by extracting the gland with acidified acetone, precipitating with higher concentrations of acetone, and extracting the precipitate with sodium phosphate solution from which it is finally salted out with ammonium sulfate (71,72). The hormone has a molecular weight of 20,000 and an isoelectric point of 4.7–4.8; it contains 2.3% sulfur (54). Administration of the hormone results in hyperfunction of the adrenal cortex. It is remarkable that the hormone retains its activity after 50% hydrolysis by pepsin (72*a*). The biological activity of the hormone is lost when its free amino, carboxyl, or tyrosine groups are substituted (72*a*).

Prolactin, the *lactogenic hormone* of the anterior lobe, is a protein having a molecular weight of 22,000 and an isoelectric point of pH 7.5 (73). It has been separated from the other hormones of the hypophysis (74–76). The hormone enhances the growth of the milk ducts and of the mammary gland.

The *gonadotropic activity* of the hypophysis was originally ascribed to the action of a single hormone. Later, it was found, however, that the hormone could be resolved into two hormones with different activities. One of them, which was precipitated by ammonium sulfate at pH 5–6, caused luteinization in the ovary and was called *luteinizing hormone* (LH) (77). Later the designation was altered to ICSH (interstitial-cell-stimulating hormone), because it was found that the hormone acts also on the interstitial cells of the male sex gland. The hormone is salted out by ammonium sulfate. The second gonadotropic hormone is precipitated by larger amounts of ammonium sulfate; it enhances the development of ovarian follicles and has been called *follicle-stimulating hormone* (FSH).

The two gonadotropic hormones are separated from one another by precipitation with ammonium sulfate or by extraction of the gland with aqueous pyridine and precipitation of the ICSH by ethanol (78–80). Both hormones have a high content of carbohydrates and are typical glucoproteins. The luteinizing hormone from hog hypophysis had a molecular weight of 100,000; it contained 4.5% mannose and 5.9% hexosamine (81). The luteinizing hormone of sheep hypophysis contained 2.8% mannose and 2.2% hexosamine; its molecular weight was 40,000, its isoelectric point pH 4.6 (82). The follicle-stimulating hormone of the hypophysis also is a glucoprotein; it contains 1.2% mannose, 0.6% glucosamine (82*a*), and 10–13% total carbohydrate (82*b*). Its molecular weight is 70,000, the isoelectric point pH 4.5 (83).

In addition to the pituitary gonadotropic hormones another gonadotropin is produced in the placenta during pregnancy. This *chorionic gonadotropin* is of great clinical importance because it passes into the urine in the early days of pregnancy and permits diagnosis of pregnancy by means of the Aschheim-Zondek test (84). It was originally believed that the urinary gonadotropin, which had been called by Zondek "prolan," was identical with the pituitary hormones and that it was likewise a mixture of a luteinizing and a follicle-stimulating component (85,86). The dualistic theory of hormonal activity has subsequently been abandoned. The interpretation of experimental data is complicated by the fact that the urinary gonadotropin possibly acts on the ovary indirectly, by means of the hypophysis, stimulating both pituitary hormones, FSH as well as ICSH (87,88). The urinary gonadotropic hormone differs from the pituitary hormones by its resistance to heat (89,90) and by its higher carbohydrate content. Its placental origin was confirmed by the observation that it is also formed in cultures of placenta tissue (91).

The urinary gonadotropic hormone is recovered from the urine by adsorption on tungstic acid (92), benzoic acid (93), Lloyd's reagent (94), quinine (95), uranyl phosphate, or alumina (96). Since the hormone is insoluble in ethanol or acetone, but stable toward these solvents, the organic adsorbents can be dissolved, while the hormone is obtained as an insoluble residue. The hormone is eluted from the inorganic adsorbents by slightly alkaline solutions (96). It has also been adsorbed by charcoal and eluted by phenol (92).

The urinary gonadotropin is precipitated by saturation with ammonium sulfate, not by salicylsulfonic acid (97). The protein nature of the hormone is indicated by its inactivation by proteolytic enzymes; it is inactivated by pepsin, and by trypsin, but not by peptidases (98). The purified hormone contains 8.4% nitrogen, and 18% carbohydrate (99); it is free of phosphorus and sulfur (99,100). Its molecular weight is 100,000; its carbohydrate component consists mainly of hexosamine-digalactose (101).

There has also been found in the serum of pregnant mares a chorionic gonadotropin which contains 25% carbohydrate; its isoelectric point is near pH 2.6 and its molecular weight is 60,000–80,000 (99). Since the chorionic gonadotropin is inactivated by salivary amylase, it has been concluded that its carbohydrate component is somehow essential for the hormonal activity (102).

F. Other Protein Hormones. The hormone of the *parathyroid glands* has been extracted from the organs by dilute hydrochloric acid. Other proteins are precipitated from the extract by adjusting the reaction to the isoelectric point pH 5, whereupon the hormone is then salted out at this pH (103). The hormone has also been precipitated from the acid extract by acetone (104). It is not denatured by hot dilute hydrochloric acid. One unit of the hormone is defined as the amount which raises the blood calcium level of 10 kg. dogs by 1 mg.% in 16 hours. Pure preparations contain approximately 300 units per milligram nitrogen. The hormone seems to be split by proteolytic enzymes, for it is ineffective when administered orally.

It is not quite clear whether or not the term hormone should be applied to *renin*, the so-called renal hormone. Renin is an enzyme-like substance, which converts hypertensinogen into hypertensin (105). Hypertensinogen is a fraction of the plasma globulins produced in the liver (106), while hypertensin is a polypeptide prepared in crystals (107) which is involved in the regulation of blood pressure (108). The behavior of hypertensin (angiotonin) toward proteolytic enzymes is similar to that of synthetic tyrosyl-lysyl-glutamyl-tyrosine (109). Renin is probably a proteolytic enzyme (110), since the conversion of hypertensinogen into hypertensin is also brought about by pepsin (111). Renin is, however, not identical with the renal cathepsin (112). Hypertensin is inactivated by another enzyme called hypertensinase (113).

Secretin, a protein derivative from the duodenal mucosa, is assumed to be an activator of the secretion of pancreatic juice. Secretin is split by trypsin; it is precipitated by 50% saturation with ammonium sulfate and contains 13.8% nitrogen (114). The molecular weight of secretin is less than 1800; the molecule contains no free amino groups (115).

Since secretin is not formed in an endocrine gland, it is doubtful whether it should be called a hormone. The same criticism has to be voiced with regard to the other so-called hormones from the stomach, the intestines, and other organs. Although the presence of these hormones has been asserted on the grounds of their physiological action, it has not yet been proved by chemical methods (116).

G. Action of Protein Hormones. It must be admitted that we are not yet able to explain satisfactorily the hormonal action of the protein hormones. No special prosthetic group has been discovered in any of them except for thyroglobulin. Possibly the carbohydrate group of the gonadotropic factors is somehow responsible for their hormone action. Most of the protein hormones act on a single organ or organ system. We have to assume that the protein hormone is bound by the cells of the organ in which it causes some change. Thus, the thyrotropic hormone is certainly bound by thyroid cells, the adrenocorticotropic hormone by cells of the adrenal cortex. Since we do not know of any special groups in the protein hormones, complementary shape of hormone and of organ protein has to be taken into consideration as a possible means of achieving the mutual combination. In other words, thyroid cells may contain a antithyrotropic grouping able to fix the thyrotropic hormone, which has been transported to the gland by the blood plasma. Similarly the proteins of the gonads might combine with gonadotropic hormones by means of antigonadotropic groupings of their molecules. Such a combination of hormone and organ has not yet been proved; it is a tentative speculation. Possibly combination of the hormone with the cells of the organ where it acts suffices to give rise to the action observed.

From the description of the protein hormones it is evident that most of them are proteins of low molecular weight. Many of them are resistant to acids, organic solvents, and heat. This indicates that their molecules are rigid units with a definite internal structure. The small molecular size enables the hormone molecules to penetrate cellular membranes, so that they can be released from the site of their production in case of necessity and can also penetrate the site of their action. It is obvious, however, that all this requires experimental confirmation and that we are still far from having an understanding of hormonal action.

References

1. J. B. Collip, *Ann. Intern. Med.* **9,** 150 (1936).
2. B. Zondek, F. Sulman, *Proc. Exptl. Biol. Med.* **37,** 343 (1947).
3. A. Bussard, *Ann. inst. Pasteur* **75,** 14 (1948).
4. H. Selye, C. Bachmann, D. L. Thompson, J. B. Collip, *Proc. Exptl. Biol. Med.* **31,** 1113 (1934).
5. E. P. Reineke, *Vitamins and Hormones* **4,** 207 (1946).

5a. C. H. Harington, The Thyroid Gland. Oxford Univ. Press, London, 1938.
6. A. Oswald, *Z. physiol. Chem.* **27,** 14 (1899).
7. M. Heidelberger, W. Palmer, *J. Biol. Chem.* **101,** 433 (1933).
8. G. L. Foster, *J. Biol. Chem.* **83,** 345 (1929).
9. C. H. Harington, S. S. Randall, *Biochem. J.* **25,** 1032 (1931).
10. Y. Derrien, R. Michel, K. O. Pedersen, J. Roche, *Biochim. et Biophys. Acta* **3,** 436 (1949).
10a. H. P. Lundgren, J. W. Williams, *J. Physic. Chem.* **43,** 989 (1939).
11. I. Snapper, A. Grünbaum, *Brit. J. Exptl. Path.* **17,** 361 (1936).
12. P. von Mutzenbecher, *Z. physiol. Chem.* **261,** 253 (1939).
13. E. P. Reineke, C. W. Turner, *J. Biol. Chem.* **161,** 613 (1945).
14. J. Roche, R. Michel, R. Lafon, *Biochim. et Biophys. Acta* **1,** 453 (1947).
15. C. H. Harington, *J. Chem. Soc.* **1944,** 193.
16. J. Wolff, I. L. Chaikoff, *J. Biol. Chem.* **174,** 555 (1948).
17. E. B. Astwood, *Harvey Lectures* **40,** 195 (1945).
17a. H. Jensen, The Chemistry and Physiology of Insulin. Am. Ass. Adv. Sci. Washington, 1944.
18. F. G. Banting, C. H. Best, *J. Lab. Clin. Med.* **7,** 251, 464 (1922). C. H. Best and D. Scott *J. Biol. Chem.* **57,** 709 (1923).
19. H. Dudley, *Biochem. J.* **18,** 147 (1924).
20. J. J. Abel, E. M. K. Geiling, *J. Pharmacol. Exptl. Therap.* **31,** 65 (1927).
21. V. du Vigneaud, H. Jensen, O. Wintersteiner, *J. Pharmacol. Exptl. Therap.* **32,** 267 (1938).
22. C. H. Harington, *Biochem. J.* **23,** 384 (1929).
23. N. McCormick, E. Noble, *J. Biol. Chem.* **59,** XXIX (1924).
24. M. Gutfreund, *Biochem. J.* **42,** 544 (1948).
25. G. L. Miller, K. J. I. Andersson, *J. Biol. Chem.* **144,** 459 (1942).
25a. J. L. Hall, *J. Biol. Chem.* **139,** 175 (1941).
26. H. Jensen, D. Wintersteiner, *J. Biol. Chem.* **98,** 281 (1938).
26a. E. Brand, *Ann. N. Y. Acad. Sci.* **47,** 187 (1946).
27. K. Freudenberg, W. Dirscherl, M. Eyer, *Z. physiol. Chem.* **187,** 89 (1930).
27a. K. G. Stern, A. White, *J. Biol. Chem.* **117,** 95 (1937).
28. V. du Vigneaud *et al., J. Biol. Chem.* **94,** 233 (1931).
29. K. Freudenberg, T. Wegmann, *Z. physiol. Chem.* **233,** 159 (1935).
30. F. Sanger, *Nature* **160,** 295 (1946).
31. M. B. Glendening, D. M. Greenberg, H. Fraenkel-Conradt, *J. Biol. Chem.* **167,** 125 (1947).
32. J. A. V. Butler, E. C. Dodds, D. M. P. Philipp, J. M. L. Stephen, *Biochem. J.* **41,** XXIII (1947); **44,** 224 (1949).
32a. J. A. V. Butler, *Abstracts 1st Intern. Congr. Biochem.*, p. 124 (1949).
33. F. Sanger, *Biochem. J.* **39,** 507 (1946).
34. F. Sanger, *Nature* **162,** 491 (1948).
34a. F. Sanger, *Ann. Repts. on Progress Chem. Chem. Soc. London* **45,** 283 (1949).
35. D. A. Scott, A. M. Fisher, *Biochem. J.* **29,** 1048 (1935).
36. H. C. Hagedorn, B. N. Jensen, I. Wodstrup-Nielsen, *J. Am. Med. Assoc.* **106,** 177 (1936).
37. A. Rothen, B. F. Chow, R. O. Greep, H. B. van Dyke, *Cold Spring Harbor Symposia Quant. Biol.* **9,** 272 (1941).
37a. D. F. Waugh, *J. Am. Chem. Soc.* **68,** 247 (1946); **70,** 1850 (1948).
38. P. Wassermann, I. A. Mirsky, *Endocrinology* **31,** 115 (1942).
38a. C. A. Villee, A. B. Hastings, *J. Biol. Chem.* **181,** 131 (1949).

38*b*. W. C. Stadie, *Science* **110,** 550 (1949). C. R. Park, M. E. Krahl, *J. Biol. Chem.* **181,** 247 (1949).
39. E. W. Sutherland, F. C. Cori *et al.*, *J. Biol. Chem.* **175,** 663 (1948); **180,** 825 (1949).
40. J. J. Abel, *J. Pharmacol. Exptl. Therap.* **40,** 139 (1940).
41. J. G. Pierce, V. du Vigneaud, *J. Biol. Chem.* **182,** 359 (1950).
41*a*. H. van Dyke, B. F. Chow, R. O. Greep, A. Rothen, *J. Pharmacol. Exptl. Therap.* **74,** 190 (1942).
42. A. M. Potts, T. F. Gallagher, *J. Biol. Chem.* **154,** 349 (1944).
43. I. G. Farbenindustrie, German Pat. 550,935 (1932).
44. R. L. Stehle, *J. Biol. Chem.* **102,** 573 (1933).
45. O. Kamm *et al.*, *J. Am. Chem. Soc.* **50,** 513 (1928).
46. V. du Vigneaud *et al.*, *J. Biol. Chem.* **100,** XCIV (1938).
47. K. Freudenberg, E. Weiss, H. Biller, *Z. physiol. Chem.* **233,** 172 (1935).
48. J. B. Gulland, S. Randall, *Biochem. J.* **29,** 378 (1935).
49. B. Zondek, L. Krohn, *Naturwissenschaften* **20,** 134 (1932).
50. F. G. Dietel, *Klin. Wochschr.* **13,** 796 (1934).
51. A. Jores, *Z. Exptl. Med.* **94,** 289, 293 (1934).
52. E. Glaser, O. Haempel, *Naturwissenschaften* **19,** 1021 (1931).
53. C. H. Li, H. M. Evans, Monograph on Hormone Conference, Am. Ass. Adv. Sci., Washington (1945).
54. C. H. Li, H. M. Evans, *Vitamins and Hormones* **5,** 198 (1947). C. H. Li, *Ann. Rev. Biochem.* **16,** 291 (1947).
55. H. L. Fevold, M. Lee, F. L. Hisaw, E. J. Cohn, *Endocrinology* **26,** 299 (1940).
55*a*. B. Houssay, *Ann. Rev. Biochem.* **4,** 288 (1935).
56. C. H. Li, C. Kalman, H. M. Evans, *Arch. Biochem.* **23,** 512 (1949).
56*a*. P. M. Cotes, E. Reid, F. G. Young, *Nature* **164,** 209 (1949).
57. H. M. Evans, R. Cornish, M. E. Simpson, *Proc. Exptl. Biol. Med.* **27,** 101 (1929).
58. L. Hewitt, *Biochem. J.* **23,** 718 (1929).
59. H. B. van Dyke, Z. Wallen-Lawrence, *J. Pharmacol. Exptl. Therap.* **40,** 413 (1929).
60. M. Reiss, A. Hochwald, H. Druckrey, *Endokrinologie* **13,** 1 (1933).
61. H. Teel, *Science* **69,** 405 (1929).
62. C. H. Li, H. M. Evans, M. F. Simpson, *J. Biol. Chem.* **159,** 353 (1945).
63. A. E. Wilhelmi, J. B. Fishman, J. Russell, *J. Biol. Chem.* **176,** 735 (1948).
64. C. H. Li, H. M. Evans, M. E. Simpson, *Science* **108,** 624 (1948).
64*a*. E. L. Smith, D. M. Brown, J. B. Fishman, A. E. Wilhelmi, *J. Biol. Chem.* **177,** 305 (1949).
65. I. Rowlands, A. Parkes, *Biochem. J.* **28,** 1829 (1934).
66. A. Loeser, *Klin. Wochschr.* **11,** 1271 (1932).
67. L. S. Ciereszko, *J. Biol. Chem.* **160,** 585 (1945).
68. A. White, in Chemistry and Physiology of Hormones. Science Press, Lancaster, Pennsylvania, 1945, p. 1.
69. R. K. Anderson, H. L. Alt, *Am. J. Physiol.* **119,** 67 (1937).
70. H. Eitel, H. A. Krebs, *Klin. Wochschr.* **12,** 615 (1933).
71. C. H. Li, H. M. Evans, M. Simpson, *J. Biol Chem.* **149,** 413 (1943).
72. G. Sayers, A. White, C. N. H. Long, *J. Biol. Chem.* **149,** 425 (1943).
72*a*. C. H. Li, *Abstracts Ist Intern. Congr. Biochem.*, p. 386 (1949).
73. C. H. Li, H. M. Evans, *J. Biol. Chem.* **146,** 627 (1942).
74. R. W. Bates, O. Riddle, *J. Pharmacol. Exptl. Therap.* **55,** 365 (1935).
75. A. White, R. W. Bonsnes, C. N. H. Long, *J. Biol. Chem.* **143,** 447 (1942).

76. A. White, *Physiol. Revs.* **26,** 574 (1946).
77. H. Jensen, M. E. Simpson, S. Tolksdorf, H. M. Evans, *Endocrinology* **25,** 57 (1939).
78. R. O. Greep, H. B. van Dyke, B. F. Chow, *J. Biol. Chem.* **133,** 289 (1940).
79. H. L. Fevold, *J. Biol. Chem.* **128,** 83 (1939).
80. Z. Wallen-Lawrence, *J. Pharmacol. Exptl. Therap.* **51,** 263 (1934).
81. B. F. Chow, H. B. van Dyke, R. O. Greep, A. Rothen, T. Shedlovsky, *Endocrinology* **30,** 650 (1942).
82. C. H. Li, M. E. Simpson, H. M. Evans, *J. Am. Chem. Soc.* **64,** 367 (1942).
82*a*. C. H. Li, personal communication.
82*b*. H. Fraenkel-Conradt, M. E. Simpson, H. M. Evans, *Proc. Soc. Exptl. Biol. Med.* **45,** 627 (1940).
83. C. H. Li, *Federation Proc.* **8,** 219 (1949).
84. B. Zondek, *Klin. Wochschr.* **8,** 157 (1929); B. Zondek, F. Sulman, *Vitamins and Hormones* **3,** 297 (1945).
85. B. Zondek, *Deut. med. Wochschr.* **56,** 300 (1930).
86. H. L. Fevold, F. L. Hisaw, *Am. J. Physiol.* **109,** 655 (1934).
87. H. M. Evans *et al.*, *Endocrinology* **16,** 601, 607 (1934).
88. J. B. Collip, H. Selye, D. L. Thompson, J. E. Williamson, *Proc. Soc. Exptl. Biol. Med.* **30,** 665 (1933).
89. F. A. Askew, A. S. Parkes, *Biochem. J.* **27,** 1495 (1933).
90. H. B. van Dyke, Z. Wallen-Lawrence, *J. Pharmacol. Exptl. Therap.* **47,** 163 (1934).
91. G. Gey, G. Seeger, L. Hellman, *Science* **88,** 306 (1938).
92. S. Katzman, E. A. Doisy, *J. Biol. Chem.* **106,** 125 (1934).
93. S. Katzman, E. A. Doisy, *J. Biol. Chem.* **98,** 739 (1932).
94. L. Davy, E. L. Sevringhaus, *Proc. Soc. Exptl. Biol. Med.* **30,** 1422 (1933); cited by D. L. Thomson and J. B. Collip, *Ann. Rev. Biochem.* **3,** 225 (1934).
95. C. Funk, P. Zefirow, *Biochem. J.* **26,** 619 (1932).
96. M. Reiss, F. Haurowitz, *Z. exptl. Med.* **68,** 371 (1929).
97. F. Dickens, *Biochem. J.* **241,** 507 (1930).
98. M. Reiss, A. Schaeffner, F. Haurowitz, *Endokrinologie* **8,** 22 (1931).
99. H. P. Lundgren, S. Gurin, C. Bachman, D. W. Wilson, *J. Biol. Chem.* **142,** 367 (1942); **128,** 525 (1939); **133,** 467, 477 (1940).
100. F. Marshall, *Nature* **130,** 170 (1932).
101. S. Gurin, C. Bachman, D. W. Wilson, *J. Biol. Chem.* **133,** 467, 477 (1940).
102. J. S. Evans, J. Hauschildt, *J. Biol. Chem.* **145,** 335 (1942).
103. J. B. Collip, *J. Biol. Chem.* **63,** 395 (1925).
104. M. V. L'Heureux, H. M. Tepperman, A. E. Wilhelmi, *J. Biol. Chem.* **168,** 167 (1947).
105. P. Edman, U. S. von Euler, E. Jorpes, O. Sjöstrand, *J. Physiol.* **101,** 284 (1942).
106. I. H. Page *et al.*, *Am. J. Physiol.* **135,** 214 (1941).
107. I. H. Page, O. M. Helmer, *J. Exptl. Med.* **71,** 29 (1940).
108. H. Goldblatt, *Physiol. Revs.* **27,** 120 (1947).
109. A. A. Plentl, I. H. Page, *J. Biol. Chem.* **163,** 49 (1946).
110. O. Schales, *J. Am. Chem. Soc.* **64,** 561 (1942).
111. H. Croxatto, R. Croxatto, *Rev. soc. argentina biol.* **17,** 439 (1941).
112. O. Schales, M. Holden, S. S. Schales, *Arch. Biochem.* **6,** 165 (1945).
113. A. A. Plentl, I. H. Page, *J. Biol. Chem.* **147,** 143 (1943).
114. J. Mellanby, *Proc. Roy. Soc. London* **B111,** 429 (1932).
115. G. Agren, O. Wilander, *Biochem. Z.* **259,** 365 (1933).
116. H. Jensen, *Ann. Rev. Biochem.* **13,** 347 (1944).

CHAPTER XIV

Role of Proteins in Immunological Reactions

A. Antigens. Immunity was first observed to arise as a result of bacterial infection. Human beings who had recovered from certain infectious diseases became resistant toward a repeated infection by the same microbe. It was found that this resistance was due to the capacity of the blood serum to specifically agglutinate, dissolve, or render susceptible to the attack of phagocytes the bacteria whose infection had been overcome. In order to explain these phenomena Ehrlich postulated the presence of *antibodies* in the immune serum and defined those substances which were responsible for the formation of antibodies as *antigens*.

In 1897 it was demonstrated by Kraus (1) that soluble substances, in addition to bacteria and cells, can also act as antigens. Antigens are precipitated by their corresponding antibodies. This test, the *precipitin test*, is the simplest and sometimes the only method applicable for differentiating between species-specific proteins. Its great importance for protein chemistry is obvious.

It was originally believed that protein antigens are essentially different from bacterial or cellular antigens. It was later found, however, that bacteria and cells are not uniform antigens, but that each bacterium and each cell consists of a mosaic of different substances, many of them antigenic, others nonantigenic. Most of the proteins found in body fluids and in somatic cells or bacteria are antigenic. Carbohydrates, lipids, and other substances are not antigenic, in general, *i.e.*, they are not able to induce the formation of antibodies.

It has long been realized that some small molecules such as those of iodine, picryl chloride, and other nitro compounds, when injected parenterally, are able to cause a condition of allergy, due to the formation of antibodies against derivatives of the substances injected. All these substances readily combine with proteins *in vitro;* it is assumed that they also combine with proteins at the site of injection and that the conjugated proteins thus formed are the true antigens (2). Similar results have been obtained with lipids, which also act as antigens when mixed with protein solutions. The antigen precursors of low molecular weight have been called proantigens (3) and it is assumed that proteins are necessary for the conversion of proantigens into true antigens.

Since most proteins are digested by pepsin or trypsin, it is understandable that antigens lose their antigenicity if administered orally. It is necessary to inject them *parenterally* in order to produce antibodies.

Each of the natural proteins is specific as an antigen. Antibodies produced by the injection of one protein give precipitates only with the same protein, not with other proteins. Only in those cases where the test antigen is very similar to the injected antigen are cross reactions observed. Thus antibodies to horse serum proteins are also able to precipitate donkey serum protein. Similarly ovalbumin from ducks' egg is precipitated by antibodies to ovalbumin from hens' egg (4). On the other hand, myoglobin is serologically quite different from hemoglobin although both substances contain the same hemin (5). Evidently the specificity is due to the protein component and not to the hemin. Hemoglobin of man and of the beef are serologically different; however a slight relationship is indicated by inhibition tests (6).

Proteins possess not only species specificity but also organ specificity. The proteins of blood serum differ serologically from the hemoglobin or from muscular proteins of the same animal. However, some of the globulin fractions separated by fractionation with ammonium sulfate are very similar and can hardly be distinguished from each other by the precipitin test (7). Ferritin (see Chapter XI, Sect. D) is species-specific, but has no organ specificity (8).

It was found by Landsteiner (2) that the specificity of proteins is not due to the protein molecule as a whole, but is associated only with certain *chemical groups* of the molecule. This was proved by coupling proteins with different chemical groups. The preferred method employed by Landsteiner was the coupling of proteins with diazo compounds. The advantages of this method are: (*1*) diazo derivatives of practically all substances can be prepared, so that any desired groups can be linked to the protein molecule; and (*2*) the coupling of diazo compounds with proteins takes place at 0° at slightly alkaline reaction of pH 9, where most proteins are not denatured. The efficiency of this method is demonstrated by many examples, some of which will be discussed.

In order to determine whether antibodies are adjusted specifically to optical isomers, Landsteiner coupled proteins with D- and L-tartaric acid. Diazo compounds of these acids were prepared by condensing them with nitroaniline, reducing the nitrotartranilic acid to the amino compound and diazotizing the latter:

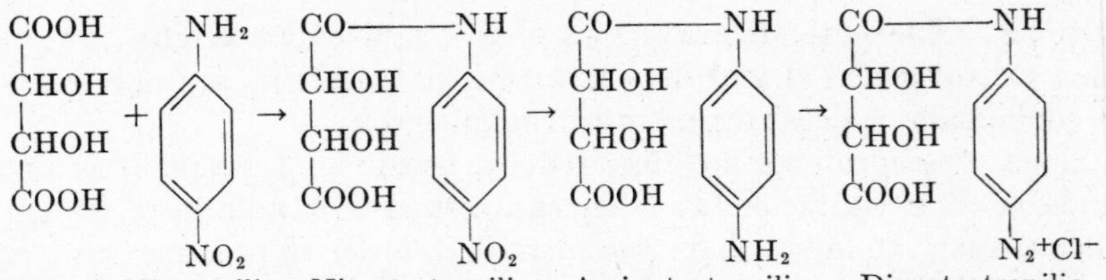

COOH·CHOH·CHOH·COOH + NH_2–C_6H_4–NO_2 → CO–NH–C_6H_4–NO_2 (CHOH·CHOH·COOH) → CO–NH–C_6H_4–NH_2 (CHOH·CHOH·COOH) → CO–NH–C_6H_4–$N_2^+Cl^-$ (CHOH·CHOH·COOH)

Tartaric acid · Nitroaniline · Nitrotartranilic acid · Aminotartranilic acid · Diazotartranilic acid

The diazo compounds combine readily with the tyrosine and histidine molecules of the protein, forming colored azo proteins:

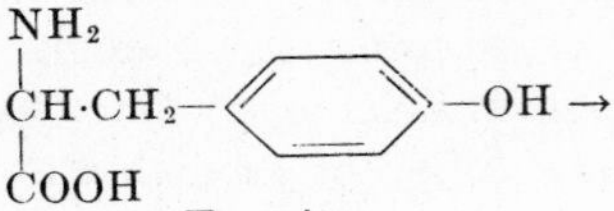

NH_2·CH(CH_2–C_6H_4–OH)·COOH →

Tyrosine

NH_2·CH(CH_2–C_6H_2(OH)(N=N–C_6H_4–NH·CO·CHOH·CHOH·COOH)$_2$)·COOH

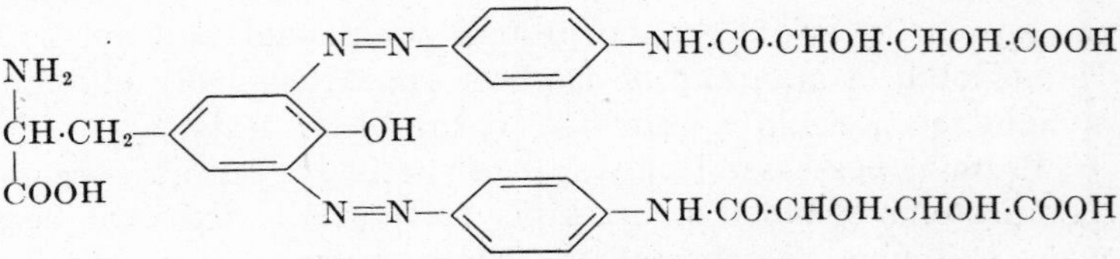

Bis (-azotartranilic acid)-tyrosine

In this experiment Landsteiner found that D- and L-tartranilazoproteins act differently as antigens. Antibodies to one of them do not react with the antigen responsible for the other (9). Similarly leucylglycine and glycylleucine were differentiated from each other (10). In another series of experiments it was shown, that *o*-, *m*-, and *p*-aminophenyl sulfonic acid, when their diazo derivatives are coupled with proteins, give quite different antigens (11). It is evident from these and many other examples that the specificity of the artificially conjugated proteins depends mainly on the chemical groups introduced into the molecule. Thus, antibodies to arsanilazo horse serum protein are able to precipitate arsanilazoovalbumin and other arsanilazo proteins. By the chemical treatment the proteins lose their species specificity. If a large number of azo groups is introduced into the horse serum globulin molecule, it is not precipitated by antibodies to horse serum globulin. Similarly the species specificity of serum globulin is lost, when its molecule is iodinated or acetylated after a certain minimum number of iodine atoms or acetyl groups has been introduced into the protein molecule (12).

Not all the groups which may be introduced into protein molecules have the capacity to alter the serological specificity and to give rise to the formation of specific antibodies. It is only *polar groups*, chiefly acidic groups such as —COOH, —SO_3H, —AsO_3H_2 (2), or basic groups, such as quaternary ammonium groups (13), which determine the serological specificity of antigens. Evidently the determinant groups of the natural proteins are also polar groups. Although we do not yet know the kind of chemical group responsible for the specificity of natural proteins, it seems that this specificity is due not to a single type of group but to a specific arrangement of different polar groups on the surface of the protein molecule (12).

The antigenic properties of proteins are destroyed when the proteins are split by proteolytic enzymes. Denaturation results in a change or a partial loss of the original antigenicity of the native protein. Antibodies against native ovalbumin react only weakly with denatured ovalbumin (14). Injection of denatured ovalbumin leads to the formation of antibodies which react specifically with denatured ovalbumin (15). On the other hand no significant differences were found in the antigenic activity of horse serum globulin in the native and denatured state (15*a*). It is very difficult to determine quantitatively the antigenicity of denatured proteins because they tend to form aggregates and, thus, to increase the amount of the precipitate. The lower antigenicity of denatured proteins is probably due to the fact that they are hydrolyzed by proteolytic enzymes more readily than native proteins (see page 127) so that they are split in the organism before they arrive at the site of antibody formation.

Gelatin, which is prepared by the heat treatment of collagen, is nonantigenic, a fact which was originally attributed to this protein's lack of tyrosine. However, gelatin does not acquire antigenic properties even when it is coupled with tyrosine (16), with diazo compounds (17), or with iodine (18). There are several reasons for the nonantigenicity of gelatin: (*1*) it is a heat-treated denatured protein and, accordingly, has no definite internal structure (19); (*2*) it is not deposited in the sites of antibody formation, but is rapidly excreted from the organism (17,18); (*3*) gelatin contains large amounts of glycine. Since glycine contains no side chain in the α-position, the peptide chain of glycyl peptides can rotate freely around the longitudinal axis and can in this way suffer distortion (20). Accordingly, the peptide chain of gelatin is flexible and does not possess the rigid structure which is one of the prerequisites for the serological specificity of proteins.

The essentiality of a definite, rigid structure for the antigenicity of proteins is demonstrated by the loss of this property when proteins are exposed to extremely high pressures. Serum proteins lose their capacity to act as antigens if they are exposed to a pressure of 6000 atmospheres (21).

Although the serological specificity of proteins is a very characteristic property, which remains unchanged under normal conditions, it can be altered by combining the protein with foreign molecules or by the formation of complexes of two or more proteins. If serum globulin is cautiously heated in the presence of serum albumin, a complex with new serological properties is formed (22). Similarly the specificity of proteins is changed by iodination (23,24). The specificity of the iodinated proteins is due to their diiodotyrosine groups. Antibodies to these proteins do not react, however, with thyroglobulin, the iodoprotein of the thyroid gland (25). This indicates that the diiodo groups of thyroglobulin are situated in the interior of the large thyroglobulin molecule and that they are not accessible to the diiodotyrosine antibodies. Obviously only those groups of the antigen molecule which are accessible and reactive can be determinant for its specificity.

Summarizing we can say that the antigenic property of a molecule is dependent on the following conditions: (*1*) the molecule must contain a protein as a carrier of determinant groups; (*2*) the protein must have a certain minimum size; (*3*) its internal structure must be rigid and must not change with time; and (*4*) the protein must carry on its surface a number of strongly polar groups.

The nonantigenicity or very weak antigenicity of insulin and of many pituitary hormones is probably due to their low molecular weight. We still have no idea why the yellow enzymes (flavoproteins) are not antigenic (26). Other enzymes, such as urease, are very active as antigens.

The protein component of the antigen is not necessary for its combination with the antibody. Antibodies against arsanilazo protein also combine with arsanilic acid or with arsanilazotyrosine (27,28). Moreover, the reaction between sulfanilazo protein and the corresponding antibody is inhibited by smaller molecules containing the same phenylsulfonic acid group (2). They are called haptens, because they are bound by the antibody (Greek: haptein = to bind, to hold). Sometimes haptens even give precipitates with the corresponding antibodies, but they differ from true antigens in that they are not able to induce the formation of antibodies when injected parenterally.

B. Antibodies. The presence of antibodies is revealed by their specific reaction with the antigen. Antibodies to cellular antigens or to bacteria are able to agglutinate them or to cause cytolysis or bacteriolysis. Antibodies to soluble proteins give precipitates with these proteins. Toxins are detoxified by combination with their antibodies. All these phenomena are manifestations of essentially the same reaction, the *combination of antibody with antigen.* If whole cells or bacteria are used as immunizing agents, there are formed a multitude of antibodies directed toward the different antigenic substances present in the injected antigen complex. The situation is much simpler if soluble substances such as pure proteins are used as antigens. In such a case only antibodies against a uniform antigen are formed.

The early workers in the field of immunology found that the antibodies reside in the *globulin fraction* of the immune sera, an observation which led to the assumption that antibodies are more or less loosely attached to the serum globulins. If the immune sera are fractionated by means of ammonium sulfate the antibodies are found mainly in the γ-globulin fraction (29). Further fractionation of the globulins with ethanol reveals the presence of antibodies in the subfractions II-1,2 and 3 and in fraction III-1 (29*a*). Some of the antibodies are precipitated as euglobulins upon dialysis against distilled water, while others are found to occur in the pseudoglobulin fraction (29*b*). Immune sera generally contain larger amounts of γ-globulins than those found in normal sera. In addition to the α-, β-, and γ-globulins normally present in the sera, immune serum occasionally contains a new fraction, T, which migrates between the β- and the γ-fraction in electrophoresis. The T-fraction also contains antibodies (30,31). The blood sera of many newborn animals such as foals (32) or rabbits (33) are poor in globulins; this agrees with the finding that antibodies are absent from the sera of newborn animals (34).

Antibodies closely resemble the γ-globulins of normal serum in their physicochemical properties. In general, their isoelectric point is near pH 6 (35) and in the blood of rabbits and monkeys their molecular weight is 157,000; in that of horses, sheep, or beef it is 920,000 (36). Hydrolysis of the antibody fractions furnishes the same amino acids that are found in hydrolyzates of normal γ-globulins (37). Normal rabbit globulins and rabbit antibodies had the same amino acid sequence consisting of aspartic acid, valine, leucine, alanine with a terminal amino group at the alanine molecule (37*a*).

The question of whether antibodies are serum globulins or are bound to serum globulins, can be solved by employing specific methods for the purification of antibodies. These methods consist, essentially, of two steps: (*1*) formation of an antigen–antibody precipitate; and (*2*) dissociation of the precipitate and isolation of pure antibody. The first successful experiments of this kind were performed by Felton (38), who precipitated antigenic polysaccharides of pneumococci by the homologous immune sera and dissociated the precipitate by treating it with barium hydroxide; the antibodies were dissolved while the barium salts of the polysaccharides were insoluble. Heidelberger and coworkers succeeded in dissociating similar precipitates by treating them with concentrated solutions of sodium chloride (39,40). When azo protein precipitates were treated, in the author's laboratory, with dilute acids in the presence of neutral salts, most of the antibody was split off, while the antigen and an undissociated portion of the antibody remained undissolved (41). The antibody solutions obtained by these procedures contain globulins of the same type as described above. Since more than 90% of these globulins are precipitated by the homologous antigen, there is convincing evidence that these globulins are indeed identical with the true antibodies.

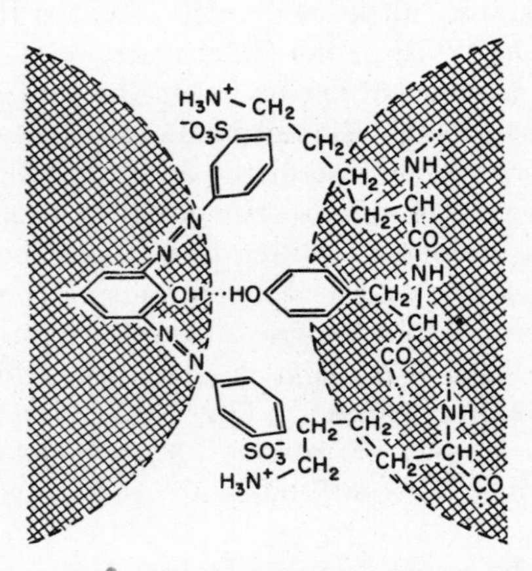

FIG. 46. Combination of *m*-azophenylsulfonic acid protein (left) with antibody (right) (44*a*).

Antibodies differ from normal serum globulins, as well as among themselves, by their specificity. Each antibody combines only with the antigen responsible for immunization, and with no other. In an effort to explain this specific property of antibodies to combine with the homologous antigen, Breinl and the author have advanced a theory according to which *antibodies are globulins whose molecules are adapted complementarily to the determinant groups of the antigen molecules* (42). It is contended that the polar groups of the antigens interfere with the formation of globulins from their component amino acids, with the result that the normal process of globulin formation is modified and globulins of a different shape are produced (42–44).

The complementariness of the antibody surface is most probably accomplished by a definite kind of folding of the peptide chains (45), and by the presence of ionic groups of the opposite sign in the bonding area of the antibody molecule (Fig. 46). Although the *site of formation* of the normal serum globulins is not certainly known, it is generally assumed that they arise in the reticuloendothelial or macrophage cells of the liver, the bone marrow, and the spleen (46). It was found that the injection into rabbits of arsanil-azo-globulin, a powerful antigen, resulted in a deposition of most of the antigen in the liver and the bone marrow of the injected animals (28). When phosphovitellin containing P^{32} was injected into rabbits, it was rapidly bound by the liver and the lung (46*a*). This supports the view that these organs are fundamentally involved in the process of antibody formation.

While the blood plasma of rabbits and horses contains large amounts of *soluble antibodies*, that of other animals such as the guinea pig have only slight amounts of precipitable antibodies, even after these animals have been sensitized by the injection of soluble antigens. The allergic state of such animals is demonstrated by an intensive anaphylactic shock, when they are reinjected with the same antigen. The *antibodies of animals of this type*, apparently, do not pass into the blood plasma. They belong to the *insoluble proteins*. It seems that these, too, are complementarily adapted to the antigen molecules and combine selectively with them (47). Antibodies have also been extracted from lymphatic cells and it has been proposed that a portion of the antibodies arises in these cells (48,49,49*a*) or in plasma cells (49*b*). It is the author's belief that antibodies can be formed in *all cells* in which proteins are formed, provided the cells are able to bind the molecules of the injected antigen (49*c*).

From the results of experiments with amino acids containing N^{15}, it appears that the formation of antibodies in the organism takes place at approximately the same rate as the formation of normal serum globulins; the half life of the antibody globulins is about 2 weeks (50). When rabbits were injected with antibodies to bacterial polysaccharides and N^{15}-amino acids, no uptake of N^{15} by the preformed antibodies was observed (50). On the other hand, however, C^{14}-leucine was demonstrated to be incorporated into passively administered antibodies in similar experiments (51). It is not yet clear, therefore, whether the antibody molecules undergo some rearrangement in the organism of the injected animal.

The formation of antibodies, just as that of other proteins, also depends on the nutritional state of the organism; the quantity of antibody formed is much higher in well fed animals than in those maintained on a poor diet (52). In frogs the antibody titer of the blood depends on the body temperature; it is much higher at 20 than at 8°C.; at low temperatures the antibodies are adsorbed on the liver cells so that the antibody titer of the blood is lowered (53).

In order to explain the *specificity of antibodies* it was asserted by some authors that the determinant group of the antigen molecule passes into the antibody molecule and that antibodies are merely globulins which carry this determinant group (54). This was definitely disproved by the finding that antibodies to iodo proteins, bromo proteins, arsanilazo proteins, and phospho proteins contain no iodine, bromine, arsenic, and phosphorus, respectively (55). The assumption that antibodies contain the determinant group of the antigen is also irreconcilable with the fact that one molecule of an antigen induces the formation of a large number of antibody molecules; if bacteria are injected as an antigen, the amount of antibody formed is approximately 600 times as large as the amount required for the agglutination of the injected bacteria (56).

It had originally been assumed that each antigen gives rise to the formation of a single type of antibody, complementarily adapted to the determinant group of the antigen molecule. If we inject antigens containing two or more different types of determinant groups per molecule, different types of antibodies are obtained. The injection of a globulin into whose molecules iodine and azophenylarsonic acid has been introduced, leads to the formation of antibodies against the diiodotyrosine group and other antibodies against the azophenylarsonic acid group (57). The two types of antibodies are separated by precipitating the first of them with iodoovalbumin, the second one by arsanilazoovalbumin. Addition of iodoarsanilazoovalbumin gives no further precipitate.

On the other hand, injection of arsanil-sheep serum globulin induces the formation of at least three types of antibodies: (*1*) anti-arsanil, (*2*) anti-sheep, and (*3*) antiarsanil-sheep (58). The last of these antibodies is precipitated by arsanil-sheep serum globulin, but not by arsanilazoovalbumin, nor by sheep serum globulin. It is evident from these experiments that the specificity of the antibody molecules depends on the arrangement of the determinant groups of the antigen molecule; if an antigen (A + B) is injected which contains the determinant groups A and B in separated positions on its surface, antibodies of the types anti-A and anti-B will be formed, but no antibodies of the type anti-AB; if A and B are adjacent, then anti-AB will be formed in addition to anti-A and anti-B (58*a*) (see Figs. 47 and 48).

It is evident from these findings that *immune serum will inevitably contain a variety of antibodies*, even if a single type of antigen is used for immunization. The *multiplicity of antibodies* is due not only to the fact that they are complementarily adapted to different portions of the antigen molecule, but also to their somewhat imperfect adaptation. Since antibody molecules are built up of amino acids and since the peptide chains cannot be distorted beyond a certain limit, the complementary adaptation of the antibody molecule to the antigen molecule will approach being, but will never really be, perfect (see Fig. 49). In

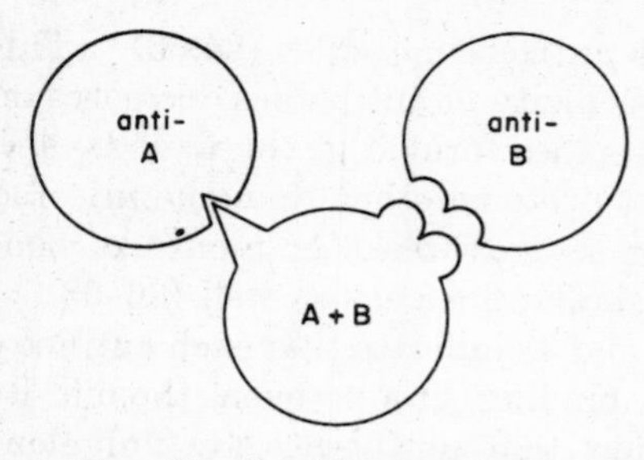

FIG. 47. Combination of antigen and antibody. A and B are two different determinant groups of the antigen (A + B).

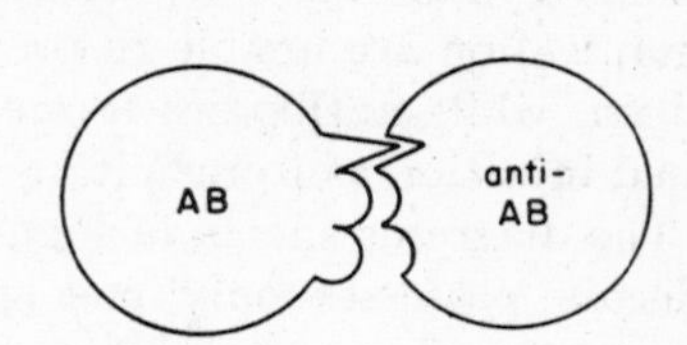

FIG. 48. Combination of antigen and antibody. AB is an antigen containing the two determinant groups A and B in juxtaposition.

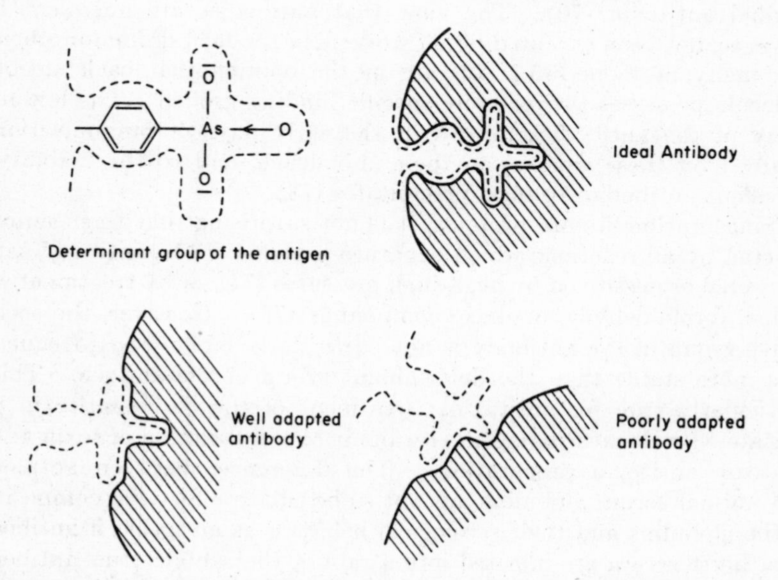

FIG. 49. Determinant phenylarsonic acid groups of an antigen and different types of antibodies.

other words, the immune serum will contain well adapted and poorly adapted antibody molecules (13,59–62). Therefore, even crystalline protein antigens such as ovalbumin give rise to the production of more than one type of antibody (62).

It seems that all intermediates between normal serum globulins and well adapted antibodies are present in immune sera (63). Some authors go so far as to assume that all globulins of an immune serum are antibodies, *i.e.*, are structurally adapted to antigen molecules (64,65). This opinion is based on the fact that the specificity of antibodies decreases on prolonged immunization; actually antibodies formed in the first days of immunization are unable to precipitate proteins other than the injected antigen, while antibodies formed after several weeks or month of continued injection can precipitate other similar antigens as well (66–68).

The diagrams shown in Figures 47 and 48 indicate that each antibody molecule possesses only one specific binding group, even though its antigen may be multivalent. The view that antibodies are univalent (58,69) is in agreement with the observation that diphtheria antitoxin, whose molecular weight is 184,000, is split by pepsin into a fully active antitoxin (mol. wt. 98,000) and an inactive product; obviously the specific binding group is present only in one of the two halves of the original antitoxin (70). The view that antibodies are univalent has, however, not been accepted by all workers in the field of immunochemistry; many of them (45,71,72) are of the opinion that each antibody molecule possesses two or more specific binding groups. The low reactivity of the antibodies formed in the early days of immunization is ascribed by these workers to their univalence, and to the inability of univalent antibodies to form precipitates (73).

Since antibodies are proteins, it is not surprising that their action is affected by all reactions which denature proteins. The antibody action is lowered or destroyed by heat, high pressures (74), or by treatment with iodine, formaldehyde, or diazo compounds (75). However, the specific active group of the antibody is not particularly labile (15*a*); frequently it is more stable than the determinant group of the antigen. This is particularly true for antitoxins; treatment of the toxin–antitoxin precipitate with denaturing agents results in the destruction of toxin and in nontoxic antitoxin preparations. The differences between antibodies and normal serum globulins are not sufficient to affect the composition of the globulins and their serological behavior as antigens; if antibodies from horse serum are injected into a rabbit, the rabbit forms antibodies against normal horse serum globulin which also precipitate horse serum antibodies (76).

The formation of antibodies in the living organism too frequently is regarded as an abnormal phenomenon having nothing to do with the processes continually taking place in the normal organism. Antibody formation is, however, protein formation and we have no reason for assuming that antibodies arise by a process differing greatly from that by which proteins are synthesized (49*c*,77). The formation of proteins in the living cells will be discussed later (Chapter XVII). It may be anticipated, however, that this process probably takes place in two phases (49*c*): (*1*) the formation of a replica of the expanded protein template and (*2*) the folding of this two-dimensional replica to give a three-dimensional globular protein molecule. Antigens would interfere mainly with the second phase of protein formation. The polar groups of the antigen probably disturb the normal process of folding so that the globular particle formed will be adapted complementarily to the polar determinant groups of the antigen (49*c*). These determinant, polar groups of the antigen exert electrostatic forces which give rise to a "field effect" (78). The size of the determinant area of polar groups varies from antigen to antigen; since glycylleucine is serologically different from leucylglycine (see above, Sect. A) we have to conclude that the specificity of antibodies is not determined by single groups of the antigen, but by the whole area of adjacent polar groups; it is understandable for the same reasons that antibodies to a peptide are able to combine with the analogous peptamine (79):

$$\underset{\text{Peptide}}{H_2N\cdot R\cdot CO\cdot NH\cdot R\cdot COOH} \xrightarrow{-CO_2} \underset{\text{Peptamine}}{H_2N\cdot R\cdot CO\cdot NH\cdot RH}$$

Attempts have been made to synthesize antibodies *in vitro* by exposing normal serum γ-globulins to mild denaturing agents in the presence of an antigen (80). The denatured γ-globulins give, however, nonspecific precipitates with the antigens used in these experiments, so that no definite conclusions can be drawn concerning the *in vitro* synthesis of antibodies (81,82).

C. Combination of Antigens with Antibodies. All immunological reactions are based on the same primary reaction, the combination of antigen with antibody. Precipitation, agglutination, cytolysis, or other more complicated reactions may occur secondarily. The simplest of all the antigen–antibody reactions is the precipitation of a soluble antigen by the homologous antibody. If we use an antigen which is labeled by a colored group, by isotopes, or by an element which can be determined by chemical analysis, we are able to carry out quantitative analyses and to examine the composition of the precipitates under different conditions. Such analyses have been made by using labeled antigens such as hemoglobin, iodinated proteins, phosphoproteins, azo proteins, and hemocyanin.

The first analyses of this kind were carried out by Wu (83). Investigations with more refined methods demonstrated that the antibody/antigen ratio in the precipitates increases with an increase of this ratio in the antibody–antigen mixture before precipitation (42,84–86). The antibody/antigen ratio in the precipitate depends on the size of the antigen employed (87). If cells are used as the precipitating antigen, the layer of antibody molecules bound to their surface is certainly negligibly small compared with the volume of the cell. The reverse is true if small molecules are employed as antigens; in some precipitates only 2–3% of the precipitate is formed by the antigen, while the bulk of the precipitate consists of antibody.

If the molecular weights of antigen and antibody are known, we are able to calculate the molecular ratio antibody/antigen in the precipitate. This ratio is sometimes astonishingly high. Thus thyroglobulin–antithyroglobulin precipitates contain up to 60 molecules of antibody per

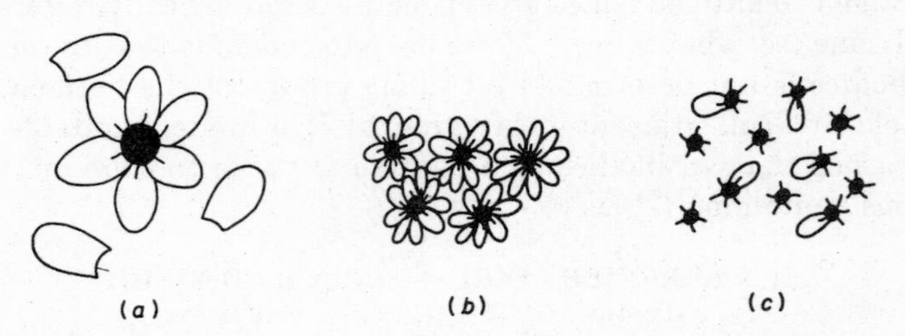

FIG. 50. Combination of antigen molecules (black) with antibody molecules (white). (*a*) antigen-antibody complex formed by multivalent antigen molecule and univalent antibody molecules (antibody in excess). (*b*) precipitate formed by the nonspecific aggregation of antigen-antibody complexes. (*c*) soluble complexes in an excess of antigen.

thyroglobulin molecule (88). Likewise arsanilazoglobulin is able to bind approximately 50 molecules of antibody to each of the antigen molecules (85). The simplest picture of such a precipitate is that of antigen–antibody complexes, each of them consisting of an antigen molecule as nucleus, to which numerous antibody molecules are attached (Fig. 50). If the complexes formed attain a certain size they become unstable and form insoluble aggregates in the same manner as euglobulins and other similar proteins such as edestin. The formation of the aggregates is inhibited in the same way as the aggregation of euglobulins, by the addition of neutral salts, or by acids or bases (85). Precipitation is enhanced by ninhydrin and other nonspecific reagents (88*a*).

Precipitates of antigens and antibodies are usually soluble in an excess of the antigen. This is attributed to the formation of many small complexes containing only one antibody molecule per antigen molecule (71) (Fig. 50). Precipitates produced by horse antibodies are soluble in an excess of horse antibody, whereas precipitates produced by rabbit antibody are not dissolved by an excess of the rabbit antibody. This is particularly surprising when the antigen injected is a foreign serum globulin; in such a case both the antigen and antibody used are serum globulins possessing very similar physicochemical properties. The different action of horse antibodies and of rabbit antibodies indicates that an essential difference exists between these two types of antibodies. The inability of the rabbit antibody to dissolve the precipitate is probably due to the univalence of this antibody; obviously univalent antibodies are not able to combine with more than one antigen molecule and to form a framework consisting of alternate antigen–antibody units. The difference between a framework and the aggregate shown in Figure 50 is that in the aggregate formed by univalent antibodies the antigen–antibody complexes are held together by nonspecific bonds between adjacent complexes (89), whereas the framework theory postulates bonding only by specific bonds. The difference between these two views disappears when we are dealing with precipitates such as that of thyroglobulin–antithyroglobulin, where each thyroglobulin molecule combines with approximately 60 antibody molecules. Obviously, only very few of the lattice forming bonds can be specific in such a case. Since antigen–antibody precipitates produced by horse antibodies are soluble in an excess of antibody (90*a*,*b*) we have to assume that antibodies produced in the horse are probably multivalent. The properties of antibody from horse serum depend, however, on the mode of injection (90*a*).

While the problem of the valence of antibodies is not yet definitely solved, there is no doubt that antigen molecules are multivalent, *i.e.*, that they possess more than one group to which antibody is bound. This has been proved by small hapten molecules possessing one, two, or three determinant groups; those containing only one determinant group are not able to form precipitates with antibodies adapted to these groups. Precipitates are formed, however, by some of the bivalent or tervalent haptens (91). Likewise a hapten possessing the binding groups R and X is precipitated by a mixture of anti-R and anti-X, but not by one of these antibodies alone (R = *p*-azophenyl-azophenyl-arsonic acid, X = *p*-azophenylazobenzoic acid) (92). The interpretation of these experiments is rendered difficult by the fact that some of the haptens might form aggregates consisting of many hapten molecules and possessing more than two or three determinant groups (93,93*a*).

The formation of an insoluble precipitate depends not only on the number of binding groups in the antigen and antibody molecule, but also on the degree of their polarity, on the hydrophilic or hydrophobic properties of these groups, and on their sterical arrangement (94). Evidently the antibody can combine only with those molecular groups of the antigen which are situated on the surface of the antigen molecule, not with endo-groups in the interior of the globular antigen molecule (85).

An attempt has been made to gain insight into the antibody–antigen reaction applying the law of mass action (95). The main obstacle confronting these attempts is that the reaction between antigen and antibody is only partially reversible; some of the precipitates are not dissolved in an excess of antigen, although their formation is inhibited by the same excess of antigen (96). If the symbol G is used for one antigen molecule and B for one antibody molecule, the reaction between antigen and antibody is represented by the reactions (73):

$$G + B \rightleftharpoons GB \quad (1)$$
$$GB + B \rightleftharpoons GB_2 \quad (2)$$
$$GB_2 + B \rightleftharpoons GB_3, \text{ etc.} \quad (3)$$

In later phases, reactions of the type $2\ GB_3 \rightarrow G_2B_6$ or ring closure by end-to-end aggregation of long chains may occur (97). If antigen–antibody aggregates combine by nonspecific bonds, linkages of the type B-B will be formed. In some cases the occurrence of nonspecific bonds has been proved by the formation of common agglutinates of different pairs of antigen and antibody. In other instances no such coagglutination could be observed (97). The linkage of antibody molecules to the surface of virus particles has been rendered visible by electron micrography (98).

The forces involved in the mutual linkage of antigen and antibody are electrostatic forces operating between polar groups; they have been discussed in Chapter X (Sect. A) where it was emphasized that they operate only over very short distances, because their intensity decreases as r^6, *i.e.*, as the sixth power of the distance between the two poles (98*a*). Although these forces are very weak, in general, they become very powerful if they are exerted simultaneously by a large number of polar groups. This is possible only when these polar groups belong to two large molecules whose surfaces are complementarily adjusted to each other. The mutual distance between antigen and antibody surface is of the order of 4 Å; differences of 0.1 Å considerably alter the mutual forces of attraction. It is understandable, therefore, that differences such as those between *o*-, *m*-, and *p*-derivatives of the same compound are highly significant in the mutual attraction of antigen and antibody molecules (99).

The free energy change accompanying the combination of a hapten with its antibody is approximately 1510 cal. per mole (100). Direct calorimetric determination of the heat of the reaction hemocyanin + antihemocyanin furnished a value of 3 cal. per gram nitrogen, *i.e.*, 40,000 cal. per antibody molecule bound (101).

The precipitation is inhibited by extremely high pressures (102).

This indicates that the combination of antigen with antibody is accompanied by a release of water molecules. Most probably antigen as well as antibody molecule undergo partial dehydration in the immediate region of their mutual combination, so that the two monomolecular water layers which originally surround each of the reacting components are replaced by layers common to both. The free energy change of the reaction $GB_n \rightarrow GB_{n-1} + B$ can be calculated from the equilibrium constant, K, according to van't Hoff's equation:

$$\Delta F = -RT \ln K$$

The value $\Delta F = +9800$ cal. per mole of antibody has been found for the reaction $GB_8 \rightarrow GB_7 + B$, where G is metanil-sheep serum pseudoglobulin and B the homologous antibody (103).

The antigen–antibody reaction has also been investigated in monomolecular films. If ovalbumin is adsorbed to a chromium plate, and dipped into an antibody solution, a monomolecular film of antibody molecules is deposited on the surface of the antigen film (104). However, no antigen is deposited when the antibody is adsorbed to the metal and dipped into the antigen solution (104). Alternate toxin and antitoxin films have been prepared in a similar manner (105). Reports that antigen and antibody combine by means of long-range forces through plastic films over distances of more than 100 Å (106) are probably due to the diffusion of the reacting particles through cracks or holes of the thin plastic film (107,108).

Since antigens and antibodies are proteins, the reaction taking place between these two compounds is disturbed by all those factors which affect protein molecules. Erroneous results are obtained when the reaction is carried out at other than neutral reactions (82), when merthiolate or similar substances are used as disinfectants (109), or when the antigen is masked by combination with other colloids; thus the precipitation of virus by anti-virus is prevented by heating the virus with serum albumin (110); when the serum albumin layer covering the virus particles is digested by pepsin, precipitation takes place once again.

D. Complement (111). If red blood cells are injected into animals of other species, antibodies are formed which are able to agglutinate the red cells. The true antigens responsible for the formation of these agglutinins are the so-called blood group substances discussed in Chapter XI, Sect. B. Agglutinins and other antibodies are not destroyed by heating to 56°C.; therefore agglutination is not affected by keeping the immune serum at 56° for 30 minutes. If, however, unheated serum is used, hemolysis is observed in addition to agglutination of the red cells. The hemolysis is brought about by a thermolabile complex in the serum called complement. The usual source of complement is guinea pig serum, which is rich in this material.

In contrast to antibody, complement is not a specific substance. Complement from guinea pig serum renders possible the lysis of red cells of various species by the specific antibodies and also the lysis of bacteria by antibacterial antibodies. The lytic system consists in all these cases of (*1*) the antigenic cell or bacterium undergoing lysis, (*2*) the specific antibody obtained by injection of the antigenic cells or bacteria into a foreign species (rabbit, horse), and (*3*) complement.

Complement is discussed at this point because it is a complex of two or more proteins which have the special property of causing cellular antigens to be subject to lysis by antibodies. It has been shown that complement consists of at least four components: the so-called midpiece, the end piece, the third component, and the fourth component. The abbreviation C′1, C′2, C′3, and C′4, respectively have been proposed for these components. The four components of complement are separated from each other by fractional precipitation with ammonium sulfate (112).

C′1, the midpiece, is a globulin-like substance, salted out by 1.39 *M* ammonium sulfate; it forms about 0.6% of the serum proteins and is a euglobulin with an isoelectric point near pH 5.1 (112). C′1 contains 16.3% nitrogen, 0.1% phosphorus, and 2.7% carbohydrate; it is destroyed by heat. C′2, the end piece, is an albumin-like protein, salted out by 2.0–2.2 *M* ammonium sulfate; C′2 combines with C′4 to form a complex which has the properties of a euglobulin; this complex contains 14.2% nitrogen and 10.3% carbohydrate and has an isoelectric point near pH 6.3–6.4; it forms about 0.18% of the serum proteins (112). C′2 is destroyed by acids (112). C′3 is inactivated by yeast, C′4, by ammonia.

It has been known for many years that complement is bound by antigen–antibody complexes. Since, owing to its hemolytic action, very small amounts of complement can be identified, the complement fixation test is one of the most sensitive tests used to prove the combination of antigen with antibody. Red blood cells which are treated with the homologous agglutinins combine at first with C′1, C′2, and C′4, then with C′3 (113). The quantitative determination of each of these four components is very difficult, because each of them requires the presence of the three other components, and because their concentrations in the blood serum are very low.

Heidelberger and coworkers (114) determined complement by adsorbing it to antigen–antibody precipitates and analyzing for nitrogen in the precipitate before and after this adsorption. They found that the total amount of complement was 24–32 γ nitrogen per milliliter serum (114). The author, using a gravimetric method, found 0.15–0.20 mg. complement per milliliter of serum (115). It is not yet clear why complement is bound by antigen–antibody complexes, but not by antigen or antibody independently, and why it is bound by complexes of antigen with the antibodies of rabbit, rat, pig, or sheep blood, but not by complexes of antigen with antibodies of horse, dog, or mouse blood or of human blood (116). Complement, as has been pointed out, is not species-specific; human complement and complement of the guinea pig are mutually replaceable (117).

The action of complement is not yet fully understood. Its lability and the fact that it renders possible lysis of cells and bacteria suggest that it is an enzyme (113,115). This view is supported by the finding that hemolysis of one red blood cell requires only 6×10^4 molecules of complement, while requiring approximately 10^{10} molecules of oleate (115). Evidently one molecule of complement is more active than 100,000 molecules of oleate.

E. Other Immunological Phenomena. Although we are not yet able to explain satisfactorily all of the phenomena of immunology, it seems that the fundamental feature of every one is a primary combination of antigen with antibody. In some instances a secondary reaction of the antigen–antibody complex with complement follows. It has been proved, however, that precipitation, agglutination, cytolysis, and other immunological phenomena are different manifestations of the same antibody; antibodies against pneumococcal polysaccharides are able to precipitate the specific polysaccharides, to agglutinate the cocci, to dissolve them or to render them susceptible to phagocytosis (118). The same antibodies are able to protect men and animals against infections with virulent pneumococci (119,120).

It was mentioned previously that we have to assume the presence of insoluble antibodies in the structural proteins of certain cells. These are responsible for the so-called anaphylactic reactions, observed after the reinjection of an antigen in a sensitized organism. It is evident from this example that some of the immunologic reactions, such as the anaphylactic reactions, are detrimental to the organism and may even lead to its death. Nevertheless they are based on the same phenomenon, the presence of antibodies in the organism into which an antigen has been introduced parenterally. The term "allergy" is sometimes used for this altered reactivity of the organism, caused by the presence of antibodies.

It is a well known fact that many species of animals are immune to certain bacteria, while other species are easily infected. The natural immunity is due either to the presence in the higher organism of proteins which act as antibodies to the invading bacteria, or to the absence of "complementary" surfaces to which the bacteria or their products could be bound. It seems that the existence of such complementary surfaces is one of the prerequisites for the infection of higher organisms (121).

One of the outstanding enigmas of immunology which remains to be explained is the persistence of immunity over periods of many years or even over the whole lifetime of the immunized organism. In such organisms the presence of antibody has been proved (122). It is very difficult to decide whether, in such cases, small amounts of the antigen are still present in the organism, actively causing the continued formation of antibody. This may be true for some virus diseases in which immunity lasts for a very long time (2). Small amounts of the mitigated virus may persist in the organism and so give rise to the formation of antibodies. It is even more astonishing that the antigenic polysaccharides of pneumococci injected into mice in doses of 0.5 mg., are found in the organs of the injected animals after periods of several months (123). These findings support the view that even in those cases where immunity persists for long periods, antibodies are formed in the same way as outlined in the preceding sections, namely by the modifying influence of antigen molecules on the process of protein synthesis. This would also explain the so-called anamnestic reaction, *i.e.*, the appearance of large amounts of antibody when small amounts of an antigen are reinjected a long period after the first immunization. This sudden increase in the titer of the serum would then be due to the passage of antibodies from the tissues to the blood stream; a true anamnestic formation of antibodies has never been proved convincingly (125).

In order to explain the long persistence of immunity and the anamnestic reaction Burnet (124) has advanced the view that antibody production goes on even in the absence of antigens; the formation of antibody is ascribed to the action of specific enzymes which have been modified by the antigen (124). This view is hardly reconcilable with the fact that the organism is able to produce antibodies against arsanilic acid, sulfanilic acid, and against other synthetic products of the chemical industry. It is difficult to believe that enzymes producing proteins complementary to these synthetic products could exist in living organisms. It is much easier to assume that these synthetic antigens act directly, as templates for complementarily adapted protein molecules (see Chapter XVII, Sect. G).

References

1. R. Kraus, *Wiener klin. Wochschr.* **10,** 431 (1897).
2. K. Landsteiner, The Specificity of Serological Reactions. Harvard Univ. Press, Cambridge, 1946.
3. P. Gell, C. R. Harington, R. V. Pitt Rivers, *Brit. J. Exptl. Path.* **27,** 267 (1946).
4. S. B. Hooker, W. C. Boyd, *J. Immunol.* **30,** 41 (1936).
5. L. Kesztyüs, V. Várterész, *Z. Immunitätsforsch.* **105,** 372 (1945).

6. F. Haurowitz, P. Schwerin, *Rev. Faculté sci. univ. Istanbul*, **A9**, 120 (1944).
7. F. Haurowitz, K. Sarafyan, M. Yenson, S. Berkol, P. Schwerin, *Rev. faculté sci. univ. Istanbul*, **A5**, 1 (1940).
8. S. Granick, *J. Biol. Chem.* **149**, 157 (1943).
9. K. Landsteiner, J. van der Scheer, *J. Exptl. Med.* **50**, 407 (1929).
10. K. Landsteiner, J. van der Scheer, *J. Exptl. Med.* **55**, 781 (1932).
11. K. Landsteiner, H. Lampl, *Biochem. Z.* **86**, 343 (1918).
12. F. Haurowitz, K. Sarafyan, P. Schwerin, *J. Immunol.* **40**, 391 (1941).
13. F. Haurowitz, *J. Immunol.* **43**, 331 (1942).
14. F. Haurowitz, F. Bursa, *Rev. faculté sci. univ. Istanbul* **B10**, 283 (1945).
15. C. F. C. MacPherson, M. Heidelberger, *J. Am. Chem. Soc.* **67**, 585 (1945).
15*a*. J. O. Erickson, H. Neurath, *J. Gen. Physiol.* **28**, 421 (1945).
16. R. F. Clutton, C. D. Harington, T. H. Mead, *Biochem. J.* **31**, 764 (1937).
17. F. Haurowitz, M. Tunca, P. Schwerin, *Biochem. J.* **37**, 247 (1943).
18. F. Haurowitz, M. Tunca, *Bull. faculté med. Istanbul* **7**, 4040 (1944).
19. A. Wormall, *Nature* **154**, 332 (1944).
20. H. Neurath, *J. Am. Chem. Soc.* **65**, 2093 (1943).
21. M. Macheboeuf, J. Basset, *Bull. soc. chim. biol.* **18**, 118 (1936).
22. A. Kleczkowski *et al.*, *Brit. J. Exptl. Path.* **22**, 188, 192, 208 (1941).
23. F. Obermayer, E. Pick, *Wiener klin. Wochschr.* **19**, 327 (1906).
24. A. Wormall, *J. Exptl. Med.* **51**, 73 (1930).
25. M. Adant, P. Spehl, *Compt. rend. soc. biol.* **117**, 230, 232 (1934).
26. V. Várterész, L. Kesztyüs, *Z. Immunitätsforsch.* **99**, 217 (1941).
27. J. R. Marrack, F. C. Smith, *Brit. J. Exptl. Path.* **13**, 394 (1933).
28. F. Haurowitz, F. Breinl, *Z. physiol. Chem.* **205**, 259 (1933).
29. A. Tiselius, *Biochem. J.* **31**, 1464 (1937).
29*a*. J. L. Oncley *et al.*, *J. Am. Chem. Soc.* **71**, 541 (1949).
29*b*. F. Haurowitz, P. Tanasoglu, *Istanbul Seririyati* **26**, 63 (1944).
30. J. van der Scheer, R. Wyckoff, *Science* **91**, 485 (1940).
31. J. R. Marrack, *Ann. Rev. Biochem.* **11**, 629 (1942).
32. A. Polson, *Nature* **152**, 413 (1943).
33. F. Haurowitz, P. Schwerin, unpublished experiments.
34. M. L. Orcutt, P. E. Howe, *J. Exptl. Med.* **36**, 291 (1922).
35. A. Tiselius, *J. Exptl. Med.* **65**, 641 (1937).
36. M. Heidelberger, F. E. Kendall, *J. Exptl. Med.* **65**, 455 (1937). E. A. Kabat, *Science* **89**, 372 (1936).
37. E. L. Smith, R. D. Greene, *J. Biol. Chem.* **171**, 355 (1947).
37*a*. R. R. Porter, *Biochem. J.* **46**, 473 (1950).
38. L. D. Felton, *J. Immunol.* **22**, 453 (1932); J. H. Northrop, W. Goebel, *J. Gen. Physiol.* **32**, 705 (1949).
39. M. Heidelberger, K. O. Pedersen, A. Tiselius, *Nature* **139**, 165 (1936).
40. M. Heidelberger, E. A. Kabat, *J. Exptl. Med.* **67**, 181 (1938).
41. F. Haurowitz, M. Bilen, P. Schwerin, S. Tekman, *Biochem. J.* **41**, 304 (1947).
42. F. Breinl, F. Haurowitz, *Z. physiol. Chem.* **192**, 45 (1930).
43. J. Alexander, *Protoplasma* **14**, 296 (1931).
44. S. Mudd, *J. Immunol.* **23**, 423 (1932).
44*a*. F. Haurowitz, in Kallos, Fortschritte der Allergielehre, Karger, Basel and New York, 1939.
45. L. Pauling, *J. Am. Chem. Soc.* **62**, 2643 (1940).
46. W. H. Taliaferro, H. W. Mulligen, *Indian Med. Research Mem.* **29**, 1 (1937).
46*a*. T. Banks, J. C. Boursnell, H. M. Dewey, G. E. Francis, R. Tupper, A. Wormall, *Biochem. J.* **43**, 518 (1948).

47. F. Haurowitz, *Lancet* **152,** 149 (1947).
48. W. E. Ehrich, T. N. Harris, *Science* **101,** 28 (1945).
49. T. F. Dougherty, J. H. Chase, A. White, *Proc. Soc. Exptl. Biol. Med.* **57,** 295 (1944).
49*a*. A. White, *Ann. Rev. Physiol.* **11,** 355 (1949).
49*b*. W. E. Ehrich, D. L. Drabkin, C. Forman, *J. Exptl. Med.* **90,** 157 (1949).
49*c*. F. Haurowitz, *Quart. Rev. Biol.* **24,** 95 (1949).
50. R. Schoenheimer, S. Ratner, D. Rittenberg, M. Heidelberger, *J. Biol. Chem.* **144,** 541, 555 (1942).
51. E. Kooyman, D. H. Campbell, *J. Am. Chem. Soc.* **70,** 1297 (1948).
52. P. R. Cannon, *Advances in Protein Chem.* **2,** 135 (1945).
53. K. Bizzett, *J. Path. Bact.* **60,** 87 (1948).
54. P. Jordan, *Z. Immunitätsforsch.* **97,** 330 (1940).
55. F. Haurowitz, M. Vardar, P. Schwerin, *J. Immunol.* **43,** 327 (1942).
56. S. B. Hooker, W. C. Boyd, *J. Immunol.* **21,** 113 (1931).
57. F. Haurowitz, P. Schwerin, *J. Immunol.* **47,** 111 (1943).
58. F. Haurowitz, P. Schwerin, *Brit. J. Exptl. Path.* **23,** 146 (1942).
58*a*. F. Haurowitz, *Abstracts 1st Internat. Congr. Biochem.*, p. 459 (1949).
59. K. Landsteiner, J. van der Scheer, *J. Exptl. Med.* **71,** 445 (1940).
60. J. R. Marrack, *Ergeb. Enzymforsch.* **7,** 292 (1938).
61. S. B. Hooker, *J. Allergy* **8,** 118 (1937).
62. M. Heidelberger, F. E. Kendall, *J. Exptl. Med.* **62,** 697 (1935).
63. F. Haurowitz, R. Cindi, P. Schwerin, *Bull. faculté med. Istanbul* **9,** 265 (1946).
64. P. Grabar, *Bull. soc. chim. biol.* **26,** 298 (1944).
65. W. C. Boyd, H. Bernard, *J. Immunol.* **33,** 111 (1937).
66. S. B. Hooker, W. C. Boyd, *Proc. Soc. Exptl. Biol. Med.* **47,** 197 (1941).
67. A. M. Pappenheimer, *J. Exptl. Med.* **71,** 263 (1940).
68. M. E. Adair, J. Hamilton, *J. Hyg.* **39,** 170 (1939).
69. T. Teorell, *J. Hyg.* **44,** 227 (1946); T. E. Banks *et al.*, *Nature* **165,** 111 (1950).
70. M. L. Petermann, A. M. Pappenheimer, Jr., *J. Physiol.* **45,** 1 (1941).
71. J. R. Marrack, The Chemistry of Antigens and Antibodies. His Majesty's Stationary Office. London, 1938.
72. M. Heidelberger, F. E. Kendall, *J. Exptl. Med.* **61,** 559 (1935).
73. E. A. Kabat, M. Heidelberger, *J. Exptl. Med.* **66,** 229 (1937); **71,** 271 (1940).
74. W. C. Boyd, *J. Exptl. Med.* **83,** 401 (1946).
75. F. Breinl, F. Haurowitz, *Z. Immunitätsforsch.* **77,** 176 (1932).
76. H. P. Treffers, M. Heidelberger, *J. Exptl. Med.* **73,** 125 (1941).
77. P. Grabar, *Abstracts 1st Intern. Congr. Biochem.*, p. 446 (1949).
78. H. Erlenmeyer, E. Berger, *Biochem. Z.* **252,** 22 (1932).
79. K. Landsteiner, J. van der Scheer, *J. Exptl. Med.* **69,** 705 (1939).
80. L. Pauling, D. H. Campbell, *J. Exptl. Med.* **76,** 211 (1942).
81. F. Haurowitz, S. Tekman, *Compt. rend. ann. et arch. soc. turque sci. phys. et nat.* **13,** 81 (1947).
82. F. Haurowitz, P. Schwerin, S. Tunç, *Arch. Biochem.* **11,** 515 (1946).
83. H. Wu, *Proc. Soc. Exptl. Biol. Med.* **25,** 853 (1928); **26,** 737 (1929).
84. M. Heidelberger, F. E. Kendall, *J. Exptl. Med.* **50,** 809 (1929); **62,** 467, 697 (1935); **65,** 647 (1935).
85. F. Haurowitz, *Z. physiol. Chem.* **245,** 23 (1936).
86. J. R. Marrack, F. Smith, *Brit. J. Exptl. Path.* **12,** 30, 182 (1931).
87. S. B. Hooker, W. C. Boyd, *J. Gen. Physiol.* **17,** 341 (1934); *J. Immunol.* **30,** 38 (1936).

88. H. E. Stokinger, M. Heidelberger, *J. Exptl. Med.* **66**, 251 (1937); *J. Am. Chem. Soc.* **60**, 247 (1938).
88*a*. F. Tayeau, *Abstracts Ist Intern. Congr. Biochem.*, p. 455 (1949).
89. S. B. Hooker, W. C. Boyd, *J. Immunol.* **33**, 337 (1937).
90*a*. M. Heidelberger, H. P. Treffers, J. Freund, *J. Exptl. Med.* **86**, 77, 96 (1947).
90*b*. M. Cohn, A. M. Pappenheimer, *J. Immunol.* **63**, 291 (1949).
91. L. Pauling, D. Pressman, D. H. Campbell, C. Ikeda, M. Ikawa, D. Brown, *J. Am. Chem.* **64**, 2994, 3003, 3010, 3020 (1942).
92. L. Pauling, D. Pressman, D. H. Campbell, *Science* **98**, 263 (1943).
93. W. C. Boyd, J. Behnke, *Science* **100**, 13 (1944).
93*a*. A. B. Pardee, L. Pauling, *J. Am. Chem. Soc.* **71**, 143 (1949).
94. W. C. Boyd, *J. Exptl. Med.* **75**, 407 (1942).
95. M. Heidelberger, *Bact. Revs.* **3**, 49 (1939).
96. M. Mayer, M. Heidelberger, *J. Biol. Chem.* **143**, 567 (1942).
97. A. D. Hershey, *J. Immunol.* **45**, 249 (1943); **47**, 77 (1943); **48**, 381 (1944).
98. W. M. Stanley, T. F. Anderson, *J. Biol. Chem.* **139**, 325 (1941).
98*a*. D. Pressman, L. Pauling, *J. Am. Chem. Soc.* **71**, 2893 (1949).
99. L. Pauling, D. Pressman, *J. Am. Chem. Soc.* **67**, 1003 (1945).
100. D. Pressman, A. L. Grossberg, L. Pence, L. Pauling, *J. Am. Chem. Soc.* **68**, 250 (1946).
101. W. C. Boyd, J. B. Conn, D. C. Gregg, G. B. Kistiakowsky, R. M. Roberts, *J. Biol. Chem.* **139**, 787 (1941).
102. D. H. Campbell, F. H. Johnson, *J. Am. Chem. Soc.* **68**, 725 (1946).
103. F. Haurowitz, R. Sowinski, unpublished experiments.
104. A. Rothen, K. Landsteiner, *Science* **90**, 65 (1939).
105. I. Langmuir, V. J. Schaefer, *J. Am. Chem. Soc.* **59**, 1406 (1937).
106. A. Rothen, *J. Biol. Chem.* **168**, 75 (1947).
107. F. Karush, B. Siegel, *Science* **108**, 107 (1948).
108. S. Singer, *J. Biol. Chem.* **182**, 189 (1950).
109. D. P. Pressman, A. L. Grossberg, *Science* **101**, 253 (1945).
110. A. Kleczkowski, *Brit. J. Exptl. Path.* **26**, 33, 41 (1945).
111. M. Heidelberger, M. Mayer, *Advances in Enzymol.* **8**, 71 (1948).
112. L. Pillemer, E. E. Ecker, J. L. Oncley, E. J. Cohn, *J. Exptl. Med.* **74**, 297 (1941).
113. L. Pillemer, S. Seifter, F. Chu, E. E. Ecker, *J. Exptl. Med.* **76**, 93 (1942).
114. M. Heidelberger *et al.*, *J. Exptl. Med.* **73**, 681, 695 (1941).
115. F. Haurowitz, M. M. Yenson, *J. Immunol.* **47**, 309 (1943).
116. E. A. Kabat, *J. Exptl. Med.* **69**, 103 (1939).
117. O. G. Bier, G. C. Leyton, M. Mayer, M. Heidelberger, *J. Exptl. Med.* **81**, 449 (1945).
118. L. D. Felton, G. Bailey, *J. Immunol.* **11**, 197 (1926).
119. O. T. Avery, W. F. Goebel, *J. Exptl. Med.* **54**, 431 (1931).
120. C. M. MacLeod, R. Hodges, M. Heidelberger, W. Bernhard, *J. Exptl. Med.* **82**, 445 (1945).
121. S. Fazekas, D. M. Graham, *Australian J. Exptl. Biol. Med. Sci.* **27**, 83 (1948).
122. M. Heidelberger *et al.*, *J. Exptl. Med.* **83**, 303 (1946).
123. L. D. Felton, G. Kaufmann, B. Ottinger, *Federation Proc.* **8**, 402 (1949); *J. Immunol.* **61**, 119 (1949); see also P. D. McMaster, H. Kruse, *Federation Proc.* **9**, 387 (1950).
124. F. M. Burnet, The Production of Antibodies. Macmillan, Melbourne, 1941.
125. E. Fischel, M. LeMay, E. A. Kabat, *J. Immunol.* **61**, 79 (1949).

CHAPTER XV

Toxins (Toxic Proteins)

A. General Remarks. Many of the toxic substances found in the animal and the plant kingdom are proteins or peptides. Some of them have been isolated in crystalline form during the last few years. The properties of these toxic substances vary according to their origin. It seems advisable, therefore, to classify them according to their composition and to the material from which they have been prepared.

B. Bacterial Toxins (1). (*a*). *Exotoxins.* The *exotoxins* are toxic substances produced by various bacteria which pass from the bacterial cell into the culture medium or into the organism of the host. The exotoxins of *Corynebacterium diphtheriae*, *Clostridium botulinum* and *Clostridium tetani* have been purified and isolated as crystals. All these, which are extremely toxic, are typical proteins of the globulin type.

Diphtheria toxin has been purified by fractional precipitation with ammonium sulfate. The molecular weight of the purified toxin is 74,000; the axial ratio of the molecules is 4.7 to 1 (1*a*). The toxin is rendered innocuous by treatment with formaldehyde, which indicates that amino groups are essential for the toxic action (2). The toxin is a globulin-like protein which is destroyed by heat and by proteolytic enzymes. It combines readily with iron porphyrins; possibly, the toxin forms the protein component of a respiratory enzyme (1).

Crystalline *tetanal toxin* has been obtained by precipitation with methanol at slightly acid reaction, low ionic strength and temperatures of −8 to −5°C. (3). Crystalline tetanal toxin is a very labile globulin with an isoelectric point of pH 5.1 and a sedimentation constant, $s = 4.5$. It is inactivated even at 0°C., when kept at that temperature for a long time (4), undergoing conversion into an nontoxic, flocculating dimer, which is still precipitated by the homologous antibody (4).

The molecular weight of the crystalline *exotoxin of Clostridium botulinum* is approximately 1,000,000 (5,6). The isoelectric point is 5.6, the frictional ratio, f/f_0, is 1.45; the axial ratio, a/b, is very high, about 10 (5,6). Although the toxin is crystalline and, apparently, uniform, the antibody/antigen ratio is not constant; the maximum of antibody molecules bound to one toxin molecule is 60 (5).

The toxin of *Clostridium welchii* (7) has been purified to a certain extent by fractionation with ammonium sulfate and ethanol. It seems to be a α-lecithinase, splitting phosphocholine from lecithin or sphingomyelin (7*a*). *Scarlet fever toxin* was adsorbed on Lloyd's reagent, eluted with alkaline buffer, and precipitated with ammonium sulfate. The toxin is rather stable to brief heating to 100°C., and to the action of pepsin and trypsin; its molecular weight is approximately 14,000, its isoelectric point pH 5.55. Here again, amino groups are essential for the toxicity (8,9).

The mode of action of these exotoxins is not yet entirely known. Some of them have a great affinity for nerve tissue and are able to paralyze the nervous system. The lethal dose of botulinus toxin required to kill a mouse is 0.00005 γ or approximately 20 million molecules of the toxin (10). This low value suggests that the toxin acts as a catalyst (11), producing toxic products or starting a chain reaction (10).

The toxins of *Corynebacterium diphtheriae, Clostridium botulinum,* and *Clostridium tetani* are typical antigens. Their injection into rabbits induces the formation of powerful antitoxins, which combine with the toxins and thus abolish their toxic properties. Toxins and antitoxins neutralize one another in definite proportions and it is possible to titrate one against the other to determine their amounts.

(*b*). *Gramicidin and Tyrocidin.* Toxins of a type different from those discussed in the preceding section were discovered in *Bacillus brevis,* a soil bacterium (12,13). The toxins are extracted from the bacteria by ethanol and are insoluble in water. By the addition of ether to the alcoholic solution a toxic substance called *tyrocidin* is precipitated, while a second toxin, called *gramicidin,* remains dissolved. Gramicidin and tyrocidin are peptides of an unusual type; they have neither free amino groups nor free carboxyl groups and are probably *cyclopeptides* formed by a closed peptide ring (14). Unlike other natural peptides and the proteins, gramicidin and tyrocidin contain D-amino acids (15) and also ornithine and ethanolamine (16).

The simplest of these cyclopeptides is gramicidin S (17); it is (-L-valyl-L-ornithyl-L-leucyl-D-phenylalanyl-L-prolyl)-cyclopeptide (16,18).

The molecule of gramicidin from *B. brevis* is formed by the following amino acids: six molecules of D-leucine, six L-tryptophan, four DL-valine, four L-alanine, and two glycine; moreover the molecule contains two molecules of ethanolamine (16). By countercurrent extraction it was found that gramicidin, contrary to the original view, is not a homogeneous substance, but a mixture of several polypeptides (18*a*,18*b*). The composition of tyrocidin is: three phenylalanine, two glutamic acid, two aspartic acid, two ornithine, two tryptophan, two proline, two leucine, two valine, and three ammonia (13). Gramicidin is extremely toxic for gram-positive bacteria, tyrocidin for both gram-positive and gram-negative bacteria. Although both peptides cause bacteriostasis, they cannot be used therapeutically because they are also considerably toxic to man. Similar antibiotic polypeptides were isolated from other bacteria (18*d*). One of these, aërosporin (polymyxin A) is remarkable in its content of α,γ-diaminobutyric acid (18*c*).

(*c*). *Endotoxins.* Bacterial *endotoxins* are found in *Eberthella typhosa*, in *Vibrio cholerae*, and in the different types of *Salmonella dysenteriae*. These endotoxins are extracted from the bacteria by trichloroacetic acid or by diethylene glycol; in contradistinction to the proteins they resist the action both of trypsin (19) and heat.

The endotoxins are complexes formed by a carbohydrate, a phospholipid, and a protein or peptide; they are present in the smooth S-forms of bacteria, but not in the rough R-forms (19). In addition to the somatic O-antigens, so-called H-antigens have been found in the bacterial flagellae (20). The endotoxin of dysentery bacteria of the *Shiga* type has been extracted from the bacteria by diethylene glycol; it is cleaved into its components by treatment with 90% phenol (21). The serological specificity of the endotoxin is determined by the carbohydrate component; the isolated carbohydrate is a hapten (see Chapter XIV, Sect. A), which acquires antigenic characteristics upon combination with the protein (21). A similar endotoxin has been prepared from dysentery bacteria of the *Flexner* type (22).

Other endotoxin complexes have also been prepared from *Brucella melitensis* (23) and from *Eberthella typhosa* (24). The latter substance, purified by fractionation with acetone, contains 50–60% of a carbohydrate, 3–4% of lipid, and about 30% of a peptide-like component (24). It may be mentioned, finally, that tuberculin from tubercle bacilli is also a protein derivative; fractionation of tuberculin with ethanol and by electrophoresis furnished two polysaccharides, at least three proteins, A, B, and C, and a nucleoprotein, D. The typical skin reaction is produced by protein A (25,26). It is remarkable that the proteins of the tubercle bacilli are toxic only for the infected organism, not for the normal organism (26*a*).

C. Other Toxins (27). The toxins of snakes (28), of certain insects such as bees and wasps, and also certain vegetable toxins are proteins or protein derivatives whose toxic actions vary widely. Proteolysis, hemolysis, hemagglutination, clotting, and effects on the nervous system have been observed (27). Some of the snake venom toxins have been purified to a certain extent; crotoxin, the toxin of the rattlesnake *Crotalus terrificus*, has been obtained in crystalline form and found to contain 4% sulfur (29). Crotoxin, which has a molecular weight of 20,000, is split by the reducing action of cysteine (30). The purified toxin of the snake

Bothrops jararaca contains no sulfur or phosphorus (31). The toxin of *Naja flava*, the African cobra, is free of dithio and of sulfhydryl groups; it is inactivated by oxygen (32) and by HCN (39); 1 g. of the toxin has a minimum lethal dose of 1–2 million mouse units (32). It is one of the most toxic substances known. The physicochemical properties of the snake toxins are similar to those of globulins; in electrophoresis experiments the hemolytic and the neurotoxic activity was found mainly in the T-fraction of the globulins (33).

The mode of action of the snake venoms is not yet understood. Most probably they are able to react as proteolytic, lipolytic or coagulating enzymes (27). The hemolysis caused by these and also by bacterial toxins has been attributed to their action on lecithin, which is hydrolyzed and converted to lysolecithin, containing only one fatty acid residue (33*a*). The spreading factor of snake venoms is probably (34) identical with hyaluronidase (see page 247). A powerful amino acid oxidase has been found in the venom of *Vipera aspis* (35).

Toxins have also been found in the albumin fraction of certain plants, mainly in legumes. The best known of these toxins are abrin from *Abrus precatorius,* crotin from *Croton tiglium,* and ricin. Ricin, the toxin of castor beans, has been crystallized and the pure toxin found to be a protein with a molecular weight of 77,000–85,000 and an isoelectric point of pH 5.2–5.5 (36). Ricin is the strongest plant agglutinin among 262 species examined (37). It is remarkable that only red cells of blood group A are agglutinated by the toxin from *Lima beans* (37).

To the toxic proteins also belongs paramecin, the toxic factor of *Paramecium aurelia;* it is found in the "killer" variety of paramecia and is toxic for the "sensitive" type of paramecia (38). Paramecin, which is inactivated by proteolytic enzymes and by desoxyribonuclease, is probably a nucleoprotein (40).

In conclusion, it must be emphasized that we know next to nothing about the nature of all these toxins. In many of them the toxic group can be neutralized by formaldehyde or by certain aromatic acids, such as diiodosalicylic acid, which contain negative substituents (39). This suggests that amino groups are involved in the toxic action. Other toxins, however, while inactivated by the reduction of their dithio to two sulfhydryl groups, retain their antigenicity even when the toxic groups are so inactivated. Evidently the antigenic properties of the toxins are not solely due to their toxic groups.

References

1. A. M. Pappenheimer, Jr., *Advances in Protein Chem.* **4,** 123 (1948).
1*a*. M. L. Petermann, A. M. Pappenheimer, Jr., *J. Phys. Chem.* **45,** 1 (1941).

2. M. Eaton, *J. Immunol.* **33,** 419 (1937).
3. L. Pillemer, R. Wittler, D. B. Grossberg, *Science* **103,** 615 (1946).
4. L. Pillemer, D. H. Moore, *J. Biol. Chem.* **173,** 427 (1948); M. S. Dunn, M. N. Camien, L. Pillemer, *Arch. Biochem.* **22,** 374 (1949).
5. C. Lamanna, B. Doak, *J. Immunol.* **59,** 231 (1948).
6. A. Abrams, G. Kegeles, G. A. Hottle, *J. Biol. Chem.* **164,** 63 (1946).
7. M. J. Boyd, M. A. Logan, A. A. Tytell, *J. Biol. Chem.* **167,** 899 (1947).
7*a*. H. G. McFarlane, *Biochem. J.* **42,** 587 (1948).
8. E. S. G. Barron, G. F. Dick, C. M. Lyman, *J. Biol. Chem.* **137,** 267 (1941).
9. L. E. Krejci, A. H. Stock, E. B. Sanogar, E. O. Kramer, *J. Biol. Chem.* **142,** 785 (1942).
10. F. W. Putnam, C. Lamanna, D. G. Sharp, *J. Biol. Chem.* **176,** 401 (1948).
11. D. Herbert, E. W. Todd, *Biochem. J.* **35,** 1124 (1941).
12. R. D. Hotchkiss, R. J. Dubos, *J. Biol. Chem.* **132,** 791 (1940).
13. R. D. Hotchkiss, *Advances in Enzymol.* **4,** 153 (1946).
14. F. Sanger, *Biochem. J.* **40,** 261 (1946).
15. F. Lipmann, R. D. Hotchkiss, R. J. Dubos, *J. Biol. Chem.* **141,** 163, 171 (1941).
16. A. H. Gordon, A. J. P. Martin, R. L. M. Synge, *Biochem. J.* **37,** 86, 313 (1943); **38,** XXXI (1944); **41,** 596 (1947).
17. A. N. Belozerskiĭ, T. S. Paskhina, *Biokhimya* **10,** 352 (1945).
18. R. L. M. Synge, *Biochem. J.* **39,** 351 (1945).
18*a*. J. D. Gregory, L. C. Craig, *J. Biol. Chem.* **172,** 839 (1948).
18*b*. R. L. M. Synge, *Biochem. J.* **44,** 542 (1949).
18*c*. T. S. G. Jones, *Biochem. J.* **42,** LIX; **43,** XXVI (1948).
18*d*. O. Wintersteiner, J. D. Dutcher, *Ann. Rev. Biochem.* **18,** 559 (1949).
19. A. Boivin, *Bull. soc. chim. biol.* **23,** 12 (1941).
20. E. A. Kabat, *J. Immunol.* **47,** 513 (1943).
21. W. T. J. Morgan, S. N. Partridge, *Biochem. J.* **35,** 1140 (1941).
22. W. F. Goebel, F. Binkley, E. Perlman, *J. Exptl. Med.* **81,** 315 (1945).
23. A. A. Miles, N. W. Pirie, *Brit. J. Exptl. Path.* **20,** 83, 109, 278 (1939).
24. W. T. J. Morgan, S. N. Partridge, *Brit. J. Exptl. Path.* **23,** 151 (1942).
25. F. B. Seibert, K. O. Pedersen, A. Tiselius, *J. Exptl. Med.* **68,** 413 (1938).
26. F. B. Seibert, *Chem. Revs.* **34,** 107 (1944); *Am. Rev. Tuberc.* **59,** 86 (1949).
26*a*. G. Brownlee, *Ann. Reports Chem. Soc. London* **45,** 292 (1949).
27. C. H. Kellaway, *Ann. Rev. Biochem.* **8,** 545 (1940).
28. E. A. Zeller, *Advances in Enzymol.* **8,** 459 (1948).
29. K. H. Slotta, H. Fraenkel-Conradt, *Nature* **142,** 213 (1939).
30. N. Gralèn, T. Svedberg, *Biochem. J.* **32,** 1375 (1938).
31. D. von Klobusitzky, P. König, *Z. physiol. Chem.* **255,** 1 (1938).
32. F. Micheel, F. Jung, *Z. physiol. Chem.* **239,** 217 (1936).
33. A. Polson, F. J. Joubert, D. A. Haig, *Biochem. J.* **40,** 265 (1946).
33*a*. R. C. Bard, L S. McClung, *J. Bact.* **56,** 665 (1948).
34. E. Chain, E. S. Duthrie, *Brit. J. Exptl. Path.* **21,** 324 (1940).
35. E. A. Zeller, A. Maritz, *Helv. Chim. Acta* **27,** 1888 (1944).
36. E. A. Kabat, M. Heidelberger, A. E. Bezer, *J. Biol. Chem.* **168,** 629 (1947); M. Kunitz, M. McDonald, *J. Gen. Physiol.* **32,** 25 (1948).
37. W. C. Boyd, R. M. Reguerra, *J. Immunol.* **62,** 333 (1949).
38. T. Sonneborn, *Cold Spring Harbor Symposia Quant. Biol.* **11,** 236 (1946).
39. G. Wellers, *Bull. soc. chim. biol.* **30,** 684 (1948).
40. W. J. Van Wagtendonk, *J. Biol. Chem.* **173,** 691 (1948).

CHAPTER XVI

The Supply of Amino Acids for Protein Biosynthesis

Protein synthesis is the cardinal manifestation of life, and yet the manner in which it is achieved is still the great problem of biochemistry and of biology. During growth and reproduction, there is necessarily an increase in the rate of synthesis of proteins within the cell. Since proteins consist of peptide chains composed of amino acids, amino acids are regarded as precursors of proteins. Plants and some bacteria and molds can produce the amino acids required for protein synthesis from inorganic nitrogen sources, sometimes even from molecular nitrogen, where it seems that the first reaction is the reduction of N_2 to ammonia; the first product of nitrogen assimilation is glutamic acid, as has been found by using isotopic nitrogen, N^{15} (1). The energy required for the incorporation of nitrogen into organic compounds is furnished by coupled oxidations; that is proved by the fact that the assimilation of nitrogen is retarded by carbon monoxide or by sulfides, both of which typically inhibit the respiratory enzymes (1).

In contrast to the bacteria which are able to assimilate nitrogen and to the plants which produce all of their amino acids and proteins from inorganic sources, the higher animals must rely upon a continual supply of certain amino acids, which are furnished by the food in the form of proteins. The consumed proteins are split in the digestive tract by proteolytic enzymes and the liberated amino acids are absorbed and incorporated into the specific body proteins.

The preliminary phase of protein formation in the animal organism is evidently the proteolytic cleavage of orally ingested proteins. Other important phases of protein elaboration include the synthesis of certain amino acids from other organic substances and the formation of proteins from the various types of amino acids then at hand.

A. Enzymatic Hydrolysis of Proteins. The proteolytic enzymes have been described in Chapter XII, and it is clear from the facts mentioned there that many of these enzymes can be isolated in a very pure, crystalline state. Some of them occur in the gastrointestinal tract and function there to cleave the proteins ingested with the food and thus convert them into amino acids which can be readily absorbed. Proteolytic enzymes, however, also occur in all the body cells, where their presence is revealed by the phenomenon of autolysis, *i.e.*, the lysis of the cell following cessation of life activities. This lysis proceeds even under strictly sterile conditions and, hence, is not caused by bacteria. It is fundamentally different from putrefaction, which frequently is accompanied by proteolysis. While the enzymes causing proteolysis in putrefaction are the proteolytic enzymes of the multiplying bacteria, those responsible for autolysis are cellular enzymes identical with, or closely related to, cathepsin.

Proteolysis is, essentially, the hydrolytic conversion by cleavage of peptide bonds of the type, RCONHR′ into RCOOH + H_2NR'. The increase in carboxyl and amino groups is a measure of the extent of proteolysis (see Chapter III, Sect. B). While there is no doubt that proteolysis consists mainly of the hydrolytic cleavage of peptide bonds, it is not yet clear whether or not the first phase of the action of proteolytic enzymes involves something more than this. The uncertainty concerning the occurrences in the initial phase arises from the observation that the incipient stage of proteolysis is frequently accompanied by an abnormal decrease in the total volume of the solution (2). Hydrolysis of peptide bonds is accompanied by an uptake of free water molecules and should, therefore, result in a decrease of the volume (see Chapter III, Sect. B) by 15–25 ml. per mole. Actually contractions as high as 50 ml. per mole were found for lactoglobulin (2).

The physical properties of the protein solution are drastically changed in the *first phases of proteolytic cleavage;* the viscosity is lowered and the protein loses its property of being coagulated by heat. This is frequently due to the conversion of the protein into peptides of lower molecular weight. Thus, in the peptic digestion of ovalbumin, the amount of protein which cannot be coagulated by heat is proportional to the number of amino groups liberated (3). On the other hand, no increase in free amino groups was observed in the initial phases of the tryptic hydrolysis of gelatin or of casein (4). This would mean that the drastic changes in viscosity are not caused by the cleavage of peptide bonds. Possibly some very loose bonds between subunits of the protein molecule are cleaved in this stage of the enzyme action, in which event the enzyme could then be said to function as a *depolymerase.*

It has been pointed out before that many of the globular proteins in their native state are *resistant to proteolytic enzymes,* but that they become susceptible to the enzymes after denaturation. Denatured hemoglobin is split by papain about 100 times more rapidly than native hemoglobin (5). Native collagen is hardly attacked by trypsin, while heated collagen is readily hydrolyzed (6). The same is valid for ovalbumin, and for the serum globulins (7). Serum albumin, which is not attacked by trypsin in aqueous solutions, is hydrolyzed in 30% ethanol (8). The resistance of native proteins to the action of proteolytic enzymes is probably due to the absence of points of attack for the enzyme molecules; when the peptide chains of the protein molecule are unfolded by denaturation, the structures required for enzyme action become accessible and proteolysis occurs. The groups required for the action of trypsin are the basic side chains of arginine or lysine (see page 249). These are, apparently, beneath the surface of the globular molecules of the native protein inaccessible to the enzyme, although they are titrable, *i.e.*, accessible to the small hydrogen ions. The appearance of these groups in the surface of the unfolded, denatured protein molecules not only explains their hydrolysis by trypsin but would also account for the establishment of intermolecular saltlike bonds and the formation of insoluble coagulates (see page 132).

If we represent the native protein by the symbol N and the denatured protein by D, then the equilibrium $N \rightleftharpoons D$ will be shifted to the right by the addition of proteolytic enzymes, for these enzymes will attack primarily the denatured protein and will in this way effect a continual conversion of N into D (9,10). It is not impossible that the first phase of enzyme action consists in an acceleration of the $N \rightleftharpoons D$ conversion and that the enzyme in this way acts as a *denaturase.*

The view that the cleavage of denatured proteins is facilitated by the unfolding of their peptide chains is supported by the fact that wool keratin becomes digestible by the purely mechanical procedure of grinding it; ground wool, unlike native wool, is attacked by trypsin (11). The promotion of enzymatic action by the unfolded state of the peptide chains is also shown by experiments with monomolecular protein films at the water–air interface; expanded protein films are readily digested, while solutions of the same proteins are more resistant to the enzymes (12).

The fact that denatured proteins are more readily digested than native proteins is surprising for the biologist, because animals, with the one exception of man, ingest native proteins with their food. One must not conclude that denatured protein, such as that present in boiled food, is more appropriate for human and animal nutrition than native protein, however, since proteins are rapidly denatured in the strongly acid gastric juice at a pH of 1–2. The protein exposed to the action of pepsin is, therefore, denatured protein. However, in those pathological conditions where the gastric juice is almost neutral, denatured protein will certainly be split more readily than native proteins by the enzymes of the intestinal tract (7).

The work of Bergmann and his school has shown that definite chemical side chains of peptides are required for enzymatic hydrolysis. Thus, basic side chains must be available for tryptic digestion to proceed and aromatic and/or acidic side chains for hydrolysis by pepsin. The groups attacked by the different enzymes are shown in the formula of the tetrapeptide tyrosyl-lysyl-glutamyl-tyrosine (13):

```
    OH                 NH2                                    OH
    |                  |                                      |
  (C6H4)              CH2                                   (C6H4)
    |                  |                  COOH                |
    |         ¦       CH2         ¦        |         ¦        |
    |         ¦(a)     |          ¦(b)    CH2        ¦(c)     |
    |         ¦       CH2         ¦        |         ¦        |
   CH2        ¦        |          ¦       CH2        ¦       CH2
    |         ¦       CH2         ¦        |         ¦        |
H2N—CH—CO—————NH—CH—CO————————NH—CH—CO————————NH—CH—COOH
              ¦                   ¦                  ¦
```

The bond *a* is split by chymotrypsin, because its CO group is that of tyrosine, an aromatic amino acid. Bond *b* is cleaved by trypsin which attacks peptide bonds formed by the carboxyl groups of basic amino acids. Pepsin and carboxypeptidase are not able to split bonds *a* or *b*; they do cleave, however, the bond *c*; cleavage by pepsin takes place because the NH group at *c* belongs to an aromatic amino acid; cleavage by carboxypeptidase is due to the adjacent terminal carboxyl group (14).

As was mentioned in Chapter XII peptide bonds are not the only groups attacked by the enzymes, since hydrolytic cleavage also occurs if the peptide bond is replaced by an ester bond. We do not yet know how far we can vary the structures of the peptides to be split without impairing the action of the hydrolyzing enzymes. Slight variations which affect only the velocity of the enzymatic hydrolysis are certainly possible; thus, at pH 4.0 pepsin is able to split not only carbobenzoxyglutamyltyrosine, but to a certain extent, also cysteyltyrosine or tyrosylcysteine (15). The limits of these variations and the range of specificity of the different proteolytic enzymes are yet to be determined (16).

Another unsolved problem of great importance is the actual *mode of cleavage* of the protein molecule. Two different mechanisms for this process are imaginable: (*a*) splitting off of amino acids from the point of attack of the enzyme, so that the length of the peptide chain forming the protein molecule is reduced stepwise until it has been entirely converted into amino acids; (*b*) splitting of the protein macromolecule into large subunits, then into smaller fragments and finally into amino acids. Intermediate mechanisms between (*a*) and (*b*), or combinations of both, are also imaginable. A clear-cut answer concerning the mechanism of proteolysis is important not only from the theoretical, but also from the biological and physiological viewpoint. If proteolysis takes place according to (*a*), protein will be transformed directly into amino acids and only a negligibly small amount of the intermediate polypeptide will be formed for a short period of time. If, however, proteins are split into large fragments, these will be present in larger amounts and noticeable alterations of the osmotic pressure and of other physicochemical properties of the cellular medium will result.

The experimental work of Kühne (1885) and of Hofmeister and his school had demonstrated that intermediary products of protein breakdown are formed when proteins are treated with the enzyme mixtures of the gastric juice or of pancreatic juice. The name *albumose* was given to products which could still be salted out by saturation with ammonium sulfate, but were not coagulated by heat. Products which were neither salted-out nor coagulated by heat were called *peptones*. It is obvious that albumoses and peptones are not uniform substances, but are mixtures of higher and lower polypeptides; moreover, some amino acids such as cystine or tyrosine are salted-out together with albumoses and peptones; work on these substances has, therefore, been discredited. The elucidation of these intermediates of the proteolytic breakdown is, however, one of the most promising experimental approaches to a solution of the problem of protein structure.

The few attempts thus far made to determine the mechanism of enzymatic protein breakdown have not furnished unequivocal results. When ovalbumin is exposed to the action of pepsin, about 35% of the protein is converted into peptides of a molecular weight of less than 1000, 25% into peptides of the weight 1000–10,000, 10% into fragments of a molecular weight between 10,000 and 30,000, and 30% into still larger fragments (3). On the other hand, the reaction of pepsin with ovalbumin in acetic acid furnished only small peptides of a molecular weight of approximately 1000 and no intermediates between 44,000 and 1000 (17), so that the proteolysis was compared with an explosive disintegration whereby the large molecule is split into many small products without an accumulation of intermediates. In other words, there is a rapid splitting of a limited number of peptide bonds, but not a slow splitting of many bonds. Such *"all-or-none" splitting* was also observed when crystalline serum albumin or globulin was exposed to the action of crystalline trypsin, or when serum albumin or fibrin were hydrolyzed by pepsin (18).

While large amounts of free amino acids are formed when crude preparations of pancreatin act on casein or other proteins, no amino acids are formed when casein is exposed to the action of crystalline trypsin (19). On the other hand, however, free amino acids are liberated when fibrin is hydrolyzed by pepsin (18). It is evident from these contradictory reports that the mechanism of proteolysis varies according to the protein and the enzyme employed and that we do not yet understand the mechanism of proteolysis. Nor is it certain whether proteolytic enzymes are able to split peptide bonds other than those linking L-amino acids to each other. The existence of D-peptidases has been postulated (20,21), but has not been proved convincingly (22).

The indispensability of bivalent metal ions for the action of some peptidases has already been noted. On the other hand proteolytic enzymes such as cathepsin or papain are activated by the addition of cyanides or sulfides. Possibly reduced glutathione or another similar reducing substance is a prerequisite for the autolysis of cells (23).

Proteolytic cleavage is sometimes dependent on the presence of certain substances which act as *cosubstrates;* thus, glycylanilide which is not split by papain, is split if acetylphenylalanylglycine is added as cosubstrate; the explanation for this surprising phenomenon is that the added cosubstrate forms an intermediary product, acetylphenylalanylglycylglycylanilide, which is secondarily split into the unchanged cosubstrate, aniline and glycine (24).

Acetylphenylalanylglycine + glycylanilide
↓
acetylphenylalanylglycylglycylanilide
↓
acetylphenylalanylglycylglycine + aniline
↓
acetylphenylalanylglycine + glycine
(↑ returns to acetylphenylalanylglycine)

This sequence of reactions shows that proteolysis and protein synthesis are closely linked to each other and that in some cases, at least, hydrolytic breakdown involves the *intermediary synthesis* of larger molecules.

It must be borne in mind, however, that peptide breakdown does not necessarily mean peptide hydrolysis, and that peptides might be oxidized directly, without having been converted into free amino acids. Such a mode of breakdown is suggested by the occurrence of *dehydropeptidases* in almost all organs (25). The dehydropeptidases catalyze the hydrolysis of dehydrogenated peptides:

$$NH_2CHR{\cdot}CO{\cdot}NH{\cdot}\underset{}{\overset{\overset{\displaystyle CHR}{\|}}{C}}{\cdot}COOH \rightarrow NH_2CHR{\cdot}COOH + NH_3 + \overset{\overset{\displaystyle CH_2R}{|}}{C}O{\cdot}COOH$$

The reaction products are ammonia, a keto acid, and an amino acid or peptide. It is worthy of note that dehydropeptides are hydrolyzed by organ extracts more rapidly than are peptides (25) and that they are also split by the enzymes of the pancreatic juice (26,27). These facts all tend to suggest that oxidation of proteins and peptides might sometimes occur without, or previous to, hydrolytic cleavage of the peptide bonds.

B. Protein Supply by the Food. Essential and Nonessential Amino Acids (27*a*, 31). Amino acids are the raw material for protein synthesis. Those which can be formed from other organic compounds in the organism of man or of other higher animals are called endogenous or nonessential amino acids. Glycine, alanine, serine, aspartic and glutamic acids, proline, hydroxyproline, arginine, cystine, and cysteine are amino acids which fall in this category. The other group of amino acids, which must be introduced into the organism with the food, is comprised by the so-called exogenous or essential amino acids. The nature of the essential and nonessential amino acids has been elucidated mainly by the work of Rose, who proved that valine, leucine, isoleucine, threonine, methionine, phenylalanine, lysine, and tryptophane are *essential amino acids;* they cannot be produced in the bodies of higher animals (28–32). Although histidine, tyrosine, and arginine can be formed slowly from other substances, the rate of their formation under the stress of growth or of disease is too slow for the maintenance of normal conditions, and these must then be supplied to the organism along with the food; they are therefore called semiessential amino acids (33).

Amino acid requirements vary from species to species. While arginine is dispensable for the dog (34) both histidine and arginine are essential for the rat (31). It is astonishing that the amino acid requirements of certain bacteria and molds are more pronounced than those of man and of other vertebrates. It was mentioned in Chapter III (Sect. D) that not only valine, leucine, isoleucine, and lysine, but also the "nonessential" amino acids, glycine, proline, and glutamic acid, can be determined microbiologically. This implies that these amino acids, although some of them are synthesized in the organism of higher animals, cannot be formed in the microbes used for their determination. It is particularly interesting and significant that the amino acid requirement of the fungus *Neurospora crassa* can be altered drastically by mutations (35).

The protein of the ingested food had long been considered simply as a material which furnishes nitrogen and amino acids. It was attempted, therefore, to determine a *protein minimum* necessary for the maintenance of the normal state of health. It was soon found that this is impossible, that some of the proteins such as those of milk, meat, or eggs have a higher biological value than collagen or proteins of vegetable origin (36). The reason for this different biological value of proteins is evident from Table I (p. 32), which shows that the high biological value of casein, myosin, or ovalbumin is due to their high content of essential amino acids. Some of the vegetable proteins are deficient in lysine and collagen is deficient in the sulfur-containing amino acids. Obviously it is impossible to supply all the essential amino acids by feeding only these proteins.

We have to abandon, therefore, the concept of a protein minimum and rather to express protein requirements in terms of the individual amino acids (37).

While it is hardly possible to determine reliable protein minima, approximate determinations are necessitated at times when shortages require that foodstuffs be rationed. In such cases the nutritional value of the protein mixture present in the rationed food has to be determined. Estimations of this kind vary within wide limits. The minimum protein requirement has been estimated to be approximately 60–70 g. protein per day (38,39). Persons, such as farmers or lumbermen, who do strenuous work require more than 100 g. of protein per day (40). Analyses of the average low-money diet in the United States shows a protein content of about 61 g. per day, while the average "excellent" diet contained 75 g. and the average "poor" diet less than 50 g. protein per day (41). Even smaller amounts of protein are certainly sufficient, provided they are rich in the essential amino acids. Thus, it has been reported that a person lived for 7 years on a diet containing only 30 g. protein per day and including no meat; the protein requirement was covered by milk, cheese, and vegetable proteins (42). This is certainly an exceptional case. The other extreme is represented by the diet of the Eskimos, who live on a diet of meat and fat, almost free of carbohydrates. Their average protein intake amounts to 300 g. protein per day (43).

It is evident from the data reported that there exists no definite protein optimum. The protein supply must furnish a minimum of each of the essential amino acids and a minimum of nitrogen necessary for the endogenous formation of the nonessential amino acids. If proteins rich in essential amino acids are used, the daily supply of 35–50 g. protein, postulated by Chittenden at the beginning of this century, is certainly sufficient. If, on the other hand, the proteins ingested are poor in, or devoid of, some of the essential amino acids, the deficiency must be compensated for by supplying in the diet other proteins which contain these amino acids; the total protein requirement will be considerably higher in such cases.

Since the amino acid composition varies from protein to protein (see Table I, p. 32) one should expect great variations in the amino acid content of different types of diet. Analyses of the most important foodstuffs reveal, however, that the total amino acid content of their protein mixtures are well balanced and do not vary very widely. The proteins of milk, serum, eggs, meat, fish meat, brain, corn germ, soybean, and fibrin contain 1–2% cystine and cysteine, 5–7% arginine, 2–3% histidine, 5–8% lysine, 3–5% tyrosine, 1–2% tryptophan, 4–6% threonine, 4–6% valine, 10–20% leucine, and 3–5% isoleucine (44). Evidently the proteins of all these foodstuffs can replace each other in the diet without any serious consequences for the organism. In contrast to these proteins, hemoglobin, gelatin, keratin, and gluten are deficient in one or another of the essential amino acids and can therefore not be regarded as equivalent to the above-named proteins (44).

Since the proteins of the ingested food are hydrolyzed in the gastrointestinal tract and converted into amino acids, one might expect that proteins can be replaced by their hydrolyzates or by amino acid mixtures of the same composition. Actually it has been found that a mixture of L-amino acids duplicating the composition of β-lactoglobulin evoked the same growth response in mice as native β-lactoglobulin (44*a*). Replacement of proteins by amino acids is particularly important in those diseases where the digestive tract is injured so that oral feeding is impossible. In such instances the protein supply can be furnished by the intravenous injection of amino acids (45).

The assumption that the artificial mixture of amino acids given parenterally is in all respects equivalent to the corresponding amount of the protein fed orally is not so well founded as was formerly believed. It has been found that vomiting resulted in dogs when the injected amino acid mixture contained glutamic acid (46), and that an amino acid mixture containing more than 10% glycine caused toxic symptoms and cessation of growth in rats (47). Since glycine as well as glutamic acid are important components of the proteins of the food and of the somatic proteins formed in the organism, it is surprising that they should have such deleterious effects. One must remember, however, that they are turned over very rapidly in the normal organism, so that their concentration in the body fluids is always kept very low; the high concentration of these amino acids in the blood serum produced by feeding or injecting the free amino acids is very different from the low physiological concentration and may be held accountable for the injuries described.

A second difference between protein, on the one hand, and amino acid mixture, on the other, is that some of the intermediates of proteolysis formed in the gastrointestinal tract seem to possess a special biological role. Peptones produced by the peptic or tryptic digestion of insulin, trypsin, or certain other proteins contain a factor required for the growth of various strains of lactobacilli (48). This factor, called *strepogenin*, is possibly formed in the intestines and might be of importance for the growth of intestinal bacteria. The composition of strepogenin is not yet known; it can be replaced to a certain extent by serylglycylglutamic acid (49). It is assumed therefore, that strepogenin has a composition similar to that of the tripeptide. It is not yet known whether strepogenin is of any importance for the mammalian organism.

The important result of these new findings is, however, that they furnish an explanation for the fact that the biological value of amino acid mixtures can be different from the value of a protein containing an equivalent amount of these amino acids.

The same conclusion has to be drawn from experiments on tissue cultures. Fibroblasts are not able to grow on a medium containing amino acids as the only source of nitrogen (50). Proteins are more favorable for the nutrition of the tissue cultures than amino acids or peptides (51). The proteins seem to be adsorbed on the cellular surfaces and digested there by the cellular enzymes; actually the tissues grow more rapidly when trypsin or papain are added to their cultures (52). Similar results were obtained with whole organisms; the hydrolyzate of lactalbumin or serum albumin had only 50% of the biological value of the corresponding proteins (53). The utilization of intravenously injected peptides seems to be still less satisfactory than that of amino acids; most of the injected peptides pass unchanged into the urine (54). All these findings prove that the most desirable mode of protein intake in higher organisms is the *oral* consumption of proteins, and that the parenteral administration of proteins, peptides or amino acids is an inadequate procedure although it may be of the greatest value in those cases where the normal mode of nutrition is impossible.

The body proteins maintain their specific structure and their specific amino acid composition even under abnormal conditions. It has repeatedly been attempted to alter the composition of these proteins by an abnormal mode of nutrition. Actually it has been reported that the amino acid content of egg albumin (55) and of muscle proteins can be altered to a certain extent by starving experimental animals (56). Similar changes in the arginine/lysine ratio of serum proteins were found in persons suffering from hunger edema (57). It is not yet clear, however, whether these changes are caused by the production of abnormal proteins or by changes in the ratio of the components of the normal protein mixtures forming ovalbumin, muscle protein, and serum protein, respectively.

C. Endogenous Formation of Nonessential Amino Acids. The fundamental scheme of the endogenous formation of amino acids, which remained obscure until relatively recently, was revealed by using molecules labeled with isotopic nitrogen or carbon atoms. The principal findings of these investigations are shown in Scheme I. As is evident from the diagram, the mother substances of the endogenous amino acids are pyruvic acid, oxaloacetic acid, and α-ketoglutaric acid. These three keto acids are formed as oxidation products in the intermediary metabolism of carbohydrates and fats, as well as proteins. It has been known for several years that ketoglutarate is oxidized to succinate,

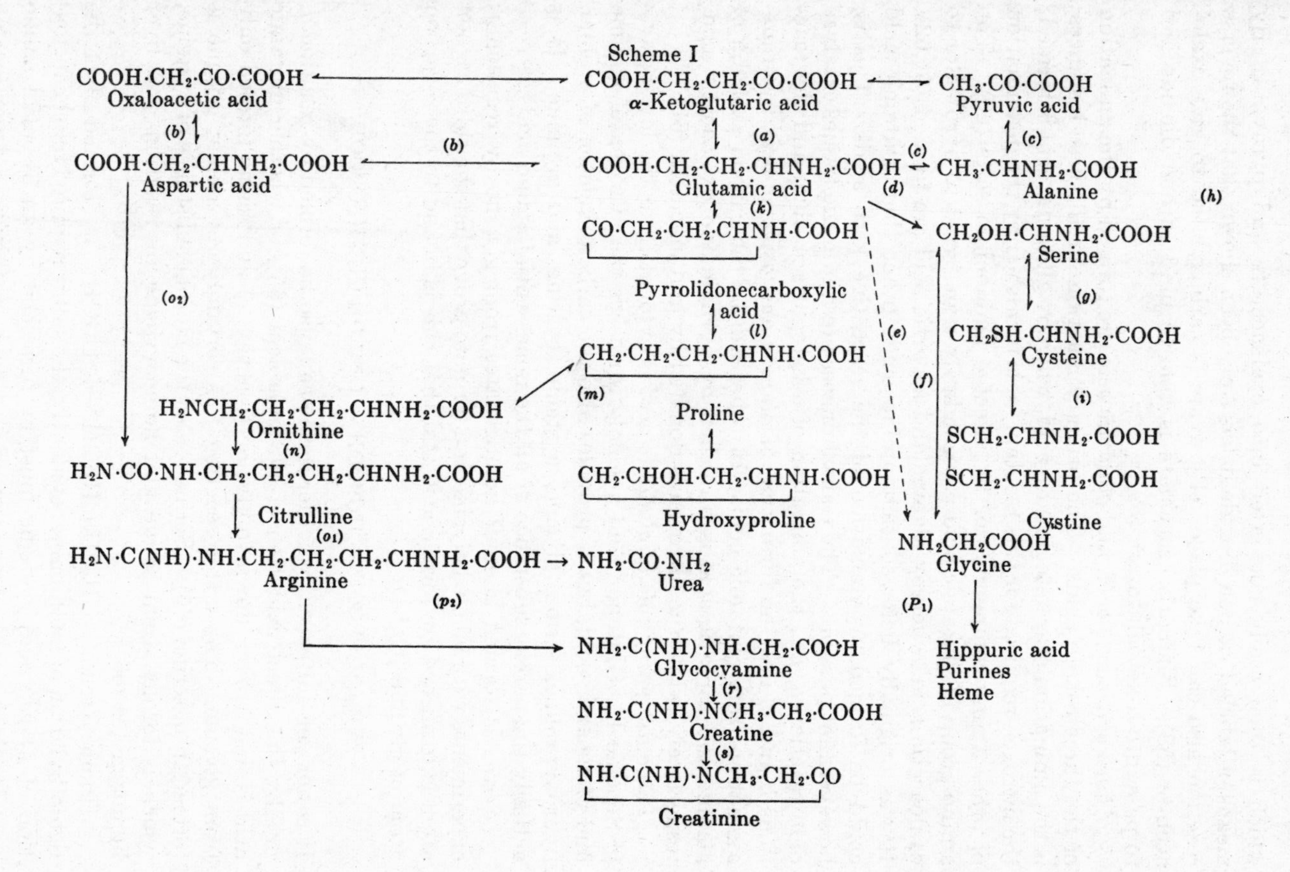
Scheme I
COOH·CH2·CO·COOH
Oxaloacetic acid
COOH·CH2·CH2·CO·COOH
α-Ketoglutaric acid
CH3·CO·COOH
Pyruvic acid
(b)
(a)
(c)
COOH·CH2·CHNH2·COOH
Aspartic acid
(b)
COOH·CH2·CH2·CHNH2·COOH
Glutamic acid
(c)
CH3·CHNH2·COOH
Alanine
(d)
(h)
(k)
CO·CH2·CH2·CHNH·COOH
CH2OH·CHNH2·COOH
Serine
(o2)
Pyrrolidonecarboxylic acid
(g)
(l)
(e)
CH2SH·CHNH2·COOH
Cysteine
CH2·CH2·CH2·CHNH·COOH
(m)
(f)
(i)
H2NCH2·CH2·CH2·CHNH2·COOH
Ornithine
(n)
Proline
SCH2·CHNH2·COOH
SCH2·CHNH2·COOH
H2N·CO·NH·CH2·CH2·CH2·CHNH2·COOH
CH2·CHOH·CH2·CHNH·COOH
Citrulline
Hydroxyproline
Cystine
(o1)
NH2CH2COOH
H2N·C(NH)·NH·CH2·CH2·CH2·CHNH2·COOH → NH2·CO·NH2
Glycine
Arginine
Urea
(p2)
(P1)
NH2·C(NH)·NH·CH2·COCH
Glycocyamine
Hippuric acid
Purines
Heme
(r)
NH2·C(NH)·NCH3·CH2·COOH
Creatine
(s)
NH·C(NH)·NCH3·CH2·CO
Creatinine

which is then easily converted into oxaloacetate and pyruvate. By means of labeled carbon dioxide it has since been shown that the reverse reaction also can take place. Pyruvate is carboxylated to give oxaloacetate (58). Similarly, succinate is able to bind carbon dioxide and to pass into α-ketoglutarate (59).

Alanine, aspartic acid, and *glutamic acid* are formed by the amination of the three α-keto acids. The primary reaction, in all three instances, is the amination of α-ketoglutaric acid, whereby glutamic acid is formed; the nitrogen required for this reaction, *a*, is furnished by the deamination of other amino compounds or by injected ammonium salts (60). The amino group of glutamic acid is secondarily transferred to pyruvic or to oxaloacetic acid, whereby alanine and aspartic acid are formed (61,62). It was originally believed that amino acids other than glutamic acid could be formed by amination of the respective keto acids. This is, however, not possible. The transaminases present in the tissues catalyze only reaction *a, i.e.*, the amination of α-ketoglutaric acid, and the reactions *b* and *c, i.e.*, the formation of *alanine* and *aspartic acid* by transamination from glutamic acid. In other words, the carbon skeleton of alanine and aspartic acid is furnished by pyruvic and oxaloacetic acid, respectively, while the nitrogen is donated by glutamic acid (61).

The *outstanding role of glutamic acid* is evident from the lower parts of Scheme I. Glutamic acid not only furnishes the nitrogen of alanine and of aspartic acid, but it provides also the carbon skeleton of proline, hydroxyproline, serine, glycine, cysteine, cystine, and arginine. It is actually the parent substance of all the nonessential amino acids.

Serine is formed in liver homogenates from glycine by reaction *f*; experiments with labeled glycine and formate prove that the third carbon atom is furnished by formic acid and that this is bound to the α-carbon atom of glycine (63,64):

$$NH_2CH_2C^{13}OOH + HC^{14}OOH \rightarrow C^{14}H_2OH{\cdot}CHNH_2{\cdot}C^{13}OOH$$

It is not yet quite clear whether serine can also be formed by reaction *d*, *i.e.*, by the direct oxidation of glutamic acid (65), or whether glutamic acid is first broken down to glycine (reaction *e*) and serine formed only from glycine. The latter reaction *f* is certainly reversible; glycine is formed from serine (65). Serine is also the mother substance of cysteine, which is formed from serine and homocysteine by reaction *g* in liver homogenates (66).

Homocysteine, $CH_2SH{\cdot}CH_2{\cdot}CHNH_2{\cdot}COOH$, is formed by the demethylation of methionine; evidently, the sulfur required for the formation of cystine and cysteine must be furnished by an essential amino acid, methionine; the formation of cystine is, in this way, dependent on the presence of sufficient amounts of methionine. Only the sulfur atom, not the carbon atoms, of cysteine, are furnished by methionine, as was demonstrated by using methionine labeled with S^{35} and with C^{13} (67). Cystathionine is formed as an intermediate in reaction *g* (68,69):

$$\underset{\text{serine}}{HOOC\cdot CHNH_2\cdot CH_2OH} + \underset{\text{homocysteine}}{HSCH_2\cdot CH_2\cdot CHNH_2\cdot COOH}$$
$$\downarrow$$
$$\underset{\text{cystathionine}}{HOOC\cdot CHNH_2\cdot CH_2\cdot S\cdot CH_2\cdot CH_2\cdot CHNH_2\cdot COOH}$$
$$\swarrow \quad \searrow$$
$$\underset{\text{cysteine}}{HOOCH\cdot CHNH_2\cdot CH_2\cdot SH} \qquad \underset{\alpha\text{-aminobutyric acid}}{CH_3\cdot CH_2\cdot CHNH_2\cdot COOH}$$

Cleavage of cystathionine furnishes cysteine and α-aminobutyric acid. The latter is found in the urine of persons fed large amounts of methionine (70). That cysteine is also formed from pyruvic acid according to reaction *h* has been proved by using S^{35} added as sulfide (71). Cysteine is easily dehydrogenated to give cystine (reaction *i*); the reaction is reversible, so that cystine and cysteine can be considered interconvertible in their intermediary metabolism.

Glycine, whose formation from glutamic acid either directly (reaction *e*) or via serine (reaction *d* and *f*) has already been discussed, is used for the synthesis of hippuric acid, and is of great importance as a precursor of the purines and of the complicated ring system of the porphyrins. Experiments with labeled glycine reveal that the carbon atoms 4 and 5 of the *purine ring* system are furnished by glycine (72,73) and not by urea (74) as was previously assumed:

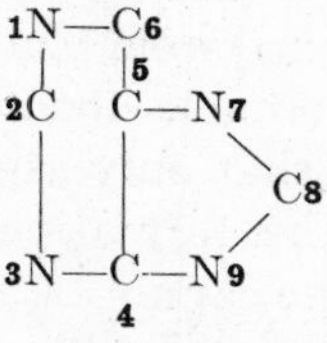

```
1N—C6
 |   |5
2C   C—N7
 |   |    \
 |   |     C8
 |   |    /
3N—C—N9
    4
```

Purine ring

The formation of *heme* from glycine has been proved by incubating glycine labeled with N^{15} and C^{14} with red blood cells of patients suffering from sickle cell anemia or with the nucleated red cells of birds (75,76). The pyrrole rings of the porphyrin system are most probably formed by the condensation of glycine with a β-ketoaldehyde (77). Porphyrins have been formed *in vitro* by condensing glycine with acetoacetaldehyde, $CH_3\cdot CO\cdot CH_2\cdot COH$ (78). The experiments with labeled amino acids also show that neither proline nor glutamic acid are precursors of the porphyrins (79). The view that proline is the mother substance of the pyrrole rings of the porphyrins has to be abandoned. The porphyrin moiety of hemoglobin injected intraperitoneally is not utilized for the formation of new hemoglobin molecules; the organism prefers the total synthesis of porphyrin from glycine to the utilization of porphyrins introduced orally or parenterally (77,80).

Proline, hydroxyproline, and *ornithine* are readily formed from glutamic acid, as shown by using N^{15}-amino acids containing deuterium (81). The first intermediary product is probably *pyrrolidonecarboxylic* acid, which is easily formed *in vitro* by heating glutamic acid and which has also been found in the urine of rats fed large amounts of glutamic acid (82). Reaction k is probably followed by reaction l, the reduction of pyrrolidonecarboxylic acid to proline (pyrrolidinecarboxylic acid). If proline labeled with deuterium and N^{15} is fed to rats, hydroxyproline, ornithine, and glutamic acid are formed from it (81). The formation of ornithine from proline is essentially an ammonolytic cleavage of the pyrrole ring (83). Reaction m is reversible; proline is formed from ornithine by splitting off ammonia (83). The reversibility of reactions l and m is also demonstrated by the formation of deuterioglutamic acid from deuterioornithine (84).

In the lower left corner of Scheme I the *urea cycle* is shown; it had long been realized that arginine is split into ornithine and urea by the enzyme arginase. It was later proved by Krebs (85) that this is in fact the way by which urea is formed in the living organism. Krebs found that the precursor of *arginine* is ornithine and that *citrulline* is formed as an intermediate (86). The carbamyl group, $—CONH_2$, of citrulline is furnished by carbamylglutamic acid $HOOC·CH_2·CH_2·$-$CH(NH·CONH_2)·COOH$, formed from glutamic acid (87). While it was originally believed that the ammonia donor of citrulline is glutamic acid, it was shown by Ratner (88) that only aspartic acid acts as a source of the ammonia required for the formation of arginine from citrulline (reactions o_1 and o_2). Arginine cannot be formed directly by the amination of α-keto-δ-guanidovaleric acid (83). The formation of urea from arginine has been confirmed by experiments in which isotopically labeled arginine was administered to animals, and the nitrogen of the recovered urea molecules shown to originate from the guanido group of arginine (89–91).

The diagram shows also the formation of *creatine* and creatinine from its precursors. The immediate precursor of creatine is guanidoacetic acid, also called *glycocyamine.* It is formed in kidney extracts from arginine and glycine (89,92). The guanido group is furnished by arginine (reaction p_2), the aminoacetic group acid by glycine (reaction p_1). Glycocyamine is methylated in liver slices in the presence of methionine (93). That the methyl group is furnished by methionine has been proved convincingly by using methionine containing a deuteriomethyl group, CD_3 (94). The methylation of glycocyamine (reaction *r*) is an aerobic reaction which does not take place in the liver homogenate; it requires unbroken cells (93).

Urinary *creatinine* is formed exclusively from creatine, as has been proved by using isotopic nitrogen (95). Reaction *s* is an irreversible reaction; creatine cannot be formed from creatinine. Possibly phosphocreatine is the immediate precursor of creatinine, for the phosphorylated compound is converted into creatine spontaneously at 37°C. (96).

Scheme I shows the endogenous formation of the natural L-amino acids. From the diagram it is evident that only three of them, alanine, aspartic acid, and glutamic acid, are formed by the amination of the corresponding α-keto acids. The reverse reaction, the deamination of amino acids to furnish α-keto acids, is the first step in the breakdown of the natural amino acids. The corresponding keto acids have been isolated as dinitrophenylhydrazones (97). Oxidative deamination of the amino acids takes place in liver and in kidney slices. Not only the natural L-amino acids, but also the D-amino acids are deaminated to yield α-keto acids (98). Since the α-keto acids are converted into the natural L-amino acids according to the diagram, it is not surprising that some of the D-amino acids such as D-phenylalanine, D-tryptophan, or D-histidine are utilized by rats just as well as the natural L-amino acids (99). However, the human is not able to utilize them; but D-lysine and D-arginine are metabolized normally in man (100). The conversion of D-amino acids into L-amino acids through deamination and reamination has been called stereonaturalization (101). D-Amino acids are present in the bacterial toxins gramicidin and tyrocidin. Kögl (102) found D-glutamic acid in the hydrolyzate of tumor proteins and considered it to be a typical component of the tumor protein. This was disproved, however, by the finding that the D-glutamic acid found was formed secondarily by racemization (103,104). The enzymes catalyzing the deamination of L-amino acids are more sensitive to poisoning and thus are destroyed more easily than the D-amino acid deaminases (98).

Acetylated amino acids have been considered possible intermediates in the mutual interconversion of α-amino and α-keto acids (105):

$$R{\cdot}CO{\cdot}COOH \rightleftharpoons R{\cdot}CH(NH{\cdot}CO{\cdot}CH_3){\cdot}COOH \rightleftharpoons R{\cdot}CHNH_2{\cdot}COOH$$

The formation of acetylated amino acids has been proved by using liver slices and deuterioacetate (106).

D. Essential Amino Acids. *Methionine* has been mentioned already as a donor both of methyl groups and of sulfur; the methyl groups are utilized for the synthesis of creatine and of choline; the sulfur for the formation of cystine and cysteine. Methionine can, however, be replaced by the corresponding α-keto compound, thiomethyl-α-ketobutyric acid, which is convertible to methionine in the organism (107). Methionine is also formed from homocysteine and choline; evidently the reaction "methionine ⇌ choline" is reversible (108).

Valine, $(CH_3)_2 \cdot CH \cdot CHNH_2 \cdot COOH$, *leucine,* $(CH_3)_2 \cdot CH \cdot CH_2 \cdot CHNH_2 \cdot COOH$, and *isoleucine* $(CH_3)(C_2H_5)CH \cdot CHNH_2 \cdot COOH$, are essential amino acids because their branched carbon chains cannot be formed endogenously (31–34). Likewise the ring systems present in phenylalanine, tyrosine, and tryptophan cannot be formed. Small amounts of tyrosine are, however, formed in the organism from phenylalanine as has been proved by using deuterioamino acids (109). Tyrosine and phenylalanine serve as indispensable precursors of adrenaline and of the thyroid hormone. Tyrosine seems also to be indispensable for the ripening of reticulocytes (110), which is attributed to hallachrome, an indole derivative formed from tyrosine. Other indole derivatives are formed from *tryptophan,* another of the essential amino acids; tryptophan is also a precursor of nicotinic acid or nicotinamide (111). *Histidine* is essential for dogs and rats, but can be formed in the human organism; we do not yet know how the imidazole ring of histidine is formed; possibly formamidinoglutaric acid, which is produced from histidine by the enzyme histidase is the precursor of histidine (112):

$$\begin{array}{c} COOH \cdot CH_2 \cdot CH_2 \cdot CH \cdot COOH \\ | \\ NH{=}CH{-}NH \end{array}$$

α-Formamidinoglutaric acid

Valine, leucine, isoleucine, tyrosine, phenylalanine, threonine, methionine, histidine and tryptophane, although essential for the organism, can be replaced in some animals by the corresponding α-keto acids or the stereoisomeric D-amino acids; the latter substances are deaminated to keto acids and these converted into the L-amino acids (113). It is possible, as mentioned above, to replace some of the L-amino acids by feeding rats the corresponding D-amino acids (99). When large amounts of D-amino acids are injected intravenously, however, death of the animals occurs; this is ascribed to the competitive inhibition of the L-amino acid oxidases by the D-amino acids and to blocking of the normal respiratory process by this inhibition (114). The fact that many of the essential L-amino acids can be replaced by α-keto acids or by D-amino acids shows that the indispensable portion of most of the essential amino acids is their carbon skeleton.

Lysine, the last of the essential amino acids to be mentioned, shows exceptional behavior in this respect. It is neither formed from the corresponding α-keto acid, nor from D-lysine (113). The deamination of lysine, as distinct from the deamination of the other amino acids, is an irreversible reaction. Lysine, in contrast to all of the other amino acids, does not incorporate N^{15} administered as ammonia or as N^{15}-amino acid (115). This singular behavior of lysine is due to the fact that its ε-amino group is less stable than the α-amino group and that lysine in the liver is rapidly converted into α-aminoadipic acid (116):

$$\underset{\text{lysine}}{NH_2{\cdot}CH_2{\cdot}CH_2{\cdot}CH_2{\cdot}CH_2{\cdot}CHNH_2{\cdot}COOH} \rightarrow \underset{\alpha\text{-aminoadipic acid}}{COOH{\cdot}CH_2{\cdot}CH_2{\cdot}CH_2{\cdot}CHNH_2{\cdot}COOH}$$

The ε-amino group of the lysine molecules of proteins is also very unstable and is destroyed by heating proteins to temperatures greater than 150°C. The nutritive value of proteins exposed to such high temperatures is lower than that of the native proteins or of those boiled at 100°C. (117).

References

1. R. H. Burris, P. W. Wilson, *Ann. Rev. Biochem.* **14,** 685 (1945).
2. K. Linderstrøm-Lang, C. F. Jacobsen, *Compt. rend. trav. lab. Carlsberg. Sèr. chim.* **24,** 1 (1943).
3. H. B. Bull, J. Hahn, Abstracts, 113th meeting Am. Chem. Soc. C50 (1948).
4. M. Sreenivasaya *et al.*, *Biochem. J.* **28,** 351 (1934).
5. H. Lineweaver, S. R. Hoover, *J. Biol. Chem.* **137,** 325 (1941).
6. E. Cherbuliez, K. H. Meyer, *Compt. rend. trav. lab. Carlsberg. Sèr. chim.* **22,** 118 (1938).
7. F. Haurowitz, M. Tunca, P. Schwerin, V. Göksu, *J. Biol. Chem.* **157,** 621 (1945).
8. E. A. Risley, A. C. Buffington, L. E. Arnow, *J. Am. Chem. Soc.* **66,** 398 (1944).
9. K. Linderstrøm-Lang *et al.*, *Nature* **142,** 996 (1938).
10. H. P. Lundgren, *J. Biol. Chem.* **138,** 293 (1941).
11. J. I. Routh, H. B. Lewis, *J. Biol. Chem.* **124,** 725 (1938).
12. E. K. Rideal, *Proc. Roy. Soc. London* **B116,** 200 (1934). J. H. Schulman and E. K. Rideal, *Biochem. J.* **27,** 1581 (1933).
13. A. A. Plentl, I. H. Page, *J. Biol. Chem.* **163,** 49 (1946).
14. J. S. Fruton, M. Bergmann, *J. Biol. Chem.* **127,** 627 (1939).
15. C. R. Harington, R. V. Pitt Rivers, *Biochem. J.* **38,** 417 (1944).
16. H. Neurath, G. W. Schwerdt, *Chem. Rev.* **46,** 69 (1950).
17. A. Tiselius, B. Erickson-Quensel, *Biochem. J.* **33,** 1752 (1939).
18. A. Beloff, C. B. Anfinsen, *J. Biol. Chem.* **176,** 863 (1948).
19. D. D. Van Slyke, R. T. Dillon, D. A. MacFadyen, P. Hamilton, *J. Biol. Chem.* **141,** 627 (1941).
20. E. Maschmann, *Naturwissenschaften* **29,** 518 (1940).
21. E. Bamann, O. Schimke, *Biochem. Z.* **310,** 131 (1941).
22. E. Waldschmidt-Leitz, M. Euner, *Z. physiol. Chem.* **282,** 120 (1947).
23. E. Maschmann, E. Helmert, *Biochem. Z.* **280,** 184 (1935); *Z. physiol. Chem.* **216,** 141 (1933).
24. O. K. Behrens, M. Bergmann, *J. Biol. Chem.* **129,** 587 (1939).
25. J. P. Greenstein, *Advances in Enzymol.* **8,** 117 (1948).
26. M. Bergmann, J. S. Fruton, *J. Biol. Chem.* **124,** 324 (1938).
27. J. Shack, *Arch. Biochem.* **17,** 203 (1948).

27*a*. A. Neuberger, *Ann. Rep. Chem. Soc. London* **38,** 283 (1942).

28. W. C. Rose, W. T. Warner, *J. Biol. Chem.* **148,** 457 (1943).

29. W. C. Rose, S. S. Fierke, *J. Biol. Chem.* **143**, 115 (1942).
30. W. C. Rose, W. J. Haines, J. E. Johnson, *J. Biol. Chem.* **146**, 683 (1942).
31. W. C. Rose, *Science* **86**, 298 (1937).
32. W. C. Rose *et al.*, *J. Biol. Chem.* **112**, 275, 283 (1935/6).
33. W. C. Rose, *Proc. Am. Phil. Soc.* **91**, 1 (1947).
34. W. C. Rose, E. E. Rice, *Science* **90**, 186 (1939).
35. G. W. Beadle, *Ann. Rev. Biochem.* **17**, 727 (1948).
36. R. H. J. Plimmer, J. L. Rosedale, W. H. Raymond, J. Lowndes, *Biochem. J.* **28**, 1863 (1934).
37. F. J. Stare, D. M. Hegsted, J. M. McKibbin, *Ann. Rev. Biochem.* **14**, 431 (1945).
38. *Bull. Natl. Research Council U. S.* No. 115 (1943); quoted by F. J. Stare, D. M. Hegsted, J. M. McKibbin, *Ann. Rev. Biochem.* **14**, 441 (1945).
39. A. Bickel, *Deut. med. Wochschr.* **1940**, 393, 423.
40. H. Kraut, H. Braunsal, *Arbeitsphysiol.* **12**, 197 (1942).
41. H. K. Stiebeling, R. M. Leverton, *Ann. Rev. Biochem.* **10**, 423 (1941).
42. I. Abelin, E. Rhyn, *Z. Vitaminforsch.* **12**, 56 (1942).
43. A. Hooygaard, quoted in *Ber. ges. Physiol. u. exptl. Pharmakol.* **129**, 154 (1941).
44. R. J. Block, D. Bolling, *Arch. Biochem.* **3**, 217 (1944).
44*a*. E. Brand, D. K. Bosshardt, Abstracts 114th Meeting Am. Chem. Soc., C38 (1948).
45. R. Elman, *Advances in Protein Chem.* **3**, 269 (1947).
46. S. C. Madden, R. R. Woods, F. W. Shull, J. H. Remington, G. H. Whipple, *J. Exptl. Med.* **81**, 439 (1944).
47. R. Gingras, R. Page, R. Gaudry, *Rev. Can. Biol.* **6**, 802 (1947).
48. H. Sprince, D. W. Woolley, *J. Exptl. Med.* **80**, 213 (1944).
49. D. W. Woolley, *J. Biol. Chem.* **162**, 383; **166**, 783 (1946).
50. E. Mayer, A. Fischer, *Skand. Arch. Physiol.* **75**, 268 (1937).
51. A. Fischer, *Arch. exptl. Zellforschg. Gewebezücht.* **19**, 255 (1937).
52. H. S. Simms, N. Stillman, *J. Gen. Physiol.* **20**, 649 (1937).
53. W. M. Cox, Jr., A. J. Mueller, *J. Clin. Invest.* **23**, 875 (1944).
54. H. N. Christensen, E. L. Lynch, J. H. Powers, *J. Biol. Chem.* **166**, 649 (1946).
55. F. A. Czonka, *Federation Proc.* **7**, 151 (1948).
56. A. Roche, *Bull. soc. chim. biol.* **16**, 270 (1934).
57. M. Florkin, G. Duchateau, *Acta Biol. Belg.* **2**, 219 (1942).
58. H. A. Krebs, L. V. Eggleton, *Biochem. J.* **34**, 1383 (1940).
59. H. G. Wood, C. H. Werkman, A. Hemingway, A. O. Nier, *J. Biol. Chem.* **139**, 483 (1941).
60. R. Schoenheimer, S. Ratner, D. Rittenberg, *J. Biol. Chem.* **130**, 703 (1939).
61. D. E. Green, L. F. Leloir, V. Nocito, *J. Biol. Chem.* **161**, 559 (1945).
62. A. E. Braunstein, M. G. Kritsmann, *Enzymologia* **2**, 129 (1937).
63. T. Winnick, I. Morning-Claesson, D. M. Greenberg, *J. Biol. Chem.* **175**, 127 (1948).
64. W. Sakami, *J. Biol. Chem.* **176**, 995 (1948); **179**, 495 (1949). D. B. Sprinson, *ibid.* **178**, 529 (1949). P. Siekievitz and D. M. Greenberg, *ibid.* **180**, 845 (1949).
65. D. Shemin, *J. Biol. Chem.* **162**, 297 (1946).
66. F. Binkley, V. du Vigneaud, *J. Biol. Chem.* **144**, 507 (1942).
67. V. du Vigneaud *et al.*, *J. Biol. Chem.* **145**, 645 (1944).
68. E. Brand, R. J. Block, B. Kassel, G. F. Cahill, *Proc. Soc. Exptl. Biol. Med.* **35**, 501 (1936).
69. F. Binkley, *J. Biol. Chem.* **155**, 39 (1944).
70. C. E. Dent, *Science* **105**, 335 (1947).

71. C. V. Smythe, *Advances in Enzymol.* **5,** 237 (1945).
72. J. C. Sonne, J. M. Buchanan, A. M. Delluva, *J. Biol. Chem.* **173,** 69, 81 (1948).
73. D. Shemin, D. Rittenberg, *J. Biol. Chem.* **167,** 875 (1947).
74. F. Barnes, R. Schoenheimer, *J. Biol. Chem.* **151,** 123 (1943).
75. I. M. London, D. Shemin, D. Rittenberg, *J. Biol. Chem.* **173,** 797, 799 (1948).
76. K. I. Altman, G. W. Casarett, R. E. Masters, T. R. Noonan, K. Salomon, *J. Biol. Chem.* **176,** 319 (1948).
77. D. Shemin, D. Rittenberg, *J. Biol. Chem.* **166,** 62, 627 (1946); N. S. Radin, D. Rittenberg, D. Shemin, *ibid.* **184,** 745 (1950).
78. H. Fischer, E. Fink, *Z. physiol. Chem.* **280,** 123 (1944).
79. D. Shemin, D. Rittenberg, *J. Biol. Chem.* **159,** 567 (1945).
80. L. L. Miller, F. S. Robscheit-Robbins, G. H. Whipple, *J. Exptl. Med.* **81,** 405 (1945).
81. M. R. Stetten, R. Schoenheimer, *J. Biol. Chem.* **153,** 113 (1944).
82. S. Ratner, *J. Biol. Chem.* **152,** 559 (1944).
83. D. Shemin, D. Rittenberg, *J. Biol. Chem.* **158,** 71 (1945).
84. M. Roloff, S. Ratner, R. Schoenheimer, *J. Biol. Chem.* **136,** 561 (1940).
85. H. A. Krebs, K. Henseleit, *Z. physiol. Chem.* **210,** 33 (1932).
86. H. A. Krebs, L. V. Eggleston, R. Hems, *Biochem. J.* **43,** 406 (1948).
87. P. P. Cohen, S. Grisolia, *J. Biol. Chem.* **174,** 389 (1948); **182,** 747 (1950).
88. S. Ratner, *J. Biol. Chem.* **170,** 761 (1947).
89. K. Bloch, R. Schoenheimer, D. Rittenberg, *J. Biol. Chem.* **138,** 155, 167 (1941).
90. D. Rittenberg, H. Waelsch, *J. Biol. Chem.* **136,** 799 (1940).
91. E. A. Evans, Jr., L. Slotin, *J. Biol. Chem.* **136,** 805 (1940).
92. H. Borsook, J. W. Dubnoff, *J. Biol. Chem.* **138,** 389 (1941).
93. H. Borsook, J. W. Dubnoff, *J. Biol. Chem.* **160,** 635 (1945); **169,** 247 (1947).
94. S. Simmonds, V. du Vigneaud, *J. Biol. Chem.* **146,** 685 (1942).
95. K. Bloch, R. Schoenheimer, *J. Biol. Chem.* **131,** 111 (1939).
96. V. Rosengart, *Nature* **154,** 829 (1944).
97. H. A. Krebs, *Z. physiol. Chem.* **217,** 191 (1933).
98. H. A. Krebs, *Biochem. J.* **29,** 1620 (1935).
99. W. C. Rose, M. Womack, *J. Biol. Chem.* **166,** 103 (1946).
100. A. A. Albanese, Abstracts 114th Meeting Am. Chem. Soc., C37 (1948).
101. Y. Kotake, S. Gotō, *Z. physiol. Chem.* **270,** 48 (1941).
102. F. Kögl, H. Erxleben, G. I. van Veersen, *Z. physiol. Chem.* **277,** 251 (1943).
103. A. C. Chibnall, E. F. Williams, E. Boyland, *Nature* **145,** 311 (1940).
104. D. Rittenberg, G. L. Foster, *J. Biol. Chem.* **133,** 737 (1940).
105. V. du Vigneaud, O. J. Irish, *J. Biol. Chem.* **122,** 349 (1936).
106. K. Bloch, E. Borek, *J. Biol. Chem.* **164,** 483 (1946).
107. W. M. Cahill, G. G. Rudolph, *J. Biol. Chem.* **145,** 201 (1942).
108. S. Simmonds, M. Cohn, J. P. Chandler, V. du Vigneaud, *J. Biol. Chem.* **149,** 519 (1943).
109. A. R. Moss, R. Schoenheimer, *J. Biol. Chem.* **135,** 415 (1940).
110. I. Gad, E. Jacobsen, C. M. Plum, *Acta Physiol. Scand.* **7,** 244 (1944).
111. H. P. Sarrett, G. H. Goldsmith, *J. Biol. Chem.* **167,** 293 (1947).
112. A. C. Walker, C. L. A. Schmidt, *Arch. Biochem.* **5,** 445 (1945).
113. S. Ratner, N. Weissmann, R. Schoenheimer, *J. Biol. Chem.* **147,** 549 (1943).
114. S. Edlbacher, O. Wiss, *Helv. Chim. Acta* **27,** 1831 (1944).
115. R. Schoenheimer, S. Ratner, D. Rittenberg, *J. Biol. Chem.* **130,** 703 (1939).
116. H. Borsook *et al.*, *J. Biol. Chem.* **176,** 1383 (1948).
117. M. Pader, D. Melnick, B. L. Oser, *J. Biol. Chem.* **172,** 763 (1948).

CHAPTER XVII

Protein Synthesis

A. Polymerization of Amino Acids in Vitro. The polymerization of amino acids and of simple peptides can be accomplished in the laboratory by various methods. Polymerization of α-aminocaproic acid was achieved by heat treatment (1). Another more convenient method used for the preparation of polyamino acids is the decarboxylation by traces of water of carbamino anhydrides (2–4):

$$n\ \underbrace{CO{\cdot}CHR{\cdot}NH{\cdot}CO}_{\text{—O—}} \rightarrow n\ CO_2 + (CO{\cdot}CHR{\cdot}NH)_n$$

The polymerization products are typical polypeptides containing amino acids linked by peptide bonds. Their molecular weight is very high and similar to that of true proteins. The close resemblance of these polymers to the natural proteins is shown by the fact that polylysine, the polymeric product of lysine, is hydrolyzed by the enzyme trypsin (5). Poly-α-glutamic acid is similar to the natural polyglutamic acid which forms the capsular substance of *Bacillus anthracis* (6,7).

Polymers have also been obtained from mixtures of amino acids treated according to one of the methods mentioned above. Thus, polymers of alanylglycylglycine containing 20 amino acids were prepared by heating the methyl ester of the tripeptide; the polymers obtained in this way were cyclopeptides free of terminal amino or carboxyl groups (8). Similarly mixed polymers were prepared by exposing to humid air mixtures of carbamino anhydrides (3). It is remarkable that the polymer of L-alanine was found to be insoluble in water, whereas the mixed polymer of D- and L-alanine was soluble (9). The insolubility of the homogeneous poly-L-alanine indicates that its peptide chains are very tightly folded so that water cannot penetrate between them; the mode of folding of poly-DL-alanine seems to be so loose that water molecules can be inserted between CO and NH groups of the peptide grid (9).

Although none of the synthetic polymers is found in nature, their formation *in vitro* is significant from the biological point of view. It is evident from the ease of formation that the energy required for peptide synthesis cannot be very high; it has been estimated to be about 3000 cal. per mole of peptide bond (10). The fundamental differences between the polymerization reactions and the *in vivo* synthesis of proteins are the following: (*1*) protein synthesis *in vivo* takes place in an aqueous medium, while all the polymerization reactions require media poor in water; (*2*) the natural proteins are formed by 15–20 different types of amino acids while the polymers are built up from a few types of amino acids; if mixtures of many amino acids are polymerized, there is no possible way of directing the various amino acids into different positions of the peptide chain; they are distributed at random in the molecule. In contradistinction to this randomness of distribution is the order of amino acids in the natural proteins, which is definite and specific for each of the natural proteins.

B. Peptide Synthesis by Enzymes. It has repeatedly been reported that amino acids or peptides are converted into proteins by the action of proteolytic enzymes. The synthetic proteins so formed were called *plasteins.* Careful repetition of these experiments with improved techniques (11) and with immunologic methods (12) showed that some of the insoluble substances formed were peptides or cyclopeptides (13) of low molecular weight. In other experiments protein formation was due to the multiplication of bacteria or molds; the composition of the proteins formed was different from that of the amino acids treated with the proteolytic enzyme. On the other hand, true protein synthesis has been observed when the peptide mixture present in Witte peptone was exposed to the action of chymotrypsin (14). Chymotrypsin also catalyzes the formation of peptides from amino acid esters (15). The energy required for this endergonic reaction is furnished by the simultaneous formation of free amino acids from one portion of the amino acid esters (15).

Since water molecules are released when amino acids combine with one another to form peptides or proteins, the synthesis is accompanied by a volume increase of the solution, while hydrolysis is accompanied by a distinct volume contraction (see Chapter III, Sect. B). Accordingly, application of high pressure should facilitate the hydrolysis of proteins. Contrary to this expectation it has been claimed that a tryptic hydrolyzate of serum albumin was reconverted to serum albumin on exposure to 6000 atmospheres at 38°C. (16).

While all reports on the enzymatic synthesis of proteins are contradictory and need further investigation, true enzymatic peptide syntheses have been accomplished by Bergmann (17), who obtained acylamino acid anilides from acylamino acids and substituted anilines by the action of papain or chymotrypsin. In this way hippurylanilide was obtained from hippurylamide and aniline by papain:

$$C_6H_5CO{\cdot}NH{\cdot}CH_2{\cdot}CONH_2 + NH_2{\cdot}C_6H_5 \rightarrow C_6H_5{\cdot}CO{\cdot}NH{\cdot}CH_2{\cdot}CO{\cdot}NH{\cdot}C_6H_5 + NH_3$$

and benzoyltyrosylglycylanilide by the action of chymotrypsin on benzoyltyrosine and glycylanilide (18):

$$C_6H_5\cdot CO\cdot NH\cdot CH(CH_2\cdot C_6H_4OH)\cdot COOH + NH_2\cdot CH_2\cdot CO\cdot NH\cdot C_6H_5$$

$$\downarrow$$

$$C_6H_5\cdot CO\cdot NH\cdot CH(CH_2\cdot C_6H_4OH)\cdot CO\cdot NH\cdot CH_2\cdot CO\cdot NH\cdot C_6H_5$$

It might seem surprising at first that the substrates used in these experiments were not the natural amino acids, but anilides and acylated amino acids. The explanation for the ease of the peptide synthesis from these substances is that the reaction products formed are *insoluble* in water and are removed from the reacting system as insoluble precipitates. Accordingly, equilibrium (1):

$$RCOOH + R'NH_2 \rightleftharpoons RCONHR' + H_2O \quad (1)$$

is displaced continuously to the right side of the equation and new amounts of peptide are formed in accordance with the law of mass action. By analogy, it has been assumed that protein synthesis in the living organism will similarly be augmented when the protein formed is insoluble. However, this assumption does not agree with the fact that the enzymatic synthesis of aniline peptides is independent of their solubility (17*a*).

Another reason for the formation of peptides from anilides and acylamino acids is that neither of these substances can form a zwitterion. Peptide synthesis from the nonionized forms (reaction 1) requires a much lower energy supply than peptide synthesis from the ionized forms (reaction 2) (19):

$$RCOO^- + R'\overset{+}{N}H_3 \rightleftharpoons RCONHR' + H_2O \quad (2)$$

since a certain amount of energy is required for the conversion of the ionized amino and carboxyl groups of amino acids in aqueous solution into the nonionized forms, COOH and NH_2.

Reactions (1) and (2) are based on the assumption that protein synthesis represents the reversal of the enzymatic hydrolysis of proteins. The soundness of this assumption has never been proved convincingly. It may well be the case that the pathways of protein synthesis and protein breakdown are different.

Several possible mechanisms have been discussed in the last few years. One of these is the coupling of protein synthesis with the oxidation of other organic substances; thus it was shown that *p*-aminobenzoic acid and glycine added to a liver homogenate combined to form a peptide; the synthesis of the peptide was associated with granular particles of the liver homogenate, and was inhibited by calcium ions (20). Similarly, hippuric acid was formed in liver homogenates from benzoic acid and glycine; the energy required for this endergonic reaction was furnished by the cleavage of adenosine triphosphate (21). Possibly phosphorylated amino acids are formed as intermediates in these reactions (22,23). Actually it has been shown that at pH 4.7 and 37°C. in phosphate solutions hippuric acid is formed spontaneously from glycine and dibenzoyl phosphate (24). No enzyme for the formation of hippuric acid is required in this case and it seems that the necessary energy is released by the cleavage of the anhydride bond between phosphoric and benzoic acid. The "activation" of amino acids by phosphorylation is the most probable explanation for the phenomenon described, although convincing proof for this theory has not yet been furnished.

According to other hypotheses advanced, the activation of amino acids can also be brought about by acetylation (25) or by reduction of the amino acids to amino aldehydes; energy is released when amino aldehydes condense with one another to form a peptide chain (26).

C. Rate of Protein Synthesis in the Living Organism. Two methods have been used extensively to determine the rate of protein formation in the living organism. In one of them use is made of *plasmapheresis*, *i.e.*, the depletion of the plasma proteins; this is accomplished by withdrawing blood from dogs at certain intervals, washing the red cells with saline solution, and reinjecting the dogs with the red cells suspended in the saline solution. In this way different amounts of plasma protein are removed from the blood plasma and the regeneration of plasma protein under various conditions is measured (27,28).

The rate of regeneration was found to be enhanced by administering casein to the dogs, while poor regeneration was observed in dogs whose protein supply consisted mainly of gelatin or zein (29). This is understandable, because gelatin and zein are deficient in some of the essential amino acids (see Table I, page 32). Hemoglobin injected intraperitoneally was much less effective than casein (30), due to the fact that hemoglobin is deficient in isoleucine (31). The maximum amount of plasma protein formed was about 1 g. per day per kg. body weight of the dogs (32).

The regeneration of the plasma proteins is greatly impaired by removal of the liver; in hepatectomized dogs the rate of formation of albumin decreases to 5% and that of globulin to 15% of the normal value (33,34). The conclusion has been drawn that the plasma proteins are formed in the liver and that a dynamic equilibrium exists between plasma and liver proteins (29). According to this view the liver protein is a pool which can be formed by or converted into plasma protein and which is different from the integral protein of the cells; this integral protein is not withdrawn from the organism by plasmapheresis.

If the red cells withdrawn from the organism are *not* reinjected, the regeneration of hemoglobin can be examined. This "double depletion" of plasma and of red cells is also counteracted by administering proteins containing all the essential amino acids (35). The maximum amount formed is about 1 g. per day per kg. body weight of the dog (35); but the sum of plasma protein and of globin formed never exceeds 1.5 g. per day. The type of protein formed depends on the amino acid composition of the administered protein; while the administration of egg proteins to doubly depleted dogs gives rise to the preferential formation of plasma proteins, feeding of beef muscle protein leads mainly to the formation of hemoglobin (36). The formation of globin, the protein moiety of hemoglobin, also takes place in the liver (37).

Protein synthesis is not restricted to the liver. Formation of proteins takes place continually in all organs, even in those of starving animals (38). Protein synthesis also occurs in tissue cultures. The type of protein formed depends on the cells of the culture and not on the protein offered as nutrient; thus chicken fibroblasts cultivated in rabbit plasma produce chicken protein and not rabbit protein. In addition to the protein of chicken fibroblasts, chicken serum proteins are also formed, as was proved serologically (39). Evidently the rabbit protein was decomposed and chicken protein was rebuilt from the breakdown products of the rabbit protein. However homologous proteins or peptones are better utilized in tissue cultures than proteins or peptones of other species (40).

A second method by which information is obtained on protein synthesis in living organisms or in tissue culture is based on the utilization of *isotopically labeled amino acids* or proteins. Attempts have been made to determine the *half-life of proteins* by means of this method. Amino acids labeled with deuterium (41), N^{15}, or with isotopic carbon were injected or introduced with the food and the isotope content of the plasma proteins was determined at different intervals (42,43).

The interpretation of these experiments with isotopes is somewhat ambiguous, because we do not know whether the isotopic amino acid administered to the organism is used only for the synthesis of one protein molecule or whether it is utilized a second or third time for the synthesis of other protein molecules. Experiments with N^{15}-glycine, in which account has been taken of these complications, indicate that about 0.2 g. plasma protein per day per kg. body weight is formed in men, and about 1 g. plasma protein in the rat (43). The rate of albumin and globulin formation was determined by feeding C^{14}-lysine; it was found that the plasma globulins are formed faster than the albumins, but that they also disappear more rapidly from the plasma (44). About 10% of the plasma proteins were replaced in 24 hr. (44). The turnover of muscle protein is much slower than that of plasma or liver protein, as shown by experiments with N^{15}-glycine (45). The lowest rate of regeneration is found in hemoglobin; only 2.5% of this protein is formed each day (41,45). The half-life of hemoglobin is about 25–30 days.

The regeneration of fetal tissue was found to proceed at a greater rate than that of adult tissues, when isotopic glycine was used as a tracer; it is not yet clear, however, whether growth is caused by an inhibition of the breakdown of proteins (46), or by an increased turnover of protein (47). The highest rate of protein formation was found to take place in the intestinal and pancreatic tissue. This is not at all strange in view of the large amounts of proteins produced with the secretions of these organs (48).

Isotopically labeled amino acids are also incorporated into the proteins of organ slices or of homogenates. The isotopic sulfur, S^{35}, of cystine or of methionine passes into the proteins of liver slices. It is not certain whether we are dealing here with true protein synthesis, since most of the isotopic amino acids can be split off again by reducing agents; apparently a portion of the sulfur-containing amino acids is fixed only by dithio bonds, which are cleaved by reducing agents (49).

The incorporation of C^{14}-glycine into the proteins of the intestinal mucosa is inhibited by azide and also by grinding of the tissue; evidently the protein synthesis is coupled with an oxidative process catalyzed by structural enzymes (50). The incorporation of alanine containing the group $C^{14}OOH$ into liver slices is likewise an aerobic process (51). Liver slices are even able to incorporate $C^{14}O_2$ into their proteins (52) and to convert C^{14}-glycine into C^{14}-serine (53). All this indicates that the protein synthesis in liver slices and in other tissues is not a simple formation of peptide bonds between amino acids, but a more complicated reaction. Labeled amino acids are not incorporated directly into proteins; they combine at first with a peptide, which is considered to be a precursor of the protein formed (54).

Radioactive isotopes have also been used to elucidate the formation of thyroglobulin; it has been found that radioiodine administered to animals accumulates only in the thyroid gland, and that thyroglobulin is formed there exclusively; other organs contain only traces of iodine, owing to the diffusion of iodides into the tissue (55). If the thyroid gland is removed by surgical operation, thyroxine is formed in the liver and the intestines, as proved by the administration of radioiodine (56).

Although much valuable information concerning protein synthesis has been derived from these experiments in which isotopically labeled substances were used as tracers, one of the main problems remains unsolved. We cannot decide on the basis of these experiments whether protein molecules are formed and then after a certain period of time are broken down, or whether they undergo a continual exchange of their constituents; such an exchange could be achieved by a temporary opening of the peptide bonds and an incorporation of amino acid molecules between the ends of the opened chains. In order to solve this problem use has been made of immunological reactions. It was reported in Chapter XIV that antibodies are found in the γ-globulin portion of the serum globulins. If we produce antibodies in a rabbit by injecting the animal with an antigen, we can differentiate the newly formed γ-globulins from the γ-globulins present prior to the injection by the ability of the former to precipitate the antigen used. Thus, injection of pneumococci of the type III into rabbits leads to the formation of anti-S III in the globulin fraction of the immune serum. When the rabbit used has also been injected with N^{15}-glycine, the isotopic amino acid is found in the newly formed antibody (57), proving that the isotopic amino acid is incorporated into the newly formed protein.

The problem of the steady incorporation of amino acids by opening and closure of the peptide chains was investigated by injecting rabbits with the serum of another rabbit previously sensitized against S I polysaccharides; the anti-S I antibodies transferred from an immunized rabbit to a normal rabbit injected with N^{15}-glycine did not undergo any alteration; the isotopic glycine was not incorporated into their molecules (57). This would indicate that the molecules of the plasma proteins do not undergo scission and closure of their peptide bonds and that they do not incorporate amino acids, but rather are broken down without intermediary resynthesis of parts of the molecules. However, C^{14}-leucine, used instead of N^{15}-glycine, is incorporated into the anti-S I antibodies (58). The experiments with isotopic carbon are more clear-cut than those with isotopic nitrogen because the latter can be lost and exchanged by deamination. Nevertheless it is very difficult to accept the conclusion that antibody globulins can undergo an exchange of their amino acids and at the same time retain their antibody function. Antibody properties are most certainly due to a complementariness of the antibody surface with the determinant antigen surface. It is difficult to imagine how this complementary shape could be maintained if the molecule were subject to a repeated exchange of its amino acids with the amino acids of the surrounding solution.

D. Nucleic Acids and Protein Synthesis. Nucleic acids are present in all cells. Owing to their occurrence in the nucleus and in the chromosomes, great importance is attributed to the nucleic acids and they are generally considered to be involved in the phenomena of growth and heredity. Since both these phenomena are closely related to the synthesis of the cellular proteins, we have to describe briefly the distribution of nucleic acids in the cells and their relation to the cellular proteins. The possible role of the nucleic acids in protein synthesis will be discussed in a subsequent section.

It was originally thought that the substances which we call nucleic acids occur only in the cellular nucleus, not in the cytoplasm, and thus followed the designation assigned them. We know today that a considerable portion of the ribonucleic acid (see Chapter XI, Sect. G) is found in the cytoplasm, while desoxyribonucleic acid is present chiefly in the nucleus and thus corresponds to the classical view. According to this old view the growth of the cell is determined by the nucleus. One should expect, therefore, that only desoxyribonucleic acid will be involved in the processes of growth and protein synthesis. Experiments carried out in the last few years have demonstrated, however, that *protein synthesis is particularly intense in those parts of the cell where ribonucleic acid is abundant, i.e.*, in the *nucleolus* and in the *cytoplasmic granules.* Large amounts of protein seem to be secreted in or around the nucleolus, which forms a small particle in the larger nucleus (59). While most of the chromatin of the nucleus is euchromatin consisting of desoxyribonucleic acid, the chromatin associated with the nucleolus contains mainly ribonucleic acid. It has been called heterochromatin. The protein formed in the environment of the nucleolus migrates toward the nuclear membrane, on the outside of which ribonucleotides and cytoplasmic proteins are produced (59). Large amounts of ribonucleates are found in growing organs and in secreting glands, *i.e.*, in organs where protein synthesis proceeds at a high rate. On the other hand, small amounts of ribonucleate are present in those organs which do not grow, even if they are biologically very active (60).

The histochemical differentiation of ribonucleates from desoxyribonucleates is based on the treatment of the cells with ribonuclease; staining or ultraviolet micrography before the treatment with the enzyme indicates the sites of both types of nucleic acids, while after treatment with ribonuclease only desoxyribonucleic acid is visible (60). Ribonucleates are turned over much more rapidly than desoxyribonucleates. 3.3% of the ribonucleate of the liver contained P^{32} 2 hr. after the injection of radioactive phosphate; in the same period only 0.1% of the desoxyribonucleate exchanged its phosphorus atoms with P^{32} (61). Nucleic acids are also necessary for the growth of tissue cultures; the labile growth factor of embryonal extracts, which is indispensable for the growth of tissue cultures, is probably a nucleoprotein (62).

Since nucleic acids are rich in phosphoric acid groups, they are distinctly acidic substances and form salt-like compounds with proteins; the formation of these artificial nucleoproteins and their relation to the natural nucleoproteins have been discussed in Chapter XI. Owing to their acidic properties the nucleic acids combine primarily with basic proteins such as protamines and histones. These basic substances have been found mainly in nuclei; it is not certain whether they occur also in the cytoplasm. It is remarkable that nuclei contain either protamines or histones, but never both types of basic proteins (63).

Protamines have been found in fish sperm cells, histones in the nuclei of nucleated erythrocytes (64). Their nucleic acid compounds are extracted from the cells by molar sodium chloride solutions; if these solutions are dialyzed, protamines diffuse through the semipermeable membranes, while the nucleic acids remain inside the dialyzer (65). The nucleic acid bound to protamines and histones is mainly desoxyribonucleic acid; ribonucleic acid is found in the residual chromosome, *i.e.*, the fraction of the nuclei which does not dissolve in molar sodium chloride; the ribonucleic acid is there combined with true *protein* and not with protamine or histone (66,67). The structural continuity of the chromosomes is not destroyed when they are treated with nucleases or with a proteolytic enzyme; destruction is achieved, however, by the successive action of nucleases and proteolytic enzymes (68).

While ribonucleic acid is probably involved in protein synthesis, desoxyribonucleic acid seems to be of some importance for the specificity of the cell, possibly also for the phenomena of heredity. Most of the desoxyribonucleic acid is found in the nucleus. The chromosomes are formed mainly by desoxyribonucleic acid; chromosomes of calf thymus contain 90–92% desoxyribonucleohistone acid, while only 2–3% desoxyribonucleate is found in the fraction which is insoluble in molar sodium chloride (66). In eggs of the sea urchin, *Arbacia*, the amount of desoxyribonucleic acid increases by 10–15 fold after fertilization, while the amount of ribonucleic acid remains unchanged (69).

Desoxyribonucleic acid is also regarded as the essential constituent of the nuclear chromatin (70) or of the genes (71), and as the agent which is able to alter the type of pneumococci (72), and of other bacteria (73). Changes in the enzymic constitution of yeast strains by extracts of other strains have also been ascribed to the action of desoxyribonucleic acid (74). Moreover desoxyribonucleic acid has been found in paramecin, the killer substance of *Paramecium aurelia* (75). Desoxyribonucleic acid is also found in the so-called structural proteins of the cell, elongated threadlike particles, which are insoluble in concentrated solutions of sodium chloride, but are dissolved by alkaline solutions of urea (76,77). In these structural proteins, and also in the chromosomes, the nucleic acid threads are oriented parallel to the protein threads (78) and not perpendicular to their longitudinal axis, as had previously been assumed.

We do not yet know whether ribonucleic acid and desoxyribonucleic acid are interconvertible, although this possibility had been discussed (60).

While most of the workers in the field of cytochemistry regard the nuclear desoxyribonucleoproteins as essential carriers of heredity and ascribe the positive Feulgen test (see Chapter XI, Sect. G) to their presence, this view is contested by Stedman and Stedman (78*a*), who attribute the basophilic properties of the cellular nucleus to an acidic protein called chromosomin. The Stedmans' views are based on the fact that the red pigment produced by the action of Feulgen reagent on desoxyribonucleic acid is water soluble, while the pigment obtained on treating nuclei with the reagent is either insoluble or adsorbed to the nuclei; moreover, chromosomes according to analyses of Stedman contain only 12–24% histone and 28–44% nucleic acid, but 33–60% chromosomin; the latter is a protein whose isoelectric point is near pH 3–4. Stedman objects to the general opinion concerning the importance of nucleoprotamines and nucleohistones in heredity, because the structure of protamines is so simple that it could hardly account for their alleged importance as carriers of heredity. It is postulated, for this reason, that only large *protein* molecules would be able to transmit the complicated pattern of hereditary characteristics. This reasoning and the criticism of the general views concerning the role of nucleoproteins in heredity and determination of specificity are certainly justified. It is, on the other hand, hard to imagine how the Feulgen test could be given by a protein devoid of desoxyribose. Further examination of the experimental findings and of their interpretations is certainly necessary.

E. Structural Protein Units in the Cell. Before discussing the mechanism of protein synthesis we have to describe the physicochemical state of proteins in the living cell, as far as it is known today. One portion of the proteins is certainly dissolved in the cellular fluid, another part present in the structural units, such as fibers or granules (79).

The high viscosity of the *cellular fluid* indicates that the proteins dissolved in this liquid have elongated, threadlike molecules. The orientation of these protein threads can, sometimes, be determined by observing them in polarized light under the microscope (78).

The same method has been used to examine *fibrous protein molecules* in cellular membranes, muscle and nerve, and other cells. In many of these membranes the proteins combine with lipids to form oriented layers. Examination of the cortical layer of sea urchin eggs (78*b*) and of nerve tissue (78*c*) shows that the lipid molecules are arranged radially, so that their longitudinal axis is directed from the center of the cells to its surface. The protein fibers, on the other hand, are oriented tangentially, so that the protein molecules form a network parallel to the surface of the cell (78*c*,80). A similar orientation of lipids and proteins has also been found in plastids of green plants; if they are examined in polarized light, they exhibit the phenomenon of layer birefringence (81).

Besides the lipoproteins, glucoproteins also form elongated particles in the cells; fertilisin, a substance involved in the fertilization of sea urchin eggs, is such a fibrous glucoprotein (82).

Small changes in the physicochemical state of fibrous proteins can hardly be detected with the instruments at our disposal at present. We can only determine the orientation of the fibers, and occasionally, their shape. One of the few tissues where alterations in the state of protein fibers can easily be detected is the transparent tissue of the lens of the eye. Physicochemical changes brought about in the lenticular protein fibers by salt solutions or by acids result in the appearance of turbidities. This method has revealed typical differences between the lenses of calves and of adult beef. While young lenses exposed to hypertonic salt solutions or to low temperatures respond to form nuclear cataract, adult lenses display a peripheral turbidity (83).

The physicochemical state of the structural proteins is highly important for the permeability of the cells and their excitability (84), their adhesiveness to other cells (85), and other properties (86). The fibrous protein particles can be made visible by electron micrography. Electron micrographs of muscle proteins (87,88), skin (89), and other organs (90) show distinctly the fibrous structure of the protein particles. One must not forget, however, that the fibrous structure is not always an intrinsic property of the protein molecules and that globular proteins such as insulin, hemocyanin, or virus proteins can also be converted into fibrous particles. This transformation from the globular to the fibrous state is frequently reversible (91).

In the last few years the attention of biochemists and cytologists has been directed to submicroscopic *granules* in the cells. These granules pass into aqueous extracts of the cells and are responsible for the turbidity of these extracts. By using aqueous salt or sucrose solutions of suitable concentration and density and by fractional centrifugation of the extracts the granules are obtained as a sediment and can be analyzed. By short centrifugation at lower velocity whole cells, cell nuclei, and larger particles, called mitochondria, are removed from the extract. Further centrifugation at higher speed furnishes the submicroscopic granules, called microsomes (92–95). Another method used for the separation of subcellular granules is chromatography (96).

The chemical analysis of the mitochondria shows that they consist largely of *ribonucleic acid*, protein, and lipids (97). The occurrence of ribonucleic acid in the mitochondria has been confirmed by many workers (98–100). Desoxyribonucleic acid has never been found in the granules. The mitochondria also contain important enzymes such as cytochrome oxidase, peroxidase (98), fatty acid dehydrogenase (101), and particularly the enzymes involved in the tricarboxylic acid cycle (102), moreover some of the hydrolytic enzymes such as trypsin, cathepsin, amylase, and ribonuclease (60). It seems that the smallest granules are particularly rich in enzymes (92).

For all these reasons, and with a consideration of the connection between content of ribonucleic acid and protein synthesis, it has been suggested that the *submicroscopic particles* are the *fundamental units* of living organisms and that they are endowed with the *power of self-duplication* (102*a*,103). The size and the properties of these granules resemble those of the viruses; actually, it is sometimes impossible to decide whether one is dealing with a virus or with subcellular granules (104). It seems appropriate, therefore, to give a brief survey of our knowledge about the viruses, the smallest living units known, before we discuss further the fundamental question of self-reproduction or, in other words, the problem of the synthesis of specific proteins in the living cell.

F. Virus Particles (105). Virus particles were purified and isolated for the first time in the crystalline state by Stanley, who succeeded in recrystallizing tobacco mosaic virus by fractionation with ammonium sulfate. The virus behaved in some respects like a pure protein, since it could be dissolved and then recrystallized by increasing the concentration of ammonium sulfate; on the other hand, the virus crystals seemed to be "living" because they multiplied in plants inoculated with a trace of the crystals, increasing in amount in a period of 4 days to about one million times that inoculated (106).

Understandably, the fact that a crystalline preparation could multiply aroused the interest of all biologists and chemists. Crystallizability had always been considered to be a property of lifeless material such as minerals, and due to a rigid, unchangeable structure. Since life, on the other hand, implies a continual change of composition, crystallizability was believed to be irreconcilable with all ideas concerning the nature of living substance. We must not forget, however, that crystalline shape implies no more than a regular repetition of structural elements. If many small structural elements are the same in size and shape, and if they aggregate in such a manner that a regular three-dimensional lattice of identical particles is formed, this lattice will appear to our eye as a crystal, even if the interior of each of the particles undergoes a continual rearrangement of its atoms and molecules. The same is also true for the molecules of lifeless crystals. Many of their molecular groups undergo continual oscillation, as is indicated by infrared spectroscopy and by other physicochemical methods.

The great importance of the virus particles for the problem of protein synthesis is evident from the fact that all, even the simplest viruses, contain protein and nucleic acid (107). While desoxyribonucleic acid has been found in the higher viruses, whose composition is more complicated, the lower viruses contain only ribonucleic acid. Owing to their nucleic acid content the virus proteins are acidic proteins; in the interisoelectric range they combine with serum albumin and other proteins to form mesomorphous fibers, which are insoluble at low ionic strength (108).

The shape and the structure of the viruses is maintained by their proteins, not by the nucleic acid. The latter can be split off by enzymes without any change in the shape and the structure of the virus particles (109). The activity of the virus, its ability to reproduce, is lost after exposure of the virus to nucleases (109).

The crystallizability of the virus is not impaired by the loss of its nucleic acid component; turnip yellow mosaic virus was obtained in crystals as nucleoprotein and also as crystalline protein after removal of the nucleic acid (110). Examination of the virus particles in polarized ultraviolet light showed that the planes of all purine rings of the nucleic acid component are parallel to each other and that they are perpendicular to the longitudinal axis of the elongated particles (111).

The molecular weight of the tobacco mosaic virus particles was found to be close to 50 million (112). This high value, determined by ultracentrifugation, was confirmed by examination of flow birefringence and electron microscopy. Similar values were found for other types of viruses. The molecular weight of the rabbit papilloma virus is about 20 million (113); that of a bacteriophage isolated from staphylococci was found to be 300 million (114). According to electron micrographs, the tobacco mosaic virus particles are elongated rods, 15 mμ thick and 300 mμ long (115). The diameter of the influenza virus is approximately 100–210 mμ (116). In concentrated urea solutions the tobacco mosaic virus is depolymerized to particles of molecular weight 100,000 (117). Disintegration of the virus protein has also been achieved by treatment with sodium dodecyl sulfate (118).

The size and the diameter of virus particles vary within wide limits; the smallest virus particles, such as those of foot and mouth disease, have a diameter of approximately 10 mμ, while the largest viruses, such as that of psittacosis, have an average diameter of approximately 275 mμ (112). The largest viruses exceed small bacteria in size. Only the vegetable viruses are crystalline rodlike particles. Animal viruses do not crystallize. The chemical composition of the smaller viruses is very simple; they contain protein and nucleic acid, but are almost free of carbohydrates and lipids. The larger virus particles have a much more complicated composition, containing not only lipids but also different enzymes (119). An analysis of the T-2 bacteriophage of *Escherichia coli* revealed the following composition: 51% protein, 5–6% lipid, 40% nucleic acid; one sixth of the nucleic acid was ribonucleic acid and five sixths desoxyribonucleic acid (120).

The amino acid composition of the virus protein has been determined in the T-4 phage of *E. coli*. It is most striking that the amino acid content of the virus protein was almost identical with the amino acid content of the coli bacteria (121). This similarity of the amino acid pattern suggests that the virus protein is formed by some rearrangement of amino acids of the host and that no deamination or any other catabolic alteration would be necessary when *host protein is converted into virus protein*. On the other hand, however, it was found that $N^{15}H_3$ added to the culture medium passed into the virus while bacterial nitrogen was not utilized by the virus (122). This would mean that the virus protein is formed from the culture medium and not from the bacterial protein. About 75% of the virus phosphorus was formed from the labeled phosphorus of the medium, while 25% was furnished by bacterial phosphorus (122). It is very difficult to interpret these findings. Possibly the host bacteria furnish the enzymes required for the synthesis of virus protein (122).

Because of their small size, their crystalline shape, and their self-reproducibility, the virus particles represent one of the most interesting subjects of biological research. If they are alive, they are certainly the simplest of all living units. But are they really living? In spite of the extensive discussion of this paramount problem by the foremost workers in this field, no satisfactory answer can be given at the present time. The main difference between viruses and other living beings, such as bacteria, is that viruses multiply only in living cells. The presence of a living host cell is an indispensable prerequisite for the growth of the virus. Dead tissues constitute a barrier beyond which multiplying virus cannot pass (125). We are not aware of the reason for this phenomenon. It may have something to do with the surface properties of the structural elements in the host cells. It seems that viruses cannot exist in homogeneous solutions, but that they must either adhere end-to-end to other particles of the same virus or be attached to structural elements of the host cells (123).

Since the viruses can be recrystallized in the same way as typical proteins, they are regarded as molecules by many workers and the particle weight determined by sedimentation or by electron micrography is called the molecular weight. However, the particles of a virus preparation are not quite uniform in size; the measured molecular weights are average values and it is doubtful whether we can rightly call the virus particles molecules (124).

The multiplication of viruses bears some resemblance to the autocatalytic conversion of proenzymes into enzymes. A small amount of trypsin is able to convert large amounts of trypsinogen into trypsin; similarly considerable amounts of pepsinogen are converted into pepsin by traces of pepsin (150). We can stress the analogy between virus growth and enzyme activation by saying that inoculation of trypsinogen with trypsin results in a multiplication of trypsin. Or emphasizing the other side of the problem we can call the protein of the living host a provirus and say that the virus catalyzes the conversion of provirus to virus (125,150). Evidently it is a matter of definition and nomenclature whether we choose to call the viruses living or lifeless (123) and we must admit that no definite criterion for rendering an unequivocal decision on this fundamental problem exists at the present time.

G. Mechanism of Protein Synthesis (126). In the preceding sections of this chapter the few data available concerning protein synthesis by polymerization and by enzymatic condensation were reported and an attempt was made to correlate protein synthesis with certain parts of the cell or with other metabolic events. The results of the pertinent observations can be summarized in the following manner: (*1*) protein synthesis seems to take place in or around the nucleolus, in small granular particles of the cytoplasm, and also in virus particles; (*2*) the sites of protein synthesis are rich in ribonucleic acid. When we attempt to construct a reasonable picture of the mechanism of protein synthesis, founded on these few facts, we have to abandon the safe basis of experimental research; we can at best advance some more or less vague speculations and try to decide whether or not they are reconcilable with our present knowledge of the physicochemical properties of proteins.

The main problem with which we are confronted is to account for the high degree of *specificity of the protein formed*. We have seen in preceding chapters of this book that each species has its specific proteins, that many of the organs have their own unique specific proteins which differ from those of other organs of the same individual, and that each cell always produces the same specific protein. We have heard, moreover, that this specificity is attributable to a specific amino acid content, to the specific order of the amino acids in the peptide chain, and to the specific mode of folding of the peptide chains, so that the same globular protein particle is always formed. How can we explain these facts? The explanation given by most workers in this field is that the cell must contain some unchangeable pattern which acts as a *template*, a mold by which the protein is formed. Although no one has ever seen such a template or proved its presence, we have to accept its existence, because we have hardly any other alternative explanation for the continual production of specific and identical protein molecules.

The next questions to be asked are: (*1*) is the shape of the protein molecule formed identical with that of the template or is the protein molecule a negative print of the template? (*2*) is the template itself composed of proteins, nucleic acids, nucleoproteins, or other material? Very divergent answers have been given to these questions by different workers. While some assume that protein synthesis is essentially reproduction, *i.e.*, formation of a *positive replica*, others assume the formation of *negative replicas*. Likewise there is no agreement concerning the *role of the nucleic acids* in reproduction of proteins. The following possibilities have been considered (60):

(*a*) The nucleic acids form a spatial matrix for the formation of protein molecules.

(*b*) The nucleic acids combine with proteins to form insoluble nucleoproteins; in this manner the newly formed protein is removed from the solution so that the equilibrium between protein precursors and protein is shifted toward the latter and thus protein synthesis is furthered.

(*c*) Nucleic acids act as a source of energy for the synthesis of proteins; it is imaginable that energy could be furnished by oxidation of their pentose residues or of the purine derivatives.

(*d*) Nucleic acids furnish the material required for the formation of coenzymes. Ribose, adenine, and phosphoric acid, present in nucleic acids, could be utilized for the synthesis of flavin adenine nucleotides and also pyridine nucleotides.

Let us discuss first the question of whether protein molecules are formed as positive or as negative replicas of the postulated cellular templates. We know that protein molecules consist of long peptide chains and that these peptide chains are folded so that a three-dimensional globular protein molecule is formed. The diameter of this particle is about 20–100 Å. We know of no forces which could be exerted by a possible matrix and operate over such long distances. The forces operating between ions and polar groups (see Chapter X, Sect. A) decrease very rapidly with an increase of the mutual distance and can hardly operate over more than 4–5 Å. The magnitude of these forces depends obviously on the size of the two areas between which they are operating and it is imaginable that in a vacuum forces between large areas would be effective over ranges even longer than 4 or 5 Å. In biological systems, however, we deal not with a vacuum, but with a situation where there are always water molecules present; these are polar particles possessing a high dielectric constant. The electrostatic attraction and repulsion will therefore be reduced by water molecules very considerably. It will be only $1/80$ of the force exerted in a vacuum. In other words, electrostatic forces cannot operate in aqueous systems over distances of more than 4–5 Å. Obviously the direct reproduction by intermolecular forces of a globular molecule with a diameter of 20–100 Å is irreconcilable with our present knowledge on the range and effectiveness of intermolecular forces.

The idea that *the reproduction of protein molecules can only take place in the expanded state, in a monomolecular film,* was advanced a number of years ago (127,128) and is the only concept reconcilable with our knowledge of the laws governing intermolecular forces (129–131). We have to assume, accordingly, that the peptide chains of the protein to be formed are synthesized in an expanded monomolecular film on the surface of the template, and that the folding of the peptide chains and the conversion of the two-dimensional peptide layer into the three-dimensional protein globule is a secondary process, apart and distinct from the true synthesis of the peptide chain.

Physicochemical considerations have led the author to the belief that *the two-dimensional peptide structure is a true positive replica of the template.* This seems at first sight contradictory to the view that complementariness is essential for the relations between enzyme and substrate or antigen and antibody. We have seen in Chapter XIV that antibodies are proteins whose shape is adjusted complementarily to the shape of the antigen molecules, suggesting that antigens act as a template and that antibody molecules are negative prints of this template. This view, which is supported by all our experience on the formation of antibodies and on antigen–antibody reactions, can very well be reconciled with the view on protein synthesis in monomolecular films, when we assume that the *antigen acts as a template in the second phase of protein synthesis*, in the formation of a globular antibody particle from the expanded protein film. Accordingly, the globular antibody particle is complementarily adapted to the globular antigen molecule and not to an expanded antigen film.

The synthesis of antibodies is a special case of protein synthesis, but is certainly not different from the synthesis of other proteins such as normal serum globulins. We have no reason to assume two different types of protein synthesis. We must also postulate, therefore, that the molecules of proteins formed in normal cells are adapted complementarily to determinant groups of template molecules in their neighborhood. If we accept this viewpoint, the concept of complementariness has to be generalized. The term *autoantibodies* has been proposed (132) to describe the proteins formed in a normal organism; it is assumed that they are adapted complementarily to specific templates present in the site of protein synthesis. Only if these normal templates are covered or coated by a foreign antigen will the normal process of folding of the expanded peptide chain be disturbed and antibodies to the injected antigen be formed (129).

The concept of a template which acts as a mold for the formation of a *negative* complementary print, has been used by many authors to explain the formation of proteins, genes, and enzymes (133,134). The formation of abnormal proteins in cancer has been attributed to an abnormal pattern of the template in cancerous tissue (136), *e.g.*, to the planar ring systems of carcinogens (135) or to their electronic structure (137). The author shares the belief of Pauling (138) that all specific biological reactions are due to the same intermolecular forces, which are in turn dependent upon atomic contact and the process of replica formation. Extending this concept, the author believes that *the first step of protein synthesis* is essentially the formation of a *positive replica of a primary template, both present as expanded monomolecular films*, and that *the second step is the formation of a negative globular replica, complementarily adapted to a secondary globular template.*

If we accept this concept of protein synthesis in the living cell, we have to answer also the questions which arise as to the nature of the templates and their mode of action. What, exactly, is the two-dimensional template for the formation of the expanded protein film? Is it a protein, a nucleic acid, or something else? The fact that nucleic acids always abound at the sites of protein synthesis has led numerous authors to the view that they constitute the templates for protein synthesis and that they confer upon the newly formed protein the specificity typical for each species of the vegetable or animal kingdom. Nucleic acids are polar molecules; they have many negatively charged phosphoric acid groups, polar hydrophilic hydroxyl groups in their sugar components, and also basic groups in their purine or pyrimidine bases. Undoubtedly they are able to exert strong forces on adjacent molecules. There is convincing evidence available that nucleic acids combine with proteins (see Chapter XI, Sect. G) and that protein molecules and nucleic acid molecules become distorted when they combine with each other (139).

It has been assumed that the positively charged groups of the basic amino acids of the protein combine with the negatively charged phosphoric acid groups of the nucleic acids, and that in this way a negative replica of the nucleic acid template is formed (134,140). It seems to the author that the strongly acidic properties of nucleic acids are not an argument in favor of their possible role as a template because the acidic character of nucleic acids is so strong that they combine with most proteins in a quite nonspecific manner. Moreover, nucleic acids consist of only seven or eight different units: adenine, guanine, cytosine, uracil, thymine, phosphoric acid, and ribose or desoxyribose. It is very difficult to imagine that a nucleic acid template should determine such small differences as those between human and bovine serum albumin, which differ slightly in their amino acid compositions (141). We do not yet know whether nucleic acids are species-specific. If they are not specific, they cannot form specific templates. If they are specific, one can hardly imagine how they could direct the different amino acids into their specific positions in the peptide chain to be formed. The phosphoric acid groups of the nucleic acids would mainly combine with the basic amino acids of the proteins.

Although we do not yet know whether nucleic acids are specific with regard to the sequence of their bases, we know that they consist of mononucleotide units and that each of these possesses a phosphoric acid group. The distances between these groups are equal in the extended polynucleotide molecule. The negative charges of the phosphoric acid groups repel one another, so that the molecule has a tendency to remain in the expanded state. How this more or less regular molecule should direct the formation of the infinite number of specific proteins is a question for which there is no imaginable answer afforded by our present knowledge of nucleic acids.

Let us abandon, therefore, the assumption that the primary template for the formation of a monomolecular protein film consists of nucleic acids, and let us examine the view that *the primary template is formed by a protein layer*. According to this view, the formation of the expanded protein film would essentially be the *duplication* of another expanded film (129,130). We have to imagine in such a case that each of the L-amino acids of the template layer attracts L-amino acids of the same type from the surrounding cellular medium and that the amino acids forming this second layer are linked to each other by the action of non-specific enzymes of the cathepsin or papain type. In this manner the first layer would be duplicated as shown by the diagram in Figure 51, where the peptide chains of the template (T) and of the replica (R) are formed by lysine, alanine, tyrosine, aspartic acid, and leucine. This

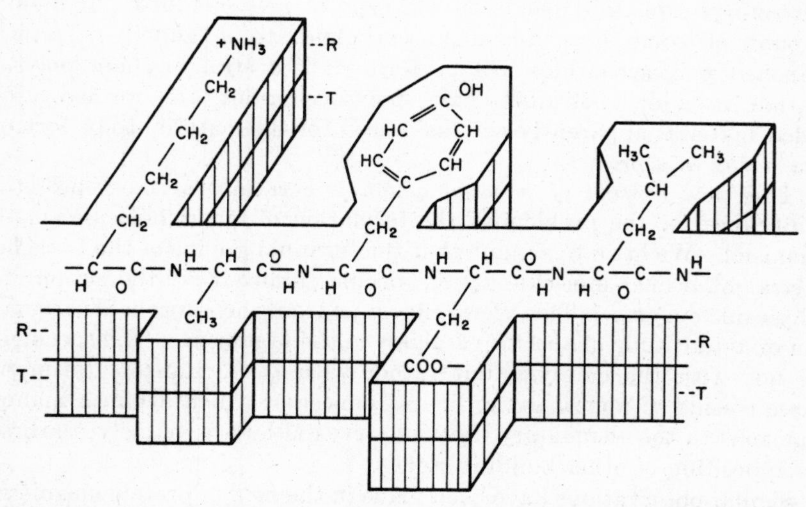

FIG. 51. Duplication of a protein template (129). Peptide chain of the template and replica is formed by lysine, alanine, tyrosine, aspartic acid, and leucine. T, template; R, replica.

view seems to be reconcilable with well established chemical and physico-chemical concepts. The decisive part of the entire mechanism is the first phase of the process, the specific adsorption of amino acids to amino acids of the same type in the template layer. This phenomenon is similar to the well known phenomenon of *crystallization*. We know that crystallization is extremely specific.

If we saturate a solution of different amino acids with one of them so that a portion of the amino acid added remains undissolved, and if we then slowly evaporate the mixture, only molecules of the same amino acid will be adsorbed to the undissolved crystal particles, which will accordingly grow in size. We will never find that another amino acid is built into the growing crystal lattice. If we then go on to concentrate the solution to such an extent that a second or third amino acid becomes insoluble, these will form separate crystals in most cases. We see from this example that the apposition of dissolved molecules to an insoluble lattice of the same molecule is a highly specific process.

The high specificity of crystallization and its analogy to biological specificity has been stressed by many chemists and biologists (127–129, 138,142). The idea of a solid particle of some substance forming a nucleus for further apposition of the same substance has received a very decided emphasis by recent findings in other fields of biochemistry. One of these new discoveries is the role played by glycogen in the enzymatic formation of new glycogen molecules. It has been found by Cori and Cori (143) that the enzymatic synthesis of polysaccharides from glucose-1-phosphate depends on the type of *primer* added. If a small amount of some branch-chained carbohydrate is added as primer, branched polysaccharides will be formed; if a straight-chain polysaccharide is added, straight-chain polysaccharides are formed. The added material apparently acts as a seed for the material to be formed, as a *starter* or a *primer*.

This new *concept of priming action* is certainly of most profound significance for the problem of the formation of macromolecules in the organism. We have to assume that the terminal groups of the branched or straight primer molecule act as specific organizer for the action of a nonspecific enzyme. This view relieves us from the improbable assumption of a multitude of specific catalysts in the organism. The specificity lies not with the catalyst, but rather with the organizers (primers). These consist of noncatalytic, lifeless molecules which act in a manner analogous to the elementary units of a crystal lattice, namely, to direct the apposition of other building stones.

Similar observations have been made in the field of protein chemistry. It was found that hemocyanin, the copper-containing respiratory chromoprotein of invertebrates is split into subunits of one half or one eighth of the original molecular weight by exposure of the protein solution to pH 8.5, and that reassociation at pH 6.85 to form the original units occurs quite specifically. Fragments of hemocyanin from *Helix pomatia* recombined with fragments of the same hemocyanin, but not with fragments derived from the hemocyanin of *Littorina littorea* (144).

From all these observations on the specificity of crystal growth, primer action, and recombination of subunits, it is evident that *molecules of the same type attract each other preferentially* under certain conditions. The forces giving rise to this mutual attraction are in some cases purely electrostatic forces of the ion–ion type; the simplest illustration of this type of attraction is the growth of a sodium chloride crystal, which is mainly due to the mutual attraction of positive sodium ions and negative chloride ions. This explanation fails when we try to explain the formation of crystals of nonelectrolytes such as naphthalene. Although naphthalene contains no ionic groups, nor polar hydroxyl or keto groups, only naphthalene molecules will be deposited on a naphthalene crystal from a naphthalene solution containing other similar hydrocarbons. The reason for this specificity of crystal growth is that the *shape* of the dissolved naphthalene molecules is congruent with the shape of those present in the crystal lattice so that they fit better than other molecules into the gaps between uneven parts of the lattice. It is evidently a purely topochemical phenomenon, a phenomenon occurring at the surface of the solid phase. Although this surface can adsorb many different substances, it will always preferentially adsorb molecules of the same kind.

The fact that the affinity between molecules of the same type is higher than that between molecules of different types is very well known to physical chemists. The magnitude of this bond energy can be determined by measuring the heat of fusion or the heat of solution. The melting point of a pure substance is always higher than that of a mixture of this substance with a contaminant. In other words, more energy is required for the separation of molecules of the same type than for the separation of molecules of different types. Obviously the force of attraction is much higher when it is contributed by the mutual attraction between ionic groups of opposite charge; this is the reason that crystals of the ionic type are hard and have high melting points, while crystals of the nonpolar type are soft and melt at low temperatures.

The phenomenon of crystallization renders understandable the apposition of amino acids on the corresponding amino acids of the expanded protein template. It might be objected that the amino acids of the template are present as component amino acid residues of a peptide chain and not as free amino acids and that they differ, therefore, from the free amino acids of an aqueous solution. This is certainly true. The bulk of most amino acid molecules, however, is formed by the residue present in peptide chains, as shown by a comparison between leucine and the leucyl residue:

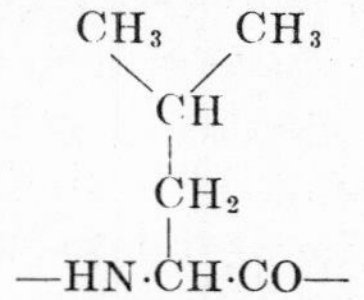

```
CH3   CH3              CH3   CH3
   \ /                    \ /
    CH                     CH
    |                      |
    CH2                    CH2
    |                   +  |
—HN·CH·CO—            H3N·CH·COO-
Leucyl residue          Leucine
```

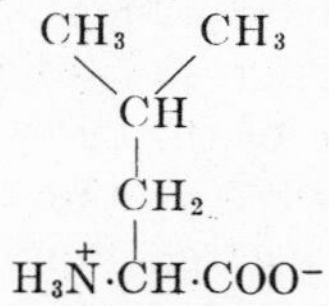

Leucine dissolved in the cellular fluid will certainly fit better than any other amino acid onto the leucyl residues of the peptide chain of the template (see Fig. 51).

According to our hypothesis, the amino acids deposited on the template are converted into a peptide chain. This phase of protein synthesis is catalyzed by *enzymes*. There is no evidence for specificity of the enzymes involved in this catalysis, nor a necessity to postulate the existence of specific enzymes. The proteoytic enzymes isolated from the organs are nonspecific. They catalyze the hydrolysis of quite different proteins of animal and vegetable origin. The same enzymes are able to catalyze the synthesis of peptides from amino acids, as was shown convincingly by experiments of Bergmann and coworkers (17,18) We have discussed these observations in a preceding section. There it was also emphasized that protein synthesis might proceed through a course of events differing widely from a mere reversal of proteolysis (see above, Sect. B). The important point is, however, that we have *no indication for the presence of specific enzymes, i.e.*, for enzymes catalyzing the hydrolysis or the formation of specific proteins. The specificity of the synthesized protein is sufficiently explained by the specificity of the template, which causes a specific mode of apposition of the amino acids on the template surface.

Before discussing the second phase of protein synthesis, the folding of the peptide chains, we must endeavor to answer two questions: (*a*) What is the role of the nucleic acids? (*b*) How does the template protein film differ from the duplicated protein film? Why does only the latter fold to form the globular protein molecule, whereas the template film remains expanded and insoluble?

It seems that both questions can be answered by a single answer. *The role of the nucleic acids is, apparently, to maintain the template protein film in the expanded state*, a state in which proteins do not remain unless exposed to the stress of interface forces. These forces cause the peptide chains to unfold and to remain in the expanded, unfolded state of the monomolecular film. It is imaginable, and quite probable, that different types of nucleic acids will act differently as carriers of the protein template and it is imaginable that replacement of a nucleic acid by a foreign nucleic acid might influence the duplication to a certain extent. But the influence of foreign substances on this first phase of protein synthesis, on the duplication of the protein film of the template, cannot be very pronounced unless the protein template is damaged.

While the protein film which forms the template is insoluble, the duplicated film folds to form the globular protein molecule. Since each peptide layer is about 8–10 Å thick, the globular protein particles can consist only of a small number of peptide layers. We do not know whether they really form folds or whether several two-dimensional subunits combine to form the globular particle. In Chapter XI (Sect. F) we had reported that hitherto only the hemoglobin molecule has been investigated in this respect. The structure suggested for hemoglobin is shown in Figure 52 (145). The molecule consists of four peptide layers each of them formed by a peptide chain folded five times in a zigzag manner.

Immunochemical experiments lead us to the conclusion that the three-dimensional protein molecules are complementarily shaped to injected *antigens*, which *apparently interfere in the process of folding* and *impress upon the protein molecule a negative print of their determinant groups.* In the absence of foreign antigens, polar molecules in the cellular contents act in the same way so that the proteins formed are "auto-antibodies" (132), *i.e.*, shaped complementarily to some determinant structure of the normal cellular constituents. These may be the structures of lipids, carbohydrates, proteins, or nucleic acids. Landsteiner has proved convincingly that practically all polar groups interfere in antibody synthesis, even such synthetic products of the chemical industry

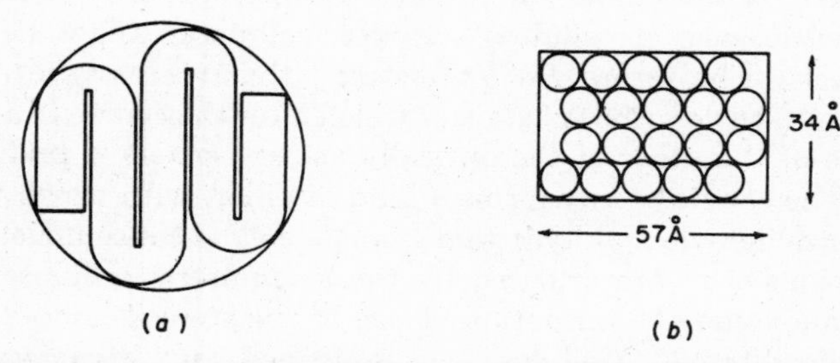

FIG. 52. Hemoglobin molecule (145). (*a*) basal section showing folded peptide chains; (*b*) vertical section showing packing of chains.

as azo compounds or nitro compounds. There is no reason why any of the polar cellular constituents should not act in the same way. If we are dealing with higher organisms, we can say nothing about the chemical nature of these *three-dimensional templates* which preside at and *interfere with the second phase of protein synthesis, with the formation of the three-dimensional protein molecule from the two-dimensional protein film.* In the simplest viruses, however, there occur practically no carbohydrates, or lipids, but only protein and nucleic acids. Nevertheless we find there an intensive synthesis of protein. It can be concluded, therefore, that here, and possibly also in higher organisms, the secondary templates consist mainly of proteins and/or nucleic acids, possibly of nucleoproteins.

In *viruses* we have to expect a further simplification in protein synthesis, because there is only one component, the virus protein. This must assume the role of the two-dimensional and also that of the three-dimensional templates at the same time, unless molecules of the host cell take over these roles. It is imaginable that certain parts of the virus protein, linked to nucleic acid, act as expanded template for the first phase of protein synthesis, while another portion of the same protein in the globular state acts as template for the formation of three-dimensional globules from the two-dimensional films.

Are the templates of protein synthesis catalysts? Is the antigen injected to be considered a catalyst? While many biochemists answer this question positively, it is the opinion of the author that a distinction should be made between catalysts and those substances which alter the course of a reaction without affecting its velocity. The difference between these two types of substances is evident from the fundamental experiments of Bredig, discussed extensively by Sevag (146).

Bredig had found that optically active mandelonitrile was obtained from benzaldehyde and hydrogen cyanide, when the catalyst, diethylamine, was linked to cellulose (147). Evidently, the asymmetric course of the reaction is here brought about by the asymmetric structure of cellulose, not by the amine whose basic groups functions as a catalyst, even in the absence of cellulose. Hence, cellulose cannot be called a true catalyst. The term "*Pfeilersubstanz*" (pillar substance) has been proposed (148) to describe substances which alter the course of a reaction, so that one or the other of the optically active isomers is preferentially formed. The cellulose fiber forms a kind of pillar, with which the molecules of benzaldehyde and hydrogen cyanide collide continuously; during these collisions they are oriented by the asymmetric cellulose fibers in such a manner that the formation of one of the stereoisomeric mandelonitriles is facilitated. Cellulose can be called an "organizer" or an "inductor" of asymmetric synthesis and can thus be differentiated from the true catalyst, the amine. The term "organizer" seems to be more adequate, because it indicates that the main function of cellulose is to organize the reaction in such a fashion that it does not proceed at random but rather in some definite direction. In an analogous manner the hypothetical templates of our proposed mechanism of protein synthesis do not catalyze this synthesis, but adsorb amino acids in a specific manner, enabling the enzyme to form peptide chains of a definite and specific order and preventing, in this way, the formation of randomly composed peptide chains.

Summarizing, we can say that the *mechanism of protein synthesis* outlined in the preceding paragraphs consists of the following phases:

(*1*) Specific adsorption of amino acids to identical amino acid residues of an expanded protein layer.

(*2*) Action of a nonspecific enzyme on the adsorbed amino acids, so that an expanded protein film (duplicate of the protein template) is formed.

(*3*) Folding of the two-dimensional protein film so that a three-dimensional globular protein molecule is formed. The shape of the three-dimensional molecule will depend on the shape and electrostatic field of polar groups of adjacent cellular constituents or of antigens brought into the cell from outside.

One of the essential points of this hypothesis is the assumption that enzymes are nonspecific and that the specificity of the synthesized proteins is caused by the specific shape and electrostatic field of the template surface. This statement is based on the experience that none of the well known enzymes acts species specifically. Thus, chicken pepsin acting on swine pepsinogen produces swine pepsin and not chicken pepsin (150). Likewise proteins of plants and animals are hydrolyzed with equal ease by vegetable and animal enzymes.

In spite of these experiences some authors believe in the existence of enzymes producing specific proteins. Burnet (149), for reasons discussed in a preceding chapter (see page 298) assumes that antibodies are produced not only in the presence of the sensitizing antigen, but also when the antigen has been destroyed by or eliminated from the sensitized organism. Antibody production, according to Burnet, is a function not only of the cell originally stimulated but of its descendants. This view is based on the experience that adaptive enzymes are formed in fungi or bacteria "trained" in a medium containing a foreign substrate.

The existence of enzymes responsible for the formation of specific proteins can neither be proved nor disproved at present, so that no experimental decision is possible. The main objection to be raised against these views is that they are hardly reconcilable with the physicochemical theories on the action of catalysts. We are not able to imagine a catalyst producing a species-specific peptide chain by combining amino acids in a definite order. The action of each of the well known catalysts and enzymes is restricted to a single molecular group at a time. Having terminated its action the enzyme can repeat the same type of action. However, we cannot imagine an enzyme which catalyzes the linkage of, say, tyrosine to the amino end of a peptide chain, and as a next step catalyzes the apposition of alanine, then glutamic acid, cysteine, and other amino acids. All our experience on enzyme action shows that always a certain type of reaction is preferred and that changes of the mode of action do not occur. This difficulty is avoided in the hypothesis presented above by the assumption that the specificity of the protein formed is caused by the adsorption of amino acids to a specific template pattern.

In our discussion we have differentiated between "enzymes" on the one hand and "proteins" on the other. One must not forget, however, that all enzymes are proteins, and that many of the proteins which had been considered to be devoid of enzymatic action were found to be enzymatically active, when suitable substrates for their action were discovered. Northrop (150), who has proved that enzymes are formed from zymogens, assumes that proteins in an analogous manner are formed from "proteinogens." The first step in protein synthesis, according to Northrop, is the formation of a "type" protein, the proteinogen, from amino acids, and the second step the autocatalytical formation of individual proteins from the proteinogens (150). Since we do not yet know what is the mechanism of the conversion of zymogens into enzymes or of proteinogens into proteins this interesting view cannot yet be discussed critically.

In the last few years the problem of protein synthesis has been receiving attention from points of vantage in the field of *genetics*. Experiments on the irradiation of fungi or bacteria led to the discovery of mutant strains which differ from the original strain in their inability to produce a certain amino acid. The use made of such strains for the determination of some amino acids was mentioned in Chapter III (page 24). Geneticists have concluded from such experiments that the production of the respective amino acid in the normal strain is due to the activity of a definite enzyme and that this enzyme is produced by a definite gene. If this gene is damaged by radiation, the enzyme will not be formed and the amino acid will not be produced. Accordingly a one-to-one relation between a gene and a definite enzyme is assumed (151, 151*a*).

How does this assumption and how does the assumption of genes as producers of enzymes and other proteins fit with the picture outlined above? Are the genes identical with the two-dimensional or the three-dimensional templates? Are they proteins or nucleoproteins? An answer to these questions is certainly of the greatest interest. A satisfactory answer is hardly possible at the present time, however, since our views on protein synthesis and on the nature and action of genes are more or less speculative. Nevertheless, an attempt to reconcile the two hypotheses is justified by the importance of the problem and by the lack of experimental proof.

The *gene*, according to the geneticist, is the unit of inheritance, the ultimate factor endowed with the property of self-duplication. This gene is certainly not identical with the secondary three-dimensional template of our concept on protein synthesis. We can reject this possibility on the basis of immunological experiments. Injection of an antigen changes, as we have seen, the secondary three-dimensional templates, so that antibodies, a new kind of protein, are formed. The allergic state of the organism injected with the antigen is, however, not a hereditary trait. The offspring of the immunized animal does not produce antibodies. Its secondary templates, apparently, are those of normal animals of the same species.

Genes are, however, affected by radiation (152) and by certain chemical substances such as mustard gas (153). Both radiation and mustard gas act on proteins and also on nucleic acids (154). The result does not indicate, therefore, whether the genes are formed by proteins, nucleic acids, or both. From genetic data it has been inferred that the shape of the genes is rodlike and that their length is approximately 1250 Å, their diameter 50–200 Å (155). These dimensions are not very different from those of the fibrous protein molecules. It will be recalled (see Chapters VIII and IX) that collagen, myosin, fibrinogen and other fibrous proteins show spacings of approximately 700 Å when examined by X-ray analysis or electron micrography. It may well be, therefore, that the gene is a protein macromolecule or a nucleoprotein molecule, although we cannot prove it or exclude other possibilities. Our assumption that genes are nucleoprotein templates and that their specificity is due to their protein component seems to be reconcilable with the few experimental data available.

Frequently an enzyme nature has been assigned to the gene, an assumption which is neither necessary nor probable (155). We have discussed above the differences between specific organizers, or inductors, and nonspecific enzymes. The gene is certainly specific and it has most probably the properties of an organizer. We do not know whether the nonspecific procedure of the formation of a peptide chain from amino acids is catalyzed by the gene or by some nonspecific enzyme. There is no necessity to identify the two. The fact that enzymes extracted from the cells are not specific suggests that they are different from the genes. It is not astonishing that the subtle process of the formation of species-specific proteins is disturbed by radiation and that mutations may occur. It is surprising, however, that this effect is caused by *a single quantum hit per cell.* Since one photon can hardly affect more than a restricted portion of a protein molecule, it has been concluded that the gene or the cell must consist of a single large molecule with a labile center whose injury is conducted to other parts of the cell by a kind of amplifier effect (156,157).

In this connection another similar assumption may be mentioned, according to which fibrous proteins are able to function as electron conductors, probably by means of hydrogen bonds formed between parallel peptide chains (158–160). This view is hardly reconcilable with the fact that living matter is neither metallike nor deeply colored, like graphite, and that it does not show the phenomenon of electron conductivity.

The fact that a single quantum hit can result in the destruction of an entire cell or alter the properties of a whole gene can be explained by less contradictory assumptions. We know that denatured proteins are digested by enzymes at a much higher rate than native proteins. We know, on the other hand, that proteins are denatured by radiation. It has been found, moreover, that proteins denatured by ultraviolet radiation are digested by trypsin at a greater velocity than native proteins (161). We can assume, therefore, that the quantum hit causes local ionization and, thereby, denaturation of the protein; it creates, in this manner, a point of attack for the endocellular enzymes. These are now able to attack the hit peptide chain, to digest it, and to enlarge the area of damage from the initial point of quantum hit to remote parts of the gene or the cell. It is understandable, therefore, that a single quantum hit may have serious consequences for a relatively large biological unit (162,163).

If the *genes are identical with the primary two-dimensional templates of protein synthesis,* we have to assume that the first phase of protein synthesis, the formation of the two-dimensional protein replica, goes on in the nucleus. For, genes are present only in the nuclei. We do not know whether the second phase of protein synthesis, the formation of the globular three-dimensional molecule from the two-dimensional replica takes place in the nucleus. The fact that this second part of protein synthesis is altered by antigens suggests that it takes place in the cytoplasm. This assumption is in agreement with Caspersson's finding (59) that proteins are secreted from the nucleus into the cytoplasm.

It agrees also with recent findings on type-specific substances of the cytoplasm of *Paramecium aurelia* (164). According to these findings the type of *Paramecium aurelia* can be altered by treating paramecia with an antiserum produced by rabbits which had been injected with the same type of paramecia. It seems that the antibody of the rabbit serum combines with some type-specific substance of the paramecia and that then another similar substance present in the same paramecia takes over the control of protein synthesis, so that the progeny manifests the new trait and transmits it through many vegetative fissions.

If we assume that the cytoplasm contains various secondary three-dimensional templates and that these compete with one another, we can understand that elimination of one of these templates will cause the production of another type of globular protein particle from the same type of expanded protein film produced. The peptide chains of the primary protein films will be the same; the mode of folding or of aggregation of these films may differ from type to type and may be dependent on the shape of the cytoplasmic templates.

The purpose of these speculations has been to show that an agreement between the physicochemical picture of protein synthesis and the ideas of modern physical chemistry and biology is possible. This agreement has been achieved by eliminating all that is contradictory to established physicochemical conceptions or irreconcilable with experimental results. It would have been more satisfactory to base a theory of protein synthesis on experimental facts. However, since these are not available, the emergency method of science, speculation, has been invoked. Scientific work is not possible without a leading idea. Advancing a new hypothesis may therefore be allowed in a field where no proven theories exist.

References

1. H. Staudinger, H. Schnell, *J. Makromol. Chem.* **1,** 44 (1947).
2. H. Leuchs, *Ber.* **39,** 857 (1906).
2*a*. K. Freudenberg, *Ann.* **537,** 197 (1938).
3. Y. Go, H. Tani, *Bull. Chem. Soc. Japan* **14,** 510 (1939).
4. R. B. Woodward, C. H. Schramm, *J. Am. Chem. Soc.* **69,** 1551 (1947).
5. E. Katschalski, J. Grossfeld, M. Frankel, *J. Am. Chem. Soc.* **69,** 2564 (1947).
6. W. Hanby, S. Waley, J. Watson, *Nature* **161,** 132 (1948).
7. E. J. Ambrose, W. E. Hanby, *Nature* **163,** 483 (1949).
8. G. Schramm, G. Thumm, *Z. Naturforsch.* **3b,** 218 (1948).
9. W. T. Astbury *et al.*, *Nature* **162,** 595 (1948).
10. F. Lipmann, *Federation Proc.* **8,** 597 (1949).
11. H. H. Strain, K. Linderstrøm-Lang, *Enzymologia* **5,** 86 (1938).
12. E. W. Flosdorf, S. Mudd, E. W. Flosdorf, *J. Immunol.* **32,** 441 (1937).
13. A. Virtanen, H. K. Kerkkonen, T. Laaksonen, *Acta Scand. Chem.* **2,** 933 (1948); **3,** 520 (1949).
14. H. Tauber, *J. Am. Chem. Soc.* **71,** 2952 (1949).
15. M. Bremer, H. R. Müller, R. W. Pfister, *Helvet. Chim. Acta* **33,** 568 (1950).
16. S. E. Bresler *et al.*, *Isvest. Akad. S.S.S.R.* **13,** 392 (1949).
17. M. Bergmann, H. Fraenkel-Conradt, *J. Biol. Chem.* **119,** 707 (1937); J. S. Fruton, *Advances in Protein Chem.* **5,** 1 (1949).
17*a*. S. Fox *et al.*, *Arch. Biochem.* **25,** 13, 21 (1950).
18. M. Bergmann, J. S. Fruton, *J. Biol. Chem.* **124,** 321 (1938).
19. K. Linderstrøm-Lang, *Bull. Soc. Chim. Biol.* **22,** 339 (1940).
20. P. P. Cohen, R. W. McGilvery, *J. Biol. Chem.* **169,** 119; **171,** 121 (1947).
21. H. Borsook, J. W. Dubnoff, *J. Biol. Chem.* **168,** 397 (1947).
22. F. Lipmann, *Advances in Enzymol.* **1,** 154 (1941).
23. P. P. Cohen, *Ann. Rev. Biochem.* **14,** 357 (1945).
24. H. Chantrenne, *Nature* **160,** 603 (1947); *Biochem. et Biophys. Acta,* **4,** 484 (1950).
25. D. Rittenberg, D. Shemin, *Ann. Rev. Biochem.* **15,** 247 (1946).
26. K. Linderstrøm-Lang, *Ann. Rev. Biochem.* **8,** 37 (1939).
27. D. Melnick, G. R. Cowgill, E. Burack, *J. Exptl. Med.* **64,** 877 (1936).
28. S. C. Madden, W. E. George, G. S. Waraich, G. H. Whipple, *J. Exptl. Med.* **67,** 675 (1938).
29. S. C. Madden, G. H. Whipple, *Physiol. Revs.* **20,** 194 (1940).
30. L. L. Miller, F. S. Robscheit-Robbins, G. H. Whipple, *J. Exptl. Med.* **81,** 405 (1945).
31. J. M. Orten, J. E. Bourque, A. U. Orten, *J. Biol. Chem.* **160,** 435 (1945).
32. F. S. Robscheit-Robbins, L. L. Miller, G. H. Whipple, *J. Exptl. Med.* **82,** 311 (1945).
33. H. Tarver, W. O. Reinhardt, *J. Biol. Chem.* **167,** 395 (1947).
34. G. H. Berryman, J. L. Bollmann, F. C. Mann, *Am. J. Physiol.* **139,** 556 (1943).

35. F. S. Robscheit-Robbins, L. L. Miller, G. H. Whipple, *J. Exptl. Med.* **82,** 311 (1945); **85,** 267 (1947).
36. F. S. Robscheit-Robbins, G. H. Whipple, *J. Exptl. Med.* **89,** 339 (1949).
37. G. H. Whipple, F. S. Robscheit-Robbins, W. B. Hawkins, *J. Exptl. Med.* **81,** 171 (1945).
38. H. Borsook, J. W. Dubnoff, *Ann. Rev. Biochem.* **12,** 183 (1943).
39. K. Landsteiner, R. C. Parker, *J. Exptl. Med.* **71,** 231 (1940).
40. A. Fischer, *Acta Physiol. Scand.* **4,** 207 (1942).
41. H. H. Ussing, *Science* **94,** 209 (1941).
42. R. M. Fink *et al., J. Exptl. Med.* **80,** 455 (1944).
43. D. B. Sprinson, D. Rittenberg, *J. Biol. Chem.* **707,** 715 (1949).
44. L. L. Miller *et al., J. Exptl. Med.* **90,** 297 (1949).
45. R. Schoenheimer, The dynamic State of Body Constituents. Harvard Univ. Press, Cambridge, 1932.
46. D. Rittenberg *et al., Federation Proc.* **7,** 180 (1948).
47. F. Friedberg, M. P. Schulman, D. M. Greenberg, *J. Biol. Chem.* **173,** 437 (1948).
48. F. Friedberg, *Science* **105,** 314 (1947).
49. J. B. Melchior, H. Tarver, *Arch. Biochem.* **12,** 301, 309 (1947).
50. T. Winnick, F. Friedberg, D. M. Greenberg, *Arch. Biochem.* **15,** 160 (1947).
51. I. Frantz, R. Lotfield, W. Miller, *Science* **106,** 544 (1947).
52. C. B. Anfinsen, A. Beloff, A. B. Hastings, A. K. Solomon, *J. Biol. Chem.* **168,** 771 (1947); T. Peters, C. B. Anfinsen, *ibid.* **182,** 171 (1950).
53. T. Winnick, I. Moring-Claesson, D. M. Greenberg, *J. Biol. Chem.* **175,** 127 (1948).
54. C. Deasy, H. Borsook *et al., Federation Proc.* **8,** 194 (1949).
55. I. Perlman, I. L. Chaikoff, M. E. Morton, *J. Biol. Chem.* **139,** 433 (1941).
56. M. E. Morton, I. L. Chaikoff, W. O. Reinhardt, E. Anderson, *J. Biol. Chem.* **147,** 757 (1943).
57. M. Heidelberger, R. Schoenheimer, S. Ratner, D. Rittenberg, *J. Biol. Chem.* **144,** 541, 555 (1942).
58. E. Kooyman, D. H. Campbell, *J. Am. Chem. Soc.* **70,** 1293 (1948).
59. T. Caspersson, *Symposia Soc. Exptl. Biol.* No. 1, 137 (1947); R. Jeener, D. Szafarz, *Arch. Biochem.* **26,** 54 (1950).
60. J. Brachet, Un Symposium sur les Proteines, Desoir, Liège, 1946, p. 123; *Arch. Biol.* **53,** 151, 167 (1940).
61. E. Hammarsten, G. Hevesy, *Acta Physiol. Acta* **11,** 335 (1946); see also S. S. Furst *et al., J. Biol. Chem.* **183,** 251 (1950).
62. A. Fischer, *Acta Physiol. Scand.* **3,** 54 (1941).
63. E. Stedman, E. Stedman, *Symposia Soc. Exptl. Biol.* No. 1, 232 (1947).
64. A. E. Mirsky, *Cold Spring Harbor Symposia Quant. Biol.* **12,** 143 (1947).
65. A. W. Pollister, A. E. Mirsky, *J. Gen. Physiol.* **30,** 101, 117 (1946).
66. A. E. Mirsky, H. Ris, *J. Gen. Physiol.* **31,** 7 (1947).
67. J. N. Davidson, *Ann. Rev. Biochem.* **18,** 153 (1949).
68. B. P. Kaufman, *Science* **109,** 443 (1949).
69. G. Schmidt, L. Hecht, S. Thannhauser, *J. Gen. Physiol.* **31,** 203 (1948).
70. A. Claude, *Trans. New York Acad. Sci.* **4,** 79 (1942).
71. A. Boivin, R. Vendrely, C. Vendrely, *Compt. rend.* **226,** 1061 (1948).
72. M. McCarty, O. T. Avery, *J. Exptl. Med.* **83,** 89, 97 (1948).
73. A. Boivin, R. Vendrely, *Experientia* **3,** 32 (1947).
74. S. Spiegelman, *Cold Spring Harbor Symposia Quant. Biol.* **11,** 256 (1946).
75. W. J. Van Wagtendonk. *J. Biol. Chem.* **173,** 691 (1948).
76. J. Banga, A. Szent-Györgyi, *Science* **92,** 514 (1940).

77. J. Brachet, R. Jeener, *Biochim. et Biophys. Acta,* **1,** 13 (1947).
78. W. Schmidt, *Naturwissenschaften* **26,** 413 (1938).
78*a*. E. Stedman, E. Stedman, *Nature* **152,** 556 (1943).
78*b*. J. Runnström, L. Monné, R. G. W. Wyckoff, *J. Colloid Sci.* **1,** 421 (1946).
78*c*. F. O. Schmitt, *Advances in Protein Chem.* **1,** 44 (1944).
79. A. Frey-Wyssling, Submicroscopic Morphology of Protoplasm. Elsevier Co. New York, 1948.
80. F. O. Schmitt, R. S. Bear, K. J. Palmer, *J. Cellular Comp. Physiol.* **18,** 31 (1941).
81. A. Frey-Wyssling, E. Steinmann, *Biochem. et Biophys. Acta* **2,** 434 (1948).
82. J. Runnström, S. Lindwall, A. Tiselius, *Nature* **153,** 285 (1944).
83. F. Haurowitz, A. Löwenstein, *Arch. Augenheilk.* **122,** 654 (1929).
84. J. F. Danielli, *Biochem. J.* **39,** LII (1945).
85. K. Dann, *Biol. Bull.* **93,** 274 (1947).
86. A. Frey-Wyssling, *Naturwissenschaften* **28,** 385 (1940).
87. W. T. Astbury, R. Reed, L. C. Spark, *Biochem. J.* **43,** 282 (1948).
88. M. A. Jakus, C. E. Hall, *J. Biol. Chem.* **167,** 705 (1947).
89. J. Gross, F. O. Schmitt, *J. Exptl. Med.* **88,** 555 (1948).
90. R. Reed, K. Rudall, *Biochim. et Biophys. Acta* **2,** 7 (1948).
91. F. O. Schmitt, A. Denues, *Ann. Rev. Physiol.* **10,** 1 (1948).
92. H. Chantrenne, *Biochim. et Biophys. Acta* **1,** 437 (1947).
93. G. A. LePage, W. C. Schneider, *J. Biol. Chem.* **176,** 1021 (1948).
94. G. H. Hogeboom, W. C. Schneider, G. E. Palade, *J. Biol. Chem.* **172,** 619 (1948).
95. W. C. Schneider, V. R. Potter, *J. Biol. Chem.* **177,** 893 (1949).
96. V. T. Riley, M. L. Hasselbach, S. Fiala, M. W. Woods, D. Burk, *Science* **109,** 361 (1949).
97. A. Claude, *Science* **87,** 467 (1938); *J. Exptl. Med.* **84,** 51 (1946).
98. K. G. Stern, *Cold Spring Harbor Symposia Quant. Biol.* **7,** 312 (1939).
99. H. Chantrenne, *Enzymologia* **11,** 213 (1944).
100. J. N. Davidson, *Symposia Soc. Exptl. Biol.* No. 1, 77 (1946).
101. E. P. Kennedy, A. L. Lehninger, *J. Biol. Chem.* **172,** 847 (1948).
102. E. P. Kennedy, A. L. Lehninger, *J. Biol. Chem.* **179,** 957 (1949).
102*a*. A. Claude, *Science* **97,** 451 (1943); *Advances in Protein Chem.* **5,** 423 (1949).
103. J. Brachet, H. Chantrenne, *Acta biol. Belg.* **4,** 451 (1942).
104. T. Sonneborn, *Am. Naturalist* **82,** 26 (1948).
105. S. E. Luria, *Bact. Revs.* **11,** 1 (1947); *Science* **111,** 507 (1950).
106. W. M. Stanley, *Science* **81,** 644 (1935); *J. Biol. Chem.* **121,** 205 (1937).
107. H. S. Loring, *J. Biol. Chem.* **130,** 251 (1939).
108. M. A. Lauffer, *Arch. Biochem.* **13,** 145 (1947).
109. G. Schramm, *Ber.* **74,** 532 (1941).
110. R. Markham, R. Matthews, K. Smith, *Nature* **162,** 88 (1948).
111. A. Butenandt, H. Friedrich-Freska, S. Hartwig, G. Scheibe, *Z. physiol. Chem.* **274,** 276 (1942).
112. W. M. Stanley, *Ann. Rev. Biochem.* **9,** 553 (1940).
113. J. W. Beard, R. G. W. Wyckoff, *Science* **85,** 201 (1937).
114. J. H. Northrop, *J. Gen. Physiol.* **21,** 335 (1938).
115. G. A. Kausche, H. Ruska, *Naturwissenschaften* **27,** 292 (1939).
116. T. F. Anderson, L. A. Chambers, W. Henle, *Ann. Re. Biochem.* **12,** 600 (1943).
117. V. L. Frampton, A. M. Saum, *Science* **89,** 84 (1939).
118. M. Sreenivasaya, N. W. Pirie, *Biochem. J.* **32,** 1707 (1938).
119. W. M. Stanley, in D. E. Green, Currents in Biochemical Research. Interscience, New York, 1946, p. 1.

120. A. E. Hook, D. Beard, A. R. Taylor, D. G. Sharp, J. W. Beard, *J. Biol. Chem.* **165,** 241 (1946).
121. A. Polson, R. G. W. Wyckoff, *Science* **108,** 501 (1948).
122. S. S. Cohen, *Bact. Revs.* **13,** 1 (1949); L. M. Kozloff, F. Putnam, *J. Biol. Chem.,* **181,** 207 (1950).
123. N. W. Pirie, *Ann. Rev. Biochem.* **15,** 573 (1946).
124. T. E. Rawlins, *Science* **96,** 425 (1942).
125. M. Dixon, *Nature* **139,** 153 (1937).
126. A. H. K. Petrie, *Biol. Revs. Cambridge Phil. Soc.* **18,** 105 (1943).
127. L. T. Troland, *Am. Naturalist* **51,** 321 (1917).
128. H. J. Muller, *Sci. Monthly* **44,** 210 (1937).
129. F. Haurowitz, *Quart. Rev. Biol.* **24,** 93 (1949).
130. M. Delbrück, *Cold Spring Harbor Symposia Quant. Biol.* **9,** 122 (1941).
131. H. Eyring, F. H. Johnson, R. Genzler, *J. Phys. Chem.* **50,** 453 (1946).
132. A. Tyler, *Physiol. Revs.* **28,** 180 (1948).
133. S. Emerson, *Ann. Missouri Botan. Garden* **32,** 243 (1945).
134. H. Friedrich-Freska, *Naturwissenschaften* **38,** 376 (1940).
135. E. Boyland, *Ann. Rev. Biochem.* **18,** 217 (1949).
136. P. Rondoni, *Schweiz. Med. Wochschr.* **78,** 419 (1948).
137. P. Rondoni *et al., Experientia* **5,** 357 (1949).
138. L. Pauling, *Nature* **161,** 707 (1948).
139. J. P. Greenstein, H. W. Chalkey, *Ann. Missouri Botan. Garden* **32,** 179 (1945).
140. L. Jansen, *Protoplasma* **33,** 410 (1939).
141. E. Brand *et al., J. Am. Chem. Soc.* **67,** 1524 (1945).
142. J. B. S. Haldane, in Needham and Green, Perspectives in Biochemistry. Cambridge Univ. Press, Cambridge, 1937, p. 1.
143. C. F. Cori, G. T. Cori, *J. Biol. Chem.* **135,** 641 (1940); *Federation Proc.* **4,** 234 (1944).
144. A. Tiselius, F. L. Horsfall, Jr., *J. Exptl. Med.* **69,** 83 (1939).
145. M. F. Perutz, *Research* **2,** 60 (1949).
146. M. Sevag, Immunocatalysis. Thomas, Springfield, 1945.
147. G. Bredig, F. Gerstner, *Biochem. Z.* **250,** 414 (1932).
148. W. Kuhn, *Z. angew. Chem.* **49,** 215 (1936).
149. F. M. Burnet, The Production of Antibodies. Macmillan, London, 1941.
150. J. H. Northrop, Crystalline Enzymes. Columbia Univ. Press, New York, 1948.
151. G. W. Beadle, *Chem. Revs.* **37,** 15 (1945).
151*a*. S. Emerson, *Cold Spring Harbor Symposia Quant. Biol.* **14,** 40 (1950).
152. H. J. Muller, *Science* **66,** 382 (1927).
153. C. Auerbach, J. Robson, *Nature* **157,** 302 (1946).
154. D. Elmore, J. M. Gulland, D. O. Jordan, H. Taylor, *Biochem. J.* **42,** 308 (1948).
155. H. J. Muller, *Am. Naturalist* **69,** 405 (1935); *Proc. Roy. Soc. London* **B134,** 1 (1947).
156. P. Jordan, *Naturwissenschaften* **26,** 537 (1938).
157. E. Wassink, *Vakblad voor Biologen* **26,** 13 (1946).
158. W. Schmidt, *Z. Naturforsch.* **2b,** 98 (1947).
159. K. G. Denbigh, *Nature* **154,** 642 (1944).
160. A. H. Szent-Györgyi, *Nature* **157,** 875 (1946).
161. F. Haurowitz, A. Ţümer, *Enzymologia* **13,** 229 (1949).
162. D. Mazia, G. Blumenthal, *Proc. Natl. Acad. Sci. U.S.* **34,** 328 (1948).
163. B. Katchman, A. McLaren, *J. Polymer Sci.* **3,** 138 (1948).
164. T. Sonneborn, *Science* **107,** 459 (1948); *Advances in Genetics* **1,** 264 (1947).

Index

B

C

I

K

L

Q

R

S

T

U

V

W

X

Y

Z